Automotive Collision Estimating and Repair

ANDRE G. DEROCHE

*Instructor in Autobody
Repairing and Repainting
Red River Community College
Winnipeg, Manitoba, Canada*

PRENTICE HALL, Englewood Cliffs, New Jersey 07632

Library of Congress Cataloging-in-Publication Data

```
Deroche, A. G.
    Automotive collision estimating and repair.

    Includes index.
    1. Automobiles--Collision damage--Estimates.
2. Automobiles--Bodies--Maintenance and repair--
Estimates.  I. Title.
TL255.D46  1988        629.28'7          88-2482
ISBN 0-13-054222-9
```

Editorial/production supervision and
   interior design: Tom Aloisi
Cover design: 20/20 Services, Inc.
Manufacturing buyer: Bob Anderson

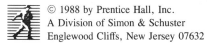
Printed in the United States of America

10 9 8 7 6 5 4 3 2 1

ISBN: 0-13-054222-9

Prentice-Hall International (UK) Limited, *London*
Prentice-Hall of Australia Pty. Limited, *Sydney*
Prentice-Hall of Canada Inc., *Toronto*
Prentice-Hall Hispanoamericana, S.A., *Mexico*
Prentice-Hall of India Private Limited, *New Delhi*
Prentice-Hall of Japan, Inc., *Tokyo*
Prentice-Hall of Southeast Asia Pte. Ltd., *Singapore*
Editora Prentice-Hall do Brasil, Ltda., *Rio de Janeiro*

Dedication

The author would like to dedicate this book to all the young people who have the fortitude and determination to become successful estimators, adjusters, or autobody technicians.

The author would also like to thank the following people: Steve Chanas, Edward Debeuckelaere, Orest Dobinsky, B. J. Small, and W. L. Williams of the Red River Community College staff.

I would also like to thank my wife Helen for her understanding and encouragement, which provided the time and support that are required when involved in this type of project, and my daughter for her typing skills and the time she devoted to this book.

Contents

Preface

This book was written for a number of reasons: first, for the student or apprentice who has been in the autobody trade and wants to learn about estimating or the latest techniques in the repair of major collision damage on unibody vehicles. Second, this text will also be very helpful for upgrading a technician's knowledge of the new methods that should be used to repair the newer vehicles.

The text will also be of great use to personnel who are connected with the body shop, such as management, the insurance claims department, and others who want to broaden their information background. The text will also help familiarize personnel in body shops or body repair equipment salespeople with how the work should be done.

Automotive estimating and collision repair, like any other occupation or trade, involve the theory of why and how. To be skilled in any occupation means that certain techniques of the occupation must be done over and over until they can be done without any errors and have become a habit. A qualified estimator or autobody technician must master all the methods and operations described in this text and be able to respond easily to all the questions at the end of each chapter.

Chapter 1 describes the fundamental technical knowledge and specialized skills that are required of an estimator, along with a pleasant and helpful personality. It points out the growing market for estimators in body shops and in the insurance industry as adjusters. The estimator must learn the latest developments in the construction of vehicles, as well as part names and new materials that are being used. The chapter also covers the types of glass used.

The estimator must be able to read vehicle identification numbers, understand the betterment factor as used on damaged or used tires, and make use of the estimating tips on the repair of wheels, bumper systems, air-conditioning systems, transmissions, and different types of steering. The estimator must know how door hardware and weather stripping are installed. It is also important that the estimator and technician be able to describe different types of damages, both direct and indirect, and understand how panels are constructed.

Chapter 2 deals with how the insurance industry works generally and the reason why estimates are used. Labor time is also discussed and how it is developed, as well as the meaning of different terms used in the industry. The estimating of time on sheet-metal repair is covered, as well as the retail price per hour charge-out rate for body shops; different types of estimates are covered and explained, as well as how and why vehicles are written off. The betterment and depreciation factors on parts of vehicles are discussed and explained.

Chapter 3 covers material on how to understand the collision estimating manuals, such as right and left part numbers and interchangeable parts. The different terms used to describe different types of operations are defined. Pages from collision manuals are given, which include the operations required and what must be excluded from or added to the time estimate. The zone system of estimating is explained, as well as how damage is analyzed. Exercises are provided so that the student may learn how to write and complete an estimate properly.

Chapter 4 covers the different types of plastics, where they are used, and the different tests made for their identification. Methods are given on how to repair the many different types of plastics used on the modern vehicle.

Chapter 5 covers methods of using the MIG welder and how to troubleshoot when problems occur. A very important section covers the methods to be used when repairing the modern unibody vehicle. The chapter covers the sectioning of front frame rails, A, B, and C pillars, rocker panels, and floor pans with inserts or by a lap-joint method to restore integrity to the construction of the vehicle.

Chapter 6 covers the different types of frames used in the industry, gauging methods, and new methods of construction used in the unibody vehicle. Also covered are the methods used to diagnose different damage conditions and how the repairs should be carried out, as well as wheel alignment and the balancing of wheels and tires.

Chapter 7 covers the repair of the major types of collision damage in great detail; these are presented in the front-end, side, turret-top, and rear-end damage sequence. Many illustrations are used to show how the repairs are achieved and the end results. The illustrations clearly show actual on-the-job applications of some of the latest hand tools, hydraulic jacking equipment, and portable and stationary body and frame straighteners. Variations in the alignment, welding, and metal-working procedures required when repairing high-strength steel vehicles are described.

Chapter 8 covers the methods used by the manufacturer to increase the corrosion protection of vehicles so that they will last longer. What causes corrosion is also covered, as well as the use of special metal to retard it, how to use weld-through primer, the cleaning of the weld, and the application of epoxy primers and undercoats inside and out. Different types of sealers and their uses and how undercoating is applied to protect metal surfaces are described.

The student, tradesperson, estimator, trainee, or adjuster trainee who desires to increase his or her knowledge may want to read and study the two following textbooks: *Autobody Refinishing Handbook*, by A. G. Deroche, and *The Principles of Auto Body Repairing and Painting*, by A. G. Deroche and N. N. Hildebrand, both available from Prentice-Hall, Inc., Englewood Cliffs, New Jersey.

Andre G. Deroche

Acknowledgments

The author wishes to acknowledge the help and encouragement of the many companies and individuals that helped to make this book possible. Special credit is due to the following companies.

Auto Body Connection, Erie, Pennsylvania, 16501

Applied Power (Canada) Mississauga, Ontario, Canada

ARN-WOOD CO., Inc. @ Chief Automotive Systems, Inc., Grand Island NE 68802

Bear Manufacturing Co., Toronto, Ontario, Canada

Chart Industries Ltd., Pickering, Ontario, Canada

Chrysler Canada, Windsor, Ontario, Canada

E.S.D. Enterprises, Warren, Manitoba, Canada

Firestone Canada, Inc., Hamilton, Ontario, Canada

Ford Motor Company, Oakville, Ontario, Canada

General Motors of Canada, Oshawa, Ontario, Canada

Inter-Industry Conference on Auto Collision Repair, Des Plaines, Illinois, USA

Mitchell Information Services, Inc., San Diego, California, USA

National Automobile Dealers Used Car Guide Co., McLean, Virginia, USA

Pro Auto Ltd., Vermette, Manitoba, Canada

## CHAPTER ONE

Fundamentals of Writing an Estimate

1-1 THE ESTIMATOR AND THE KNOWLEDGE REQUIRED

A good estimator is invaluable to a body shop or insurance company as the estimator is the person who deals with the customer, whether for an insurance claim or not. In the body shop the estimator must be able to write an estimate that is accurate and easy for the insured customer to understand. The estimator must also be able to deal with the noninsurance customer and with the estimator or adjustor representing an insurance company.

The estimator must keep up to date with all changes that occur in the repair field, whether in frame repair, body repair, or painting. In recent years the good estimator has had to deal with great change in the automobile industry in methods of construction, types of materials used, and methods and types of paint used.

Manufacturers have changed the construction of the average family automobile by changing from a rear-wheel drive to a front-wheel drive power train. This has meant a great change in the types of metals used and in the engineering design of these vehicles. The qualified estimator has had to understand the power trains, transmissions, rear axles and the transaxles used in these newer types of automobiles. Knowledge of the design and types of brakes and types of rear axles and front suspension parts is required

for the estimator to be a good troubleshooter when investigating problems and attempting to make sound, practical decisions (Fig. 1-1).

When the estimator is required to write an estimate when examining a collision or a noncollision type of repair, the estimate must be fair in price to the customer, insurance company, and body shop. The estimator must examine the damage and, if it is from a collision, decide whether the damaged parts must be replaced or are repairable. It is unwise to estimate for all new parts both from an economical and practical standpoint, as some parts may be repairable or replaced with quality used parts available from a recycler.

It is always easier to list for new parts, but if the estimator followed this procedure, the estimated price would often be too high and the job lost to another shop. Therefore, the estimator must be able to judge how seriously damaged the parts are, what parts can be repaired, and what parts can be replaced by either new or recycled parts so that the written estimate is a fair price for the job to be done.

If the vehicle has been extensively damaged, the estimator must know the value of vehicle so that when the estimate is finished the amount of money required for the repairs will not exceed the market value of the vehicle. Through day-to-day exposure to making estimating

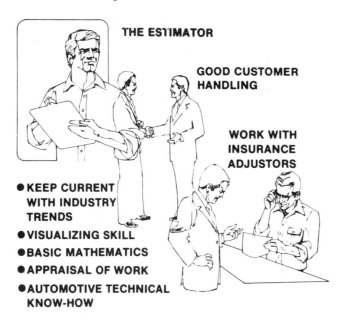

FIGURE 1-1 A broad range of skills is required by a qualified estimator. (Courtesy of Ford Motor Company of Canada Ltd.)

decisions and after making many estimates, the estimator will become proficient. The estimator must review his or her estimates after each vehicle has been repaired to check if a profit or loss occurred on the particular job. If the estimator does a careful analysis of the written estimates and the vehicle repair cost established after completion, it will help to develop the necessary decision-making skills (Fig. 1-2).

The type of facility used as a shop can have a great effect on the number of estimated vehicles that the shop will repair. Customers prefer to do business with a clean, efficient, and friendly shop. The type of equipment in the shop and the ability of the technicians to perform and do the work on time will affect the profit and loss on any job done in the shop. These factors will also help determine to a great degree what parts need be replaced and what parts can be repaired.

The market for good estimators is always growing as the amount of vehicles on the highways is always increasing (Fig. 1-3). The growing number of vehicles leads to more traffic congestion, which usually leads to more traffic accidents. These accidents can be minor "fender benders" or more extensive major collisions, or the vehicle may be written off due to the cost of the repairs.

FIGURE 1-2 Decision making is part of an estimator's job. (Courtesy of Ford Motor Company of Canada Ltd.)

FIGURE 1-3 North American vehicle numbers increase every year. (Courtesy of Ford Motor Company of Canada Ltd.)

FIGURE 1-4 A professional estimator must build his or her work on a solid foundation of technical knowledge. (Courtesy of Ford Motor Company of Canada Ltd.)

Accidents can happen on lightly traveled roads as well as congested highways. Usually, on lightly traveled roads one- or two-vehicle accidents occur, but on congested highways multiple-vehicle accidents are fairly common. Accidents are caused by weather conditions, dangerous driving methods, and very often lack of courtesy by the driving public. Damaged vehicles are driven or towed to insurance service centers or body shops to obtain estimates on the particular damage so that repair procedures may proceed.

It is therefore easy to see the need that increases every year for professionally qualified, ethical estimators to enter the field of professional estimating. A qualified estimator with the desire to succeed in this profession on a full-time basis has excellent opportunities. But to be successful, it is necessary that the estimator master the required fundamentals (Fig. 1-4).

1-2 AUTOMOTIVE DESIGN TRENDS

Auto manufacturers have spent a great deal of money and time in designing vehicles that are safer to drive and also get more miles per gallon, or use less liters of gasoline per 100 kilometers. These new vehicles were redesigned and downsized, and the weight was reduced by using new building techniques and new types of thinner-gauge metal in structural members and body panels. To accomplish this without jeopardizing the strength and safety of automobiles, design engineers have turned more and more to the use of lightweight plastics, aluminum, and high-strength steel (HSS), also known as high-strength, low-alloy steel (HSLA).

Steel is produced from iron, carbon, and certain additional alloy materials, such as chromium, manganese, nickel, and others, each mixed according to a specific formula, giving it certain properties. One of these properties is yield strength, the resistance that a particular type of steel possesses to permanent stretching.

Steel possessing a yield strength of up to 35,000 psi (241,000 kPa) is called mild steel and up until 1980 was used extensively in manufacturing automobiles of standard or conventional as well as unitized body construction (described later in this chapter).

Steel with a yield strength of 40,000 to 150,000 psi (276,000 kPa to 1034 MPa) is called high-strength steel and is used on all late-model automobiles of unitized body construction.

Steel, when examined under a microscope, is found to be composed of small particles or grains, arranged in a general pattern or structure (Fig. 1-5). When precise amounts of certain alloys are added to basic steel at the furnace in the steel mill, this grain structure is altered, imparting special qualities to the steel, qualities such as greater yield strength, hardness, flexibility, or resistance to corrosion. Mild steel is composed of large grains that are widely spaced; high-strength steel has far smaller grains that are more densely packed together (Fig. 1-6). The interlocking of the grains and the forces of attraction of the grains to each other give high-strength steel its superb strength.

There are three main reasons why automobile manufacturers are using high-strength steel wherever possible:

1. It enables them to reduce the weight of the vehicle by cutting down the gauge or thickness of its structural members and sheet-metal panels, without sacrificing strength.
2. Most autobody parts can be made of high-strength steel without changing existing dies or tooling.
3. Manufacturers have found the use of high-strength steel to be the cheaper method of reducing the weight of the automobiles rather than aluminum or plastics.

Following is a brief description of some of the different high-strength steels produced and for what body parts each type is used:

*   Rephosphorized steel, which has a yield strength of 40,000 psi (276,000 kPa), is used in rear rails, rear seat backs, seat cushions, A pillars, and various suspension parts.
*   Nitrogenized steel, which also has a yield strength of 40,000 psi (276,000 kPa), is used in front side rails, tie-down reinforcements, and various brackets.
*   High-strength, low-alloy steel with a yield strength of 50,000 psi (345,000 kPa) is used for window regulator arms and suspension brackets.
*   High-strength, low-alloy steel with a yield strength of 80,000 psi (552,000 kPa) is used for rear suspension cross-members and track bars.
*   Ultrahigh-strength steel, which has a yield strength of 85,000 psi (586,000 kPa), is specially processed (cold rolled, full hard) and used for rear-door guard beams. When processed with a yield strength of 120,000 psi (827 MPa), it is employed in front and rear bumper reinforcements, and when processed

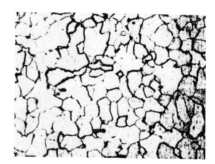

1977 Pontiac frame rail (mild steel) grain structure before heating. Note the large grains and loose arrangement. (400X magnification)

FIGURE 1-5   Grain structure of Pontiac (mild steel) frame rail before heating. (Courtesy of Blackhawk, Division of Applied Power of Canada Ltd.)

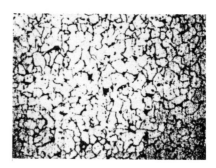

Ford Escort front inner rail (HSS) grain structure before heating. Note the smaller grains and tighter arrangement than in the mild steel (400X)

FIGURE 1-6   Grain structure of Ford Escort H.S.S. frame rail before heating. (Courtesy of Blackhawk, Division of Applied Power of Canada Ltd.)

with a yield strength of 140,000 psi (965 MPa), it is used for front-door guard beams.
*   Martensitic steel, which has a yield strength of 150,000 psi (1034 MPa), is the strongest, hardest, and most brittle steel produced and is used for front-door guard beams.

All auto manufacturers recommend that all welding on late-model automobiles of high-strength-steel construction be done using only the MIG (metal inert gas) welding process, that the use of the oxyacetylene torch be restricted and limited to heating only in the repair of automobiles, and that it be used very carefully and sparingly and only when absolutely necessary, as discussed in Chapter 6. Manufacturers recommend that no heat whatsoever be used on parts made of martensitic or ultrahigh-strength steel.

Some high-strength-steel parts should not be heated beyond 1200°F (643.3°C) for more than 3 minutes; others, made of high-strength steel and high-strength, low-alloy steel, if heated beyond 700°F (371.1°C), begin to lose strength, and if heated to 1000°F (537.7°C), revert to the strength level of plain, low-carbon steel (Fig. 1-7).

Since this loss of strength can lead to future failure of a structural member or part, insurance claim adjusters, estimators, autobody repair shops, and body technicians all have an interest in seeing to it that proper repair methods are used.

Structural failure on a repaired automobile will occur,

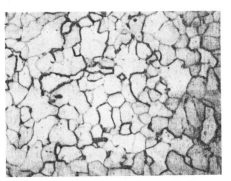

1977 Pontiac frame rail (mild steel) grain structure before heating. Note the large grains and loose arrangement. (400X magnification)

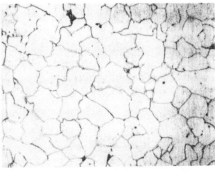

Pontiac rail after heating to 1700°F for 2 minutes and air cooling. Note that the structure is almost unchanged from the unheated sample. (400X)

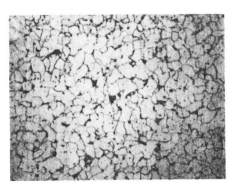

Ford Escort front inner rail (HSS) grain structure before heating. Note the smaller grains and tighter arrangement than in the mild steel. (400X)

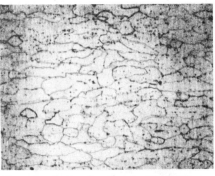

Escort rail after heating to 1050°F for 2 minutes and air cooling. Note that the grains have grown larger and the arrangement has gotten looser. (400X)

FIGURE 1-7 Effect of heat on the granular structure of mild- and high-strength steel. (Courtesy of Blackhawk, Division of Applied Power of Canada Ltd.)

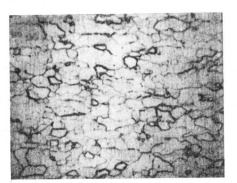

Escort rail after heating to 1200°F for 2 minutes and air cooling. Note that the grains have remained about the same size, but don't appear to fit together as well. (400X)

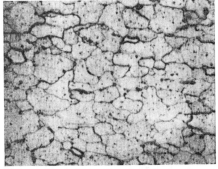

Escort rail after heating to 1700°F for 2 minutes and air cooling. Note that both grain size and structure have deteriorated almost to the level of mild steel. (400X)

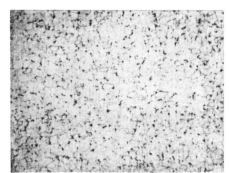

General Motors X-car front rail (HSS) grain structure before heating. Note the still smaller grains and even tighter arrangement (400X)

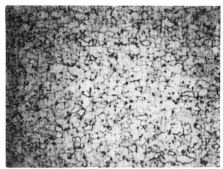

X-car rail after heating to 1050°F for 2 minutes and air cooling. Note that there is almost no change in grain size or structure at this temperature. (400X)

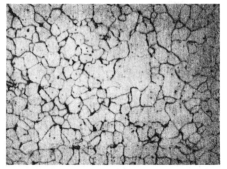

X-car rail after heating to 1200°F for 2 minutes and air cooling. Note that the grains have started to gobble each other up, and that the arrangement has gotten slightly looser. (400X)

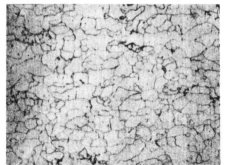

X-car rail after heating to 1700°F for 2 minutes and air cooling. Note that some parts have deteriorated more than others despite the even heating, and some areas are approaching the appearance of mild steel. (400X)

FIGURE 1-7   (cont.)

if at all, after the car is back on the road. The failure will be in the metal adjoining the weld, leading to a critical loss of strength, which causes the part to crack and tear under stress or load.

In the standard or conventional body construction (Fig. 1-8), the body and the frame are two entirely separate units and are held together at various points by means of body bolts that are usually tightened with torque wrenches to the manufacturer's specifications. Rubber insulators and various thicknesses of shim stock separate the body and frame at these points; they prevent squeaks from developing and road noises from being transmitted through the frame to the body. If necessary, by either removing or adding shims at these points, easy and accurate alignment of the body and frame is obtained. Frames used in this type of construction can be of the perimeter or ladder type; these are described and illustrated in Chapter 6.

In unitized body construction, which includes the newer unitized, HSS-constructed automobiles, both the frame and the body are made from a large number of sheet-

metal panels of varying sizes and shapes (Fig. 1-9). These are assembled and welded into a single unit. This type of construction gives an overall rigidity to the integral body construction. The strength that these bodies possess is drawn from each of the many individual panels, which, after they have been welded together, make up the body shell. The necessary attachments required to hold the power train and the suspension system are built into the reinforced floor pans, side rails, and cross-members; these are called the *underbody* section. It is this section that provides the greatest amount of strength to the body. This type of construction eliminates the independent body and frame and is dealt with in detail in Chapter 6.

One of the latest types of unitized body construction, employing "space-frame" technology, gives great structural strength to the automobile and also keeps its overall weight to a minimum (Fig. 1-10). The all-steel framework, composed of six modular units (Fig. 1-11), each made up of many smaller parts of different types of high-strength steel, is automatically welded together. The welded space

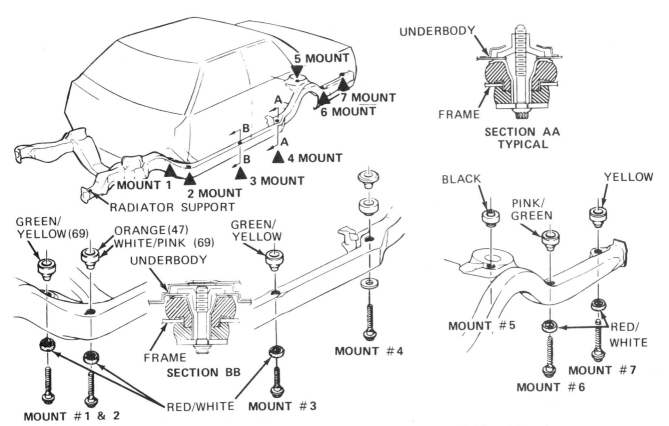

FIGURE 1-8 Typical frame and body mounts: two-door coupe (1947) and four door (1969). (Courtesy of General Motors of Canada Ltd.)

frame is clamped in a "mill and drill fixture" that drills holes in their exact location on all mounting pads to which the exterior Enduroflex panels (Fig. 1-12) are then attached.

Some manufacturers also employ what is known as a modified form of unitized body construction (Fig. 1-13), consisting of half frame and half unitized body construction. The frame consists of short, stubby side rails that usually extend from behind the front doors to the front of the vehicle and are joined by lateral cross-members. This frame provides support for the front-wheel suspension, engine, transmission, steering mechanism, and front-end sheet metal. The rear section of the vehicle has the frame built into the underbody section and forms an integral part of the body.

When an automobile is brought into the autobody shop for repairs, the estimator and the autobody technician should know the correct name of all the many parts, assemblies, and sections of an automobile body. Not only will this knowledge enable them to repair, align, and replace damaged parts in accordance with the shop estimate, but it will enable them to order parts intelligently, thereby eliminating the needless delivery of wrong repair parts and greatly assisting in preparing estimates when the opportunity arises.

Figure 1-14 shows typical sheet-metal body parts, panels, and assemblies.

An automobile body is generally divided into four sections: the front, the upper or top, the rear, and the underbody. These sections are further divided into even small units, called *assemblies,* which in turn are divided into smaller units, called *parts.*

The front section is composed of a number of assemblies, such as the grille, the hood, the right and left fender, and the cowl assembly.

The cowl assembly, one of the largest of all assemblies, is composed of the shroud upper panel, shroud vent panel, windshield glass support, instrument panel, front-body hinge pillar to rocker panel, and the dash panel.

The roof panel is usually the largest of all body panels and is supported by the upper inner windshield frame, the front-body hinge pillars, the longitudinal roof bows on its sides, and the inner back window panel at the rear. The center of the roof panel is reinforced by the roof bow.

The quarter-panel assemblies are located in the rear section of the automobile and are composed of the lower inner rear quarter-panel, wheelhouse panel, and outer rear quarter side panel.

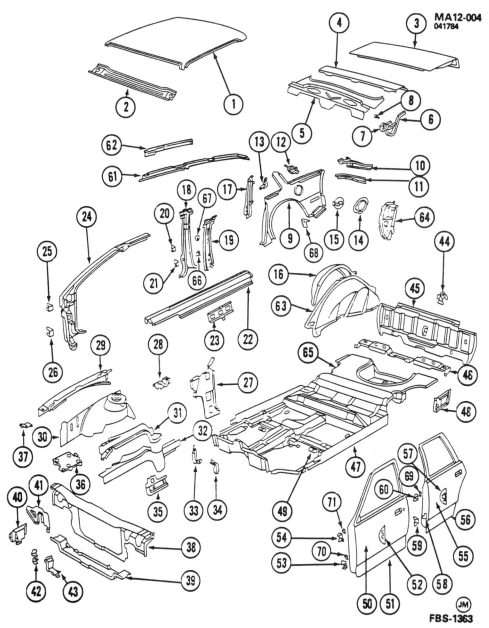

MA12-004
041784

FBS-1363

1. **PANEL:** Roof (Exc AD3)
   PANEL: Roof (1982 W/AD3)(1985 W/AD3)
   PANEL: Roof-W/FULL VINYL (CB5) (1984–85)
2. **FRAME:** W/S Inr Upr
3. **LID:** Compt
4. **PANEL:** Compt Frt
5. **PANEL:** R/Seat To Bk Wdo
6. **STRAP:** Hge C/Lid & Supt
7. **BOX:** Hge C/Lid-RH
   BOX: Hge C/Lid-LH
8. **PIN:** Compt Lid Hgw
9. **PANEL:** Qtr Otr-RH
   PANEL: Qtr Otr-LH
10. **EXTENSION:** Q/Otr To R/Pnl-RH
    EXTENSION: Q/Otr To R/Pnl-LH
11. **RETAINER:** Tr On R/Pnl-RH (1982)
    RETAINER: Tr On R/Pnl-LH (1982)

12. **EXTENSION:** Q/Otr Pnl At B/W-RH
    EXTENSION: Q/Otr Pnl At B/W-LH
13. **FILLER:** Q/Wdo Lwr Cor-RH
    FILLER: Q/Wdo Lwr Cor-LH
14. **FILLER:** Q/Otr Pnl At Tank
15. **DOOR:** Fuel Tank Fil
16. **PANEL:** W/H Otr-RH
    PANEL: W/H Otr-LH
17. **PANEL:** Lk Plr Inr Upr-RH ''C'' Pillar
    PANEL: Lk Plr Inr Upr-LH
18. **PANEL:** C/Plr Otr-RH ''B'' Pillar
    PANEL: C/Plr Otr-LH
19. **PANEL:** C/Plr Inr-RH
    PANEL: C/Plr Inr-LH
20. **STRAP:** Hge Upr Bdy Si-RH
    STRAP: Hge Upr Bdy Si-LH
21. **STRAP:** Hge Lwr Bdy Si-RH

FIGURE 1-9 1982–1987 A19 body sheet metal. (Courtesy of General Motors of Canada Ltd.)

STRAP: Hge Lwr Bdy Si-LH
22. PANEL: Rkr Otr-RH
    PANEL: Rkr Otr-LH
23. REINFORCEMENT: Rkr Otr Pnl
24. PANEL: Hge Plr-RH "A" Pillar
    PANEL: Hge Plr-LH
25. STRAP: Hge Upr Bdy Si-RH
    STRAP: Hge Upr Bdy Si-LH
26. STRAP: Hge Lwr Bdy Si-RH
    STRAP: Hge Lwr Bdy Si-LH
27. REINFORCEMENT: Hge Plr Inr Pnl-RH
    REINFORCEMENT: Hge Plr Inr Pnl-LH
28. HINGE: Hood-RH
    HINGE: Hood-LH
29. RAIL: M/Compt Si Upr-RH
    RAIL: M/Compt Si Upr-LH
30. PANEL: M/C Si & W/H-RH
    PANEL: M/C Si & W/H-LH
31. RAIL: M/Compt Si Otr-RH
    RAIL: M/Compt Si Otr-LH
32. RAIL: M/Compt Si Inr-RH
    RAIL: M/Compt Si Inr-LH
33. EXTENSION: M/C Si Otr F/Rail-RH
    EXTENSION: M/C Si Otr F/Rail-LH
34. EXTENSION: M/C Si Inr Rail-RH
    EXTENSION: M/C Si Inr Rail-LH
35. RAIL: Mtr Comps Si Otr-RH
    RAIL: Mtr Comps Si Otr-LH
36. TRAY: Battery (1982–83 W/4.3T Exc H.D. Bat)
    TRAY: Battery (1982–83 W/4.3T & H.D. Bat)
    TRAY: Battery (1984–85 W/4.3T Exc H.D. Bat)
    TRAY: Battery (1984–85 W/4.3T & H.D. Bat)
37. EXTENSION: Mtr Compt Frt To Upr Rail-RH
    EXTENSION: Mtr Compt Frt To Upr Rail-LH
38. PANEL: Mtr Compt Frt
39. BAR: R/End Lwr Tie
40. EXTENSION: Mtr Compt Si Rail Frt-RH
    EXTENSION: Mtr Compt Si Rail Frt-LH
41. EXTENSION: Mtr Compt Frt Pnl To Rail-RH
    EXTENSION: Mtr Compt Frt Pnl To Rail-LH
42. SUPPORT: Bar F/End Lwr
43. REINFORCEMENT: F/End Lwr Tie Bar-RH
    REINFORCEMENT: F/End Lwr Tie Bar-LH
44. STRIKER: Lid C/Lid
45. PANEL: R/End

46. SUPPORT: R/End Fin Pnl (OLDS Only)
47. PAN: Compartment
48. FILLER: Pan Compt To Qtr Pnl-RH
    FILLER: Pan Compt To Qtr Pnl-LH
49. COVER: Floor Pan Gage & Drn Hole
    COVER: Compt Pan Gage & Drn Hole (1982–83)
    COVER: Compt Pan Gage & Drn Hole (1984–85)
50. DOOR: Frt-RH
    DOOR: Frt-LH
51. PANEL: F/D Otr-RH
    PANEL: F/D Otr-LH
52. BAR: F/D Otr-RH
    BAR: F/D Otr-LH
53. STRAP: Hge F/D Lwr Door Si-RH
    STRAP: Hge F/D Lwr Door si-LH
54. STRAP: Hge F/D Upr Door Si-RH
    STRAP: Hge F/D Upr Door Si-LH
55. DOOR: Rr-RH
    DOOR: Rr-LH
56. PANEL: R/D Otr-RH
    PANEL: R/D Otr-LH
57. BAR: R/D Otr-RH
    BAR: R/D Otr-LH
58. PLATE: Anc R/D Lwr Hge Dr Si
59. STRAP: Hge R/D Lwr Do Si-RH
    STRAP: Hge R/D Lwr Do Si-LH
60. STRAP: Hge R/F Upr Do Si
61. RAIL: Si Rf Inr-RH
    RAIL: Si Rf Inr-LH
62. RAIL: Si Rf Otr-RH
    RAIL: Si Rf Otr-LH
63. PANEL: W/H Inr-RH
    PANEL: W/H Inr-LH
64. EXTENSION: Q/Otr to R/End Pnl Lwr-RH
    EXTENSION: Q/Otr to R/End Pnl Lwr-LH
65. PAN: Compartment
66. PLATE: R/D Lwr Hge Body Si Anc-RH (1983–85)
    PLATE: R/D Lwr Hge Body Si Anc-LH (1983–85)
67. PLATE: R/D Upr Hge Body Si Anc-RH (1983–85)
    PLATE: R/D Upr Hge Body Si Anc-LH (1983–85)
68. SUPPORT: Filler Neck Stone Shield (1983–85)
69. PLATE: R/D Upr Hge Dr Si Anc
70. PLATE: F/D Lwr Hge Dr Si Anc
71. PLATE: F/D Upr Hge Dr Si Anc

FIGURE 1-9   (cont.)

The automobile body is divided into three distinctly separate compartments and these are serviced by the following assemblies. Doors provide easy access to the body compartment, hoods to the engine compartment, and the deck lids to the luggage compartment. They are all similar in design and construction in that each is made with an outer panel whose flanged edges are folded over and spot-welded to a box-type frame or inner construction, thus giving them a great deal of strength. All are mounted on hinges and equipped with locks for easy opening and closing.

Rocker panels are rust-proofed assemblies of box-type construction and are composed of the outer door-opening rocker panel, the rear outer rocker panel reinforcement, and the front outer-rocker panel reinforcement. They are located directly below the doors and are not only spot-welded to the sides of the floor pans, thereby greatly reinforcing the underbody section, but also to the cowl assembly in front and the rear quarter-panel assembly at the rear.

The front and rear bumpers (Figs. 1-15, and 1-16) provide a certain amount of protection to the automobile

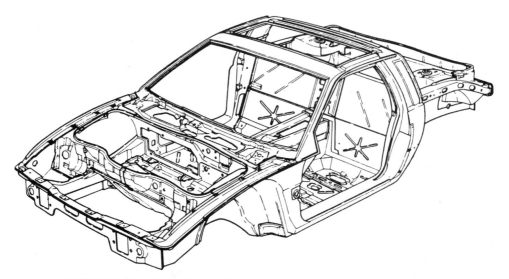

FIGURE 1-10 Space frame. (Courtesy of General Motors of Canada Ltd.)

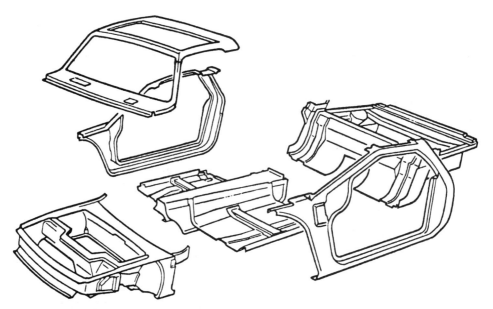

FIGURE 1-11 Space frame modules (Courtesy of General Motors of Canada, Ltd.)

and enhance its appearance. The bumpers are held in position by means of brackets, shock absorbers or isolators that are bolted to each end of the frame side rails, commonly called *frame horns.*

Slotted holes, either in the brackets or in the frame horns, off-center washers, and cam-equipped bolts are employed in the installation and adjustment of automobile bumpers.

On automobiles of standard or conventional body construction, most of the front-end sheet-metal parts (Fig.

1-17) are bolted together, but in automobiles of unitized body construction most of the parts (except those that have to be removed for periodic servicing) are spot-welded together. These methods vary somewhat from model to model and from year to year, however, and are predetermined by the design and styling of a particular automobile and the assembly system employed by the manufacturer.

The grilles are usually held in place by screws, bolts, or even rivets and are die-cast or made out of plastic, aluminum, or stamped sheet metal, which is then chrome

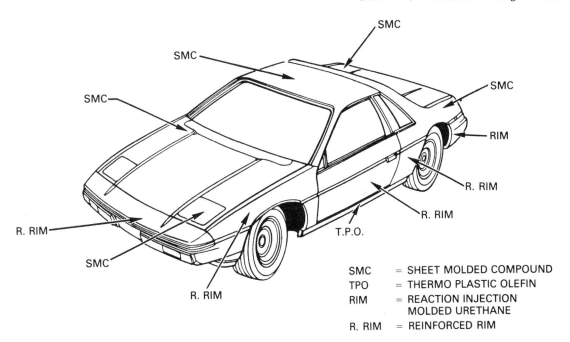

SMC	= SHEET MOLDED COMPOUND
TPO	= THERMO PLASTIC OLEFIN
RIM	= REACTION INJECTION MOLDED URETHANE
R. RIM	= REINFORCED RIM

FIGURE 1-12 All-plastic Enduroflex exterior body panels. (Courtesy of General Motors of Canada Ltd.)

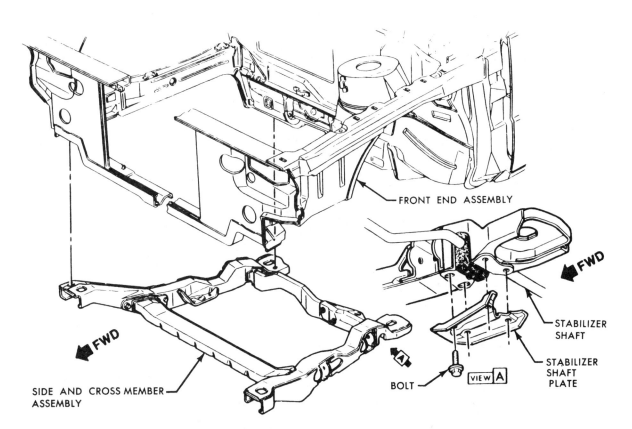

FIGURE 1-13 Side and cross-member assembly. (Courtesy of General Motors of Canada Ltd.)

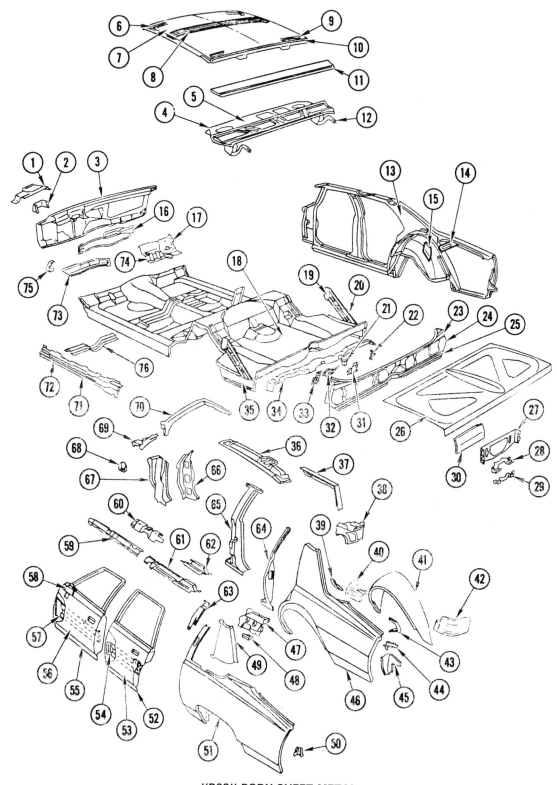

"B69" BODY SHEET METAL

1. **PLATE ASM:** Fender on Dash Mounting.
2. **SUPPORT ASM:** Fender Skirt (exc. Olds & Cadillac).
3. **PANEL ASM:** Dash.
4. **REINFORCEMENT:** Rear Seat to Back Window.
5. **PANEL:** Rear Seat to Back Window.
6. **FRAME:** Windshield Inner Upper.
7. **PANEL:** Roof Outer.
8. **BOW:** Roof No.1

FIGURE 1-14 Body shell components and sheet metal. (Courtesy of General Motors of Canada Ltd.)

9. **PANEL:** Back Window Inner Upper (''C'' Styles).
10. **PANEL:** Back Window Upper (''B'' Styles).
11. **PANEL:** Compartment Front.
12. **BOX ASM:** Rear Compartment Lid Hinge.
    STRAP & LINK ASM: Rear Compartment Lid Hinge.
    ROD: Compartment Lid Hinge Torque.
    PIN: Rear Compartment Lid Hinge.
13. **PANEL:** Quarter Inner Upper.
14. **BRACE:** Compartment Gutter to Wheelhouse (Chev.).
15. **BRACE:** Compartment Lid Hinge to Wheelhouse.
16. **REINFORCEMENT:** Dash Panel (Cadillac).
17. **FILLER:** Floor Pan to Rocker Inner Front.
18. **PAN ASM:** Compartment.
19. **BRACE:** Wheelhouse to Compt. Pan Diagonal Front (Cadillac).
20. **BRACE:** Wheelhouse to Compt. Pan Diagonal (Cadillac).
21. **PLATE:** Compartment Lid Mechanical Closing (Cadillac).
22. **STRIKER:** Compartment Lid Lock.
23. **PANEL:** Rear End Upper (Buick).
24. **PANEL:** Rear End.
25. **PANEL:** Rear End Lower (Buick ''C'').
26. **PANEL ASM:** Compartment Lid.
27. **POCKET ASM:** License Plate. Mounting (Chev. & Pontiac).
28. **SUPPORT:** License Plate (Pontiac).
29. **SUPPORT:** Tail Lamp & Rear End Panel Mounting (Pontiac).
30. **PANEL:** Rear End Finish (Pontiac).
31. **SUPPORT ASM:** Rear Bumper Skid (Olds).
32. **REINFORCEMENT:** Rear End Panel Center (Buick).
33. **REINFORCEMENT:** Rear End Panel At License Plate (Chev. & Pontiac)
34. **BAR ASM:** Compartment Pan Rear Cross.
35. **FILLER:** Quarter Panel to Compartment Pan.
36. **RAIL:** Side Roof Inner.
37. **RAIL ASM:** Side Roof Outer.
38. **EXTENSION:** Rear Seat to Back Window (''C'' Styles).
39. **FILLER:** Quarter Panel at Back Window Lower (''C'' Styles).
40. **REINFORCEMENT:** Quarter Outer Panel.
41. **PANEL:** Wheelhouse Outer.
42. **SHIELD:** Tailpipe & Frame-On Wheelhouse.

43. **FILLER:** Quarter Outer to Rear End Panel Upper (Pontiac).
44. **SUPPORT:** Rear End Finish Panel to Rear End (Pontiac).
45. **EXTENSION:** Compartment to Quarter Panel Filler (''B'' Styles).
46. **PANEL:** Quarter Outer.
47. **GUTTER:** Quarter Window Run (''D'' Styles).
48. **FILLER:** Quarter Panel to Back Window Reinforcement (''D'' Styles).
49. **PANEL:** Quartr Ouarter Rear (''D'' Styles).
50. **SUPPORT:** Rear End Finish Panel (Cadillac).
51. **PANEL:** Quarter Outer Front (''D'' Styles).
52. **DOOR ASM:** Rear.
53. **PANEL:** Rear Door Outer.
54. **BAR ASM:** Rear Door Outer.
55. **DOOR ASM:** Front.
56. **PANEL:** Front Door Outer.
57. **BAR ASM:** Front Door Outer.
58. **REINFORCEMENT:** Front Door Outer Panel-At Mirror.
59. **RAIL ASM:** Front Side Roof Outer (''D'' Styles).
60. **RAIL ASM:** Front Side Roof Inner ''D'' Styles).
61. **RAIL ASM:** Rear Side Roof Outer (''D'' Styles).
62. **RAIL:** Rear Side Roof Inner (''D'' Styles).
63. **PANEL ASM:** Body Lock Pillar Inner Upper (''D'' Styles).
64. **PANEL ASM:** Body Lock Pillar Outer ''C'' Pillar.
65. **PILLAR ASM:** Center ''B'' Pillar.
66. **REINFORCEMENT ASM:** Front Body Hinge Pillar.
67. **PANEL:** Front Body Hinge Pillar Lower.
68. **PLATE:** Front Fender on Pillar Mounting.
69. **BRACE:** Windshield Lower Frame Reinforcement.
70. **RAIL ASM:** Windshield Side Frame & Reinforcement-Front. ''A'' Pillar.
71. **PANEL:** Rocker Outer (''B, C'' Styles).
72. **PANEL:** Rocker Outer-Front (''D'' Styles).
73. **REINFORCEMENT:** Dash Panel (Cadillac).
74. **BRACE ASM:** Dash to Chassis Frame.
75. **SUPPORT ASM:** Dash Panel Reinforcement to Chassis (Cadillac).
76. **REINFORCEMENT:** Front Seat Cross Bar Underbody (Exc. Buick).

FIGURE 1-14 (cont.)

plated. Figure 1-18 shows a typical grille assembly and the method used in securing it to the sheet metal.

Front-end sheet metal refers to all the panels from the cowl assembly forward, such as the right and left fender panels and their inner skirts, sometimes called wheelhouses (Fig. 1-19), the hood panel, stone deflector panel, and so on.

These panels, when assembled, cover the front sections of the frame and front wheel suspension system, keeping water, dirt, and dust raised by the wheels from splashing and covering the outer panels and windows of the body and making driving more comfortable and less hazardous. They also form a suitable compartment in which the engine can operate. The front-end sheet metal is held in position by such parts as the radiator support, the tie-bar assembly, and the valance panel (Fig. 1-20).

The top mounting bracket or flange, located near the rear end of many front fender panels, is bolted to the upper section of the lower shroud side panel (cowl assembly) (Fig. 1-21) and to the rocker panel at the bottom.

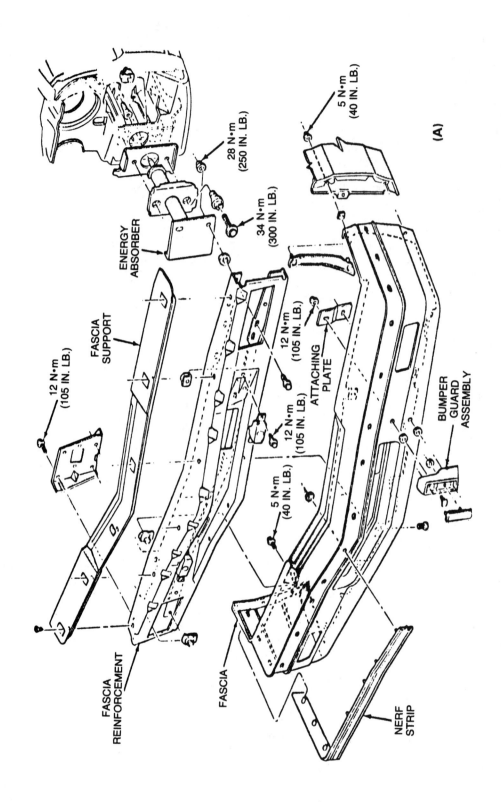

28 N·m (250 IN. LB.)

34 N·m (300 IN. LB.)

ENERGY ABSORBER

5 N·m (40 IN. LB.)

(A)

FASCIA SUPPORT

12 N·m (105 IN. LB.)

12 N·m (105 IN. LB.)

12 N·m (105 IN. LB.)

ATTACHING PLATE

BUMPER GUARD ASSEMBLY

5 N·m (40 IN. LB.)

FASCIA REINFORCEMENT

FASCIA

NERF STRIP

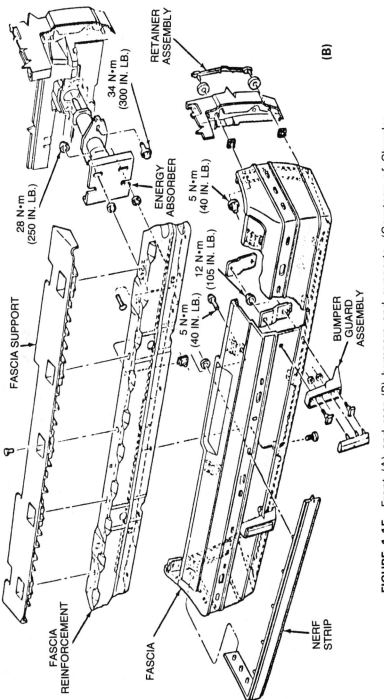

FIGURE 1-15 Front (A) and rear (B) bumpers and supports. (Courtesy of Chrysler Canada.)

RETAINER ASSEMBLY

(B)

34 N•m (300 IN. LB.)

28 N•m (250 IN. LB.)

ENERGY ABSORBER

5 N•m (40 IN. LB.)

FASCIA SUPPORT

12 N•m (105 IN. LB.)

5 N•m (40 IN. LB.)

BUMPER GUARD ASSEMBLY

FASCIA REINFORCEMENT

FASCIA

NERF STRIP

15

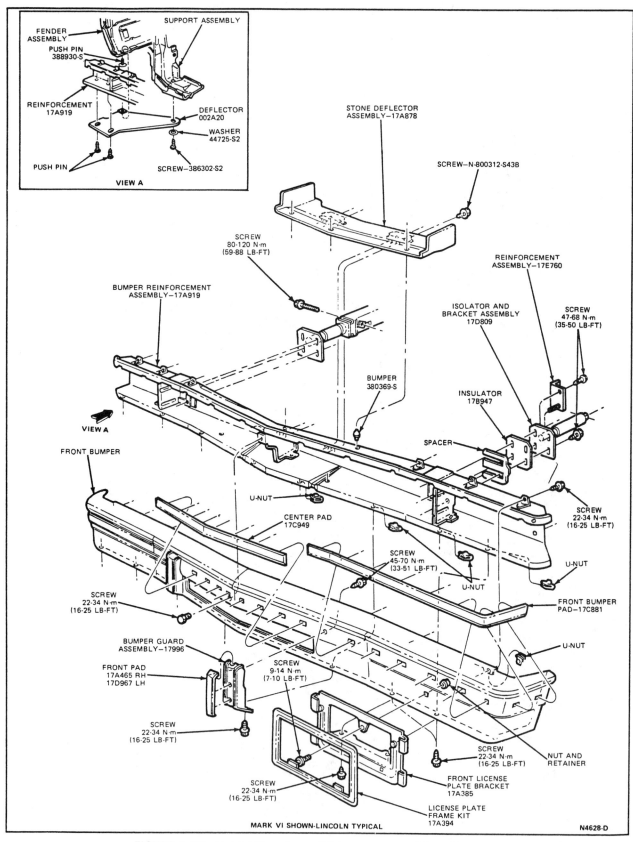

FIGURE 1-16 Front (A) and rear (B) bumper assemblies. (Courtesy of (A) Ford Motor Company of Canada Ltd. and (B) General Motors of Canada Ltd.)

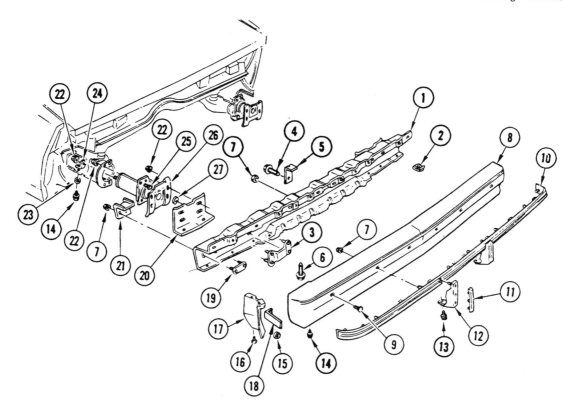

1. REINFORCEMENT
2. NUT
3. PLATE
4. BOLT
5. STRAP
6. SCREW
7. NUT
8. FACE BAR
9. BOLT
10. STRIP
11. CUSHION
12. GUARD
13. BOLT
14. BOLT

15. NUT
16. RETAINER
17. FILLER PANEL
18. REINFORCEMENT
19. SKID PLATE
20. SUPPORT
21. SKID PLATE
22. NUT
23. WASHER
24. BRACKET
25. BOLT
26. ABSORBER
27. RETAINER

FIGURE 1-16 (cont.)

The front of the fender panel is attached to the radiator support, which in turn is attached to the front of the frame horn. Shims are used to vary the height of the front of the fender between the frame and the radiator support (Fig. 1-22).

The hood panel not only serves as a finish panel to fill in the large space between the two front fenders, but it also prevents water from falling on the engine. It pivots on large hinges that are usually attached to either the cowl or front fender or both. It is held down at the front by a locking

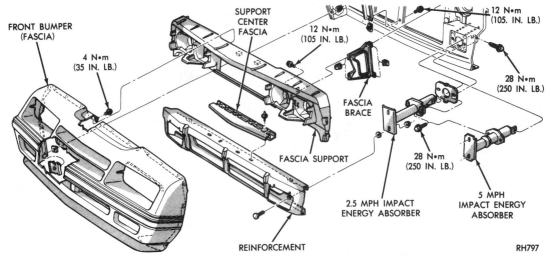

FIGURE 1-16C. Front cover and bumper assembly. (Courtesy of Chrysler Canada.)

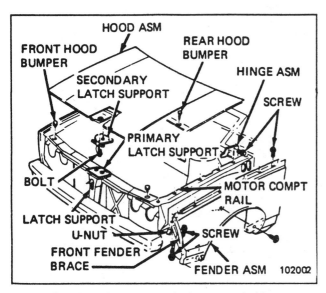

FIGURE 1-17 Front-end sheet metal. (Courtesy of General Motors of Canada Ltd.)

mechanism composed of a lock bolt and a lock plate (Fig. 1-23) or a remote-control hood latch (Fig. 1-24). Stationary as well as adjustable rubber bumpers are used to keep it cushioned and aligned in its opening and at the correct height (level) with the front fenders and the upper shroud (cowl) assembly panel. To perform the necessary adjustments and to obtain proper alignment of the body and the front-end sheet metal, the technician must be familiar with all adjustment methods that can be used (Fig. 1-25).

Auto manufacturers are making more use of fiberglass and resin to form such parts as fender extensions, header panels, quarter-panel extensions, and even hood trunk lids

and doors, depending on the car being manufactured. Flexible stone shields and impact strips for bumpers are used, as well as a front cover that is molded to the desired shape for styling the front part of the vehicle and covering the front bumper assembly (Fig. 1-16C). This cover is made from a synthetic rubberized type of material such as urethane. Kits to patch this material are available if the part is not damaged too extensively (see Chapter 4).

Many of the moldings and nameplates used are made of different plastics and are usually glued on using special adhesives. These fiberglass and resin plastics can be painted with the proper primers and flex agent (if required) is used in the paint as necessary

It is important that the estimator know the name of the moldings on a vehicle, as these items are also part of the repair estimate. Figure 1-26 shows a typical vehicle with its moldings.

1-3 DETERMINING THE EXTENT OF THE DAMAGE AND ITS COST

In recent years, many new developments have occurred due to new design or changes in materials; for safety reasons, new materials have been introduced that are able to absorb impacts (Fig. 1-27).

Glass Front, Rear and Side

The glass used on vehicles is usually safety glass for the windshield and heat-tempered glass for the side windows and the back window or backlite. Glass comes shaded with a tint if ordered by the customer as an option or as clear

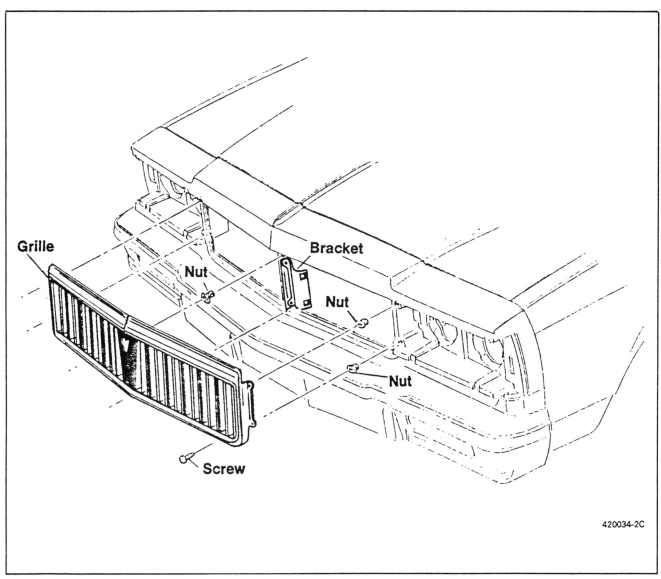

FIGURE 1-18 Grille assembly. (Courtesy of General Motors of Canada Ltd.)

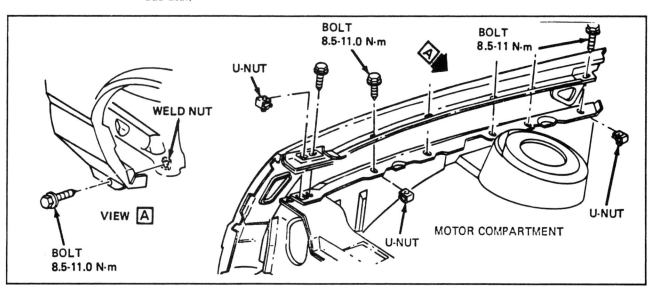

FIGURE 1-19 Fender and apron assembly. (Courtesy of General Motors of Canada Ltd.)

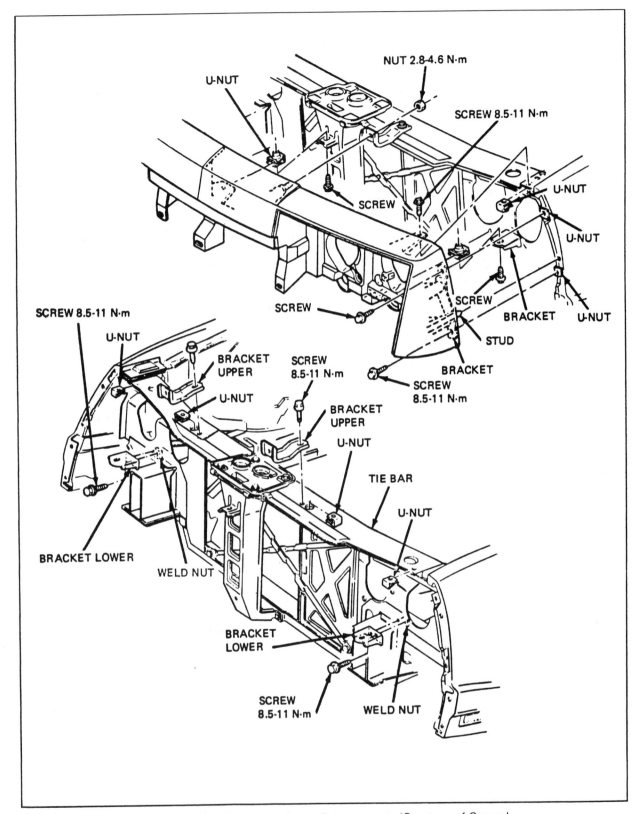

FIGURE 1-20 Header panel to radiator support. (Courtesy of General Motors of Canada Ltd.)

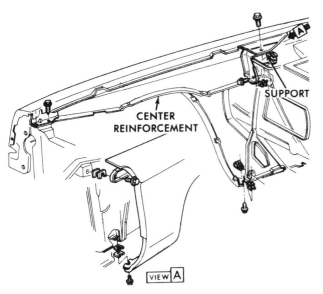

FIGURE 1-21 Attachment of front fender to cowl and rocker panel. (Courtesy of General Motors of Canada Ltd.)

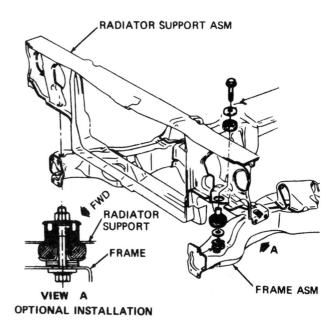

FIGURE 1-22 Attachment and shimming of radiator support to frame. (Courtesy of General Motors of Canada Ltd.)

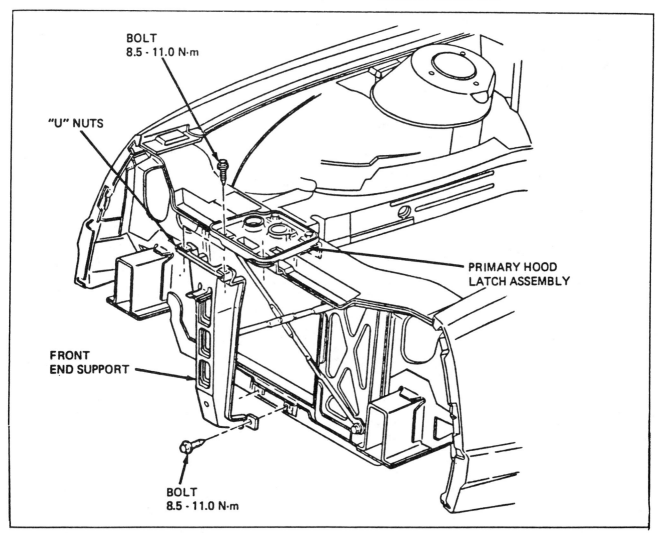

FIGURE 1-23 Hood latch support. (Courtesy of General Motors of Canada Ltd.)

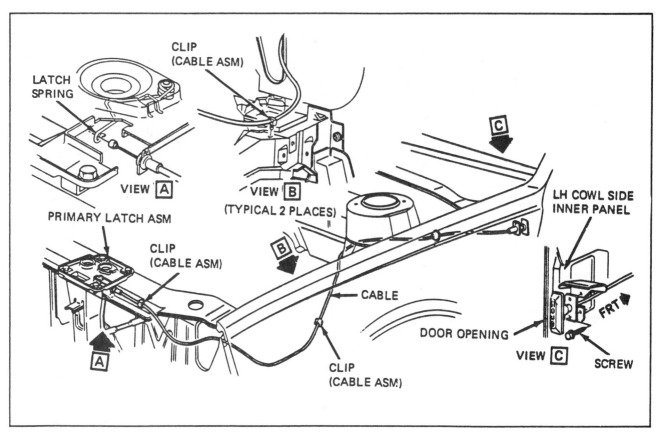

FIGURE 1-24 Remote-control hood latch assembly. (Courtesy of General Motors of Canada Ltd.)

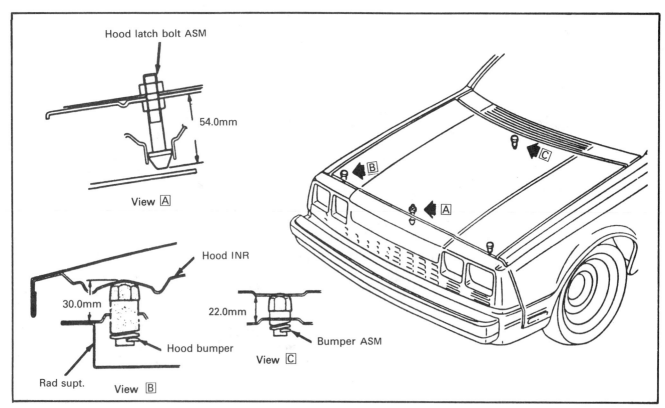

FIGURE 1-25 Series hood adjustment. (Courtesy of General Motors of Canada Ltd.)

1984-85 "A19-27" SIDE MOLDINGS BELOW BELT

1. MOLDING, F/Fdr-RH (Exc B88)
2. PLATE, Na F/D Otr Pnl "EUROSPORT"
3. MOLDING KIT, F/D Ctr-RH)Exc B88)
4. MOLDING, F/D Edge Guard-RH
5. MOLDING KIT, Rr Q/Frt Of Whl Opg-RH (Exc B88)
6. MOLDING KIT, Rr Whl Opg-RH (W/B96)(1984)
7. PLATE, Na Rr Compt Lid "CL" (Bla/Red)
8. PLATE, Na Rr Compt Lid "DIESEL"
9. PLATE, Na Rr Compt Lid "CHEVROLET"
10. PLATE, Na Rr Compt Lid "2.8V-6" (Bla/Red)
11. PLATE, Na Rr Compt Lid "2.5-FI" (Bla/Red)
12. MOLDING KIT, F/D/ Ctr-RH (Bla/Gray)
13. MOLDING KIT, R/D-RH (Bla/Gray)
14. MOLDING, R/D Edge Guard-RH
15. MOLDING KIT, Rr Qtr Frt of Whl Opg-RH (Bla/Gray)

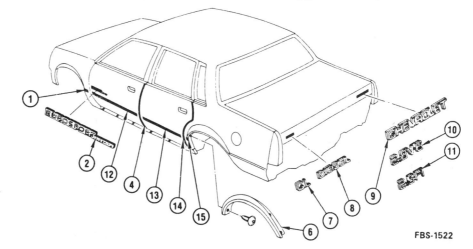

FIGURE 1-26 1984–1985 A19-27 side moldings below belt. (Courtesy of General Motors of Canada Ltd.)

FBS-1522

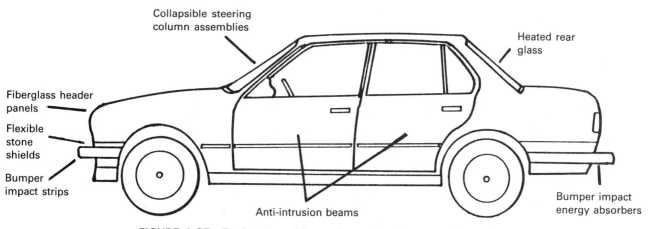

FIGURE 1-27 Engineering changes have brought many changes to the vehicle's construction.

glass if the customer does not desire the tinted glass. The windshield is made from safety glass, which has an energy-absorbing layer of clear or tinted vinyl between the two layers of the glass. The use of this type of glass construction helps reduce serious injuries when passengers hit it when the vehicle is stopped suddenly due to driver panic or an accident, because this type of glass is more resilient and will give. Regular glass breaks into sharp pieces. Yet safety glass has sufficient strength to meet specifications. The glass

used on side and backlites is tempered, and when hit hard enough to break, it will shatter in granular pieces. Some manufacturers use an etching on the glass to identify the type of glass and date of manufacture and whether it is shaded or laminated. (Fig. 1-28).

The estimator must know the details about the glass used as well as the methods of installation used by the manufacturers. On trucks and older automobiles, the windshield and back windows were held on the pinch weld

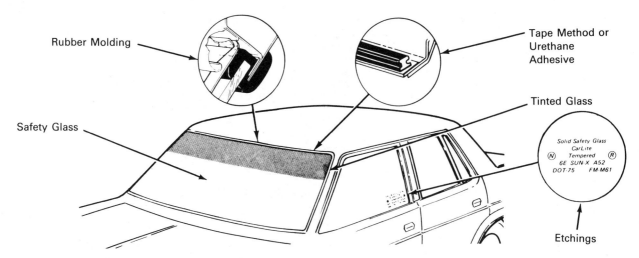

FIGURE 1-28 Details of glass construction and installation. (Courtesy of Ford Motor Company of Canada Ltd.)

flange by grooved weather stripping that held the glass in place. On more recent automobiles and even some trucks, the windshield and back lite were held with a butyl tape, but some manufacturers used urethane adhesive. Most new automobiles use urethane adhesive now, and if the windshield, backlite, or some door glass is removed for any reason, it must be replaced by using approved factory methods.

When replacing the glass held by a grooved rubber molding, caulking material must be used to seal the edge of the glass to rubber and rubber to metal. When using butyl tape, a kit consisting of butyl tape, primer and sealer must be purchased. When using urethane adhesive, a urethane kit consisting of a cleaner, primer, and adhesive must be used. These kits must be charged out to the particular job being repaired.

Some windshields have a thin, fine, drawn wire embedded between the two glass panels in the vinyl; this is used as an antenna instead of an outside radio antenna (Fig. 1-29). Most manufacturers also have as an option backlites with fine heating strips to heat the glass to help remove snow or ice and also to clear fogging on the glass (Fig. 1-30).

When the estimator writes the estimate for any glass repair, the different methods used and their cost must be reflected in the estimate for the insurance company.

Bumpers and Impact Absorbers

Changes in the law have caused many changes in the construction of the front and rear bumpers. Automobiles now have energy absorbers and bumper reinforcements, and different types of materials are used in these components. This has caused a tremendous change in estimating practices and also the repair cost involved.

There are many different types of absorbers, and if they are damaged, they are replaced with new parts or undamaged recycled parts. They are usually not repaired unless there is only very minor damage on the bolting brackets, as heat should never be used on the absorber itself.

Steering Columns

The introduction of the collapsible steering column has increased the safety of the driver when involved in a front-end collision. In a front-end collision, forward motion is suddenly severely slowed down or stopped, causing the steering column to partially collapse; passengers in the vehicle keep on moving ahead (Fig. 1-31) unless they are restrained by seat belts. The driver will hit the steering wheel and this force will be partially absorbed as the steering column is compressed further because of the high force of the impact; this collapsing will reduce the column's tendency to move into the passenger compartment.

It is important that the estimator check the steering column collapsing area carefully even if the steering wheel shows little or no damage. The damage is easily detected and, if required, column repairs and cost can be included on the estimate form.

Door Beams and Roof Reinforcements

The side doors have a strong reinforcement welded on the door frame behind the door skin. It is called a door guard beam or side-intrusion reinforcement. Its purpose is to help prevent the side doors from crushing too far inward in a severe side impact.

This beam has made repair of the outer skin more difficult, which increases the cost of repairs; the beam is in

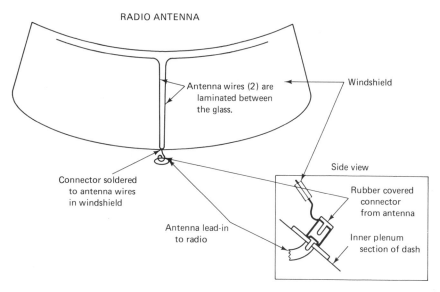

RADIO ANTENNA

IMPORTANT:

For maximum efficiency, the antenna trimmer must be adjusted to exact peak (loudest signal) with radio tuned to a weak station near 1400 kHz (140) and volume on full.

To Test Antenna for Short Circuit
1. Remove antenna lead-in from radio.
2. Connect 12 volt test light to 12 volt source and to antenna lead-in center terminal.
   A. If test light is "OFF", antenna is not shorted.
   B. If test light is "ON", disconnect antenna from lead-in socket at base of windshield. If test light turns off, short circuit was in short wire to windshield. Tape it and position it to prevent short circuit from occurring. If test light stays on, remove lead-in and repair or replace as required.

A whip antenna can be adjusted to 25–30 inches and temporarily connected to the radio to determine if antenna or lead-in is at fault. If there is considerable improvement in reception, the connector at the base of the windshield should be inspected for corrosion and loose connections. The antenna wires can be visually inspected for breaks. A crack in the glass across one of the wires would probably break the wire. If the problem is in the antenna wires or wire to the connector and cannot be repaired, a whip antenna can be installed or the windshield replaced.

FIGURE 1-29 Windshield with antenna wire. (Courtesy of General Motors of Canada Ltd.)

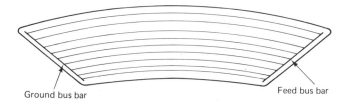

Ground bus bar   Feed bus bar

FIGURE 1-30 Backlite with heating strips.

the way when using the tools required for the repairs; this added cost must be entered on the repair estimate. The beams are sometimes removed when the outer skin is removed to achieve the required repairs; but if the beam is made from martensitic steel, it must be discarded and replaced with a new beam.

To conform to the federal safety standard for crush resistance, manufacturers have changed the construction of the roof and roof pillar for added strength. This in turn has affected the repair or replacement of these parts when damaged and has increased the cost of labor and the estimate price when repairs are required.

FORCES BEFORE COLLISION

FIRST STAGE PRIMARY COLLISION

SECOND STAGE SECONDARY COLLISION

FIGURE 1-31 Severe front impacts develop two forces. (Courtesy of Ford Motor Company of Canada Ltd.)

Protection of Occupants

Newer automobiles incorporate more safety in the engineering and manufacturing aspects of their construction. These features are designed by the manufacturer to absorb energy when the vehicle is involved in a collision (see Chapter 6). Many of these features, in addition to rust-prevention characteristics, make these vehicles more expensive to repair. Therefore, the estimator must be very careful when writing the estimate that these facts be taken into consideration.

Wheels

Most wheels used on passenger vehicles are made of steel; most manufacturers have improved their design for more tire retention in case of a blowout. The typical wheel cross-section design looks like the one in Fig. 1-32. The typical damage on a wheel will be inward lip bend, outward lip bend, and a bent rim that extends beyond the first step (Fig. 1-32).

   The estimator must examine the wheel carefully and determine if the wheel can be repaired, that is, whether inward or outward bend of the wheel lip can be straightened, thus saving the wheel. Any bend extending beyond the first step will cause excessive wobble in the wheel as it rotates and the wheel must be replaced. The estimator must indicate the size of the wheel on the estimate; some manufacturers have a code near the valve stem that must

also be included so that the proper rim is installed on the automobile.

Brakes

The brakes of the modern vehicle are disc brakes on the front, brake drums or disc brakes on the rear axle, or possibly disc brakes on both front and rear. The master cylinders now have two chambers that split the system into two separate sections. This was done so that, in the event of a rupture of a line in one part of the system, the driver would still have some braking power to stop the vehicle. A combination control valve modulates the hydraulic line pressure on vehicles with both disc and drum brakes so that the correct proportion of pressure is applied to both the front and rear brakes.

   Most vehicles have power brakes, and the estimator must take note of this fact, as well as check out the brake operating components and the hydraulic lines, both flexible and steel, to see that there are no kinks, breaks, or bent lines or leaking fluid.

1-4 THE ESTIMATOR'S JOB AND FUNCTION

The first important task for an estimator is to identify the vehicle and type of collision damage. The estimator must know the body style, model year, type of transmission, type of engine, and color of the particular vehicle.

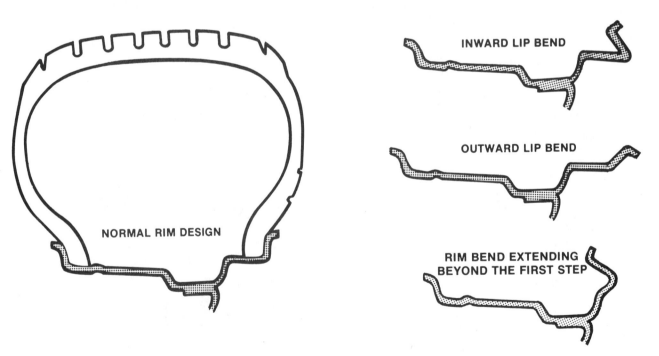

FIGURE 1-32 If wheel rim damage is not too severe, it can be straightened. (Courtesy of Ford Motor Company of Canada Ltd.)

All vehicles have a vehicle identification number located on the left side of the instrument panel and visible through the windshield. This is one of the first items that should be entered on the estimate form, as this information is used to determine vehicle specifications.

Figures 1-33 to 1-36 show the identification methods used by some manufacturers who build vehicles in the United States and Canada. Estimating manuals are used to find out what each of the vehicle identification numbers means.

Auto manufacturers also have certification labels or plates, which are placed at different locations. American Motors places its plate to the upper left corner of the firewall under the hood. Chrysler Corporation locates its plate on the radiator support or on the left front wheelhouse or inner panel. Ford Motor Company places its certification label on the left front door lock face or the door pillar. General Motors places its information plate on the radiator support (Fig. 1-37) or in the cowl area below the rear edge of the hood.

The estimator need not necessarily have been a body-repair technician to become a proficient estimator; it can be learned if enough on-the-job training is given. But the body-repair technician with two to four years of body and paint

American Motors

VEHICLE IDENTIFICATION NUMBER

LOCATION – PLATE ATTACHED TO THE UPPER LEFT CORNER OF INSTRUMENT PANEL AND BOTTOM LINE OF METAL PLATE ATTACHED TO THE UPPER LEFT CORNER OF THE FIREWALL UNDER THE HOOD.

Typical VIN interprets as follows:

1981-86

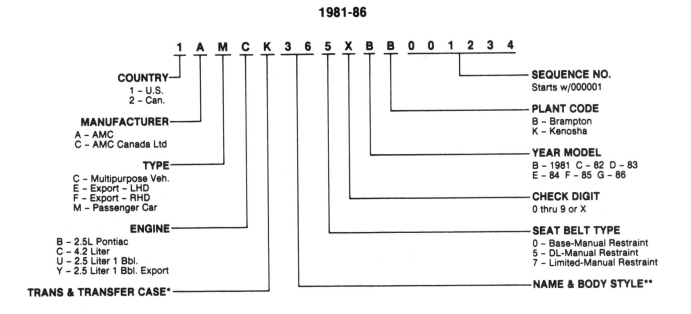

TRANS & TRANSFER CASE*

A – Automatic Column – None
C – Automatic Floor – None
C – Automatic Floor – Full/Time
G – 4-Speed Manual – Floor – Full/Time
H – 4-Speed Manual – Floor – Part/Full/Time
K – Automatic Floor – Part/Full/Time
M – 4-Speed Manual – Floor – None
N – 5-Speed Manual – Floor – Part/Full/Time
W – 5-Speed Manual – Floor – None

NAME & BODY STYLE**

05 – Concord 4 Door Sedan
06 – Concord 2 Door Sedan
08 – Concord 4 Door Wagon
35 – Eagle 4 Door Sedan
36 – Eagle 2 Door Sedan
37 – Eagle "Limited" 4 Door Wagon
38 – Eagle 4 Door Wagon
43 – Spirit 2 Door Liftback
46 – Spirit 2 Door Sedan
53 – SX-4 2 Door Liftback
56 – Kammback 2 Door Sedan

UNIT BODY/TRIM PLATE

Located on the left door and contains: Body Number, Model Number, Trim Number, Paint Code and Car Building Sequence Number.

FIGURE 1-33 Vehicle identification number. (Courtesy of Mitchell Information Services, Inc.)

American Motors

VEHICLE IDENTIFICATION NUMBER

LOCATION – PLATE RIVETED TO THE INSTRUMENT PANEL IN THE UPPER LEFT CORNER.

Contains 13 digit number and is decoded as follows:

1973-80

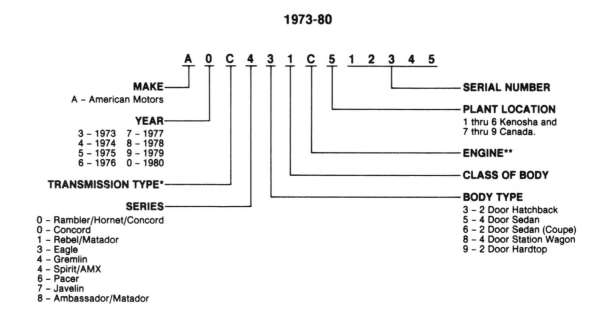

TRANSMISSION TYPE*	ENGINE**	UNIT BODY/TRIM PLATE
S – 3 Speed Manual Column Shift	A – 73-79 258 Six 1V Carb	Located on the left door and contains: Body
O – 3 Speed Manual Column Shift	B – 80 151 Four 2V Carb	Number, Model Number, Trim Number, Paint
A – Automatic Column Shift	B – 73 258 Six 1V Carb-Low Compression	Code and Car Building Sequence Number.
C – Automatic Floor Shift	C – 76-80 258 Six 2V Carb	
M – 4 Speed Manual Floor Shift	E – 73-79 232 Six 1V Carb	
F – 3 Speed Floor Shift	F – 73 232 Six 1V Carb-Low Compression	
E – 3 Speed Manual Floor Shift	G – 78-79 121 Four 2V Carb	
D – 3 Speed Floor Shift w/Overdrive	H – 73-79 304 V8 2V Carb	
	M – 73 304 V8 4V Carb	
	N – 73-78 360 V8 2V Carb	
	P – 73-76 360 V8 4V Carb	
	Z – 73-76 401 V8 4V Carb	

FIGURE 1-33   (cont.)

work repair will have a tremendous advantage over a nonexperienced trainee. From the experience gained while working, the technician will have developed knowledge on how metal behaves when it is repaired and on how to deal with the repainting of panels.

The sheet metal used today has been changed; much of it, especially in the lower areas of the vehicles, is galvanized, low carbon, zincrometal, HSLA steel, and plastic. The metal is fairly soft compared to high-carbon steel; this makes this metal ideal to use in stamping presses, which form the panels into the different shapes and sizes used in doors, fenders, hoods, trunk lids, and so on. Once this metal has been cold formed by being stamped into the different shapes required for the panels, it becomes somewhat harder.

The stamping process makes the metal harder, but not so hard that it cannot be worked and returned to its original stamped shape. In fact, automotive sheet-metal parts can be considered to have elasticity and plasticity. Elasticity is the property of stretching easily without undue tearing. Plasticity is the metal's ability to change shape without splitting or tearing as repairs are done using dollies, hammers, and often heat, and the metal can also be easily stretched.

The estimator must remember these qualities of metal when viewing damaged sheet-metal panels that must be

1985
PASSENGER CARS/FWD TRUCKS

LOCATION – UPPER LEFT SIDE OF INSTRUMENT PANEL, ALSO IN CENTER PORTION OF BOTTOM ROW OF BODY CODE PLATE

Vehicle Identification Plate contains 17 characters interpreted as follows:

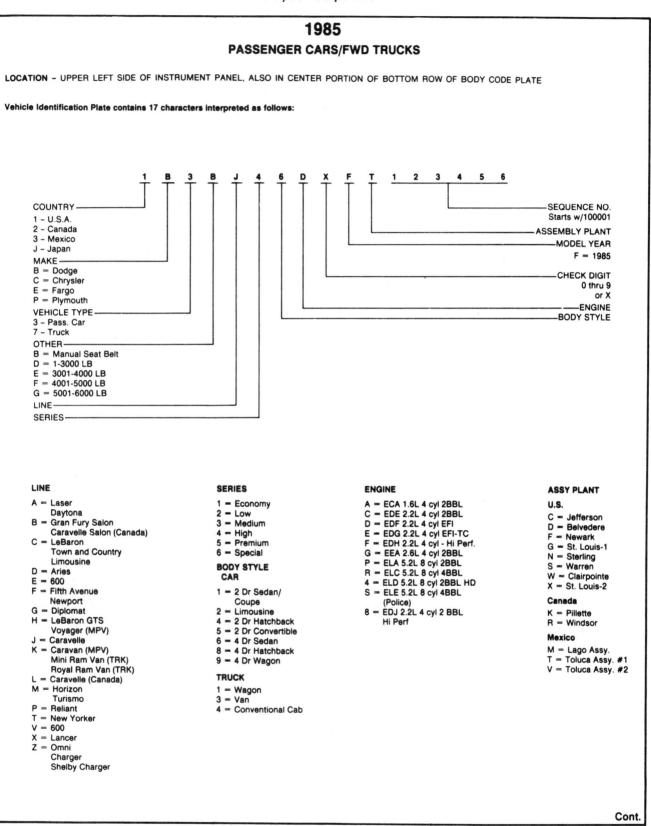

LINE

A = Laser
    Daytona
B = Gran Fury Salon
    Caravelle Salon (Canada)
C = LeBaron
    Town and Country
    Limousine
D = Aries
E = 600
F = Fifth Avenue
    Newport
G = Diplomat
H = LeBaron GTS
    Voyager (MPV)
J = Caravelle
K = Caravan (MPV)
    Mini Ram Van (TRK)
    Royal Ram Van (TRK)
L = Caravelle (Canada)
M = Horizon
    Turismo
P = Reliant
T = New Yorker
V = 600
X = Lancer
Z = Omni
    Charger
    Shelby Charger

SERIES

1 = Economy
2 = Low
3 = Medium
4 = High
5 = Premium
6 = Special

BODY STYLE
CAR

1 = 2 Dr Sedan/
    Coupe
2 = Limousine
4 = 2 Dr Hatchback
5 = 2 Dr Convertible
6 = 4 Dr Sedan
8 = 4 Dr Hatchback
9 = 4 Dr Wagon

TRUCK

1 = Wagon
3 = Van
4 = Conventional Cab

ENGINE

A = ECA 1.6L 4 cyl 2BBL
C = EDE 2.2L 4 cyl 2BBL
D = EDF 2.2L 4 cyl EFI
E = EDG 2.2L 4 cyl EFI-TC
F = EDH 2.2L 4 cyl - Hi Perf.
G = EEA 2.6L 4 cyl 2BBL
P = ELA 5.2L 8 cyl 2BBL
R = ELC 5.2L 8 cyl 4BBL
4 = ELD 5.2L 8 cyl 2BBL HD
S = ELE 5.2L 8 cyl 4BBL
    (Police)
8 = EDJ 2.2L 4 cyl 2 BBL
    Hi Perf

ASSY PLANT

U.S.

C = Jefferson
D = Belvedere
F = Newark
G = St. Louis-1
N = Sterling
S = Warren
W = Clairpointe
X = St. Louis-2

Canada

K = Pillette
R = Windsor

Mexico

M = Lago Assy.
T = Toluca Assy. #1
V = Toluca Assy. #2

Cont.

FIGURE 1-34 Vehicle identification number. (Courtesy of Mitchell Information Services, Inc.)

Chrysler Corporation

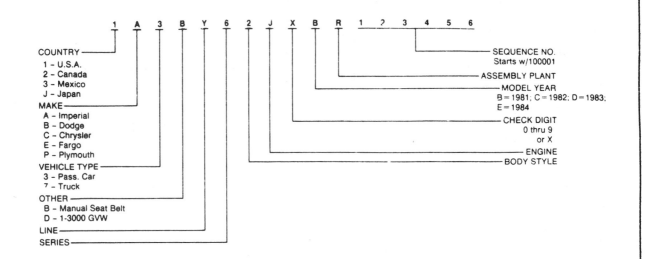

1981-84
PASSENGER CARS/FWD TRUCKS

LOCATION – UPPER LEFT SIDE OF INSTRUMENT PANEL, ALSO IN CENTER PORTION OF BOTTOM ROW OF BODY CODE PLATE

Vehicle Identification Plate contains 17 characters interpreted as follows:

```
       1  A  3  B  Y  6  2  J  X  B  R  1  2  3  4  5  6
```

COUNTRY
1 – U.S.A.
2 – Canada
3 – Mexico
J – Japan
MAKE
A – Imperial
B – Dodge
C – Chrysler
E – Fargo
P – Plymouth
VEHICLE TYPE
3 – Pass. Car
7 – Truck
OTHER
B – Manual Seat Belt
D – 1-3000 GVW
LINE
SERIES

SEQUENCE NO.
Starts w/100001
ASSEMBLY PLANT
MODEL YEAR
B = 1981; C = 1982; D = 1983;
E = 1984
CHECK DIGIT
0 thru 9
or X
ENGINE
BODY STYLE

LINE

A = Laser/Daytona
B = Gran Fury &
Caravelle (82-84)
C = LeBaron (82-84)
D = Aries
E = St. Regis (79-81)
E = "600", ES (83-84)
F = New Yorker (5th) (82-84)
LeBaron (81)
Fifth Avenue (84)
Newport (84)
G = Diplomat
H = Voyager
J = Gran Fury (81)
K = Mini Ram
Caravan
Royal
M = Horizon/TC3/Scamp
Turismo
P = Reliant
S = Cordoba
T = Newport/New Yorker (82-83)
T = E Class/New Yorker (83-84)
V = "400" (82-83)
"600" (84)
X = Mirada
Y = Imperial
Z = Omni/Rampage
Charger

SERIES

1 = Economy
2 = Low
3 = Medium
4 = High
5 = Premium
6 = Special

BODY STYLE
CAR

1 = 2 Dr Sedan
2 = 2 Dr Specialty
Hardtop
3 = 4 Dr Executive
Sedan
4 = 2+2 Hatchback
(U.S. only)
5 = 2 Dr Convertible
6 = 4 Dr Sedan
7 = 4 Dr Limousine
8 = 4 Dr Hatchback
9 = 4 Dr Wagon

TRUCK

1 = Wagon
3 = Van
4 = Conventional Cab

ENGINE

A = 1.6L (E82)
B = 1.7L (E12)
C = 2.2L (E62)
D = 2.2L (E65) TBI
E = 2.2L (E67)
Turbocharged
F = 2.2L (E69) H/Perf
8 = 2.2L H/Output
G = 2.6L (E72)
H = 3.7L (E24)
225 1 Bbl-Std
J = 3.7L (E25)
225 1 Bbl-HD
K = 3.7L (E26)
225 2 Bbl-Std
L = 3.7L (E27)
225 2 Bbl-HD
N = 5.2L (E43)
318 E.F.I.
P = 5.2L (E44)
318 2 Bbl-Std
R = 5.2. (E46)
318 4 Bbl-Std
S = 5.2L (E48)
318 4 Bbl-HD
X = 2.2L (E62)
Liq Propane Gas
4 = 5.2L (E45)
318 2 Bbl-HD
8 = 2.2L (E68)
High Output

ASSY PLANT

U.S.

A-Lynch Road
C-Jefferson
D-Belvidere
F-Newark
G-St. Louis 1
S-Warren
W-Clairpoint
X-Missouri (81-82)
St. Louis 2

CANADA

J-Tecumseh Assy
K-Pillette
R-Windsor

MEXICO

T-Toluca

FIGURE 1-34   (cont.)

1981-85

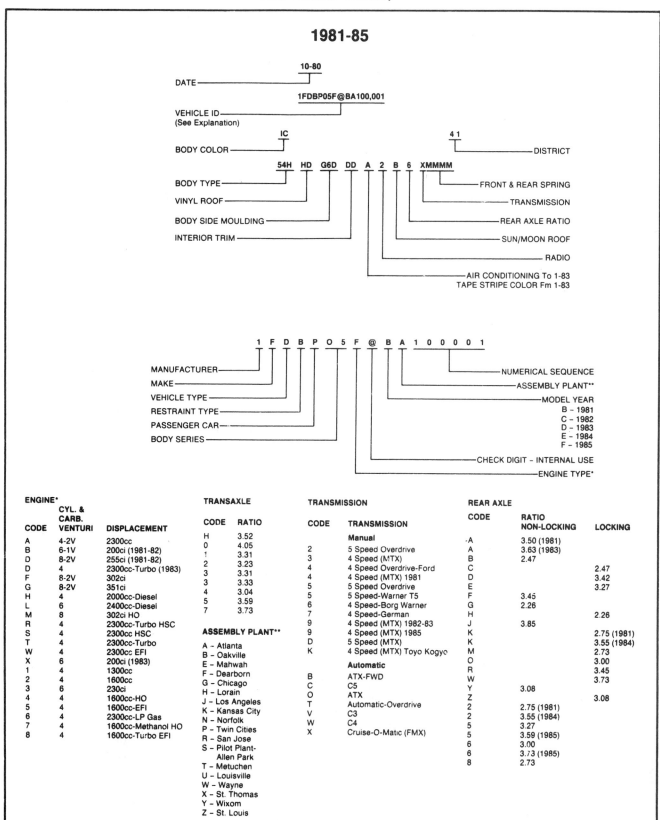

ENGINE*				TRANSAXLE		TRANSMISSION		REAR AXLE		
CODE	CYL. & CARB. VENTURI	DISPLACEMENT		CODE	RATIO	CODE	TRANSMISSION	CODE	RATIO NON-LOCKING	LOCKING
A	4-2V	2300cc		H	3.52		**Manual**	-A	3.50 (1981)	
B	6-1V	200ci (1981-82)		0	4.05	2	5 Speed Overdrive	A	3.63 (1983)	
D	8-2V	255ci (1981-82)		1	3.31	3	4 Speed (MTX)	B	2.47	
D	4	2300cc-Turbo (1983)		2	3.23	4	4 Speed Overdrive-Ford	C		2.47
F	8-2V	302ci		3	3.31	4	4 Speed (MTX) 1981	D		3.42
G	8-2V	351ci		3	3.33	5	5 Speed Overdrive	E		3.27
H	4	2000cc-Diesel		4	3.04	5	5 Speed-Warner T5	F	3.45	
L	6	2400cc-Diesel		5	3.59	6	4 Speed-Borg Warner	G	2.26	
M	8	302ci HO		7	3.73	7	4 Speed-German	H		2.26
R	4	2300cc-Turbo HSC				9	4 Speed (MTX) 1982-83	J	3.85	
S	4	2300cc HSC				9	4 Speed (MTX) 1985	K		2.75 (1981)
T	4	2300cc-Turbo		**ASSEMBLY PLANT****		D	5 Speed (MTX)	K		3.55 (1984)
W	4	2300cc EFI		A – Atlanta		K	4 Speed (MTX) Toyo Kogyo	M	2.73	
X	6	200ci (1983)		B – Oakville				O	3.00	
1	4	1300cc		E – Mahwah			**Automatic**	R	3.45	
2	4	1600cc		F – Dearborn		B	ATX-FWD	W	3.73	
3	6	230ci		G – Chicago		C	C5	Y	3.08	
4	4	1600cc-HO		H – Lorain		O	ATX	Z		3.08
5	4	1600cc-EFI		J – Los Angeles		T	Automatic-Overdrive	2	2.75 (1981)	
6	4	2300cc-LP Gas		K – Kansas City		V	C3	2	3.55 (1984)	
7	4	1600cc-Methanol HO		N – Norfolk		W	C4	5	3.27	
8	4	1600cc-Turbo EFI		P – Twin Cities		X	Cruise-O-Matic (FMX)	5	3.59 (1985)	
				R – San Jose				6	3.00	
				S – Pilot Plant- Allen Park				6	3.73 (1985)	
				T – Metuchen				8	2.73	
				U – Louisville						
				W – Wayne						
				X – St. Thomas						
				Y – Wixom						
				Z – St. Louis						

FIGURE 1-35   Vehicle identification number. (Courtesy of Mitchell Information Services, Inc.)

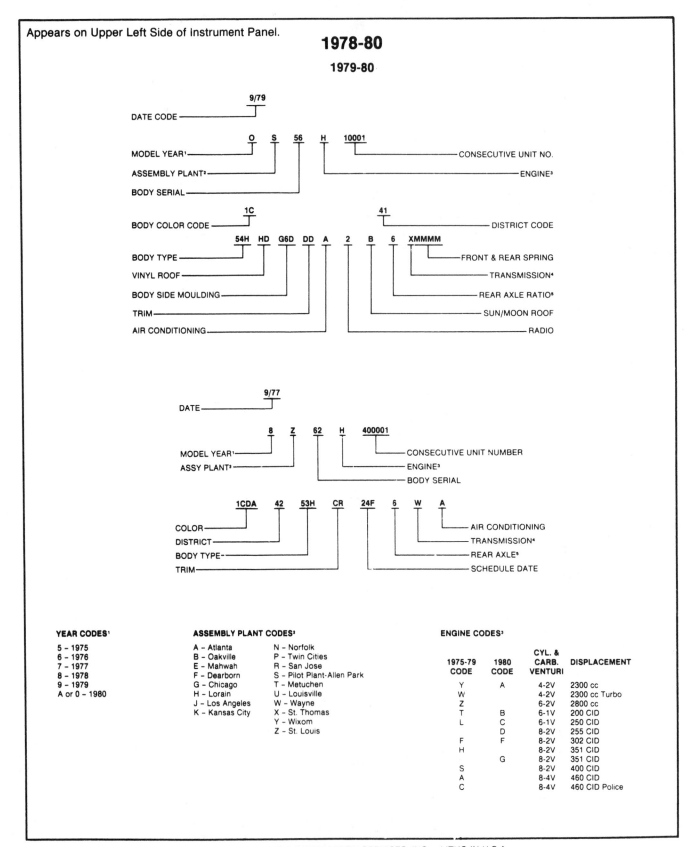

Appears on Upper Left Side of Instrument Panel.

1978-80
1979-80

FIGURE 1-35   (cont.)

CHEVROLET

LOCATION: Exc Corvette – on upper left side of instrument panel visible through windshield. Corvette – on left windshield pillar visible through windshield.

1981-86

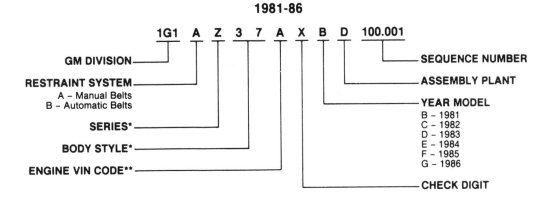

1976-80

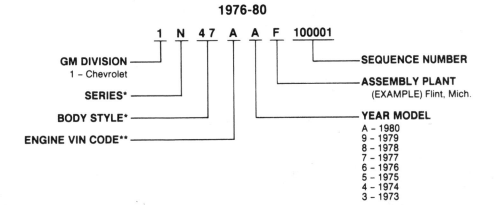

***EXAMPLE ABOVE**	**1st Position – COUNTRY**	**2nd Position – MANUFACTURER**
Z – Monte Carlo	1 United States	G General Motors
37 – Notchback Coupe	2 Canada	
	J Japan	

3rd Position – DIVISION
1 Chevrolet
2 Pontiac
3 Oldsmobile
4 Buick
6 Cadillac
7 Canada

***EXAMPLE ABOVE**
N – Caprice
47 - 2 Door Coupe

**ENGINE VIN CODES

1976-78

A – V6-231-2 Barrel
B – L4-140-2 Barrel
C – V6-196-2 Barrel
D – L6-250-1 Barrel
E – L4-98-1 Barrel
H – V8-350-4 Barrel
I – L4-85-1 Barrel
J – L4-1.6-1 Barrel
L – V8-350-4 Barrel
M – V6-200-2 Barrel
U – V8-305-2 Barrel
V – L4-151-2 Barrel
X – V8-350-4 Barrel

1979-81

1 – L4-151-2 Barrel
3 – V6-231-4 Barrel Turbo
4 – V6-252-4 Barrel
5 – L4-151-2 Barrel
7 – V6-173-2 Barrel
9 – L4-98-2 Barrel-
     Single Port Ex Man
0 – L4-98-2 Barrel-
     Dual Port Ex Man
A – V6-231-2 Barrel
C – V6-196-2 Barrel
D – L6-250-1 Barrel-77-79
D – L4-1.8 Diesel-1981
E – L4-98-1 Barrel
G – V8-350-2 Barrel
H – V8-305-4 Barrel
J – V8-267-2 Barrel
K – V6-229-2 Barrel
L – V8-350-4 Barrel
M – V6-200-2 Barrel
N – V8-350-Diesel
V – L4-151-2 Barrel
X – V6-173-2 Barrel

1982

4 – V6-252-2 Barrel
5 – L4-151-2 Barrel
C – L4-98-2 Barrel
D – L4-110-Diesel
H – V8-307-4 Barrel
J – V8-267-2 Barrel
K – V6-229-2 Barrel
L – V8-350-4 Barrel
N – V8-350-Diesel
R – L4-151-TBI
T – V6-260-Diesel-(a)
V – V6-260-Diesel-(b)
X – V6-173-2 Barrel-(c)
Z – V6-173-2 Barrel-(d)

(a) Front Wheel Drive
(b) Rear Wheel Drive
(c) 115 HP
(d) 135 HP

1983

A – V6-3.8L-2 Barrel
B – L4-2.0L-2 Barrel
C – L4-1.6L-2 Barrel
D – L4-1.8L-Diesel
F – L4-2.5L-2 Barrel
H – V8-5.0L-4 Barrel
N – V8-5.7L-Diesel
P – L4-2.0L-TBI
R – L4-2.5L-TBI
S – V8-5.0L-TBI
T – V6-4.3L-Diesel
V – V6-4.3L-Diesel
X – V6-2.8L-2 Barrel
Z – V6-2.8L-2 Barrel
1 – V6-2.8L-2 Barrel
2 – L4-2.5L-TBI
5 – L4-2.5L-TBI
6 – V8-5.7L-4 Barrel
8 – V8-5.7L-TBI
9 – V6-3.8L-2 Barrel

Cont.

FIGURE 1-36 Vehicle identification numbers. (Courtesy of Mitchell Information Services, Inc.)

General Motors

**ENGINE VIN CODES (Cont.)

1984

A – V6-3.8L-2 Barrel
B – L4-2.0L-2 Barrel
C – L4-1.6L-2 Barrel
D – L4-1.8L-Diesel
E – V6-3.0L-2 Barrel
H – V8-5.0L-4 Barrel
J – L4-1.8L-MFI*
L – V6-2.8L-2 Barrel
N – V8-5.7L-Diesel
P – L4-2.0L-EFI*
R – L4-2.5L-TBI*
T – V6-4.3L-Diesel
V – V6-4.3L-Diesel
X – V6-2.8L-2 Barrel
Y – V8-5.0L-4 Barrel
Z – V6-2.8L-2 Barrel
0 – L4-1.8L-TBI*
1 – V6-2.8L-2 Barrel
2 – L4-2.5L-TBI*
3 – V6-3.8L-MFI*
4 – V6-4.1L-4 Barrel
6 – V8-5.7L-4 Barrel
8 – V8-5.7L-CFI*
8 – V8-4.1L-DFI*
9 – V8-6.0L-DFI*
9 – V8-5.0L-4 Barrel
9 – V6-3.8L-2 Barrel
9 – V6-3.8L-SFI*

1985

A – V6-3.8L-2 Barrel
A – L4-1.9L-2 Barrel
B – V6-2.8L-2 Barrel
C – L4-1.6L-2 Barrel
C – V8-6.2L-Diesel
D – L4-1.8L-Diesel
E – L4-2.5K-TBI*
F – V8-5.0L-4 Barrel
F – V8-5.0L-MFI*
G – V8-5.0L-4 Barrel
H – V8-5.0L-4 Barrel
H – V8-5.0L-4 Barrel
J – V8-6.2L-Diesel
K – V8-5.7L-4 Barrel
L – V8-5.7L-4 Barrel
N – V6-4.3L-4 Barrel
N – V8-5.7L-Diesel
P – L4-2.0L-TBI*
R – L4-2.5L-TBI*
S – L4-2.2L-Diesel
S – V6-2.8L-MFI*
T – V6-4.8L-1 Barrel
T – V6-4.3L-Diesel
W – V6-2.8L-MFI*
W – V8-7.4L-4 Barrel
X – V6-2.8L-2 Barrel
Z – V6-4.3L-TBI*
2 – L4-2.5L-TBI*
8 – V8-5.7L-MFI*

1986

A – V6-3.8L-2 Barrel
C – L4-1.6L-2 Barrel
D – L4-1-1.8L Diesel
F – V8-5.0L EFI*
G – V8-5.0L-4 Barrel
H – V8-5.0L-4 Barrel
K – L4-1.5L-2 Barrel
M – L3-1.0L-2 Barrel
N – V8-5.7L-Diesel
P – L4-2.0L-EFI*
R – L4-2.5L-TBI*
S – V6-2.8L-MFI*
T – V6-4.3L-Diesel
V – V6-4.3L-Diesel
W – V6-2.8L-MFI*
X – V6-2.8L-2 Barrel
Z – V6-4.3L-TBI*
2 – L4-2.5L-TBI*
5 – L4-1.5L-Diesel
6 – V8-5.7L-4 Barrel
8 – V8-5.7L-MFI

*SFI – Sequential Port Fuel Injection
*CFI – Cross Fire Injection
*MFI – Multi-Port Fuel Injection
*EFI – Electronic Fuel Injection
*DFI – Digital Fuel Injection
*TBI – Throttle Body Injection

FIGURE 1-36   (cont.)

FIGURE 1-37 General Motors body identification plate on the radiator support.

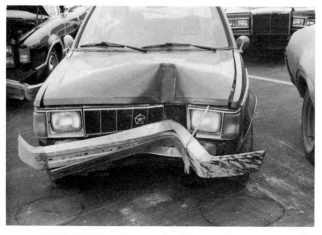

FIGURE 1-38 Head-on collision with a post.

repaired if he or she is to arrive at an accurate figure for the work required.

The estimator must know the name of the parts shown in Figs. 1-8 to 1-26 and also their locations to be able to write a proper estimate. The estimator must also know the terminology used for different types of collisions and types of damage. The following illustrations of typical types of accidents will provide the estimator trainee with the proper terms to be used.

Figure 1-38 shows a vehicle that struck a square post; this caused the bumper, grille, hood, and other parts to be damaged and require replacement or repair. This accident could be classified as a head-on collision with an object that was not moving.

Figure 1-39 shows a vehicle that was hit on the left front corner, causing extensive sheet-metal damage and a sidesway condition in the front section of the vehicle.

Figure 1-40 shows a front-end collision that occurred when the vehicle hit the back of a truck, causing mainly high sheet-metal damage; notice the bumper is hardly damaged.

Figure 1-41 shows a near head-on collision, which was a bit more severe on the right side, causing a lot of sheet-metal damage and also sidesway in the front section.

Figure 1-42 shows a vehicle that was sideswiped from the front left corner to the rear door. This type of accident causes a lot of distortion in the front and outer section and is very expensive to repair.

Figure 1-43 shows a vehicle that was hit dead center on the left side, causing damage so extensive that it was too expensive to repair and the vehicle was written off.

FIGURE 1-41   Head-on front-end collision.

FIGURE 1-39   Impact on left corner causing a sidesway condition.

FIGURE 1-42   Sideswipe collision.

FIGURE 1-40   High-impact front-end collision.

FIGURE 1-43   Damaged vehicle with double sidesway caused by dead-on side collision.

Figure 1-44 shows a vehicle that rolled over, which can be seen by the damage and direction of the damage. Damage was done to the front end sheet metal, windshield, roof panel, door, and quarter-panels. The type of roll-over, which is affected by speed, by what the vehicle hits as it is rolling, and by the type of terrain it rolls over, greatly affects the amount of damage that results. If the vehicle rolls over on soft, long grass, deep, soft snow, or in a water-filled ditch, damage will be less. Grass and snow absorb some of the impact. When a vehicle rolls over in a water-filled ditch, the panels will not usually be extensively damaged, but the water and mud will usually make a mess of the outside and inside of the vehicle. In some roll-overs on soft surfaces, the only really visible effect is liquids that have leaked inside the motor compartment.

The vandalized vehicle (Fig. 1-45) usually winds up being a total loss to the insurance company. The vehicle usually has all or most of the glass broken, most of the body panels damaged by the use of a heavy instrument, upholstery torn, and a broken dash; sometimes it has even been hit by another vehicle. Vehicles are vandalized for different reasons, and the estimator must try to find out the reason for and who did the vandalizing, as some vandalism is done for fraudulent purposes.

Stolen vehicles are sometimes vandalized and usually these vehicles receive severe abuse. The whole power train could be ruined and must be carefully checked during estimating procedures. Fluid levels should all be checked, and if possible the vehicle should be test driven to ensure that all the components are in working order. The vehicle should also be checked by an automotive technician before the estimate is completed.

Another common type of damage is the burnt-out vehicle (Fig. 1-46). Vehicles burn for a multitude of reasons; it can be due to vandalism, a forgotten cigarette, a short in the wiring harness, perhaps due to faulty repairs, or in cold climates in the winter an overheated or shorted-out interior heater. Fire in the front compartment could be due to gasoline spilling or leaking from a faulty fuel line or connection. Many burnt vehicles are investigated by the insurance companies or even the police to find out if the vehicle was burnt for fraudulent purposes, which may be a lack of money to pay for the vehicle on the costly repairs required by a burnt-out engine. The motor oil or even the engine oil pan is sometimes removed, and the oil and sediment are sent to labs to be analyzed to find out if the motor had burnt out bearings on the crankshaft.

When the estimator inspects the burnt vehicle, the amount of damage will determine the course to take. A completely gutted vehicle is unrepairable, whereas a vehicle with a slight under-the-hood fire may very possibly be repaired. When making the estimate, the estimator must take into consideration the cost of the repairs to restore the

FIGURE 1-44 Rolled-over truck.

FIGURE 1-45 Vandalized vehicle.

FIGURE 1-46 Burnt vehicle.

vehicle to original condition and the market value of an identical vehicle.

If the fire was localized for example in the engine compartment, the inspection must be very thorough. Since many of the parts are made from synthetic materials, spark-plug wires, vacuum hoses, wiring harness, electrical cables, and any rubber parts and hoses will have to be replaced. All plastic components and electric sending units of the emission controls, control systems for the air conditioning, and the battery will have to be checked and replaced as required. Most likely, it will be necessary to repair or replace the carburetor or fuel-injection system, control modules of the fuel system, fuel pump, and the distributor. Before closing the estimate, the estimator should get an automotive technician to help diagnose exactly which parts are still in good condition and which must be replaced or overhauled.

Submerged Vehicles

Vehicles are sometimes submerged due to a catastrophe, such as in a flood, loss of control when driving, or an accident forcing the vehicle into a water-filled ditch; sometimes the vehicle is pushed into a lake or river for fraudulent purposes. The submerged vehicle may sometimes be salvaged, depending on how deep the water is and how long it has been submerged (Fig. 1-47). If submerged deeply enough, water will enter the engine through the intake manifold and dip stick; the engine, manual or automatic transmission, rear axles, and transaxles will have to be drained and refilled with proper lubricant. The gas tank will have to be removed, cleaned, and replaced. The carburetor or fuel injection will need overhauling, all filters will need

FIGURE 1-47 Submerged vehicle. (Courtesy of Ford Motor Company Ltd.)

replacing, and the ignition system, starter, and alternator will need to be checked, cleaned, and overhauled as required. The braking system as well as the power brake unit will need to be cleaned and inspected, and the necessary work listed on the estimate. The automatic transmission if present will have taken in some water through the dip stick and will have to have the pan removed to drain it and change the filter. The pan and filter are then replaced and the transmission is refilled with the proper fluid. The power steering unit should also be drained and refilled.

The engine is given all necessary checks. Water is drained from the affected pistons and they are lightly lubricated; the oil pan is drained, the filter changed, and the pan is refilled before the engine is started. All electrical components and options should be checked to prevent any additional damage that could possibly happen when the engine is started.

The door trim panels, seats, and floor mats will most likely have to be removed and hosed down, allowed to air dry, and then possibly dry cleaned. The interior of the doors and any panels that have sediment deposited due to the flooding will have to be washed out or vacuumed. It may be necessary to replace the padding under the floor mats with new material.

Hail Damage

To estimate hail damage, the estimator must have knowledge of how this type of damage is repaired. No rule of thumb can be applied due to the different sizes of hailstones. This type of damage occurs in certain geographical areas of North America and is caused by atmospheric conditions. Hailstones vary from very small to some that are bigger than large chicken eggs. Their different sizes and the velocity at which they fall will cause different types of damage.

Hailstones dent body panels, break glass and plastic, and damage moldings. Hail damage is repaired by the use of many different techniques and methods. Some damage may be removed by the use of an oxyacetylene torch by a skilled technician. Smaller dents are sometimes filled with a plastic filler after grinding. Some estimators will assign a 0.3, which is 18 minutes for repairing the average smaller type of dent; but this is only a judgment estimate as the size and location of the dent will vary the time required. It may be necessary to change some damaged panels due to repair being uneconomical or repair being impossible due to panel shape and lack of accessibility to the damage. The estimator will also have to estimate the amount of time required to paint affected areas. This paint allowance is sometimes used by customers to pay part of the cost of a complete paint job, as it is often impossible to match the existing faded paint on the vehicle.

Repair Limitations on Panels

When the estimator examines a damaged panel or panels, it must be realized that there are limits on what can be repaired and what must be replaced. Depending on the estimator and/or insurance company, some variations in methods of estimating when a panel will be repaired or replaced exist. Some companies use new panels on fairly new vehicles, even when not too badly damaged, to provide customer satisfaction. Other companies will estimate for repairs as long as the repair work done will be of good quality and will not exceed the cost of removal and replacement with either good recycled or new parts.

If there is some doubt whether the repair and straightening procedures may not produce a quality job then the estimate is written using new parts on fairly new vehicles and good recycled parts on older vehicles. Usually sheet-metal panels offer the most opportunities for straightening repair procedures. Because of this sheet-metal replacement, repairs and refinishing will account for the largest amount of estimating dollars. Sheet-metal parts can be repaired by several different methods depending on the shop and technician.

Depending on their characteristics, different types of bends can be stretched, hammered, dollied, and jacked to their normal preexisting position. Stretched metal can be leveled and all stretched areas shrunk using heat, a hammer, a dolly, and the cooling of the hot metal with a water-soaked rag, Tears are welded and upset metal will have to be stretched back to a level surface. Low areas may be pulled out to alignment using many different methods, and any low area left will usually be filled with plastic fillers.

Reinforced Panels

Some sheet-metal parts, such as trunk lids, hoods, door panels, and roof panels, have high and low crowned surfaces; this gives the panels added strength. Many of these panels have fairly low crowned surfaces, such as parts of hoods and trunk lids, and manufacturers use an inside reinforcing metal panel to make them stronger and more rigid (Fig. 1-48). These inner panels are spot welded or crimped and spot welded and glued to the rest of the outer panel so as to be very rigid.

Classification of Damages

Collision damage can first be classified as direct damage, which is where the first point of impact occurred. Figure 1-49 shows a typical type of first direct damage, which occurred on the left rear corner of the vehicle, which pushed the bumper and the back section of the rear quarter-panel. The next damage is the indirect damage caused by the force of the impact driving the rear of the panel ahead. This

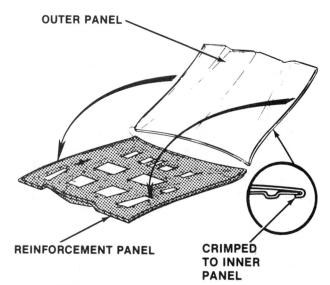

FIGURE 1-48 Typical panel construction. (Courtesy of Ford Motor Company of Canada Ltd.)

FIGURE 1-49 Typical direct and indirect damage.

caused indirect damage to the frame rail, trunk floor, quarter-panel, and outer wheel house by bending and distorting the various panels. Indirect damage is clearly visible where the quarter-panel is pushed out, and the metal severally rolled over the rear wheel opening.

The other types of damage can be grouped in five major categories: displaced metal, simple bends, rolled buckles, stretched metal, and gouged metal. Figure 1-50 shows a fairly typical displaced sheet-metal area that is held in this particular shape by the stress of the forces from the impact. When the body-repair technician removes these forces by correcting the damage, the panel will tend to move or snap back to its original location and shape without too much more effort.

FIGURE 1-50   Typical displaced metal locked in position by the bend in the styling edges.

FIGURE 1-52   Typical rolled buckle.

FIGURE 1-53   Upset rolled buckle.

Figure 1-51 shows a simple bend where the metal is depressed or pushed in to just past its natural point of elasticity. The body-repair technician finds this type of damage fairly simple to repair as it is easy to shape (D means direct damage and ID means indirect damage).

The rolled buckle in Fig. 1-52 formed when the force of the impact traveled through the slightly crowned quarter-panel, causing it to collapse near the front close to the rear edge of the door; this is not a severe rolled buckle and has only collapsed slightly at the front and rear of the quarter. The body-repair technician has to remove the stresses and the pressure that causes this type of damage.

Metal is upset when a collision forces an area of a sheet-metal panel to be reduced in its surface dimension and causes its thickness to increase in certain areas. Figure 1-53 shows a left front fender that was damaged in such a way as to reduce its dimension. Force exerted against it with the proper tools will cause the upset metal section to return to its normal position as the force rolls or pushes it back into place.

Figure 1-54 shows typical stretched panels where the collision was severe enough to put pressure on one or two areas and create separating forces. The force of the impact is severe enough to increase the area of the metal on both

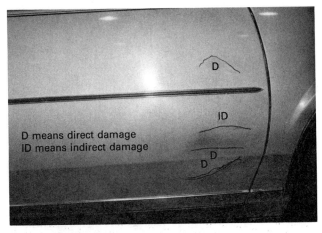

FIGURE 1-51   Direct and indirect damage.

FIGURE 1-54   Stretched and gouged metal.

the door and fender in some areas. This stretching causes the metal to decrease in thickness. This type of damage is typical stretching and gouging; an extreme stretch will cause the metal to tear.

Another type of damage that the estimator must recognize at first sight is indicated by the gap between doors and front edge and rear front fender edge. Figure 1-55 shows a fender where there is pressure on it pulling the top section ahead. This could be caused by either sidesway or the frame horn could be pushed down ahead of the cross member.

Damage in the same area occurs when the collision on a fender closes the gap between the door and fender, causing the metal to upset at the impact point of the door and fender (Fig. 1-56). This must be checked carefully, as this condition may indicate that the frame has sagged damage at that area.

In any collision, the estimator must be familiar with the different types of construction used on automobiles and trucks. The different types of frames must be identified and the type of damage (see Chapter 6 for identification and gauging methods) to enable the estimator to make a proper estimate.

The estimator must not only be familiar with the main body panel, but a thorough knowledge of the construction of passenger doors and their inner hardware is also important in obtaining an accurate estimate. Manufacturers stock repair panels as well as complete new panels. If a used door is required, it may be bought from a recycler. Some manufacturers use hinges made of heavy metal casting, stampings, or forgings; this type of hinge provides doors with built-in adjustments. Other manufacturers use stamped or forged hinges that are lighter and usually welded in position on the door and door pillars. This type of hinge allows no adjustment, and to obtain adjustment it is usually bent to fit. The striker bolt may be adjusted up and down or in and out and can be shimmed in and out from the door pillar (Fig. 1-57).

The windows in doors are moved by using regulators and rear and front glass run channels that stabilize the glass and keep it in the right position (Fig. 1-58). This type of regulator is used in many newer-model vehicles. Another system, such as in Fig. 1-59, may be used in other models of vehicles. These two different systems use a different type of hardware to achieve the same results, and the estimator must be familiar with the names of the parts in the different doors. If the regulator or glass runs are not damaged extensively, they may sometimes be repaired; but if the damage extends to the up and down mechanism, the regulator must be replaced. If the vehicle is equipped with a power unit and if any damage occurs to the power unit, it must be replaced. The glass is held by bolts through the glass and lower glass sash in Fig. 1-59, but in some other models the lower sash is attached to the glass by using epoxy adhesive (Fig. 1-60). On yet other models the glass is held in the

FIGURE 1-55 Fender edge and door edge spread apart.

FIGURE 1-56 Fender edge compressed against the door edge.

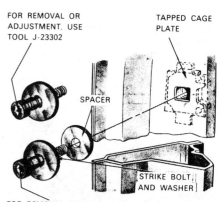

FIGURE 1-57 Door lock striker installation. (Courtesy of General Motors of Canada Ltd.)

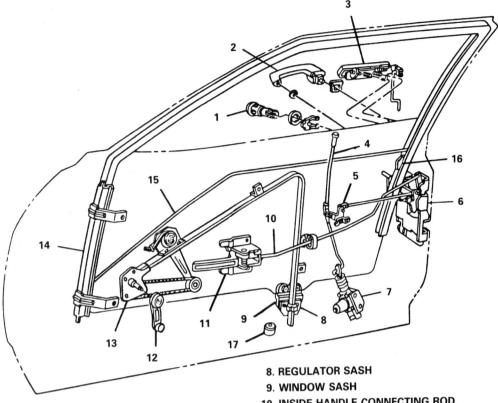

1. LOCK CYLINDER
2. OUTSIDE DOOR HANDLE (PUSH BUTTON)
3. OUTSIDE DOOR HANDLE (LIFT BAR)
4. INSIDE LOCKING ROD
5. LOCKING ROD BELL CRANK
6. DOOR LOCK
7. DOOR LOCK ACTUATOR

8. REGULATOR SASH
9. WINDOW SASH
10. INSIDE HANDLE CONNECTING ROD
11. INSIDE REMOTE HANDLE
12. WINDOW REGULATOR HANDLE
13. WINDOW REGULATOR
14. FRONT RUN CHANNEL
15. DOOR GLASS
16. PLASTIC GUIDE
17. RUBBER DOWN STOP

FIGURE 1-58   Front door hardware. (Courtesy of General Motors of Canada Ltd.)

lower channel by means of a packing strip, which by pressure holds the glass and lower channel together.

Different types of weather stripping are used to seal the openings between the door and the door frame. Where it is used determines the holding method to some degree, as well as the shape of the weather stripping. On some models the weather stripping is held on the doors by a plastic type of retainer and adhesive or only adhesive (Fig. 1-61A). On other models, the weather stripping is held to the pinch weld flange by the way the weather stripping is shaped and by using some adhesive (Fig. 1-61B).

In side collisions the lock mechanism sometimes get damaged beyond repair and will not open; it is then necessary to cut the outside panel at the right location to enable the tripping of the mechanism in the lock to open the door for closer examination. In some severe collisions where the lock is damaged, it should be replaced; the linkage can usually be straightened as it is not as readily available. The door lock mechanism is moved from an unlocked or locked position by means of attached control rods connected to the door lock and locking cylinder (Fig. 1-62). These rods are usually fairly easy to remove when the door trim panel is off. If the cylinder has to be changed, some cylinders have the proper key code stamped on them; if not, the lock cylinder may have to be sent to the supplier to have the proper tumblers inserted or a new key cut to fit it.

Using this method does away with having to buy matching cylinders for the other door, the ignition, and the truck lid as applicable when only one lock is damaged. On vehicles that have power door locks (Fig. 1-59), the estimator must check to see if they all function, as well as the inside locking rod. If a solenoid is damaged or crushed, it must be replaced as it is not repairable. Usually only on severe collisions will the mechanism in the doors be damaged enough to affect the operation of the lock holding the door in its proper location. But in severe collisions it is

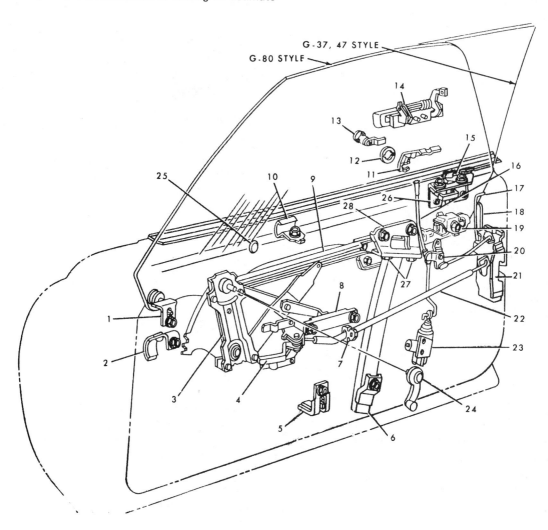

1. **Front Up-Travel Stop** (on Inner Panel)
2. **Glass Stabilizer** (on Inner Panel)
3. **Manual Window Regulator**
4. **Inside Remote Handle**
5. **Down-Travel Stop**
6. **Vertical Guide Cam Assembly**
7. **Silencer**
8. **Inner Panel Cam**
9. **Lower Sash Channel Cam**

10. **Front Belt Stabilizer and Trim Retainer**
11. **Lock Cylinder Retainer**
12. **Lock Cylinder Gasket**
13. **Lock Cylinder Assembly**
14. **Outside Handle Assembly**
15. **Rear Belt Stabilizer Pin Assembly** (on inner Panel)
16. **Inside Locking Rod**

17. **Outside Handle to Lock Connecting Rod**
18. **Lock Cylinder to Lock Connecting Rod**
19. **Rear Up-Travel Stop** (on Inner Panel)
20. **Bell Crank**
21. **Door Lock**
22. **Inside Handle to Lock Connecting Rod**
23. **Power Door Lock Actuator**
24. **Manual Window Regulator Handle**

25. **Plastic Stabilizer Button** (on Glass)
26. **Plastic Stabilizer Guide** (Riveted to Glass)
27. **Vertical Guide Upper Support** (Lower) **Screws**
28. **Vertical Guide Upper Support**

FIGURE 1-59   Door hardware G. coupe styles. (Courtesy of General Motors of Canada Ltd.)

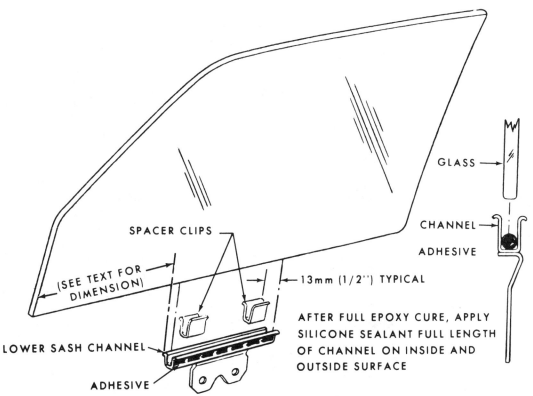

GLASS →

CHANNEL →

ADHESIVE

SPACER CLIPS

(SEE TEXT FOR DIMENSION)

← 13mm (1/2") TYPICAL

AFTER FULL EPOXY CURE, APPLY SILICONE SEALANT FULL LENGTH OF CHANNEL ON INSIDE AND OUTSIDE SURFACE

LOWER SASH CHANNEL

ADHESIVE

FIGURE 1-60 Glass to channel bonding. (Courtesy of General Motors of Canada Ltd.)

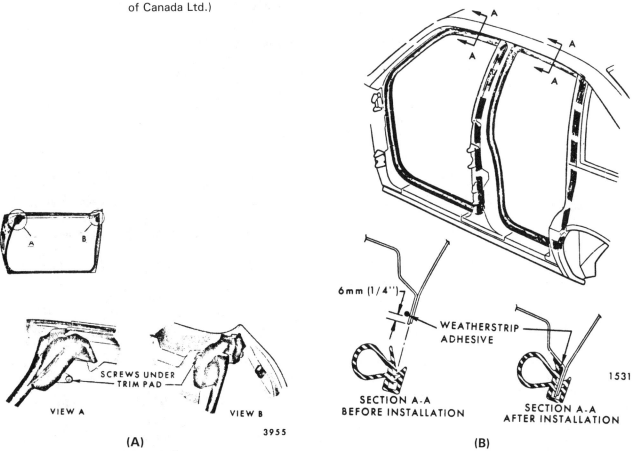

SCREWS UNDER TRIM PAD

VIEW A

VIEW B

3955

(A)

6mm (1/4")

WEATHERSTRIP ADHESIVE

SECTION A-A BEFORE INSTALLATION

SECTION A-A AFTER INSTALLATION

1531

(B)

FIGURE 1-61A. Door weather-stripping coupe styles. (B) Front and rear door opening weather-stripping installation. (Courtesy of General Motors of Canada Ltd.)

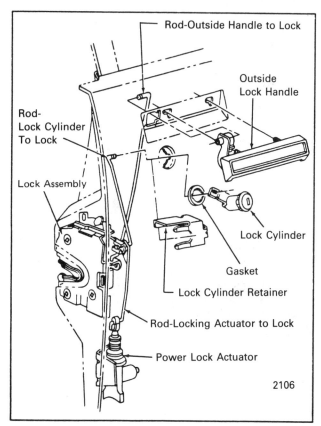

Rod-Outside Handle to Lock

Outside
Lock Handle

Rod-
Lock Cylinder
To Lock

Lock Assembly

Lock Cylinder

Gasket

Lock Cylinder Retainer

Rod-Locking Actuator to Lock

Power Lock Actuator

2106

FIGURE 1-62 Front door lock cylinder removal. (Courtesy of General Motors of Canada Ltd.)

sometimes necessary to cut the outer panel and sometimes also the inner panel around the lock mechanism to be able to open the door.

Different Types of Front Suspensions

The majority of the the new automobiles manufactured since 1980 use front-wheel drive with a McPherson strut suspension on the front; some even use a similar system on the rear wheels (Fig. 1-63).

Other vehicles use a strut-type front suspension where the spring is carried between control arm and the main front cross member (Fig. 1-64). The shock absorber is inside the spring and attached to the lower control arm and the top of the cross-member spring pocket built into the frame and cross member. The strut is located on the outside of the spring and the spindle forms part of it. This is sometimes referred to as the spring on lower control arm suspension systems. The lower ball joint and control arm place and hold the spring between them and the spring pocket, on which the bracket that holds the upper control arm is placed.

In another version of the ball joint and spring suspension system, the spring is placed between the top control arm and a tower built into the front fender apron assembly

(Fig. 1-65). This type of suspension is used on some unitized construction vehicles and is called a spring on upper control arm system.

Chrysler uses a variation of the ball joint suspension system, known as torsion bar suspension, on some models of automobiles (Fig. 1-66). The lower control arm is attached to the torsion bar, which is held firmly in a socket at the other end to stop it from moving at that end. Bumps in the road force the control arm to move up and down, which are absorbed and resisted by the torsion the bar offers to the twisting forces.

Another type of suspension is the I-beam axle and leaf springs used on heavier trucks. The spindle assembly turns on the axle by having king pins that attach it to the axle, but it can still be turned in a horizontal part of a circle.

The suspension does not need alignment every time a vehicle is involved in a front accident unless the frame, strut, lower control arm, or wheel are bent or the tire badly damaged. But the estimator must check it to be certain that no damage was done in the accident. If any parts are damaged, they may be purchased separately, either new or recycled. Some accidents, such as a roll-over, place stress on the front suspension, which could possibly move and change the front-end alignment.

CAUTION: When repairing front ends, no parts should be straightened cold or by using heat on any of the parts of the steering system, linkage, or front suspension. To straighten these parts would be against all safety aspects and is not recommended by any manufacturer.

Steering Systems

Most automobiles made today use a rack-and-pinion steering system, either manual or with power assist. A few models of automobiles and most trucks use the recirculating type of steering assembly (Fig. 1-67). The recirculating type of steering assembly used in manual steering has recirculating, round, steel ball bearings that travel in a nut up and down on the wormshaft screw thread with very little friction. This type of steering mechanism is highly resistant to collision impact that may travel from the steering linkage into the gear box.

The integral type of power steering (Fig. 1-68) functions in much the same as the manual, except that hydraulic pressure from a high-pressure pump (Fig. 1-69) attached to and turned by the engine sends oil at a high pressure through the flexible hoses into the integral power steering assembly.

On vehicles with a rack-and-pinion powered or nonpowered type of steering gear (Fig. 1-70), the turning effort from the steering wheel is also transmitted through the steering shaft, flexible coupling to the helically toothed pinion. The toothed rack is moved right to left by the

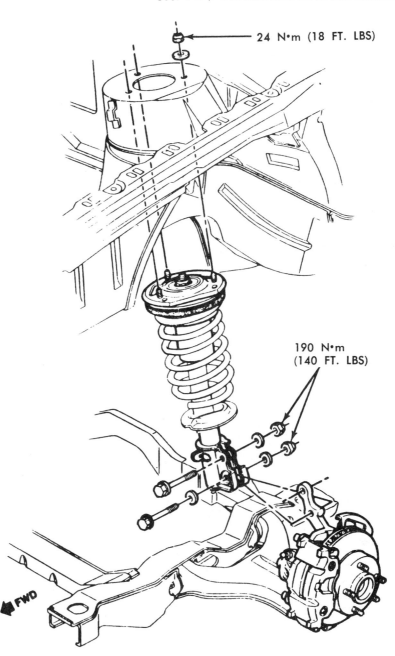

24 N•m (18 FT. LBS)

190 N•m
(140 FT. LBS)

FWD

FIGURE 1-63 McPherson strut assembly. (Courtesy of General Motors of Canada Ltd.)

rotation of the pinion gear. This movement is transmitted to the spindle arms and wheels by means of the connecting rods (or tie-rod ends), which are connected to the rack. By using this type of steering gear, manufacturers eliminate the use of certain parts, such as the idler arm, pitman arm, and drag link.

When making the estimate on a front collision, the estimator should check the rack and pinion because it could possibly be damaged or the holding brackets bent. All parts of the manual or power steering pump and steering mechanism should be inspected carefully for any damage. If any internal damage is suspected, a motor and wheel alignment technician should be called in to carefully evaluate the system.

Drive Lines and Transmissions

When a vehicle is involved in a severe front or rear collision, the transmission or transaxle, whether automatic or standard shift, and its drive should be carefully examined (Fig. 1-71). In front collisions the drive wheels should be

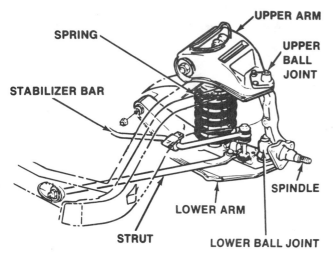

FIGURE 1-64 Typical front suspension ''spring on lower arm.'' (Courtesy of Ford Motor Company of Canada Ltd.)

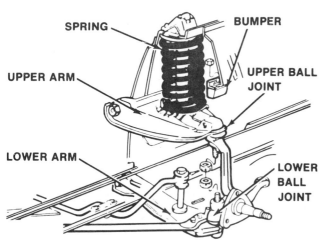

FIGURE 1-65 Typical front suspension with the spring on the upper arm. (Courtesy of Ford Motor Company of Canada Ltd.)

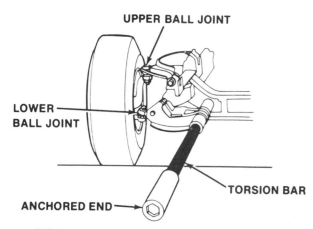

FIGURE 1-66 Typical torsion bar front suspension system. (Courtesy of Ford Motor Company Ltd.)

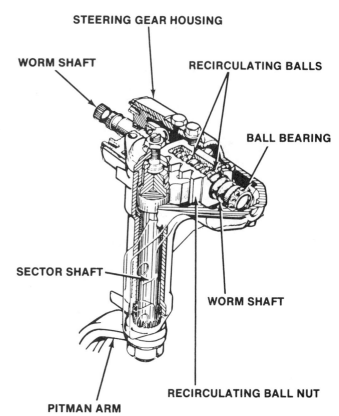

FIGURE 1-67 Typical manual steering gear assembly. (Courtesy of Ford Motor Company of Canada Ltd.)

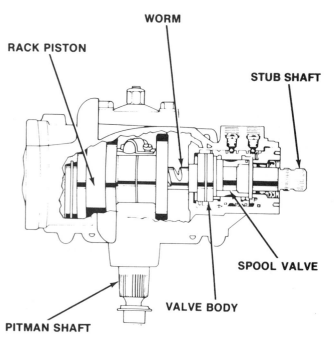

FIGURE 1-68 Typical integral power steering gear assembly. (Courtesy of Ford Motor Company of Canada Ltd.)

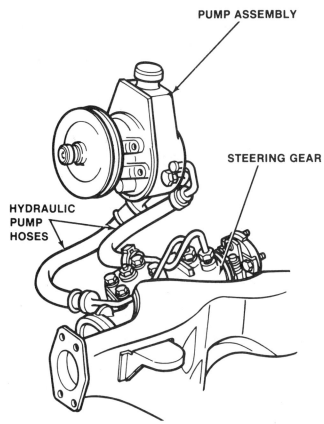

FIGURE 1-69 Typical integral power steering system. (Courtesy of Ford Motor Company of Canada Ltd.)

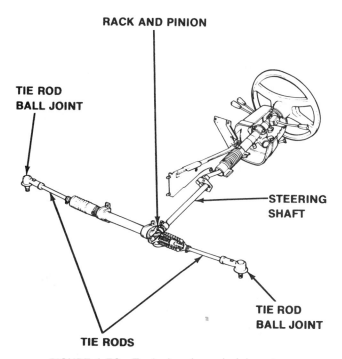

FIGURE 1-70 Typical rack- and pinion steering gear assemblies. (Courtesy of Ford Motor Company of Canada Ltd.)

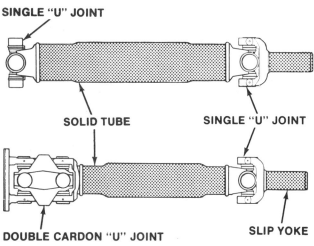

FIGURE 1-71 Drive axle and components. (Courtesy of Ford Motor Company of Canada Ltd.)

raised off the ground if possible to see if the transmission is operating properly, that is, if the engine can be started.

In a severe front collision, especially with front-wheel-drive vehicles, the transmission case is more likely to be damaged than in the vehicle driven by the rear wheels. It is possible and sometimes probable that there could be damage to the back side of the transmission and even the engine block, which is very hard to see without having the power train removed for a careful inspection. If damage is found in the transmission case, such as a crack, it can sometimes be repaired; but it usually means that the transmission will have to be removed, completely replaced by an exchange unit or repaired, and the transmission overhauled and reinstalled. This process is very expensive due to the cost of the parts and labor involved. An estimator should always get a firm quote from a technician before deciding to repair the unit; otherwise the cost could become exorbitant.

The motor and transmission mounts are installed to stop the transfer of vibrations or noise to the passenger compartment. They should be checked to see if they are bent, have moved, or have become sheared and need to be replaced. In vehicles with transaxles that are hit on a front drive wheel, the boots, joint assemblies, and axle shaft should be checked for damage, as well as the strut.

On rear-driven automobiles when hit in the front or back end in a severe collision, the drive shaft and the yoke (Fig. 1-72) should be checked for extreme movement, as a certain amount of back and forth movement is built into the driveshaft of the vehicle. The yoke can slide forward and backward a certain amount on the transmission output shaft, therefore very rarely damaging the internal operating units in the transmission.

The drive shafts used on typical rear-wheel-drive automobiles are rarely damaged since their U-joints allow

**TRANSMISSION
CASE EXTENSION**

**"U" JOINT
FRONT YOKE**

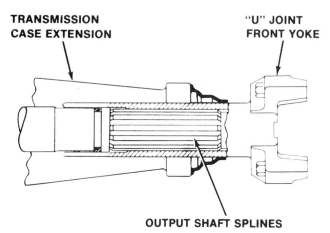

OUTPUT SHAFT SPLINES

FIGURE 1-72 Transmission output shaft connected to a front U-joint yoke. (Courtesy of Ford Motor Company of Canada Ltd.)

TRANSMISSION CASE

PAWL

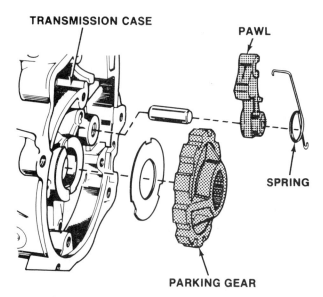

SPRING

PARKING GEAR

FIGURE 1-73 Typical parking pawl and gear used in automatic transmission. (Courtesy of Ford Motor Company of Canada Ltd.)

them to move in any direction. The front U-joint will also provide for side-to-side movement if the transmission is misaligned, preventing damage to the transmission or rear seal.

When a vehicle has been involved in a collision, if the vehicle has an automatic transmission and is parked with the shift lever in the park position, the parking pawl may break as designed if the vehicle is hit hard enough (Fig. 1-73). This is done to prevent the transmission from being damaged. If the pawl should break due to the impact, the broken section will drop into the bottom of the oil pan or transmission case. When the estimator checks this condition, it must be assured that the linkage is adjusted properly

and the transmission mount not sheared off, which would allow the transmission to move, and in its proper location. Then the shift lever of the vehicle is put in the park position and an attempt made to move the vehicle ahead or back; if it moves, the pawl is broken and only this particular section of the transmission will need to be repaired, which will be the parts, gaskets, fluid, and labor required, all of which are listed on the estimate.

In some cases in a collision the mounts will be sheared and the engine will have moved. This will make it necessary to replace the mounts, and align the power train and adjust the transmission shift and throttle linkage (Fig. 1-74).

Air-conditioning Systems

Many vehicles are bought with air-conditioning systems, either manually operated or automatically controlled. Also, after-market types of systems are installed in some vehicles.

Figures 1-74 and 1-75 show a typical installation of an air-conditioning system; regardless of manufacturer, they all have similar parts, such as a compressor, an evaporator, a receiver dehydrator or accumulator, all necessary electrical wires, solenoids, and lines to connect the components to form a closed system.

A front collision in a vehicle with an air conditioner usually damages the condenser, which is always located ahead of the radiator (Fig. 1-76), and the lines connecting the system will be damaged either slightly or completely ruptured. When the lines or condenser rupture, the refrigerant oil and the refrigerant charge discharge into the atmosphere within a few minutes; then air carrying moisture enters the system and the acid formed will cause damage to occur in the system. The system should be sealed completely when dismantled with appropriately sized plastic or rubber plugs. The receiver dehydrator will have to be changed as its moisture absorbing material will be damaged. Minor ruptures in the condenser may sometimes be repaired by a well-equipped shop specializing in such repairs. Some of the fins of the repaired or recycled condenser can be straightened by using a special comb or needle pliers. If the condenser is damaged beyond repair, it will have to be replaced with either a new or used condenser. Once the damage has been repaired, the system will have to be evacuated and recharged by putting the proper amount of air-conditioning oil and refrigerant into the system. The required amounts of refrigerant and oil as called for by factory specifications are usually marked on a plate on the compressor. This information can also be found in factory manuals or other industry publications. The labor time and costs for the parts are listed in estimating manuals to enable the estimator to arrive at a proper figure.

Compressors are very rarely badly damaged, and if repairs are required, the necessary parts may be ordered or

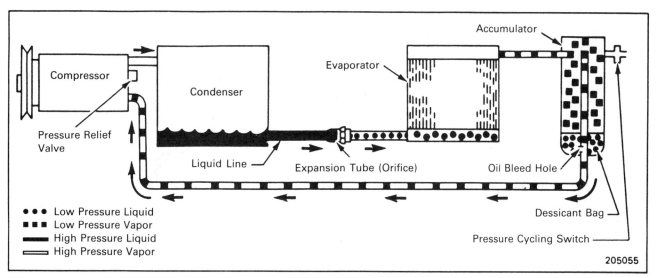

FIGURE 1-74   Typical air-conditioning system. (Courtesy of General Motors of Canada Ltd.)

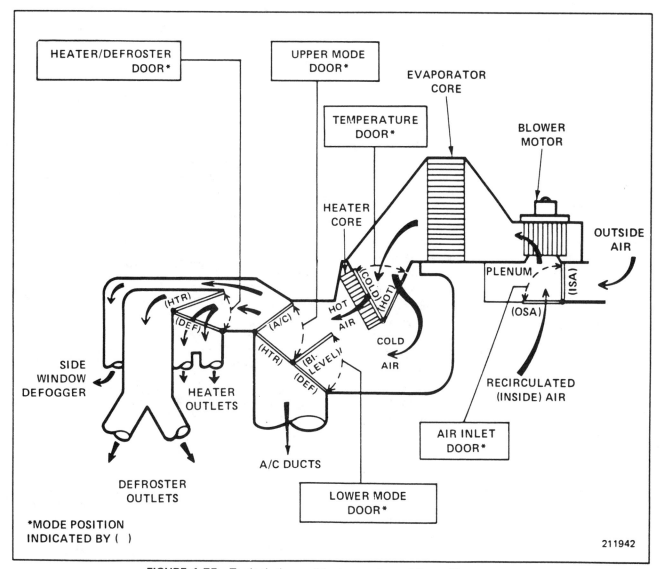

FIGURE 1-75   Typical air-conditioning system airflow. (Courtesy of General Motors of Canada Ltd.)

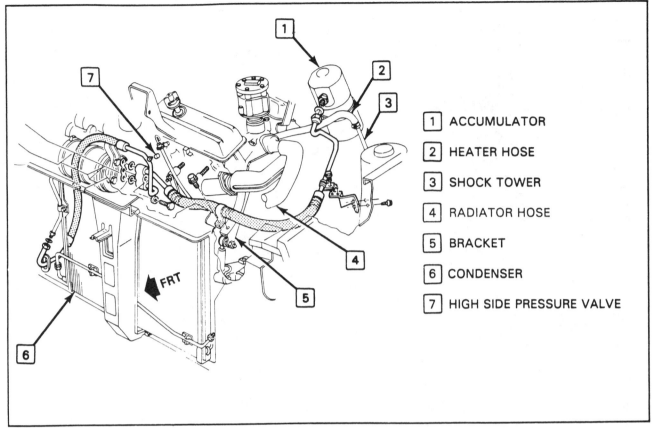

FIGURE 1-76   Typical location for air-conditioning refrigeration hoses, lines, condenser, and components. (Courtesy of General Motors of Canada Ltd.)

the compressor may be exchanged for a rebuilt unit. With the smaller engines used in many of today's automobiles, smaller compressors using less power are used for the air-conditioning system. If the compressor clutch, pulley assembly, or field coil is damaged, the part may be changed separately without opening the refrigerant system (Fig. 1-77).

If the estimator is in doubt about some of the parts that may need replacement, it would be advantageous to call in a specialist in this line of work and ask for an evaluation. The estimator will thus obtain a more accurate estimate, which will protect the insurance company, the shop, and the vehicle owner.

Bumper Systems

The bumper systems used today vary. Some vehicles have steel chrome plates or face bar assemblies; others use aluminum bumpers, and others will have a bumper system covered by a urethane cover painted the same color as the vehicle.

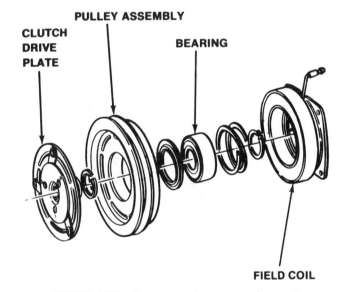

FIGURE 1-77   Damage to these parts does not require compressor overhaul. (Courtesy of Ford Motor Company of Canada Ltd.)

The bumper systems used not only have a face bar, but also reinforcements to strengthen them, as well as energy absorbers to meet safety regulations. It is more economical for insurance companies for damaged chromed bumpers to be replaced with recycled chromes parts that may have been repaired. Aluminum bumpers are either replaced with an exchange shop repaired unit or a new face bar. Most metal bars have impact cushions attached to the front of the bar to protect the shiny surface.

Insurance companies will usually install new face bars on fairly new vehicles, but as the vehicle gets older the bumpers are usually changed by using a shop repaired bumper. (see price list and availability in Appendix B). Reinforcement bars are made of steel or aluminum and can sometimes be repaired by the body shop, but mostly by the exchange shop, (see Appendix B) except when they are made of material such as martensitic steel. If not repairable or available, they must be replaced with a new part.

Bumper assemblies are usually damaged from either a front or rear collision; the amount of damage governs the type of repairs required. Most collisions are severe enough to damage the face bar, reinforcement bar, and sometimes the energy absorbers, as well as to kink and bend the frame. In very light collisions, the bumper maybe only suffer from a slight kink on the top or lower section or a slight twist, which can sometimes be repaired. When removing a bumper assembly, some of the bolts will have to be cut or they may break due to corrosion.

The estimator must estimate for the type of repair required, type of bumper and parts needed, the cost of one or two bolts, plus some additional time for removing the assembly in the remove and replace time in spite of the corroded bolts. Also, it is often necessary to repair some of the brackets if they are bent but still repairable; if not repairable, new or used parts must be used and the estimate priced accordingly.

All manufacturers use energy absorbers or isolators, which vary according to the manufacturer. If the absorbers are not collapsed after a collision, they do not need to be replaced. The end plate that attaches the bumper to the isolator may be repaired if the damage is not extensive without affecting the isolator. The mounting holes for mounting the isolators on the frame rails, especially on unibody vehicles, should be checked to see if the holes have elongated or been damaged.

Repaired and Chromed Bumpers

The price differential between new bumpers, reinforcement bar, and urethane covers and recycled parts makes it necessary that recycled parts be used as often as possible so that the estimate will not be overpriced. Bumpers are usually straightened in shops that have an exchange system avail-

able for most face bars. When a bar is repaired, the plating is stripped by dipping it into a tank that contains muriatic acid. The bar is then straightened using such tools as hydraulic presses, power hammers, large hammers, welded and grinded as required, and checked for fit against a template. The back of the bar is sandblasted to clean it; then the face of the bar is ground if required and polished.

The face bar is then put in a cleaning tank to clean the bumper. Then it is put in a tank that contains a solution of semibright nickel; this is deposited on the bar by an electric process for approximately 45 minutes. The bumper is then put in a tank containing bright nickel for 20 to 25 minutes; then it is put in a chrome-plating tank for $1\frac{1}{2}$ minutes. The bumper is then cleaned and wrapped ready for shipment to a customer.

Bumpers that are properly rechromed will look as good as a new part, but the estimator should increase the time for replacing it by at least 0.1 or 0.2 to enable the technician to fit it. Some rechromers cut corners by not plating the bumper as required, and these will usually rust or peel fairly fast. The extent of the damage to the bar will govern whether it can be repaired or junked. If it has to be scrapped, a core charge will be added to the price of the rechromed bumper. A shop should save all salvageable bars, which may be traded with the rechromer as a core to offset the price of unsalvageable cores that are junked. Sometimes the rechromer does not have the required core; in this case the repairable core is shipped to the repairing and rechroming shop, where it will be repaired and shipped, usually within 24 to 48 hours, back to the body shop.

Reputable rechromers guarantee their work, and if a bumper is found to be defective, it will be replaced immediately and they will usually pay the collision-technician time to replace it.

In some cases just a slight scratch, which could be called a cosmetic scratch, is caused; this can be repaired in some parts of the country by shops that charge a certain rate to repair a spot on a bumper.

If not too badly damaged, the urethane cover may be repaired (see Chapter 4); if not repairable, it is replaced by either a new part, a recycled part, or a remanufactured part.

When making the estimate, the estimator has options to keep the price of the repair as low as possible. These encourage the use of rechromed bars, straightened reinforcement bars, and repaired urethane covers and polished aluminum bumpers.

Wheel and Tires

A factor that should be considered when estimating collision damage to the tires and wheels is lateral or radial runout. (Fig. 1-78). If the lip of the wheel is slightly

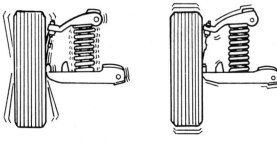

LATERAL RUN-OUT   **RADIAL RUN-OUT**

FIGURE 1-78 Conditions caused by collision damage. (Courtesy of Ford Motor Company of Canada Ltd.)

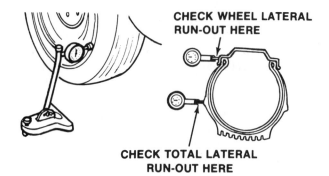

CHECK WHEEL LATERAL RUN-OUT HERE

CHECK TOTAL LATERAL RUN-OUT HERE

FIGURE 1-79 Dial gauge used to check lateral runout. (Courtesy of Ford Motor of Canada Ltd.)

damaged, it can usually be repaired and a new wheel is not required. By removing the tire, this condition can be repaired quickly; but only with a lateral runout check can it be determined if the wheel is within factory specifications. A lateral runout check is made by placing a fixed pointer or a runout gauge against the most outward portion of the first step of the wheel (Fig. 1-79) and checking as the wheel is rotated slowly to see if any gaps are present. An indicator with a dial on a fixed stand will show runout accurately in thousandths of an inch or millimeter. Excessive lateral runout will cause the wheel to wobble and wheels damaged beyond factory limits must be replaced. The maximum runout allowed is 0.070 in., slightly more than $\frac{1}{16}$ in. (1.6 mm) by factory specifications. In certain cases, lateral runout is caused by damaged hubs or axles.

The estimator must check the wheels, and if some are bent inward beyond the first step, new wheels should be listed for replacement on the estimate.

In some collisions the tires are damaged and should be closely inspected by the estimator. The tire must be inspected to see where it was hit and if any scrapes or deep cuts have made the tire carcass unsafe to use; if this is the case, the size, make, and type must be determined and listed for replacement.

Wheel damage often occurs without apparent damage to the tire; but the tire could be deflated due to a bent wheel. The tire may not show exterior damage but could possibly be damaged in the interior; in this type of situation the tire must be dismantled and checked for possible damage.

When the estimator finds that a tire or tires must be changed, the tire tread must be checked for the amount of wear caused by use before the accident. The owner is then charged for the amount of wear of the tread on the damaged tire. The insurance company will pay for the amount of tread left on the damaged tire; this is called a betterment factor since the customer will now have a new tire.

A tire tread depth gauge is used to measure the tread on damaged or undamaged tires. These tread depth gauges

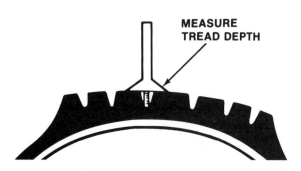

MEASURE TREAD DEPTH

FIGURE 1-80 Measuring tread depth to arrive at a betterment factor. (Courtesy of Ford Motor Company of Canada Ltd.)

are calibrated usually in increments of $\frac{1}{32}$ in. (0.8 mm) (Fig. 1-80). The estimator measures the tread depth to determine the average nonskid depth as follows. The tire is measured twice, first where the tread is worn the most and then where the tread is worn the least. The readings are totaled and divided by 2 to average the remaining tread depth. Then the same size, type, make, price, and tread depth on a new tire must be used to make an accurate calculation as to the amount of wear present.

The tread code letter is noted from a data sheet such as in Fig. 1-81 or from similar data sheets. If the tread letter is an E and the wear is $\frac{9}{32}$ in. or 7 mm, then the wear on the tire is 35%. The percentage is multiplied by the price that is listed for the particular tire from the customer's retail price list to establish the replacement charge for the tire. A tire is considered worn out when the wear bars are showing or $\frac{2}{32}$ in. (1.6 mm) total tread depth is left on the tire. The charge for the amount of wear on the tire to the owner is called a betterment factor toward the price of a new tire.

Firestone

ADJUSTMENT TREAD WEAR CHART FOR PASSENGER TIRES (EXCEPT "TEMPA SPARE"™)—AND LIGHT TRUCK TIRES

Remaining Tread	"Adj./Wt." Column Code Letters and % of Tread Worn												Remaining Tread
	X	Y	A	B	C	D	E	F	G	H	J	K	
2/32	100%	100%	100%	100%	100%	100%	100%	100%	100%	100%	100%	100%	2/32
	92	93	94	95	95	95	96	96	96	96	97	97	
3/32	85	87	88	90	91	91	92	92	93	93	94	94	3/32
	78	81	83	85	86	87	88	89	90	90	91	91	
4/32	71	75	77	80	81	83	84	85	86	87	88	88	4/32
	64	68	72	75	77	79	80	82	83	84	85	86	
5/32	57	62	66	70	72	75	77	78	80	81	82	83	5/32
	50	56	61	65	68	70	73	75	76	78	79	80	
6/32	42	50	55	60	63	66	69	71	73	75	76	77	6/32
	35	43	50	55	59	62	65	67	70	71	73	75	
7/32	28	37	44	50	54	58	61	64	66	68	70	72	7/32
	21	31	38	45	50	54	57	60	63	65	67	69	
8/32	14	25	33	40	45	50	53	57	60	62	64	66	8/32
	7	18	27	35	41	45	50	53	56	59	61	63	
9/32	0	12	22	30	36	41	46	50	53	56	58	61	9/32
		6	16	25	31	37	42	46	50	53	55	58	
10/32		0	11	20	27	33	38	43	46	50	53	55	10/32
			5	15	22	29	34	39	43	46	50	52	
11/32			0	10	18	25	30	35	40	43	47	50	11/32
				5	13	20	27	32	36	40	44	47	
12/32				0	9	16	23	28	33	37	41	44	12/32
					4	12	19	25	30	34	38	41	
13/32					0	8	15	21	26	31	35	38	13/32
						4	11	17	23	28	32	36	
14/32						0	7	14	20	25	29	33	14/32
							3	10	16	21	26	30	
15/32							0	7	13	18	23	27	15/32
								3	10	15	20	25	
16/32								0	6	12	17	22	16/32
									3	9	14	19	
17/32									0	6	11	16	17/32
										3	8	13	
18/32										0	5	11	18/32
											3	8	
19/32											0	5	19/32
												2	
20/32												0	20/32

GAUGE REMAINING TREAD DESIGN DEPTH...

AT MOST WORN AND LEAST WORN POINTS ON TREAD SURFACE

IN THESE GROOVES — Conventional Design

IN THESE GROOVES — Mud & Snow Design

All-Season Design

HOW TO FIGURE PERCENT OF TREAD WEAR ON ADJUSTMENTS

With an accurate tread depth gauge, measure remaining tread design depth in a groove nearest center of the tread. MEASURE TWICE—FIRST, WHERE THE TREAD IS MOST WORN, SECOND WHERE THE TREAD IS LEAST WORN. TOTAL THE READINGS AND DIVIDE BY TWO FOR *EXACT AVERAGE* REMAINING TREAD DEPTH.

On the chart line corresponding to the exact average remaining tread depth, under appropriate TREAD DEPTH CODE LETTER (X, Y, A, etc.) is the PERCENT OF TREAD WEAR (percent of useable tread worn off). If exact average ends in ½ (.5) use unmarked line *between* appropriate marked lines on the chart. For example, if exact average is 7.5/32 (7½/32) use line between 7/32 and 8/32.

For appropriate TREAD DEPTH CODE LETTER on tires see "Adj. Wt." column in Firestone current "Passenger Tire and Tube Price List" P701 or "Light Truck Tires—Suggested Exchange & Adjustment Base Price List" P702 —or tread depth column of Firestone current "Passenger Tire Adjustment Prices" pocket card. For retreads, see "Trade" or "Each" column of Firestone current "Factory Method Retreading & Repairing Price List" P713.

For adjustments that actually qualify as no-charge under current Firestone warranties, the percentages in the shaded area of the tread wear chart are considered to be within the first 10% of tread wear and percentages within the heavy line (above shaded area) are considered to be within the first 25% of tread wear.

THE FIRESTONE "TEMPA SPARE™" has no tread depth code letter. The tread wear chart will not accommodate this special spare tire which when new has only 4/32nds of an inch of tread design depth—and, like all highway tires is legally worn out when only 2/32nds of tread design remain. Replace an adjustable Tempa Spare on the following treadwear basis:

REMAINING TREAD DEPTH	REPLACE TO CONSUMER AT
1. 3/32 or more	No Charge
2. Less than 3/32, but more than 2.5/32	50%
3. Less than 2.5/32, but more than 2/32	75%

A180—Rev. 4/82

FIGURE 1-81 Tread wear data sheet. (Courtesy of Firestone Canada, Inc.)

QUESTIONS

1-1. What special qualities are required to be successful as a qualified estimator?

1-2. What types of steel are used in the new unibody vehicles?

1-3. Explain where an A, B, and C pillar are used in the construction of the vehicle.

1-4. What type of material is used to manufacture the flexible front cover and bumper assembly?

1-5. What type of glass is used for windshields and side windows? Explain the difference.

1-6. Explain briefly how an estimator decides if a wheel should be repaired or replaced.

1-7. Explain briefly what damage occurs when a vehicle is vandalized.

1-8. Explain briefly what damage occurs when a vehicle is submerged.

1-9. Explain what a rolled buckle is.

1-10. When a fender is compressed against the front door, what damages should the estimator look for?

1-11. Explain how some side windows are held to the lower channel.

1-12. What must the estimator do when a door cannot be opened due to collision damage?

1-13. What type of suspension is used on front-wheel-drive vehicles?

1-14. Explain how an integral power steering system functions.

1-15. What components may be damaged in a front collision in a rear-wheel-driven vehicle?

1-16. What should be done as soon as possible when an air-conditioning system is ruptured?

1-17. How is the lateral runout of a wheel checked?

## CHAPTER TWO

Understanding the Insurance and Body-Repair Industry

2-1 GENERAL KNOWLEDGE

Estimators are employed by autobody shops, adjusting firms, and insurance companies. Estimators working for the autobody repair shop may not only write estimates, but, depending on the size of the shop, may also be the supervisor and service representative. The estimator arranges for the customer's appointments for repairs and the loaner vehicles that many shops now provide for improved customer relations.

When an estimator works for an adjusting firm or insurance company, the title of the job may be changed to adjustor. Some insurance firms have estimators who write the complete estimate in service centers where the customer brings in the vehicle involved in the collision, if drivable. This customer may have previously phoned in a claim to an adjuster and was given an appointment for obtaining an estimate. Once the estimate is done and the adjuster has finished reviewing the particulars of the collision, he or she will then authorize the repairs as required as long as the cost does not exceed the value of the vehicle, minus its salvage value.

In some adjusting firms, the adjuster estimator will travel to the repair shop where the customer's vehicle is parked waiting for the adjuster to authorize repairs. The responsibility of the adjuster is to approve the collision repair shop's legitimate bid and also to satisfy the customer's legitimate damage claim to the vehicle. Many adjusters will write their own estimate without any input from the shop owner. From previous knowledge and experience, the adjuster will estimate the required labor for straightening a frame and/or for sheet-metal damage, as required. The prices for parts and replacement-part labor time are either added in by a computer or the adjuster or estimator, or a clerk may fill in the required information. The adjuster will then check and approve the completed repair estimate. A golden rule that should be followed by all shop estimators is never to criticize the customer to an adjuster and also never to criticize an adjuster to a customer. They are both valued customers, and they should always be treated as such on all matters pertaining to work relations in the shop as well as to any social obligations which are important to the employer.

The shop estimator and the adjuster must know the different terms used in the insurance industry, such as collision insurance, deductible, public liability, comprehensive insurance, and no-fault insurance. Customers who need an estimate and carry insurance do not always understand the coverage that they paid for.

Collision insurance is used to pay for repairing the insured vehicle if it is hit by an uninsured motorist, even if the insured customer caused the accident. Most collision insurance has a deductible amount that the insured must pay when the vehicle is repaired. The deductible varies depending on the policy the insured chose. The deductible is not charged to the insured person if he or she was not at fault and the other vehicle was covered by insurance.

Public liability insurance coverage protects the insured up to the value of the insurance policy that was bought, let us say $1 million. The insurance company will protect the insured from claims that result from an accident caused by the vehicle owned by the insured. The insurance company will protect the insured to the amount of the value of the policy from the loss of the insured's personal property due to a lawsuit. This insurance will also pay for the damaged property or vehicle of the other party who was not at fault in the collision.

Comprehensive or all perils coverage insurance is a type of coverage bought to protect the insured property from damages that are not covered by policies such as collision and public liability. This type of policy will pay for damages caused by fire, theft, hail, and wind.

In some states and provinces it is necessary to carry a no-fault type of insurance coverage. Some states and provinces require 100% coverage by no-fault insurance. With this type of coverage, both the insured's injuries and damage to the vehicle are paid by the insurance company regardless of who may have caused the accident. In other areas, the no-fault coverage is only on personal injuries. When vehicles that carry complete no-fault coverage are involved in a collision, the insurance companies do not make an effort to find out who was at fault when settling the claims. The no-fault insurance of bodily injuries that occur in accidents covers the medical treatment expenses required. Some companies even allow a burial expense for the driver and passengers, as well impairment payments and total and partial weekly disability payments for as long as the disability lasts. Some companies also offer an addition to an insurance policy that covers the insurer if involved with a vehicle that has no insurance coverage.

In certain states or provinces, when an insured motorist is involved in an accident, he or she is required to take the vehicle if driveable to a certain number of collision repair shops to obtain an estimate from each. In this type of situation, it is especially valuable for the shop to have a reputable, knowledgeable estimator. It is very important that the shop have a good business relationship with the customer, adjuster, and insurance companies. In great part, this is because the vehicle owner is not the paying customer, but the insurance company is, as it will authorize the repairs and payment for the repairs required.

When an accident report is made, a file with a claim number is opened, and all information pertaining to the collision will be entered in this file until it is closed upon completion of the necessary paperwork.

Computers are now being used for estimating purposes. Large companies use this service to help their local company adjusters fill in their estimates. The computer program provides recent price changes, as well as remove and replacement times for parts and paint times for different panels. These programs are costly and very few repair shops can afford this service. The repair of frames and metal panel straightening time are still estimated by the estimator. An experienced estimator is still needed even when using a computer to be able to give a comprehensive accurate estimate.

When the adjuster or estimator visits a shop to write the estimate personally, it is good practice for the shop estimator to be present, to meet the insurance representative, to show where the vehicle is, and to assist as much as is required or desired. As the estimate is being filled, the shop estimator can help the adjuster check data on the items included in the estimate and see that no items have been missed. Two people helping each other can usually do better than one. Also, if there is a problem with an item, it can be discussed on site and a decision made as to repair operations.

Some local insurance company offices or adjusters use what may be called preferred repair shops for vehicles repairs. This may occur because the shop owners are personal friends, the bids are usually on the low side, or the repairs made are of good quality. However, this type of policy usually creates an unfriendly attitude from excluded shops toward the insurance company or adjuster.

2-2 THE ESTIMATE AND ITS PURPOSE

The estimate is a legal document between a shop and a customer for specified work, which includes the type of work to be done, the parts to be repaired or replaced, and an agreed-on price. The estimate becomes a guide for the parts that need to be ordered and to inform the technician what work is to be done. The estimate becomes a guide for the parts that need to be ordered and to inform the technician what work is to be done. The customer has to sign the estimate to make the contract valid between the shop owner and the customer. A typical estimating form is shown in Fig. 2-1A and B; this type is also used as a work order for the shop. On the reverse side of the first page of the estimate form, drawings of automobiles are included; the estimator uses this to mark where the damage occurred and the color of the vehicle. Notice that the required information must be filled in on the appropriate lines. Also, the information on the bottom-left portion of the page must be read by the customer so that he or she is aware of the conditions under which the work is to be done and how it is to be paid for.

Figure 2-2 shows another type of estimate form used by many shops; notice the disclaimer on the bottom-left corner of the form. This disclaimer protects the shop as it

ESTIMATOR'S REPORT

Insurance Company _____

CLAIM NUMBER

Estimate, Inspection and Location Date _____

ADJUSTER'S NAME	ESTIMATOR'S NAME	DATE OF COMPLETION	DATE OF LOSS

INSURED   VEHICLE

NAME AND ADDRESS	LICENSE (POLICY) NUMBER	GVW	MILEAGE	AMOUNT OF DEDUCTIBLE
	YEAR, MAKE & MODEL		SERIAL NUMBER	

DESCRIPTION OF WORK TO BE DONE	RE-PAIR	REPLACE NEW	REPLACE L.K.Q.	QTY.	PART NUMBER	PARTS COST	HRS.	LABOR COST

This is purely an estimate and not a definite contract price. Owing to the impossibility of determining damage of concealed parts, we reserve the right to submit a further estimate for approval or otherwise. Prices subject to change without notice.
Authorization to Repair

I _____ the registered owner of the above described vehicle authorize the repairs to proceed.

TOTAL PARTS COST ▶	
TOTAL LABOR COST ▶	
SHOP MATERIAL	
PAINT LABOR	
PAINT MATERIAL	
SUB TOTAL	
TAX	
TOTAL COST ▶	

ONLY APPROVED ADDITIONS PAID

FIGURE 2-1A.   Typical estimate work order form.

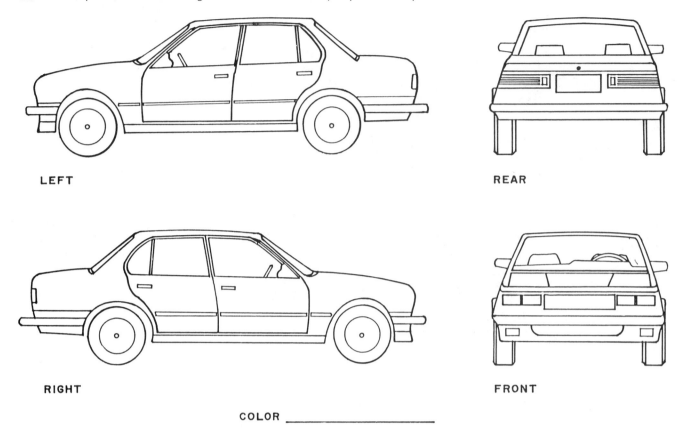

LEFT

REAR

RIGHT

FRONT

COLOR _____

FIGURE 2-1B.   Reverse side of estimate for showing vehicles where estimator can mark location of damage.

creates an open bid, which may be used if extra damage is found upon dismantling or repairing the vehicle. This extra damage has to be paid for; insurance companies realize that it is impossible to see all the parts required and the work involved in a major collision. To change the amount and type of work that must be done on the vehicle, the shop supervisor must phone the adjuster to point out what changes are required for the repair of the vehicle to bring it back to a pre-accident condition. The adjuster may give authorization for the repairs either by phone or by a personal visit to the repair shop to view the problem. The adjuster or estimator will have to fill a form similar to Fig. 2-3 to authorize the extra work; this form must be filed with the claim so that the company will know why the amount of money to be paid has increased and why the extra work was required.

When a shop always requires supplementals, insurance companies either will learn to avoid that particular shop or will examine each supplemental very carefully.

Many shops do not work on or repair motors, transmissions, rear-axle suspensions, and many of the accessories. This type of work is usually done by automotive technicians and is sublet to these types of shops.

Insurance companies do not particularly like to leave an estimate open as to the amount that will be required to repair the vehicle. The company adjuster will often ask that

the damaged assembly be dismantled to find out what the damage is and how much it is going to cost to repair it. Some repair operations may be left open, but not too often, as some shops abuse this type of estimate and may load up the bill with fictitious repairs or work to guarantee a profit for the shop. To prevent this abuse, the adjuster or estimator will ask that all damaged parts be kept on hand so that they may be personally inspected to verify if the repairs have been done per the supplemental submitted before authorization for payment is approved for the claim.

Labor Time and How It Is Established

Estimators use different methods to record the time on the estimate form. They are estimated time, flat-rate time, straight time (that is, the technician has a work order for which the time is punched on a time clock), and open time.

Estimated time is used when body repairs are to be made for which no flat-rate time has been established, such as when a panel or panels are to be repaired instead of removed and replaced. Estimated time is also used on the part of frame repairs that is called cosmetic repairs, that is, to smooth out and repair damage on rails to improve the quality of the repair. There are many operations for which there is no established time (flat rate); these include alignment procedures, sheet-metal repair, welding, and partial

OWNER		ADDRESS		PHONE BUS.		DATE	
				RES.			
YEAR	MAKE		MODEL	SERIAL NO.		LIC. NO.	

Replace	Repair	Description of Repairs	Labor hrs	Part No.	Amount
			Subtotals		

Labor	HRS	
Parts		
Painting	HRS	
Paint material		
Shop material		

Estimated by

Insurance companies   Policy #

Owner

Policy #

Third party

Adjuster

Remarks

S U B L E T	Radiator	
	Chrome	
	Frame	
Sublet total		
Tax		
Towing and storage		
TOTAL ▶		

This is purely an estimate and not a definite contract price. Owing to the impossibility of determining damage of concealed parts, we reserve the right to submit a further estimate for approval or otherwise. Prices subject to change without notice.

FIGURE 2-2 Typical estimate form.

Addition to Repair Estimate Authorization

Insurance Company or Adjusting Firm _____ A.B.C. Adjuster _____

DATE: ___ February 5, 1988 ___   CLAIM NUMBER: ___ 36hy 4065 _____

ADJUSTER: ___ John Doe _____   ESTIMATOR: ___ Tom Smith _____

OWNER OF CAR: ___ Jack Jones _____

BODY SHOP: ___ AAA Auto Collision and Painting _____

CHANGE IN REPAIR AND AMOUNT: ___ Check front end and report damage estimate ___

___ for repairs. _____

_____

_____

_____

_____

_____

_____

REASON FOR CHANGE OF REPAIR ESTIMATE: ___ McPherson strut and spindle damaged; ___

___ needs wheel alignment. Total cost $346.50 including labor. ___

_____

_____

FIELD CHECK APPROVED: YES | X | NO | | PHONE APPROVAL   YES | | NO | |

___ Repairs required to make vehicle roadworthy. ___

_____

_____

_____

| ___ Tom Smith ___ | ___ B. J. Thomas ___ |
| ESTIMATOR | ESTIMATOR SUPERVISOR |

FIGURE 2-3 Repair estimate supplement authorization form.

panel installations such as the sectioning of a panel. Repairs on seat trim and cushions, paint spot repairing, undercoating cleaning of sections of fabric, and many other items require the estimator to use his or her judgment from such previous experience.

The estimator's judgment will usually give a fair amount of time; but if there is some question on the time for the repair on an item with which the adjuster is not too familiar, an experienced technician should be consulted for advice. The estimator may also use an estimated cost to repair the item, and that is the cost of the parts plus the labor required.

The *flat-rate* time is the time published by manufacturers or estimating collision guides for the removal and replacement (or remove and install), overhaul, alignment, and overlap time. This type of information is published by the manufacturers for the payment of warranty claims, which are made when a vehicle is under a specified new-car warranty time and mileage. These published flat-rate times are also used by the auto collision repair industry for making estimates.

Another method is *straight time,* which is used when repairing such items as rattles, door locks, regulators, minor alignments on doors or hood, and the like. The technician punches time in on a time clock on a work order when the repairs are started and punches out again when the repairs have been completed, and the time is then calculated. This type of time is usually used when working on custom-built or modified vehicles for which no flat rate time may be found to cover the repair operation.

Open time is used when a component or part is believed to be damaged but it cannot be seen or proved that it is damaged. This means that extra time will be required for repairs charged to the customer; using this system honestly will protect both the customer and the body shop from extra time and charges for repairs. Typical items could be a transmission, a power steering pump, window regulators, or in fact any item that cannot be tested while the estimate is being written. The estimator should not and really cannot leave many items on open time, because it would defeat the purpose of the estimate. Open time should only be used as an item of last resort to protect both the shop and customer.

Estimating Straightening Time

No estimating collision guide will be able to give the estimator the amount of time for repairs of panels or frames on collision damage, because accidents and collision damage are all different to a certain degree and vehicles are built slightly different from one another. Therefore, the estimator must possess the knowledge and ability to determine how much time must be allowed when panels and frames are to be repaired.

The estimator must inspect the damaged vehicle very carefully, sometimes using a tape measure or gauges to determine the amount of damage and how much time will be required for repairs. The first time to be estimated is the alignment time and then the finish operations for sheet-metal damage. A rule of thumb is to use 1.0 hour per square foot (0.09 square meter) for ordinary metal collision repair and 1.5 hours per square foot (0.140 square meter) for metal that is badly stretched, gouged, or torn.

The repair process must mentally visualize different operations required and how long they will take. A few steps are similar and required for each collision repair job. These are bringing the vehicle into the shop and ordering materials and parts. Then the vehicle must be prepared for pulling the sheet metal, frame, or both frame and sheet metal at the same time. This is accomplished by lifting the vehicle on a safety stand or frame machine; then all panels that are in the way of accomplishing the repairs are removed to facilitate hook-ups. The damage is roughed out; this can also be called alignment of panel or section time. Then the sheet metal must be repaired or replaced and materials such as plastic filler are applied after final grinding of the metal is finished. The plastic filler must be sanded and shaped properly; then the paint finishing process is completed to give the customer a good collision repair job.

All the necessary times required for the different phases of the work must be added together to obtain a complete and accurate amount of time for accomplishing the repairs. The repair or replacement time as well as the customer's wishes must be considered when estimating a panel; should it be repaired or replaced? Usually, when the cost of repair approaches 60% to 75% for a panel, especially on newer vehicles, it is replaced with a new panel. When damaged to this extent, it is often very difficult to return a panel to a before-collision quality, strength, and appearance, which can be obtained from using a new panel. The customer must be satisfied with the repairs done.

If the customer is paying for the repairs, the repairs may be done as the customer desires. The estimator must explain clearly the options available to perform the repairs. If the vehicle is insured and the insurance company is paying for the repairs, the estimator may want the panel if repairable to be repaired. This is an important fact that should be established for legal reasons before asking the customer to sign the authorization to perform the necessary repairs. Sometimes, to please both the customer and insurance company, estimates for both types of repairs are written; then the customer, adjuster, and estimator can make a decision by evaluating the amount of money each method will cost.

Sometimes, because of a part shortage due to age or type of vehicle, the existing part must be repaired or replaced with good parts from a recycler. Using good recycled parts will give good-quality repair if done properly at a lower cost than using new panels. This, plus the availability of work at certain times of the year (shop work is slow and the technicians must be paid anyway), will favor repair instead of replacement if possible.

The skills of the technicians and the type of equipment the shop owns will determine to a great extent the type of work the shop prefers to do. Sometimes when adjoining panels are borderline for repair operations, it is advantageous for alignment operations that some panels be changed. These panels are changed with either new parts or good recycled parts; thus the technicians have undamaged panels to help align other panels.

When estimating a unitized vehicle for collision damages, it is important that the McPherson strut suspension and its attaching points be examined very carefully to diagnose any damage that has occurred and include it on the estimate, thus avoiding a later appreciable increase in the price for the repairs.

Shop Retail Price Per Hour

A very important part of operating a business is knowing what is required as a charge per hour to the customer to realize a profit for the shop. Many items must be considered to arrive at a charge-out rate per hour, such as wages, cost and upkeep of all equipment, and materials used in the body and paint shop. Some fringe benefits must be paid by law to employees and the shop may offer others. Fringe benefits may include social security, unemployment benefits, industrial accident insurance, paid holidays, laundering or dry cleaning of uniforms, and parking spaces; some shops offer sick benefits and insurance and even a profit-sharing system to the older employees. Another sizable cost is building overhead cost, which includes utilities, property and business taxes, building rent or repair and depreciation, heat, and telephone rentals, long-distance charges, and other applicable charges.

Some shops pay their employees on an hourly or weekly rate. The pay of the employee is the shop's cost and will continue until the job is finished. The estimator must be very careful when estimating when the shop employees are paid in this fashion, because if more time is taken to perform the repairs than estimated, the shop will lose money. If the vehicle should come back due to poor work or a mistake, the shop has to pay the employee again. Apprentices are paid less than qualified technicians but they will usually need more time to complete the repairs required. In this situation the estimator must be careful as to how the estimate is written and which technician should be chosen to do the repairs. Many shops pay their qualified technicians as per the estimated time on the estimate, which is known as piece work or flat rate. This system usually pays 40% to 50% of the shop labor rate to the qualified technician; apprentices will receive a lower rate of pay, which is usually based on an hourly or weekly pay rate. Therefore, if the shop charge-out rate is $30.50, the qualified technician will receive between $12.20 to $15.25 per hour for his work per estimated hour. The shop must not forget to include the cost of operating the business, plus a percentage that should be realized as a net profit after all costs are paid for.

Most shops have a body shop material charge that is around $4.50 or a percentage of labor per estimated hour of work, as well as a paint shop hourly charge of $14.00 or a percentage per hour of labor as required for the paint work. There also must be an extra charge when working on trucks over 1 ton as they are harder to work on and use up more room in the shop.

Most shops use the flat-rate or piece-work method of payment to technicians because it provides an incentive for the technician to work without wasting time. A good technician will usually finish the repairs before the allotted time and is rewarded financially. The average technician usually meets the time on the estimate, and the slower technician will lose some time on many jobs. This will vary the income of the technicians, but it is easier to administer for pay purposes. Any vehicle that comes back to the shop due to mistakes or errors in doing the repairs is fixed by the technician without cost to the shop for labor.

Some shops use a modified pay plan; they pay their technicians so much a week plus a bonus for any work done by the technician above the required amount of hours for the week. Using these two pay systems means that the technician will usually check the work done for any possible mistakes to prevent come backs. The estimator must ensure that all the estimates are fair to both the technicians and the shop so that a net profit is realized.

In the industry, there are usually three recognized types of estimates: the competitive bid, the noncompetitive bid, and the courtesy bid. These different types of estimates depend on the type of customer vehicle, type of work to be done, type of work done by the shop, and how busy the shop is at a particular time.

The majority of the work for most shops is insurance-paid work; other types of work may be rust or restoration work. Some shops do custom body work and paint work. There will always be some slight disagreements on the time estimated between the body and paint technician, as this type of work is usually done on a commission or piece-work basis. The estimator has to be fair to the shop, the technician, and the customer, because if the bid is too high the customer will go to another shop; if the estimate is too low the shop and technician will lose money and there will be no profit.

The Competitive Estimate

Insurance companies and customers shop around for estimates for doing either collision, rust, or custom work. The customer, whether a private individual or insurance company, wants fair value for the money paid for the work. Thus the estimate done will be competing against another shop. This means that the estimator must be friendly, show a good attitude, and explain how the work is to be done and the total cost to the customer. A very poor practice, which is sometimes used, is to get the job in the shop on a low estimate; then, once the work is started, the estimate is increased without very good reason. This type of business practice leaves a hostile feeling between the customer and the shop and is not good for public relations. A good shop is kept busy by repeat customers and their friends, who patronize the shop due to the quality of the work, the friendliness of the staff, and honest deals.

However, it is necessary at times to raise the estimate due to unforeseen or hidden damage. The best way is to call the customer and discuss the situation and arrive at a mutual agreement. It is better to lose a job than to underbid for the work, because if the customer leaves underbid work with the shop, the technicians will be tempted to take short-cuts in the work quality, the shop will most likely lose money, and the customer will not be happy with the quality of the work.

To prepare a proper comprehensive estimate takes time when cost of repairs may run to figures as high as $6000.00 or higher depending on the damage. It is sometimes impossible to write an estimate on the bigger types of repairs without missing a few items that may not be visible. Sometimes items are damaged but cannot be inspected to obtain an accurate cost for the price of repair. These items may be left open for later inspection and agreement on the repairs to be done.

Noncompetitive Estimates

The noncompetitive estimate is done by the shop estimator when a customer has a vehicle that through use, and maybe some abuse, requires that dents, nicks, scratches, and faded paint be repaired. These estimates are usually between the customer and the estimator, who come to an agreement as to the price for the repairs after inspecting the vehicle, listing the damage that must be repaired, and determining the cost of the work and materials.

The shop estimate is made with the required margin for shop profit; great detail is not required as the repairs are usually fairly simple. Only the prices of some parts that may be required and flat-rate times for some parts that may have to be removed and replaced are entered on the estimate. This will require the use of the estimating manual for part prices and time. If the estimate is needed for competition purposes or an insurance claim, the estimator who is honest and friendly, and explains why and how certain work will be done will often get the work for the shop.

Courtesy Estimates

Courtesy estimates are done when a person brings a vehicle for an estimate to a shop, but says that the work will be done at another shop, but that another estimate is needed for either insurance purposes or for comparing prices. The estimate must still be written and is done fairly often by many shops. When customers want to sell or trade their vehicle, some will want to know how much it is going to cost to repair the vehicle. By getting an estimate, they know approximately how much they can expect to receive for the vehicle.

Some courtesy estimates are dishonest because they are written by shops that work together, or they could be written by the owner of the same shop who has estimate forms from other shops. This is sometimes done by a customer who wants the vehicle repaired by a certain shop after suffering collision damage. The owner or estimator will write one estimate for the shop and then two more estimates on other shops' estimate forms which will be priced higher for the estimated repairs required. The estimates might appear legitimate and competitive, but they are not because they were written by the same person and are illegal, as this is price fixing. The customer's vehicle will be repaired at the shop preferred, but this thwarts the competitive business ethics of honest conduct.

The adjuster or estimator receiving various estimates for repairs should check the estimates very closely. The points to check are as follows:

1. The estimates may be typed instead of handwritten; the same words are used; repairs are estimated for the wrong side or part.

2. The parts list is the same on all estimates; estimated parts replacement times on one estimate are correct, but inflated on others.

3. Repair work is inflated on other estimates but are fairly close to one another; and a sure giveaway is when the estimate forms of the shops show up often.

If the adjuster finds this type of estimates on some jobs, the customer should be sent to another specified shop to have an estimate written on the damages to be repaired. Shops who write many courtesy estimates usually are known to insurance companies and develop a poor business reputation. This is a good reason for the insurance adjuster and the shop estimator to write the estimate together, as it will make for honest bidding and a shop will not then be excluded from insurance work.

Insurance discounts

Some insurance firms expect to get discounts on the parts used on a collision repair job. A shop may refuse to give this discount, but it could lose the repair work if some other shop gives discounts. A shop usually receives discounts of 20% to 25% from dealers on vehicle parts that fit vehicles manufactured in North America, but the dealers of foreign vehicles may only give discounts of around 10%. If the shop is expected to give discounts on parts to insurance companies, this will cut its profit margin. This type of pressure from an insurance company may lead some shops to substitute used parts or even repair the old part where new parts are estimated for, which is a dishonest method of doing business. Some insurance companies insist on using original parts for panel replacement, but others will use after-market jobber parts (see Appendix C for parts list). Any discount given on parts will certainly not help to pay for the time and expenses a shop incurs through ordering, picking up, paying freight, telephone charges, and other business expenses.

Discounts on glass are fairly high, but losses on broken glass can also be very expensive to the shop. Discounts of up to 50% are sometimes given to shops, but if the employees break a new windshield when installing the profit margin is much less. Many shops and insurance firms prefer that the glass-replacement companies do the replacement, as this is their type of business and they are very proficient at it. Many insurance firms receive a discount on glass replacement, especially from shops that replace glass as their main business.

Many shops install glass only when it is required that it be used as a template for fitting purposes; otherwise, this work is sublet to glass-replacement firms, which work on a bigger discount and will give the shop a small discount for the work sent to them.

2-3 THE WRITTEN-OFF OR TOTALED VEHICLE

Write-offs

A write-off or a totaled vehicle is a vehicle that due to the damage from a collision will cost more to repair, plus its salvage value, than the same vehicle may be bought for on the open market (Fig. 2-4).

The estimator or adjuster upon viewing the vehicle must write a comprehensive estimate, listing all the parts that are required, if possible, as well as the labor time required to repair the vehicle. The price of the parts, labor, body shop material, and paint shop material must be totaled

FIGURE 2-4 Written-off vehicle due to cost of repairs.

to find out the cost of the repairs required. The value of the vehicle is taken from a guide using the latest edition, such as in Figs. 2-5 and 2-6.

The values for the 1985 Oldsmobile Firenza, Cutlass, Calais, Cutlass Ciera, Delta 88 Royal, Ninety-Eight Regency, and Toronado are included in Fig. 2-5. The value is determined by the base price plus the value of the options that are part of the vehicle. From this, a high mileage and reconditioning deduction, if applicable, will be subtracted, thus reducing the value. A chart is included in the guide as to what amounts should be deducted for high mileage.

As an example, we will use a 1985 Oldsmobile Calais V.6, two-door coupe with the following options: sunroof, AM/FM radio, cruise control, two-tone paint, and air conditioning. This vehicle has an average trade-in value of $8525, an average loan value of $8450, and an average retail value of $9575. If the vehicle did not have an automatic transmission but a manual transmission a deduction of $475 would be taken off the price for trade in, loan value, and retail price.

For example, the top book value of a vehicle is $8300, the collision repair estimate is $6250, and the average or salvage yard value or bid is $2200. The amount of the estimated repairs plus the bid for the salvage exceed the market value of the vehicle by a $150. With these figures available, it is not economical to repair the vehicle and the vehicle will be sold to a recycler salvager.

There are always some exceptions to the rule, such as a premium low-mileage vehicle, which is too borderline to be written off. Figure 2-6 is to be used to answer question 2-14 at the end of the chapter.

The customer, knowing the value of the particular vehicle due to its good shape and low mileage, does not want the vehicle written off but repaired. Some insurance companies will authorize repairs up to the value of the vehicle or sell the vehicle to the customer for salvage value plus a certain amount of money; the customer is then responsible to have the vehicle repaired. Some companies will also have body shops give an estimate on the repairs to be done on a contract basis.

Some insurance companies will total vehicles at a certain percent of value of repairs plus salvage value. The insurance company adjuster will have to fill in a report on the condition of the salvage vehicle, which could be similar to Fig. 2-7. When the adjustor estimator fills in this form, the estimator must pay particular attention to the condition of the vehicle, as insurance companies usually depreciate for worn or torn upholstery. The older the vehicle is, the more depreciation that will be applied to worn or damaged parts, such as from corrosion or previous wear and tear. The adjusters are instructed to pay only for the value of the amount of the worn part that was on the vehicle before the accident. Should the insured demand new parts, the insured will have to pay the difference between the price of the new

70 OLDSMOBILE 1986-85

Av'g. Trd-In	Ins. Sym.	BODY TYPE	Model	Av'g. Loan	Av'g. Retail
1986 CUSTOM CRUISER-V8-AT-PS-AC-Cont					
	Add	Tilt Strg. Wheel			
	Add	Wire Wheel Covers			
	Add	Luggage Rack			
	Add	Third Seat S/W			
	Add	Woodgrain			
1986 NINETY-EIGHT-TORONADO AC-PW-P.Sts-FWD					
NINETY-EIGHT REGENCY-V6					
		Sedan 4D	CX69		
		Coupe 2D	CX11		
NINETY-EIGHT REGENCY BROUGHAM-V6					
		Sedan 4D	CW69		
		Coupe 2D	CW11		
TORONADO BROUGHAM-V6					
		Coupe 2D	EZ57		
	Add	Astroroof			
	Add	VinylRf(Std.98Cpe)			
	Add	CruiseCont(Std.Tor)			
	Add	RearWindDefroster			
	Add	AM/FM Stereo/Tp.			
	Add	Delco/BoseSystem.			
	Add	Tilt Strg. Wheel			
		(Std.Brghm&Toronado)			
	Add	Leather Seats			
	Add	WireWhlCov(Std.Brghm)			
	Add	2-Tone Paint			
	Add	Grande Pkg.			
1985 FIRENZA-L4-AT-PS-AC-FWD					
5575		Sedan 4D	JC69	5025	6450
5475		Coupe 2D S	JC77	4950	6350
5925		Sedan 4D LX	JD69	5350	6800
5825		Coupe 2D SX	JD77	5250	6700
5750		Cruiser Wgn	JC35	5175	6625
6100		Cruiser LX	JD35	5500	6975
150 Add		Sunroof		150	200
75 Add		AM/FM Stereo		75	100
100 Add		AM/FM Stereo/Tp.		100	125
50 Add		Power Door Locks		50	75
50 Add		Power Windows		50	75
50 Add		Power Seats		50	75
25 Add		RearWindDefroster.		25	50
50 Add		Cruise Control		50	75
25 Add		Tilt Strg. Wheel		25	50
50 Add		Wire Wheel Covers		50	75
25 Add		Luggage Rack		25	50
75 Add		2-Tone Paint		75	100
225 Add		ES Pkg.		225	300
400 Add		GT Pkg.		375	475
75 Add		Woodgrain		75	100
150 Add		6 Cyl. Engine.		150	200
325 Deduct		Manual Trans.		325	325
125 Deduct		Convent. Steer.		125	125
550 Deduct		W/out Air Cond		550	550

Av'g. Trd-In	Ins. Sym.	BODY TYPE	Model	Av'g. Loan	Av'g. Retail
1985 CUTLASS-AT-PS-AC					
CUTLASS SUPREME-V6					
6925		Sedan 4D	GR69	6250	7850
7125		Coupe 2D	GR47	6425	8050
CUTLASS SUPREME BROUGHAM-V6					
7350		Sedan 4D	GM69	6625	8275
7550		Coupe 2D	GM47	6800	8500
CUTLASS SALON-V6					
7675		Coupe 2D	GK47	6925	8625
CUTLASS SUPREME-V8					
7125		Sedan 4D	GR69	6425	8050
7325		Coupe 2D	GR47	6600	8250
CUTLASS SUPREME BROUGHAM-V8					
7550		Sedan 4D	GM69	6800	8500
7750		Coupe 2D	GM47	6975	8700
CUTLASS SALON-V8					
7875		Coupe 2D	GK47	7100	8825
8300		Cpe 2D 442	GK47	7475	9325
75 Add		Vinyl/Land Roof		75	100
500 Add		T-Top		450	600
400 Add		Astroroof		375	475
100 Add		AM/FM Stereo		100	125
125 Add		AM/FM Stereo/Tp.		125	150
50 Add		Power Door Locks		50	75
75 Add		Power Windows		75	100
75 Add		Power Seats		75	100
50 Add		RearWindDefroster.		50	75
50 Add		Cruise Control		50	75
50 Add		Tilt Strg. Wheel		50	75
150 Add		Leather Seats		150	200
75 Add		Wire Wheel Covers		75	100
75 Add		2-Tone Paint		75	100
650 Deduct		W/out Air Cond		650	650
Deduct 25% of Trade-In Value for Diesel Engine.					
1985 CALAIS-AT-PS-AC-FWD					
CALAIS-L4					
7300		Coupe 2D	NF27	6575	8225
7550		Cpe Supreme	NT27	6800	8500
CALAIS-V6					
7500		Coupe 2D	NF27	6750	8425
7750		Cpe Supreme	NT27	6975	8700
150 Add		Sunroof		150	200
100 Add		AM/FM Stereo		100	125
125 Add		AM/FM Stereo/Tp.		125	150
350 Add		Delco/BoseSystem.		325	425
50 Add		Power Door Locks		50	75
75 Add		Power Windows		75	100
75 Add		Power Seats		75	100
50 Add		RearWindDefroster.		50	75
50 Add		Cruise Control		50	75
50 Add		Tilt Strg. Wheel		50	75
75 Add		Wire Wheel Covers		75	100
75 Add		2-Tone Paint		75	100
450 Add		Calais 500 Pkg.		425	525
150 Add		Leather Seats		150	200

OLDSMOBILE 1985-84 71

Av'g. Trd-In	Ins. Sym.	BODY TYPE	Model	Av'g. Loan	Av'g. Retail
1985 CALAIS-AT-PS-AC-FWD-Cont					
475 Deduct		Manual Trans.		475	475
650 Deduct		W/out Air Cond		650	650
1985 CUTLASS CIERA-AT-PS-AC					
CUTLASS CIERA LS-L4-FWD					
6750		Sedan 4D	AJ19	6075	7650
6650		Coupe 2D	AJ27	6000	7550
7000		Cruiser Wagon	AJ35	6300	7925
CUTLASS CIERA BROUGHAM-L4-FWD					
7075		Sedan 4D	AM19	6375	8000
6975		Coupe 2D	AM27	6300	7900
CUTLASS CIERA LS-V6-FWD					
6950		Sedan 4D	AJ19	6275	7875
6850		Coupe 2D	AJ27	6175	7750
7200		Cruiser Wagon	AJ35	6500	8125
CUTLASS CIERA BROUGHAM-V6-FWD					
7275		Sedan 4D	AM19	6550	8200
7175		Coupe 2D	AM27	6475	8100
*Std. LS					
Deduct 25% of Trade-In Value for Diesel Engine.					
75 Add		Vinyl/Land Roof		75	100
150 Add		Sunroof		150	200
100 Add		AM/FM Stereo		100	125
125 Add		AM/FM Stereo/Tp.		125	150
50 Add		Power Door Locks.		50	75
75 Add		Power Windows		75	100
75 Add		Power Seats		75	100
50 Add		RearWindDefroster.		50	75
50 Add		Cruise Control		50	75
50 Add		Tilt Strg. Wheel		50	75
150 Add		Leather Seats		150	200
75 Add		Wire Wheel Covers		75	100
50 Add		Luggage Rack		50	75
100 Add		Woodgrain		100	125
125 Add		Third Seat S/W		125	150
350 Add		ES Pkg.		325	425
950 Add		GT Pkg.		875	1050
175 Add		Holiday Cpe Pkg.		175	225
75 Add		2-Tone Paint		75	100
650 Deduct		W/out Air Cond		650	650
Deduct 25% of Trade-In Value for Diesel Engine.					
1985 DELTA 88 ROYALE-AT-PS-AC					
DELTA 88 ROYALE-V6					
7700		Sedan 4D	BN69	6950	8750
7550		Coupe 2D	BN37	6800	8600
DELTA 88 ROYALE BROUGHAM-V6					
8175		Sedan 4D	BY69	7375	9300
8025		Coupe 2D	BY37	7225	9150
DELTA 88 ROYALE-V8					
7975		Sedan 4D	BN69	7200	9025
7825		Coupe 2D	BN37	7050	8875
DELTA 88 ROYALE BROUGHAM-V8					
8450		Sedan 4D	BY69	7625	9575
8300		Coupe 2D	BY37	7475	9425
8975		Sedan 4D LS	BY69	8100	10275
CUSTOM CRUISER-V8					
8575		Sta Wgn 2S	BP35	7725	9700

Av'g. Trd-In	Ins. Sym.	BODY TYPE	Model	Av'g. Loan	Av'g. Retail
500 Add		Astroroof		450	600
100 Add		Vinyl/Land Roof		100	125
125 Add		AM/FM Stereo/Tp.		125	150
75 Add		PowerDoorLocks*		75	100
100 Add		Power Windows*		100	125
100 Add		Power Seats*		100	125
50 Add		RearWindDefroster.		50	75
75 Add		Cruise Control		75	100
50 Add		Tilt Strg. Wheel*		50	75
100 Add		WireWheelCovers*.		100	125
50 Add		Luggage Rack		50	75
125 Add		Third Seat S/W		125	150
125 Add		Woodgrain		125	150
100 Add		2-Tone Paint		100	125
150 Add		Leather Seats		150	200
750 Deduct		W/out Air Cond		750	750
*Std. 98 Cpe.					
1985 NINETY-EIGHT-TORONADO AC-PW-P.Sts-FWD					
NINETY-EIGHT REGENCY-V6					
10050		Sedan 4D	CX69	9050	11475
9900		Coupe 2D	CX11	8925	11300
NINETY-EIGHT REGENCY BROUGHAM-V6					
10775		Sedan 4D	CW69	9700	12225
10625		Coupe 2D	CW11	9575	12075
TORONADO-V8					
11900		Coupe 2D	EZ57	10725	13475
600 Add		Astroroof		550	700
125 Add		Vinyl/Land Roof		125	150
		(Std. 98 Cpe)			
125 Add		CruiseCont.(Std.Tor)		125	150
100 Add		RearWindDefroster		100	125
150 Add		AM/FM Stereo/Tp.		150	200
400 Add		Delco/BoseSystem.		375	475
125 Add		Tilt Strg. Wheel		125	150
		(Std.Brghm&Toronado)			
225 Add		Leather Seats		225	300
125 Add		WireWhlCov(StdBrghm)		125	150
125 Add		2-Tone Paint		125	150
750 Add		Tor. Caliente Pkg.		675	850
1984 FIRENZA-L4-AT-PS-AC-FWD					
4725	6	Sedan 4D	C69	4275	5550
4625	7	Coupe 2D S	C77	4175	5450
5025	7	Sedan 4D LX	D69	4525	5875
4925	6	Coupe 2D SX	D77	4450	5750
4875	7	Cruiser Wgn	C35	4400	5700
5175	7	Cruiser LX Wgn	D35	4675	6025
125 Add		Sunroof		125	150
50 Add		AM/FM Stereo		50	75
75 Add		AM/FM Stereo/Tp.		75	100
25 Add		Power Door Locks		25	50
25 Add		Power Windows		25	50
25 Add		Power Seats		25	50
25 Add		RearWindDefroster.		25	50

DEDUCT FOR RECONDITIONING
1986 AUGUST 1986

DEDUCT FOR HIGH MILEAGE
MIDWEST EDITION

FIGURE 2-5 Typical page from August 1986 NADA Midwest Edition of the official used-car guide. (Courtesy of *National Automobile Dealers Used Car Guide*.)

part and the value of the used damaged part. This is known as a betterment charge to the vehicle, and this, as well as depreciation, is applied to paint, power train, batteries, upholstery, corroded panels, vinyl and convertible tops, and tires.

Paint

The paint on vehicles that are a few years old will have faded in different amounts depending on the care received and where the vehicle was parked. If the paint is badly faded, it will be impossible to match; the insured should be so notified that the parts to be painted will not match the paint on the vehicle. The insured should be informed that the insurance company only pays for the parts that are to be repainted. The shop estimator should then inform the insured that the amount of paint work paid for by the insurance company can be applied toward the cost of a new complete paint job, thus assuring a vehicle on which all the color will be the same. Many vehicle owners will take advantage of this offer, and this will provide more work for the shop and more satisfied customers.

Power Train

If the power train is damaged in a collision it may be depreciated at a reasonable amount, which may be worked out as to life expectancy according to the mileage on the vehicle.

Batteries

Batteries are usually stamped as to the date of purchase, and the betterment factor is easy to apply as to the percentage of life left in the damaged battery.

88 **PONTIAC 1985-84**

Av'g. Trd-In	Ins. Sym.	BODY TYPE	Model	Av'g. Loan	Av'g. Retail
1985 FIERO-4 Cyl.-AT-AC-Cont					
50	Add	Cruise Control		50	75
50	Add	Tilt Strg. Wheel *		50	75
75	Add	AlumWhls (Std.SE,GT)		75	100
200	Add	6 Cyl. Engine *		200	250
200	Deduct	Manual Trans		200	200
650	Deduct	W/out Air Cond		650	650
		* Std. GT			
1985 FIREBIRD-AT-PS-AC					
FIREBIRD-V6					
7050		Coupe 2D	FS87	6350	7975
8350		Coupe 2D SE	FX87	7525	9375
FIREBIRD-V8					
7250		Coupe 2D	FS87	6525	8175
8550		Coupe 2D SE	FX87	7700	9575
9550		CpeTransAm	FW87	8600	10675
575	Add	Hatchroof		525	675
100	Add	AM/FM Stereo		100	125
125	Add	AM/FM Stereo/Tp.		125	150
50	Add	Power Door Locks		50	75
75	Add	Power Windows		75	100
75	Add	Power Seats		75	100
50	Add	RearWindDefroster		50	75
50	Add	Cruise Control		50	75
50	Add	Tilt Strg. Wheel		50	75
75	Add	Aluminum Wheels*		75	100
75	Add	2-Tone Paint*		75	100
450	Deduct	4Cyl.Eng.fromV8		450	450
475	Deduct	Manual Trans.		475	475
650	Deduct	W/out Air Cond		650	650
		*Std. SE & Trans Am			
1985 BONNEVILLE-AT-PS-AC					
BONNEVILLE-V6					
6850		Sedan 4D	GN69	6175	7850
7100		Sedan 4D LE	GS69	6400	8125
7350		Sed 4D Brghm	GR69	6625	8375
BONNEVILLE-V8					
7125		Sedan 4D	GN69	6425	8050
7375		Sedan 4D LE	GS69	6650	8300
7625		Sed 4D Brghm	GR69	6875	8675
100	Add	Vinyl Roof		100	125
100	Add	AM/FM Stereo		100	125
125	Add	AM/FM Stereo/Tp.		125	150
75	Add	Power Door Locks		75	100
100	Add	Power Windows		100	125
100	Add	Power Seats		100	125
50	Add	RearWindDefroster		50	75
75	Add	Cruise Control		75	100
50	Add	Tilt Strg. Wheel		50	75
100	Add	Wire Wheel Covers		100	125
150	Add	Leather Seats		150	200
100	Add	2-Tone Paint		100	125
750	Deduct	W/out Air Cond		750	750

Av'g. Trd-In	Ins. Sym.	BODY TYPE	Model	Av'g. Loan	Av'g. Retail
1985 GRAND PRIX-AT-PS-AC					
GRAND PRIX-V6					
7025		Coupe 2D	GJ37	6325	7950
7325		Coupe 2D LE	GK37	6600	8250
7625		Coupe Brghm	GP37	6875	8575
GRAND PRIX-V8					
7225		Coupe 2D	GJ37	6525	8250
7525		Coupe 2D LE	GK37	6775	8575
7825		Coupe Brghm	GP37	7050	8875
75	Add	Landau Roof		75	100
400	Add	Power Sunroof		375	475
500	Add	T-Top		450	600
100	Add	AM/FM Stereo		100	125
125	Add	AM/FM Stereo/Tp.		125	150
50	Add	Power Door Locks		50	75
75	Add	PwrWind (Std.Brghm)		75	100
75	Add	Power Seats		75	100
50	Add	RearWindDefroster		50	75
50	Add	Cruise Control		50	75
50	Add	Tilt Strg. Wheel		50	75
150	Add	Leather Seats		150	200
75	Add	Wire Wheel Covers		75	100
175	Add	Landau Pkg.		175	225
75	Add	2-Tone Paint		75	100
650	Deduct	W/out Air Cond		650	650
1985 PARISIENNE-AT-PS-AC					
PARISIENNE-V6					
7650		Sedan 4D	BL69	6900	8700
8100		Sed 4D Brghm	BT69	7300	9225
PARISIENNE-V8					
7925		Sedan 4D	BL69	7150	8975
8375		Sed 4D Brghm	BT69	7550	9500
8175		Sta Wgn 4D	BL35	7375	9300
100	Add	Vinyl Roof		100	125
500	Add	Power Sunroof		450	600
100	Add	AM/FM Stereo		100	125
125	Add	AM/FM Stereo/Tp.		125	150
75	Add	Power Door Locks		75	100
100	Add	Power Windows		100	125
100	Add	Power Seats		100	125
50	Add	RearWindDefroster		50	75
50	Add	Luggage Rack		50	75
75	Add	Cruise Control		75	100
50	Add	Tilt Strg. Wheel		50	75
100	Add	Wire Wheel Covers		100	125
125	Add	Woodgrain		125	150
100	Add	2-Tone Paint		100	125
150	Add	Leather Seats		150	200
750	Deduct	W/out Air Cond		750	750
Deduct 25% of Trade-In Value for Diesel Engine.					
1984 1000-4 Cyl.-AT					
3275	7	H'back 5D	L68	2950	3950
3175	7	H'back 3D	L08	2875	3850
400	Add	Air Conditioning		375	475
75	Add	Power Steering		75	100

DEDUCT FOR RECONDITIONING

1986 AUGUST 1986 D

PONTIAC 1985 87

Av'g. Trd-In	Ins. Sym.	BODY TYPE	Model	Av'g. Loan	Av'g. Retail
1985 1000-4 Cyl.-AT					
3800		H'back 5D	TL68	3425	4525
3700		H'back 3D	TL08	3350	4400
450	Add	Air Conditioning		425	525
100	Add	Power Steering		100	125
75	Add	AM/FM Stereo		75	100
25	Add	RearWindDefroster		25	50
25	Add	Tilt Strg. Wheel		25	50
50	Add	Aluminum Wheels		50	75
150	Add	Sunroof		150	200
200	Deduct	Manual Trans.		200	200
1985 SUNBIRD-AT-PS-AC-FWD					
SUNBIRD-4 Cyl.					
5475		Sedan 4D	JB69	4950	6275
5375		Coupe 2D	JB27	4850	6175
5550		H'back 3D	JB77	5000	6375
5675		Sta Wgn 4D	JB35	5125	6500
SUNBIRD LE-4 Cyl.					
5775		Sedan 4D	JC69	5200	6600
5675		Coupe 2D	JC27	5125	6500
		Convertible 2D	JC67		
5975		Sta Wgn 4D	JC35	5400	6800
SUNBIRD SE-4 Cyl. Turbo					
6325		Sedan 4D	JD69	5700	7175
6225		Coupe 2D	JD27	5625	7075
6400		H'back 3D	JD77	5775	7250
150	Add	Sunroof		150	200
75	Add	AM/FM Stereo		75	100
100	Add	AM/FM Stereo/Tp.		100	125
50	Add	Power Door Locks		50	75
50	Add	PowerWind (Std.Conv)		50	75
50	Add	Power Seats		50	75
25	Add	RearWindDefroster		25	50
25	Add	Luggage Rack		25	50
25	Add	Tilt Strg. Wheel		25	50
50	Add	Wire Wheel Covers		50	75
50	Add	Cruise Control		50	75
75	Add	2-Tone Paint		75	100
	Add	1.8LTurboEng (Std.SE)			
325	Deduct	Manual Trans.		325	325
125	Deduct	Convent. Steer		125	125
550	Deduct	W/out Air Cond		550	550
1985 GRAND AM-AT-PS-AC-FWD					
GRAND AM-4 Cyl.					
7500		Coupe 2D	NE27	6750	8425
7750		Coupe 2D LE	NV27	6975	8700
GRAND AM-V6					
7700		Coupe 2D	NE27	6950	8600
7950		Coupe 2D LE	NV27	7175	8850
150	Add	Sunroof		150	200
100	Add	AM/FM Stereo		100	125
125	Add	AM/FM Stereo/Tp.		125	150
50	Add	Power Door Locks		50	75
75	Add	Power Seats		75	100
75	Add	Power Windows		75	100

Av'g. Trd-In	Ins. Sym.	BODY TYPE	Model	Av'g. Loan	Av'g. Retail
50	Add	RearWindDefroster		50	75
50	Add	Tilt Strg. Wheel		50	75
75	Add	Aluminum Wheels		75	100
50	Add	Cruise Control		50	75
475	Deduct	Manual Trans.		475	475
650	Deduct	W/out Air Cond		650	650
1985 6000-AT-PS-AC-FWD					
6000-4 Cyl.					
6825		Sedan 4D	AF19	6150	7725
6725		Coupe 2D	AF27	6075	7625
7075		Sta Wgn 4D	AF35	6375	8000
6000 LE-4 Cyl.					
7125		Sedan 4D	AG19	6425	8050
7025		Coupe 2D	AG27	6325	7950
7375		Sta Wgn 4D	AG35	6650	8300
6000-V6					
7025		Sedan 4D	AF19	6325	7950
6925		Coupe 2D	AF27	6250	7850
7275		Sta Wgn 4D	AF35	6550	8200
6000 LE-V6					
7325		Sedan 4D	AG19	6600	8250
7225		Coupe 2D	AG27	6525	8150
7575		Sta Wgn 4D	AG35	6825	8525
6000 STE-V6					
9000		Sedan 4D	AH19	8100	10050
150	Add	Sunroof		150	200
100	Add	AM/FM Stereo		100	125
125	Add	AM/FMStereo/Tp*		125	150
50	Add	PowerDoorLocks*		50	75
75	Add	Power Windows*		75	100
75	Add	Power Seats		75	100
50	Add	RearWindDefroster*		50	75
50	Add	Cruise Control*		50	75
50	Add	Tilt Strg. Wheel*		50	75
75	Add	Aluminum Wheels*		75	100
150	Add	Leather Seats		150	200
125	Add	Rally Pkg.		125	150
125	Add	Third Seat S/W		125	150
50	Add	Luggage Rack		50	75
75	Add	2-Tone Paint*		75	100
200	Add	Sport Landau Pkg.		200	250
100	Add	Woodgrain		100	125
650	Deduct	W/out Air Cond		650	650
		*Std. STE			
Deduct 25% of Trade-In Value for Diesel Engine.					
1985 FIERO-4 Cyl.-AT-AC					
6550		Coupe 2D	PE37	5900	7450
6850		Spt Coupe 2D	PM37	6175	7750
7375		Coupe 2D SE	PF37	6650	8300
8200		Coupe 2D GT	PG37	7400	9225
150	Add	Sunroof		150	200
100	Add	AM/FM Stereo		100	125
125	Add	AM/FMStereo/Tp*		125	150
50	Add	Power Door Locks		50	75
75	Add	Power Windows *		75	100
50	Add	RearWindDefroster		50	75

DEDUCT FOR HIGH MILEAGE

MIDWEST EDITION

FIGURE 2-6 Typical pages from August 1986 NADA Midwest Edition of the official used car guide. (Courtesy of *National Automobile Dealers Used Car Guide*.)

Upholstery

If the upholstery is torn or there is other damage, it is usually depreciated according to the wear caused by use and the age of the vehicle. The estimator must examine carefully the condition of the remaining upholstery on the rest of the vehicle.

Corroded Panels

In many collisions some of the panels damaged are often corroded due to age and climate. The estimator has to figure out what damage is due to the collision and what amount is due to corrosion and apportion the cost of repair accordingly.

Vinyl and Convertible Tops

Damaged vinyl and convertible tops are depreciated according to age; also, the type of care that these parts get will affect their life span. Usually, vinyl tops last more than 5 years and convertible tops more than 3 years. The adjustor or estimator must use common sense when estimating these parts. If not damaged too badly, it is possible to repair these parts, which is usually done at special upholstery shops.

Tires

The betterment factor is applied when adjusting tires (see runout in Figs. 1-78 and Fig. 1-79 for an adequate explanation).

In a collision report, the adjustor and/or estimator may be required to send pictures of the vehicle or vehicles

VEHICLE IDENTIFICATION AND CONDITION REPORT

LIC. NO.	Manitoba	CLAIM NUMBER	
YEAR	1980	ADJUSTER	John Doe
MAKE	Oldsmobile	ESTIMATOR	Tom Smith
MODEL NAME	Delta Royale	ESTIMATED DATE	Feb. 5, 1988
MODEL NO.	37	REINSPECTION SUPERVISOR	Jack Jones
BODY STYLE	2 dr coupe	REINSPECTION DATE	Feb. 15, 1988
SERIAL NO.	3n37rax 124365	LOCATION OF VEHICLE	Barrys Compound
COLOR	Green Met.	FULL SIZE VEHICLE	YES __X__ NO _____
SPEEDOMETER	KM _____ MILES 48,654	CONDITION	ABOVE AV. _____ AV. __X__
			BELOW AV. _____

	YES	NO			YES	NO		TIRES
NO. OF CYLINDERS	X			POWER STEERING	X			
TRANS. A/T	X			POWER BRAKES	X			Tread Remaining
RADIO	X			OPEN ROOF		X		
AM FM STEREO CASSETTE	X		100	VINYL ROOF	X			RF ___fair___
FACTORY AIR	X			CUSTOM WHEELS				LF ___fair___
LOCAL AIR		X		RADIAL TIRES	X			
TINTED GLASS	X			CUSTOM TIRES				RR ___fair___
POWER WINDOWS		X	75	WHEEL DISC	X		75	LR ___fair___
POWER SEATS		X						
REAR DEFOG.	X							Spare ___fair___
SUN-ROOF		X						(If tread not measured, indicate — bald, poor, fair, etc.)
TWO-TONE PAINT		X		TOTAL			100	

ESTIMATED REPAIR COST OTHER THAN NORMAL WEAR. DEDUCT FROM BASIC VALUE

GLASS		ENGINE & MOUNTS	
GRILLE & COOLING	350.00	TRANSMISSION	
DOORS		FRONT SUSPENSION	
QUARTER PANELS & FENDERS		DRIVE & REAR SUSP.	
LIGHTS		TIRES & WHEELS	
TRIM		————	
PAINT	50.00	————	
————	400.00	TOTAL	

REPAIRS $ __3600.00__   SALVAGE $ __550.00__   OBVIOUS TOTAL LOSS $ __3050.00__   MARGINAL $ __400.00__

ABOVE AVERAGE CONDITION OR EXTRA EQUIPMENT	ADD TO BASIC VALUE

ESTIMATOR'S COMMENTS ___The cost of repair would be more than resale value.___

FIGURE 2-7 Typical adjuster estimator report on a written-off salvage vehicle.

involved in the collision. A form such as in Fig. 2-7 as well as pictures, may be used to inform the insurance company of the damage.

Electronic Control Modules

Electronic control modules are used in most newer types of vehicles; they are used to control many of the functions and equipment used on a vehicle. The estimator must locate this unit when writing the estimate; manufacturers place them in different locations, and it is possible for these modules to be damaged or destroyed in a collision. The module will require repair or replacement depending on the amount of damage.

Salvaged Vehicles

Insurance companies sell their salvage vehicles by different methods. Some sell the vehicles to regional auto recyclers, who pay a certain percentage of the value of the vehicle on the market. Others receive bids from the recyclers and accept the high bid. Other companies sell their salvage vehicles at auction sales in lots of one, three, or five at a time.

The recycler brings these vehicles to the salvage yard where they are placed in rows (Fig. 2-8), waiting the dismantling of removable parts. These parts are catalogued and inventoried as to amount and location in specially built storage parts bins (Fig. 2-9). This enables the recycler to know if a certain part is in stock when a customer phones. The part is usually priced and then delivered or picked up if bought by the customer. Once the recycler has removed

FIGURE 2-9 Salvaged parts in parts bins.

all the salvageable parts, the remaining bodies of the damaged vehicles are sometimes crushed on site and transported elsewhere, where they are put in piles (Fig. 2-10); the remaining body is later crushed or shredded and the metal sold to steel manufacturers.

The older or more badly smashed the vehicle, the quicker it will be written off. The newer write-offs are sometimes bought by rebuilders, who repair these vehicles and, when these salvaged vehicles have been declared road worthy, sell them to the general public. The cost of the vehicle to the rebuilder, plus parts and labor, should not total more than the loan value of the vehicle. Using this method, the rebuilder should be able to realize a profit. Many rebuilders own and operate commercial body shops and use these vehicles to keep their staff busy during slow periods.

FIGURE 2-8 Salvage vehicles in auto-wrecking yard.

FIGURE 2-10 Vehicle bodies piled up at shredding plant.

QUESTIONS

2-1. What are some of the duties of the adjuster?

2-2. How does an adjuster write the estimate and is it a good practice to have the shop estimator help?

2-3. What is the main purpose of the estimate?

2-4. When a component may be damaged, what should the estimator or adjuster do to obtain an accurate estimate?

2-5. How is labor time established?

2-6. How does an estimator assess the amount of time required for repairing sheet metal?

2-7. When are recycled parts used?

2-8. How much do shops usually pay their qualified technicians?

2-9. What is a competitive bid?

2-10. What is a courtesy estimate?

2-11. What discount may insurance companies insist on when glass work is done?

2-12. For what reasons is a vehicle written off?

2-13. What items are taken into consideration when a vehicle may be written off?

2-14. Find the value of a 1985 6000 LE with a v6, automatic transmission, power steering, brakes, power door locks, cruise control and aluminum wheels is worth as a trade in and also an average retail price?

CHAPTER THREE

Understanding the Collision Manual and Writing Estimates

3-1 UNDERSTANDING THE COLLISION MANUAL

Estimating collision manuals are published by a few publishing companies who collect the required information and publish it for use in the repair field. Most of this information comes from the manufacturers' manuals, which give part numbers, prices, and the time required to remove and replace an item. Revisions of the collision manuals are sent to subscribers as the information is updated.

The student estimator must carefully study the information included in the first few pages of the manual. A tremendous amount of information is included in these first pages. The manual contains the information required to identify the year of make, as well as any pertinent information from the vehicle identification number (see Chapter 1). The manual information pages explain what the following terms mean and how they are used: remove and install, remove and replace, overhaul, and alignment (see Fig. 3-1).

Figures 3-2 and 3-3 explain how *labor guide allowances* are used as a guide for repair with new, undamaged parts. If used parts are used, the estimator must understand that more time is required to prepare a used, recycled part for installation on the vehicle.

Parts

The parts for each section are grouped together in exploded diagrams, and the pages with the required information guide the estimator as the required parts are included on the estimate; this helps the estimator from missing some damaged parts as they are shown together (Fig. 3-4).

Part numbers are included on each page, usually below the item, to make ordering and estimation more accurate. Many parts are not interchangeable and are labeled as right-hand and left-hand parts, but have the same price. For example, in Fig. 3-4 the Park and Signal Lamp is right-hand 915560 and left hand 915559, but both are priced at $18.40. Also, for some parts the right and left part numbers are on the same line, but the right part is always first; for example, Park Signal Lamp 915214-3. The left-hand part is the second number, but the price is the same; $22.05. This applies even when the right number is the higher or the lower; it is usually the lower number of the pair. Sometimes the right and left numbers are very different and are each listed and specified on a separate line; for example, Reinforcement in Cooling (Fig.3-4);

Reinforcement Lower to Rail R #20460098 $18.30
L #20475005 $16.45

DEFINITIONS

REMOVE AND INSTALL (R&I): Remove a part or assembly, set it aside and reinstall it later. The time quoted includes the alignment that can be done by shifting the part or assembly, except when noted otherwise in the Procedure Explanation in text.

REMOVE AND REPLACE (R&R): Remove a part or assembly, transfer bolted or clipped on parts (except when additional time is needed for mouldings, name plates, and accessories) and replace the part or assembly with a new one. Time quoted includes the alignment that can be done by shifting the part or assembly except when noted otherwise in the Procedure Explanation or in the text.

OVERHAUL (O/H): Remove an assembly, disassemble, clean and inspect it, replace needed parts, reassemble and reinstall on the vehicle making any necessary adjustments.

In the bumper and front suspension sections we show which items are included in the overhaul operation by placing "IOH" in the labor column.

However, some items that are included will also have a time allowance as they can be removed and replaced without the overhaul procedure.

OVERLAP/ADDITIONAL TIME: If adjoining parts are being replaced (e.g., quarter and rear body panels), there is an overlap in that both individual operations include common surfaces or parts attached to both panels. A deduction must, therefore, be made from the total of the individual operations to compensate for the two or more repeated operations in each sub-task. Similarly, if a part has already been removed, it makes access to other parts easier; the estimator must recognize that time to replace interior parts will be influenced by whether or not the exterior parts are on or off the vehicle.

ALIGNMENT: This includes only what can be accomplished by moving the part or assembly, or by adjusting parts of the assembly being replaced.

FIGURE 3-1 Explanation of terms. (Courtesy of Mitchell Information Services, Inc.)

Many parts are used on many different vehicle lines by the same manufacturer. Some parts are even used by different manufacturers. To find out which parts are used, an interchangeable parts manual is required. For the same manufacturer, the parts will be used on different car lines, for example, drive axles;

82–87	Celebrity	#7844745
84	Citation	#7844745
84	Omega	#7844745
84	Phoenix	#7844745
84	Skylark	#7844745

To be able to find these interchangeable parts, the estimator must compare them to similar body lines or other vehicle lines that are manufactured by the same company. Knowledge of interchangeable parts will give the estimator a wider choice in finding the required parts. Some body panels will fit more than one vehicle line; for instance, the left door on the 82–87 Celebrity and the 82–86 Pontiac 6000 have the same part number. The star in front of the part number signifies that this particular panel is interchangeable (Fig. 3-5).

The price of parts will reflect the prices used in the area at the time of the printing of the manuals. The prices used in the manuals are the manufacturers' suggested retail prices used in the particular area.

When parts are discontinued by manufacturers, the collision manual publisher will continue to carry the number, but the part number will be preceded by the letter "d" before the price of the part. This indicates the latest information available from the manufacturer.

Some manufacturers have some replacement parts that are included in special parts price programs; these parts will not have a manufacturer's suggested retail price. Mitchell manuals designate such parts by placing a symbol, such as a black box, in the price column. The price shown following the black symbol is an approximate price; the part price could be higher or lower and should be checked out by contacting the manufacturer's local parts dealer.

For glass, both the manufacturers' and the glass companies' prices are listed. These prices will not be the same. Four different types of glass from manufacturers are shown; clear, tinted, clear and heated, and tinted and heated; but glass suppliers provide only two kinds of glass: clear, with the prefix C, and tinted, with the prefix T. For the part number and price of older-model vehicle glass, contact the auto glass supplier for the required information.

Flat Rate

Flat-rate manuals give the times required for different operations when a car is repaired. The flat-rate time is the time required to remove and replace or overhaul and assembly. These times are based on new cars where no bolts are rusted. Therefore, the estimator must add extra time for rust, cutting parts, reaching attached bolts, removing and replacing of undercoat, and removing of some special materials found on some replacement parts.

GUIDE ALLOWANCES: THE OPERATION ALLOWANCES SHOWN ARE FOR REPLACEMENT WITH NEW UNDAMAGED PARTS FROM THE VEHICLE MANUFACTURERS ON NEW UNDAMAGED VEHICLES using the sequences and procedures listed in this publication. Exceptional circumstances, including all the sub-operations or extra operations, are indicated as notes throughout the text or are explained in the Procedure Explanations. The actual times taken by individual shops, etc., to replace collision-damaged parts can be expected to vary due to vehicle condition, equipment used, etc.

OPERATION ALLOWANCE DETERMINATION: Operation allowances are determined by Mitchell editors based on a combination of our data base, field checking, surveys, "hands-on" experience, and information supplied by vehicle manufacturers.

The types of vehicles covered are standard models only.

We strive for completeness in each manual, however, there will be instances in which a verified labor operation allowance has not been established at the time of publication. If an item requires replacement and can be replaced as an individual item but shows no operation allowance, a fair and equitable time should be agreed upon among all parties and recorded on your damage report.

DRILLING TIME: Allowances given are for round holes; other shapes should be estimated separately.

IMPORTANT REMINDER: Operation allowances on inner panels, rails or reinforcements are with outer panels removed.

ITEMS NOT INCLUDED:
Because of the very wide range of collision damage and vehicle conditions allowances associated with the individual operations listed do **NOT INCLUDE:**

- **ACCESS TIME:** To remove extensively damaged collision parts by cutting, pushing, pulling, etc.
- **CAULKING MATERIAL:** As used in standard factory applications to each make and model.
- **RUST RESISTANT ANTI-CORROSION MATERIAL:** Or any type of added conditioning.
- **TAR, GREASE:** Or any other materials that would interfere with repair.
- **REPAIR OR ALIGN:** Parts adjacent to the parts being replaced.
- **FREE UP PARTS:** Frozen by rust or corrosion.
- **TRANSFER TIME:** Welded or riveted brackets, braces or reinforcements from an old part to the new part.

- **REWORK PARTS:** To fit a particular year or model. Such as cutting holes for lamps, modifying a radiator support, etc...
- **PLUG AND FINISH:** Holes not needed on the parts being installed.
- **BROKEN GLASS:** Clean up.
- **DETAIL:** Or clean up for delivery essential to repair.
- **PAINT AND SHOP MATERIALS:** Additional costs.
- **MEASURE & IDENTIFY:** Structural damage to unibody vehicles.
- **ELECTRONIC COMPONENTS:** Time to R&I as necessary, includes wiring.
- **REFINISH ADDITION:** Refer to refinish prcedure section.

FIGURE 3-2   Estimating information on labor and excluded items. (Courtesy of Mitchell Information Services, Inc.)

72

ESTIMATING INFORMATION

FOOTNOTES: We draw attention to special situations or requirements with a footnote symbol (¶ or #) in the part description or Guide time. The explanation follows as closely after the callout as possible.

¶ symbol always refers to a part footnote.
# symbol always refers to a labor footnote.

BOLTED PARTS & ASSEMBLIES: For example, on a radiator support or fender apron bolted parts and assemblies include the following: washer/coolant reservoir, cruise control and accessories. On the front suspension crossmember, steering components are examples of bolted parts and assemblies.

HIGH STRENGTH LOW ALLOY STEEL: High strength low alloy (HSLA) steel information is not completely accessible from manufacturers. When informa-

tion is available we list a warning in the head notes of the section involved. We also list HSLA within the text after the name of the part we have identified.

It is recommended when replacing parts containing HSLA steel, that it be welded at factory seams unless noted otherwise, using manufacturers' suggested welding procedures.

When replacing HSLA steel parts, the recommended equipment for this operation is Metal Inert Gas (MIG) or Gas Metal Arc Welding (GMAW). Oxyacetylene equipment is not recommended to weld this material. This supercedes information published in previous Mitchell Collision Estimating Guides.

SPECIAL CAUTIONS

MAIN COMPUTER MODULE: When working with vehicles equipped with on board computers, manufacturers recommend removal if temperatures are likely to exceed 80°C (176°F) such as in paint booth dryers, ovens or any heating or welding done with a torch or electric welding equipment.

Never connect or disconnect these units with ignition switch on, or charge a battery with battery cables connected. Computer control information is listed in the Electrical Section of all Mitchell Collision Estimating Guides. There is a footnote below the listing describing the location of each unit.

STRUCTURAL GLASS: Windshields, back windows and other glass that was originally installed at the vehicle manufacturer utilizing urethane, should be

reinstalled with urethane. The urethane bonds the glass to the vehicle and makes the glass part of the vehicle's structure. Therefore, when reinstalling this glass, it once again must be part of the structure.

AIR SAFETY BAGS: To avoid accidental release of air safety bags while working on vehicle, disconnect and cover negative battery cable before starting any work on vehicle.

HUB NUT: When removing and installing the front wheel drive halfshafts on Ford Escort and Mercury Lynx models, make sure that a new hub nut and lower control arm-to-steering knuckle bolt and nut are available. These items can only be used one time. Once removed, their torque holding ability is destroyed.

FIGURE 3-3 Estimating information and special caution notes. (Courtesy of Mitchell Information Services, Inc.)

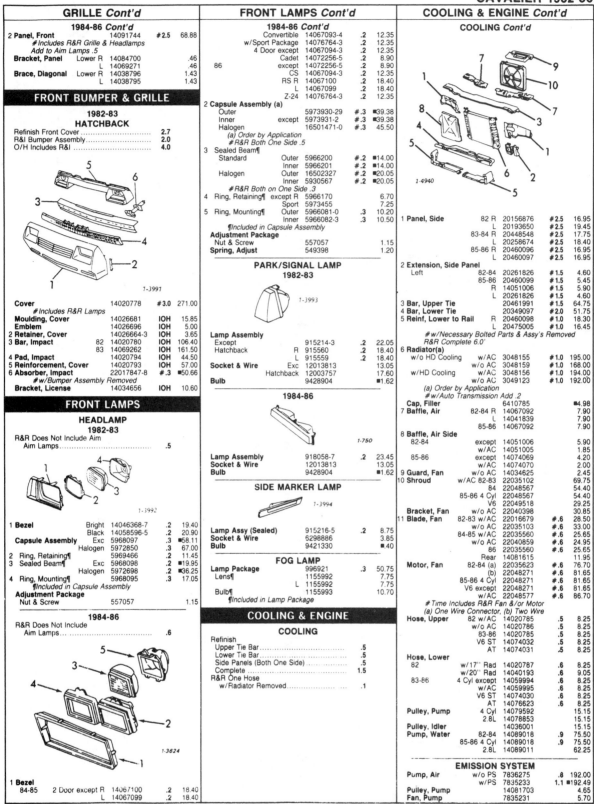

GRILLE Cont'd

1984-86 Cont'd

2 **Panel, Front**		14091744	#2.5	68.88

*# Includes R&R Grille & Headlamps
Add to Aim Lamps .5*

Bracket, Panel	Lower R	14084700		.46
	L	14069271		.46
Brace, Diagonal	Lower R	14038796		1.43
	L	14038795		1.43

FRONT BUMPER & GRILLE

1982-83
HATCHBACK

Refinish Front Cover	2.7
R&I Bumper Assembly..........................	2.0
O/H Includes R&I	4.0

Cover		14020778	#3.0	271.00

 # Includes R&R Lamps

Moulding, Cover		14026681	IOH	15.85
Emblem		14026696	IOH	5.00
2 **Retainer, Cover**		14026664-3	IOH	3.65
3 **Bar, Impact**	82	14020780	IOH	106.40
	83	14069262	IOH	161.50
4 **Pad, Impact**		14020794	IOH	44.50
5 **Reinforcement, Cover**		14020793	IOH	57.00
6 **Absorber, Impact**		22017847-8	#.3	■50.66

 # w/Bumper Assembly Removed

Bracket, License		14034656	IOH	10.60

FRONT LAMPS

HEADLAMP
1982-83

R&R Does Not Include Aim	
Aim Lamps................................	.5

1 **Bezel**	Bright	14046368-7	.2	19.40
	Black	14058596-5	.2	20.90
Capsule Assembly	Exc	5968097	.3	■58.11
	Halogen	5972850	.3	67.00
2 **Ring, Retaining¶**		5969466	.2	11.45
3 **Sealed Beam¶**	Exc	5968098	.2	■19.95
	Halogen	5972698	.2	■36.25
4 **Ring, Mounting¶**		5968095	.3	17.05

¶Included in Capsule Assembly

Adjustment Package			
Nut & Screw		557057	1.15

1984-86

R&R Does Not Include	
Aim Lamps...	.6

1 **Bezel**				
84-85	2 Door except R	14067100	.2	18.40
	L	14067099	.2	18.40

FRONT LAMPS Cont'd

1984-86 Cont'd

	Convertible	14067093-4	.2	12.35
	w/Sport Package	14076764-3	.2	12.35
	4 Door except	14067094-3	.2	12.35
	Cadet	14072256-5	.2	8.90
86	except	14072256-5	.2	8.90
	CS	14067094-3	.2	12.35
	RS R	14067100	.2	18.40
	L	14067099	.2	18.40
	Z-24	14076764-3	.2	12.35
2 **Capsule Assembly (a)**				
	Outer	5973930-29	#.3	■39.38
	Inner except	5973931-2	#.3	■39.38
	Halogen	16501471-0	#.3	45.50

*(a) Order by Application
#R&R Both One Side .5*

3 **Sealed Beam¶**				
Standard	Outer	5966200	#.2	■14.00
	Inner	5966201	#.2	■14.00
Halogen	Outer	16502327	#.2	■20.05
	Inner	5930567	#.2	■20.05

#R&R Both on One Side .3

4 **Ring, Retaining¶**	except R	5966170		6.70
	Sport	5973455		7.25
5 **Ring, Mounting¶**	Outer	5966081-0	.3	10.20
	Inner	5966082-3	.3	10.50

¶Included in Capsule Assembly

Adjustment Package			
Nut & Screw		557057	1.15
Spring, Adjust		549398	1.20

PARK/SIGNAL LAMP
1982-83

Lamp Assembly				
Except		915214-3	.2	22.05
Hatchback	R	915560	.2	18.40
	L	915559	.2	18.40
Socket & Wire	Exc	12013813		13.05
	Hatchback	12003757		17.60
Bulb		9428904		■1.62

1984-86

Lamp Assembly		918058-7	.2	23.45
Socket & Wire		12013813		13.05
Bulb		9428904		■1.62

SIDE MARKER LAMP

Lamp Assy (Sealed)		915216-5	.2	8.75
Socket & Wire		6298886		3.85
Bulb		9421330		■.40

FOG LAMP

Lamp Package		996921	.3	50.75
Lens¶		1155992		7.75
	L	1155992		7.75
Bulb¶		1155993		10.70

¶Included in Lamp Package

COOLING & ENGINE

COOLING

Refinish	
Upper Tie Bar................................	.5
Lower Tie Bar................................	.5
Side Panels (Both One Side)	.5
Complete	1.5
R&R One Hose	
w/Radiator Removed....................	.1

COOLING & ENGINE Cont'd

COOLING Cont'd

1 **Panel, Side**	82 R	20156876	#2.5	16.95
	L	20193650	#2.5	19.45
	83-84 R	20448548	#2.5	17.75
	L	20258674	#2.5	18.40
	85-86 R	20460096	#2.5	16.95
	L	20460097	#2.5	16.95
2 **Extension, Side Panel**				
Left	82-84	20261826	#1.5	4.60
	85-86	20460099	#1.5	5.45
	R	14051006	#1.5	5.90
	L	20261826	#1.5	4.60
3 **Bar, Upper Tie**		20461991	#1.5	64.75
4 **Bar, Lower Tie**		20349097	#2.0	51.75
5 **Reinf, Lower to Rail**	R	20460098	#1.0	18.30
	L	20475005	#1.0	16.45

*# w/Necessary Bolted Parts & Assy's Removed
R&R Complete 6.0'*

6 **Radiator (a)**				
w/o HD Cooling	w/AC	3048155	#1.0	195.00
	w/o AC	3048159	#1.0	168.00
w/HD Cooling	w/AC	3048156	#1.0	194.00
	w/o AC	3049123	#1.0	192.00

*(a) Order by Application
w/Auto Transmission Add .2*

Cap, Filler		6410785		■4.98
7 **Baffle, Air**	82-84 R	14067092		7.90
	L	14041839		7.90
	85-86	14067092		7.90
8 **Baffle, Air Side**				
82-84	except	14051006		5.90
	w/AC	14051005		1.85
85-86	except	14074069		4.20
	w/AC	14074070		2.00
9 **Guard, Fan**	w/o AC	14034625		2.45
10 **Shroud**	w/AC 82-83	22035102		69.75
	84	22048567		54.40
	85-86 4 Cyl	22048567		54.40
	V6	22049518		29.25
Bracket, Fan	w/o AC	22040398		30.85
11 **Blade, Fan**	82-83 w/AC	22016679	#.6	28.50
	w/o AC	22035103	#.6	33.00
	84-85 w/AC	22035560	#.6	25.65
	w/o AC	22040859	#.6	24.95
	86	22035560	#.6	25.65
	Rear	14081615		11.95
Motor, Fan	82-84 (a)	22035623	#.6	76.70
	(b)	22048271	#.6	81.65
	85-86 4 Cyl	22048271	#.6	81.65
	V6 except	22048271	#.6	81.65
	w/AC	22048577	#.6	86.70

*# Time Includes R&R Fan &/or Motor
(a) One Wire Connector, (b) Two Wire*

Hose, Upper	82 w/AC	14020785	.5	8.25
	w/o AC	14020786	.5	8.25
	83-86	14020785	.5	8.25
	V6 ST	14074032	.5	8.25
	AT	14074031	.5	8.25
Hose, Lower				
82	w/17" Rad	14020787	.6	8.25
	w/20" Rad	14040193	.6	9.05
83-86	4 Cyl except	14059994	.6	8.25
	w/AC	14059995	.6	8.25
	V6 ST	14074030	.6	8.25
	AT	14076623	.6	8.25
Pulley, Pump	4 Cyl	14079592		15.15
	2.8L	14078853		15.15
Pulley, Idler		14036001		15.15
Pump, Water	82-84	14089018	.9	75.50
	85-86 4 Cyl	14089018	.9	75.50
	2.8L	14089011		62.25

EMISSION SYSTEM

Pump, Air	w/o PS	7836275	.8	192.00
	w/PS	7835233	1.1	■192.49
Pulley, Pump		14081703		4.65
Fan, Pump		7835231		5.70

GM **Procedure Explanation Pages Must Be Used With The Above Text for an Accurate Damage Report.** 169

FIGURE 3-4 Typical page from estimating manual. (Courtesy of Mitchell Information Services, Inc.)

FRONT DOOR		
Refinish Outside ....2 Door	**2.4**	
4 Door	**2.2**	
Add for Jambs & Interior	**1.0**	
Refinish Hinge..	**.2**	
Refinish Rear View Mirror.......................	**.5**	
R&I Door Assy ....w/Manual Window	**.8**	
w/Power Window	**1.3**	
R&I Trim Panel	**.4**	
Add to Door or Outer Panel R&R		
w/Power Window	**.5**	
w/Power Lock	**.3**	
w/Theft Deterrent	**.2**	
w/Welded Hinges	**2.0**	
HSLA – High Strength Low Alloy Steel		

SHEET METAL

Door Shell					
2 Door	82-85	R	20683064	**4.5**	581.00
		L	★20618633	**4.5**	581.00
	86-87	R	20683064	**4.5**	581.00
		L	20683065	**4.5**	581.00
4 Door		R	20683052	**4.5**	565.00
		L	20683053	**4.5**	565.00
Panel, Repair¶					
2 Door		R	20462782	**5.5**	120.60
		L	20462783	**5.5**	120.60
4 Door			20460562	**5.0**	102.60
		L	20460563	**5.0**	102.60

Bar, Reinf¶ (HSLA)				
2 Door	(2)	20290589	**1.5**	90.50
4 Door		20290590-1	**1.5**	48.21
¶Included in Door Shell				

FRONT DOOR		
Refinish Outside ....2 Door	**2.4**	
4 Door	**2.2**	
Add for Jambs & Interior	**1.0**	
Refinish Hinge..	**.2**	
Refinish Rear View Mirror.......................	**.5**	
R&I Door Assy ....w/Manual Window	**.8**	
w/Power Window	**1.3**	
R&I Trim Panel	**.4**	
Add to Door or Outer Panel R&R		
w/Power Window	**.5**	
w/Welded Hinge	**2.0**	
HSLA–High Strength Low Alloy Steel		
Add To Door Shell or Outer Panel R&R		
To Drill For & Install		
One Moulding	**.3**	
Each Additional Moulding	**.2**	

Shell, Door	2 Door	R	★20618632	**4.5**	581.00
		L	★20618633	**4.5**	581.00
	4 Door	R	★20618642	**4.5**	565.00
		L	★20618643	**4.5**	565.00
Panel, Repair¶	2 Door	R	20462782	**5.5**	120.60
		L	20462783	**5.5**	120.60
	4 Door	R	20460562	**5.0**	102.60
		L	20460563	**5.0**	102.60
Bar, Reinf¶(HSLA)					
2 Door			20290589	**1.5**	90.50
4 Door			20290590-1	**1.5**	48.21
¶Included in Door Shell					

FIGURE 3-5 Interchangeable parts. (A) 1982–1987 Celebrity; (B) 1982–1986 Pontiac 6000 left door shell.

It is also necessary to estimate the time required to repair adjacent parts that cannot be aligned by shifting the assembly. Plugging holes that are not required in the used parts, the removal of brackets from an old part to weld onto the new part, and the cleaning of broken glass or checking the windshield or back window opening are all operations that require extra time above the flat-rate schedule.

The time in flat-rate manuals is given in tenths of an hour in most cases. The hour is divided into 10 parts of 6 minutes; thus shops and employees are paid accordingly in tenths of an hour on many jobs.

Overlap and/or Additional Time

When a technician repairs a vehicle, there may be parts that will have an overlap time; that is, the technician will be paid twice to do some of the job unless the time is adjusted, which is called overlap time. Therefore, a deduction of time must be made where the overlap occurs, as when common surfaces or parts are attached to both panels. The deduction is subtracted from the minor operation, which is the smaller of the time between the two parts. The larger portion is called the major operation. A general rule may be used, such as one-third deduction from the minor operation, but in some cases the estimator must use common sense. For some operations a part may have been removed that makes access to other parts easier; the estimator must recognize this fact. The estimator must also recognize that the time required to replace interior parts will be affected if the parts are off or on the vehicle.

On most jobs there are combination or overlap operations; that is, part of a job is done while doing another job. For example, a fender is removed from a vehicle and the time to remove and replace (R&R) is 2.3 hours; but to remove this fender one side of the bumper must be dropped. Since the bumper is also damaged, it must also be R&Red completely and the time given to R&R the bumper is 0.9 hour. Therefore, the R&R of the fender becomes the major operation; the minor operation is the bumper. Since the body repair technician is getting paid to remove or lower one side already, this creates an overlap of payment on the job. To obtain a proper payment on the minor operation, the flat-rate time is cut by one-third, giving the body person 0.6 hour to complete the R&R of the bumper. In making an estimate, the estimator must be careful to deduct for this overlap time; otherwise the estimate could be out of line.

Another typical area where an overlap is present is when the left or right quarter-panel and rear lower trunk are removed. The quarter-panel time is maybe 11.5 hours and the lower trunk panel is 5.0 hrs. The quarter panel is the major operation and the lower trunk panel is the minor operation. Therefore, no time is removed from the major operation, but only from the minor operation. For example,

Remove and replace quarter panel section 11.5 hours
Remove and replace lower trunk panel   5.0 hours

But by removing the overlap on the minor operation, the time for remove and replacement time will become 3.5 hours. Therefore, the time for removal and replacement will decrease from 16.5 hrs. to 15.0 hrs. If the other quarter-panel is to be removed, then a double overlap is present and another 1.5-hour deduction must be taken off the minor operation, leaving a replacement time of 2.0 hrs for this particular panel. The estimator must write the estimate with caution and be careful to remove any overlap (see Figs. 3-6 and 3-7 for details). Each manufacturer uses slightly different methods when building its vehicles and this is reflected in their flat-rate-manual times.

For the refinish times of the panels, the estimator should consult the appropriate manual page, such as in Figs. 3-6 and 3-7, which will show refinish times in detail for the panels. When a hood, fender, front door, and rear door are being painted on the same vehicle and on the same side, there is an overlap of time for some of the operations. The panels do not have to be masked individually, but are masked off from the rest of the vehicle in a section; also, the spray gun does not have to be filled or cleaned for each separate panel, and the panels are not cleaned, sanded, and prepared by themselves; it is done in one continuous operation. Therefore, the overlap time of 0.2 hour must be taken off the minor operations; these are the panels that have less paint time than the major operation, which in this case is the hood panel.

Repaint Time, Flat Rate		Minus Overlap	
Hood	3.1	Hood	3.1
Left front fender	2.4	Left front fender	2.2
Left front door	2.5	Left front door	2.3
Left rear door	2.2	Left rear door	2.0
Total time	10.2	Total time	9.6

When replacing these parts, if they must be painted on inside edges, additional time must be included in the paint time so that the technician receives the proper credit for time and pay for the job done. Some estimators will deduct 0.2 hour for paint time that is to be done on the other side of the vehicle, but this is usually a judgment call.

All manufacturers provide parts books to their dealers, as well as to suppliers such as rechromers and paint supply companies to their own jobbers. Estimators will have to contact these other businesses to obtain any information that is required, but not given in the collision manual, to complete the estimates, such as part numbers and prices. The flat-rate manuals group the parts used in order, starting at the front of the vehicle and moving section by section toward the rear of the vehicle.

The estimator consults the index in the collision manual for parts to fit a certain vehicle. The index will identify the vehicle by body style. Sequence definitions, special cautions, procedure explanations, refinish notes and explanations, paint code location, VIN interpretation, inter-change section, front unibody dimensions, labor and dollar conversion are found on the first page of the index.

The parts are grouped together in the manual with illustrations to help the estimator find the required part and the price of the item. Manufacturers do not always use the same name for some of the parts used in the body of the vehicle; an example is the front inner skirt, which may also be called the fender apron or inner fender panel. The estimator must find the proper part on the illustration, take its number, and consult the number key, which gives the name of the part and the suggested retail price. In parts books or microfiche issued by manufacturers, the item is found and then the part number; this part number is looked up in a master price list, which gives dealer price, trade price, and suggested retail price. If there is a change up on the part number, the change up must be looked up in the change up area of numbers if it is not mentioned where the part number is.

Each manufacturer uses a preferred method of numbering parts, and the estimator must learn each systems to become proficient when using parts manuals and price lists. When making an estimate, it is sometimes of the utmost importance that a parts manual be available so as to be able to identify all required parts needed for the repair operations.

It must be remembered that the automobile of the 1980s is quite different in construction than those previously built. When the vehicle is involved in a collision, the damage spreads in a cone shape (Fig. 3-8). The unibody vehicle built today is designed to absorb the impact, and when hit in a collision the body is designed to fold and collapse as the energy of the collision is absorbed. The collision forces are absorbed in an ever increasing area as they penetrate the unibody. This design allows the force of the impact to spread until completely dissipated. Figure 3-8 shows the point of impact as the tip of the cone. The direction and force of the impact will determine the center line of the cone, how deep it penetrates, and how wide the damage will spread through the unibody. The tip of the cone is the area of direct damage, and as the force of the impact penetrates through the unibody, the indirect damage spreads like a cone.

The estimator must remember that indirect damage is caused by the force of the direct damage. The indirect damage occurs toward the inner section of the unibody or toward the opposite side or end of the vehicle. Indirect damage is always the last damage to occur as a result of the impact. Repair operations on indirect damage should be done first because it is usually adjacent to undamaged panels; this will cause the straightening operations to be done in a logical order. Straightening procedures on indirect damage first helps to control subsequent pulling operations

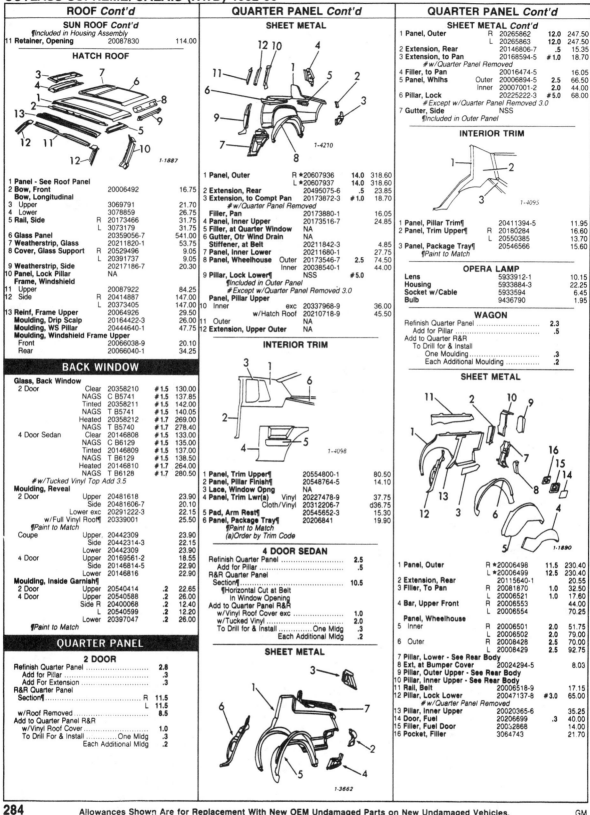

ROOF Cont'd

SUN ROOF Cont'd

¶Included in Housing Assembly

11 Retainer, Opening	20087830	114.00

HATCH ROOF

1-1887

1 Panel - See Roof Panel			
2 Bow, Front		20006492	16.75
Bow, Longitudinal			
3 Upper		3069791	21.70
4 Lower		3078859	26.75
5 Rail, Side	R	20173466	31.75
	L	3073179	31.75
6 Glass Panel		20359056-7	541.00
7 Weatherstrip, Glass		20211820-1	53.75
8 Cover, Glass Support	R	20529496	9.05
	L	20391737	9.05
9 Weatherstrip, Side		20217186-7	20.30
10 Panel, Lock Pillar		NA	
Frame, Windshield			
11 Upper		20087922	84.25
12 Side	R	20414887	147.00
	L	20373405	147.00
13 Reinf, Frame Upper		20064926	29.50
Moulding, Drip Scalp		20164422-3	26.00
Moulding, WS Pillar		20444640-1	47.75
Moulding, Windshield Frame Upper			
Front		20066038-9	20.10
Rear		20066040-1	34.25

BACK WINDOW

Glass, Back Window				
2 Door	Clear	20358210	#1.5	130.00
	NAGS C B5741		#1.5	137.85
	Tinted	20358211	#1.5	142.00
	NAGS T B5741		#1.5	140.05
	Heated	20358212	#1.7	269.00
	NAGS T B5740		#1.7	278.40
4 Door Sedan	Clear	20146808	#1.5	133.00
	NAGS C B6129		#1.5	135.00
	Tinted	20146809	#1.5	137.00
	NAGS T B6129		#1.5	138.50
	Heated	20146810	#1.7	264.00
	NAGS T B6128		#1.7	280.50

#w/Tucked Vinyl Top Add 3.5

Moulding, Reveal				
2 Door	Upper	20481618		23.90
	Side	20481606-7		20.10
	Lower exc	20291222-3		22.15
	w/Full Vinyl Roof¶	20339001		25.50
¶Paint to Match				
Coupe	Upper,	20442309		23.90
	Side	20442314-3		22.15
	Lower	20442309		23.90
4 Door	Upper	20169561-2		18.55
	Side	20146814-5		22.90
	Lower	20146816		22.90
Moulding, Inside Garnish¶				
2 Door	Upper	20540414	.2	22.65
4 Door	Upper	20540588	.2	26.00
	Side R	20400068	.2	12.40
	L	20540599	.2	12.20
	Lower	20397047	.2	26.00

¶Paint to Match

QUARTER PANEL

2 DOOR

Refinish Quarter Panel		2.8
Add for Pillar		.3
Add For Extension		.3
R&R Quarter Panel		
Section¶	R	11.5
	L	11.5
w/Roof Removed		8.5
Add to Quarter Panel R&R		
w/Vinyl Roof Cover		1.0
To Drill For & Install ......One Mldg		.3
Each Additional Mldg		.2

QUARTER PANEL Cont'd

SHEET METAL

1-4210

1 Panel, Outer	R	*20607936	14.0	318.60
	L	*20607937	14.0	318.60
2 Extension, Rear		20495075-6	.5	23.85
3 Extension, to Compt Pan		20173872-3	#1.0	18.70
#w/Quarter Panel Removed				
Filler, Pan		20173880-1		16.05
4 Panel, Inner Upper		20173516-7		24.85
5 Filler, at Quarter Window		NA		
6 Gutter, Otr Wind Drain		NA		
Stiffener, at Belt		20211842-3		4.85
7 Panel, Inner Lower		20211680-1		27.75
8 Panel, Wheelhouse	Outer	20173546-7	2.5	74.50
	Inner	20038540-1		44.00
9 Pillar, Lock Lower¶		NSS	#5.0	
¶Included in Outer Panel				
#Except w/Quarter Panel Removed 3.0				
Panel, Pillar Upper				
10 Inner	exc	20337968-9		36.00
	w/Hatch Roof	20210718-9		45.50
11 Outer		NA		
12 Extension, Upper Outer		NA		

INTERIOR TRIM

1-4098

1 Panel, Trim Upper¶	20554800-1		80.50
2 Panel, Pillar Finish¶	20548764-5		14.10
3 Lace, Window Opng	NA		
4 Panel, Trim Lwr(a)	Vinyl	20227478-9	37.75
	Cloth/Vinyl	20312206-7	d36.75
5 Pad, Arm Rest¶	20545652-3		15.30
6 Panel, Package Tray¶	20206841		19.90

¶Paint to Match
(a)Order by Trim Code

4 DOOR SEDAN

Refinish Quarter Panel		2.5
Add for Pillar		.5
R&R Quarter Panel		
Section¶		10.5
¶Horizontal Cut at Belt		
In Window Opening		
Add to Quarter Panel R&R		
w/Vinyl Roof Cover exc		1.0
w/Tucked Vinyl		2.0
To Drill for & Install ......One Mldg		.3
Each Additional Mldg		.2

SHEET METAL

1-3662

QUARTER PANEL Cont'd

SHEET METAL Cont'd

1 Panel, Outer	R	20265862	12.0	247.50
	L	20265863	12.0	247.50
2 Extension, Rear		20146806-7	.5	15.35
3 Extension, to Pan		20168594-5	#1.0	18.70
#w/Quarter Panel Removed				
4 Filler, to Pan		20016474-5		16.05
5 Panel, Whlhs	Outer	20006894-5	2.5	66.50
	Inner	20007001-2	2.0	44.00
6 Pillar, Lock		20225222-3	#5.0	68.00
#Except w/Quarter Panel Removed 3.0				
7 Gutter, Side		NSS		
¶Included in Outer Panel				

INTERIOR TRIM

1-4095

1 Panel, Pillar Trim¶		20411394-5	11.95
2 Panel, Trim Upper¶	R	20180284	16.60
	L	20550385	13.70
3 Panel, Package Tray¶		20546566	15.60

¶Paint to Match

OPERA LAMP

Lens	5933912-1	10.15
Housing	5933884-3	22.25
Socket w/Cable	5933594	6.45
Bulb	9436790	1.95

WAGON

Refinish Quarter Panel	2.3
Add for Pillar	.5
Add to Quarter R&R	
To Drill for & Install	
One Moulding	.3
Each Additional Moulding	.2

SHEET METAL

1-1890

1 Panel, Outer	R	*20006498	11.5	230.40
	L	*20006499	12.5	230.40
2 Extension, Rear		20115640-1		20.55
3 Filler, To Pan	R	20001870	1.0	32.50
	L	20006521	1.0	17.60
4 Bar, Upper Front	R	20006553		44.00
	L	20006554		70.25
Panel, Wheelhouse				
5 Inner	R	20006501	2.0	51.75
	L	20006502	2.0	79.00
6 Outer	R	20008428	2.5	70.00
	L	20008429	2.5	92.75
7 Pillar, Lower - See Rear Body				
8 Ext, at Bumper Cover		20024294-5		8.03
9 Pillar, Outer Upper - See Rear Body				
10 Pillar, Inner Upper - See Rear Body				
11 Rail, Belt		20006518-9		17.15
12 Pillar, Lock Lower		20047137-8	#3.0	65.00
#w/Quarter Panel Removed				
13 Pillar, Inner Upper		20020365-6		35.25
14 Door, Fuel		20206699	.3	40.00
15 Filler, Fuel Door		20032868		14.00
16 Pocket, Filler		3064743		21.70

Allowances Shown Are for Replacement With New OEM Undamaged Parts on New Undamaged Vehicles.

GM

FIGURE 3-6 Flat-rate times for removal of parts including quarter-panel and lower trunk panel. (Courtesy of Mitchell Information Services, Inc.)

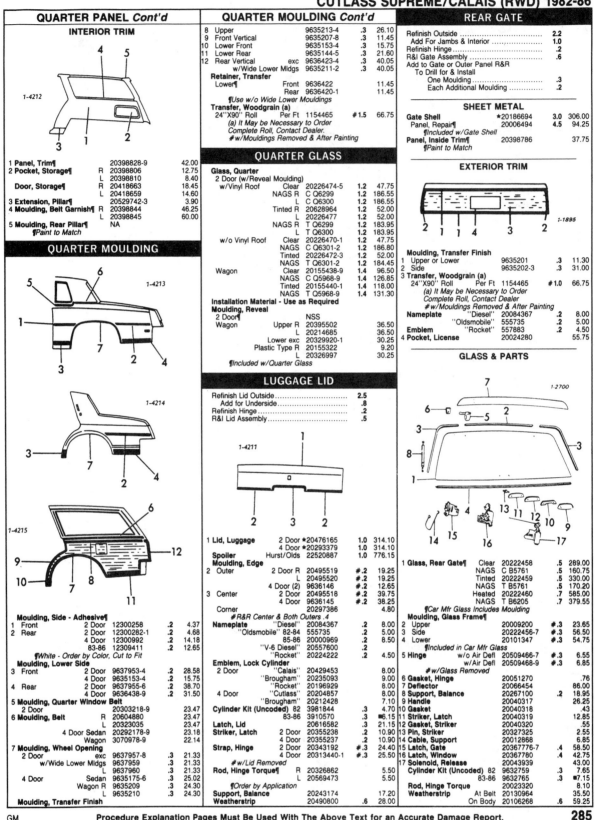

QUARTER PANEL Cont'd

INTERIOR TRIM

1-4212

1 Panel, Trim¶		20398828-9	42.00
2 Pocket, Storage¶	R	20398806	12.75
	L	20398810	8.40
Door, Storage¶	R	20418663	18.45
	L	20418659	14.60
3 Extension, Pillar¶		20529742-3	3.90
4 Moulding, Belt Garnish¶	R	20398844	46.25
	L	20398845	60.00
5 Moulding, Rear Pillar¶		NA	
¶Paint to Match			

QUARTER MOULDING

1-4213

1-4214

1-4215

Moulding, Side - Adhesive¶				
1 Front	2 Door	12300258	.2	4.37
2 Rear	2 Door	12300282-1	.2	4.68
	4 Door	12300992	.2	14.18
	83-86	12309411	.2	12.65
¶White - Order by Color, Cut to Fit				
Moulding, Lower Side				
3 Front	2 Door	9637953-4	.2	28.58
	4 Door	9635153-4	.2	15.75
4 Rear	2 Door	9637955-6	.2	38.70
	4 Door	9636438-9	.2	31.50
5 Moulding, Quarter Window Belt				
2 Door	R	20303218-9		23.47
6 Moulding, Belt	R	20604880		23.47
	L	20323035		23.47
	4 Door Sedan	20292178-9		23.18
	Wagon	3070978-9		22.14
7 Moulding, Wheel Opening				
2 Door	exc	9637957-8	.3	21.33
	w/Wide Lower Mldgs	9637959	.3	21.33
	L	9637960	.3	21.33
4 Door	Sedan	9635175-6	.3	25.02
	Wagon R	9635209	.3	24.30
	L	9635210	.3	24.30
Moulding, Transfer Finish				

QUARTER MOULDING Cont'd

8 Upper		9635213-4	.3	26.10
9 Front Vertical		9635207-8	.3	11.45
10 Lower Front		9635153-4	.3	15.75
11 Lower Rear		9635144-5	.3	21.60
12 Rear Vertical	exc	9636423-4	.3	40.05
	w/Wide Lower Mldgs	9635211-2	.3	40.05
Retainer, Transfer				
Lower¶	Front	9636422		11.45
	Rear	9636420-1		11.45
¶Use w/o Wide Lower Mouldings				
Transfer, Woodgrain (a)				
24''X90'' Roll	Per Ft	1154465	#1.5	66.75
(a) It May be Necessary to Order				
Complete Roll, Contact Dealer.				
#w/Mouldings Removed & After Painting				

QUARTER GLASS

Glass, Quarter					
2 Door (w/Reveal Moulding)					
w/Vinyl Roof	Clear		20226474-5	1.2	47.75
	NAGS R	C	Q6299	1.2	186.55
	L	C	Q6300	1.2	186.55
	Tinted R		20628964	1.2	52.00
	L		20226477	1.2	52.00
	NAGS R	T	Q6299	1.2	183.95
	L	T	Q6300	1.2	183.95
w/o Vinyl Roof	Clear		20226470-1	1.2	47.75
	NAGS	C	Q6301-2	1.2	186.80
	Tinted		20226472-3	1.2	52.00
	NAGS	T	Q6301-2	1.2	184.45
Wagon	Clear		20155438-9	1.4	96.50
	NAGS	C	Q5968-9	1.4	126.85
	Tinted		20155440-1	1.4	118.00
	NAGS	T	Q5968-9	1.4	131.30

Installation Material - Use as Required				
Moulding, Reveal				
2 Door¶		NSS		
Wagon	Upper R	20395502		36.50
	L	20214685		36.50
	Lower exc	20329920-1		30.25
	Plastic Type R	20155322		9.20
	L	20326997		30.25
¶Included w/Quarter Glass				

LUGGAGE LID

Refinish Lid Outside		2.5
Add for Underside		.8
Refinish Hinge		.2
R&I Lid Assembly		.5

1-4211

1 Lid, Luggage	2 Door	★20476165	1.0	314.10
	4 Door	★20293379	1.0	314.10
Spoiler	Hurst/Olds	22520887	1.0	776.15
Moulding, Edge				
2 Outer	2 Door R	20495519	#.2	19.25
	L	20495520	#.2	19.25
	4 Door (2)	9636146	#.2	12.65
3 Center	2 Door	20495518	#.2	39.75
	4 Door	9636145	#.2	38.25
Corner		20297386		4.80
#R&R Center & Both Outers .4				
Nameplate	"Diesel"	20084367	.2	8.00
	"Oldsmobile" 82-84	555735	.2	5.00
	85-86	20000969	.2	8.50
	"V-6 Diesel"	20557600	.2	
	"Rocket"	20224222	.2	4.50
Emblem, Lock Cylinder				
2 Door	"Calais"	20429453		8.00
	"Brougham"	555735		9.00
	"Rocket"	20196929		8.00
4 Door	"Cutlass"	20204857		8.00
	"Brougham"	20212428		7.10
Cylinder Kit (Uncoded) 82		3981844	.3	4.70
	83-86	3910570	.3	■6.15
Latch, Lid		20616582	.3	21.15
Striker, Latch	2 Door	20355238	.2	10.90
	4 Door	20355237	.2	10.90
Strap, Hinge	2 Door	20343192	#.3	24.40
	4 Door	20313440-1	#.3	25.50
#w/Lid Removed				
Rod, Hinge Torque¶	R	20326862		5.50
	L	20569473		5.50
¶Order by Application				
Support, Balance		20243174		17.20
Weatherstrip		20490800	.6	28.00

REAR GATE

Refinish Outside		2.2
Add For Jambs & Interior		1.0
Refinish Hinge		.2
R&I Gate Assembly		.6
Add to Gate or Outer Panel R&R		
To Drill for & Install		
One Moulding		.3
Each Additional Moulding		.2

SHEET METAL

Gate Shell	★20186694	3.0	306.00
Panel, Repair¶	20006494	4.5	94.25
¶Included w/Gate Shell			
Panel, Inside Trim¶	20398786		37.75
¶Paint to Match			

EXTERIOR TRIM

1-1895

Moulding, Transfer Finish				
1 Upper or Lower		9635201	.3	11.30
2 Side		9635202-3	.3	31.00
3 Transfer, Woodgrain (a)				
24''X90'' Roll	Per Ft	1154465	#1.0	66.75
(a) It May be Necessary to Order				
Complete Roll, Contact Dealer				
#w/Mouldings Removed & After Painting				
Nameplate	"Diesel"	20084367	.2	8.00
	"Oldsmobile"	555735	.2	5.00
Emblem	"Rocket"	557883	.2	4.50
4 Pocket, License		20024280		55.75

GLASS & PARTS

1-2700

1 Glass, Rear Gate¶		Clear	20222458	.5	289.00
	NAGS	C B5761		.5	160.75
		Tinted	20222459	.5	330.00
	NAGS	T B5761		.5	170.20
		Heated	20222460	.7	585.00
	NAGS	T B6205		.7	379.55
¶Car Mfr Glass Includes Moulding					
Moulding, Glass Frame¶					
2 Upper			20009200	#.3	23.65
3 Side			20222456-7	#.3	56.50
4 Lower			20101347	#.3	54.75
¶Included in Car Mfr Glass					
5 Hinge	w/o Air Defl		20509466-7	#.3	6.55
	w/Air Defl		20509468-9	#.3	6.85
#w/Glass Removed					
6 Gasket, Hinge			20051270		.76
7 Deflector			20066454		86.00
8 Support, Balance			20267100	.2	18.95
9 Handle			20040317		26.25
10 Gasket			20040318		.43
11 Striker, Latch			20040319		12.85
12 Gasket, Striker			20040320		.55
13 Pin, Striker			20327325		2.55
14 Cable, Support			20012868		6.85
15 Latch, Gate			20367776-7	.4	58.50
16 Latch, Window			20367780	.4	42.75
17 Solenoid, Release			20043939		43.00
Cylinder Kit (Uncoded) 82			9632759	.3	7.65
	83-86		9632765	.3	■7.15
Rod, Hinge Torque			20023320		8.10
Weatherstrip	At Belt		20130964		35.50
	On Body		20106268	.6	59.25

FIGURE 3-6 (cont.)

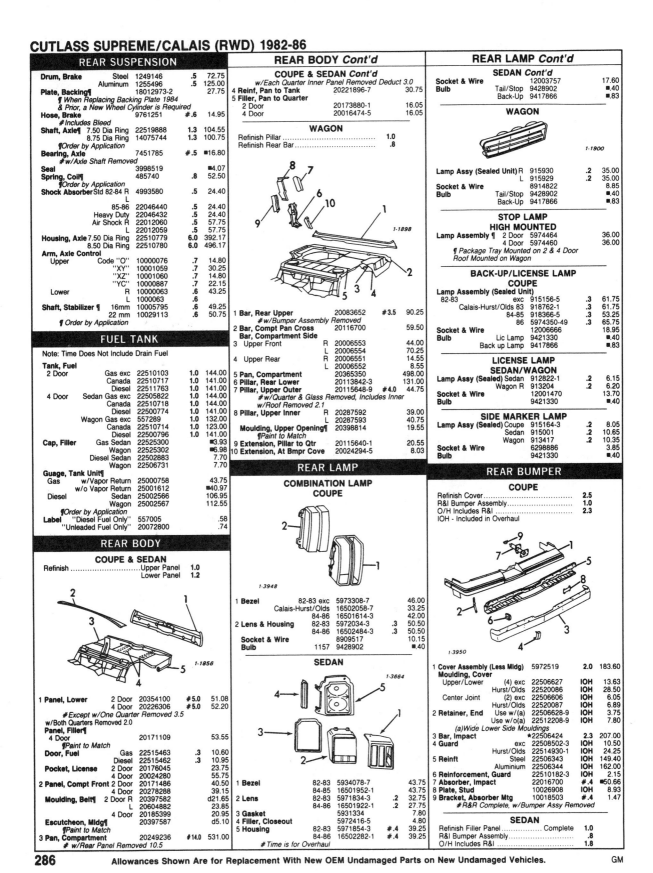

REAR SUSPENSION

Drum, Brake	Steel	1249146	.5	72.75
	Aluminum	1255496	.5	125.00
Plate, Backing¶		18012973-2		27.75
¶ When Replacing Backing Plate 1984 & Prior, a New Wheel Cylinder is Required				
Hose, Brake		9761251	#.6	14.95
# Includes Bleed				
Shaft, Axle¶	7.50 Dia Ring	22519888	1.3	104.55
	8.75 Dia Ring	14075744	1.3	100.75
¶Order by Application				
Bearing, Axle		7451785	#.5	■16.80
# w/Axle Shaft Removed				
Seal		3998519		■4.07
Spring, Coil¶		485740	.8	52.50
¶Order by Application				
Shock Absorber Std 82-84 R		4993580	.5	24.40
L				
85-86		22046440	.5	24.40
Heavy Duty		22046432	.5	24.40
Air Shock R		22012060	.5	57.75
L		22012059	.5	57.75
Housing, Axle 7.50 Dia Ring		22510779	6.0	392.17
8.50 Dia Ring		22510780	6.0	496.17
Arm, Axle Control				
Upper	Code "O"	10000076	.7	14.80
	"XY"	10001059	.7	30.25
	"XZ"	10001060	.7	14.80
	"YC"	10000887	.7	22.15
Lower	R	10000063	.6	43.25
	L	1000063	.6	
Shaft, Stabilizer ¶	16mm	10005795	.6	49.25
	22 mm	10029113	.6	50.75
¶ Order by Application				

FUEL TANK

Note: Time Does Not Include Drain Fuel

Tank, Fuel				
2 Door	Gas exc	22510103	1.0	144.00
	Canada	22510717	1.0	141.00
	Diesel	22511763	1.0	141.00
4 Door	Sedan Gas exc	22505822	1.0	144.00
	Canada	22510718	1.0	144.00
	Diesel	22500774	1.0	141.00
	Wagon Gas exc	557289	1.0	132.00
	Canada	22510714	1.0	123.00
	Diesel	22500796	1.0	141.00
Cap, Filler	Gas Sedan	22525300		■3.93
	Wagon	22525302		■6.98
	Diesel Sedan	22502883		7.70
	Wagon	22506731		7.70
Guage, Tank Unit¶				
Gas	w/Vapor Return	25000758		43.75
	w/o Vapor Return	25001612		■40.97
Diesel	Sedan	25002566		106.95
	Wagon	25002567		112.55
¶Order by Application				
Label	"Diesel Fuel Only"	557005		.58
	"Unleaded Fuel Only"	20072800		.74

REAR BODY

COUPE & SEDAN

Refinish	Upper Panel	1.0	
	Lower Panel	1.2	

1 Panel, Lower	2 Door	20354100	#5.0	51.08
	4 Door	20226306	#5.0	52.20
#Except w/One Quarter Removed 3.5 w/Both Quarters Removed 2.0				
Panel, Filler¶				
	4 Door	20171109		53.55
¶Paint to Match				
Door, Fuel	Gas	22515463	.3	10.60
	Diesel	22515462	.3	10.95
Pocket, License	2 Door	20176045		23.75
	4 Door	20024280		55.75
2 Panel, Compt Front 2 Door		20171486		40.50
	4 Door	20278288		39.15
Moulding, Belt¶	2 Door R	20397582		d21.65
	L	20604882		23.85
	4 Door	20185399		20.95
Escutcheon, Mldg¶		20397587		d5.10
¶Paint to Match				
3 Pan, Compartment		20249236	#14.0	531.00
# w/Rear Panel Removed 10.5				

REAR BODY Cont'd

COUPE & SEDAN Cont'd

w/Each Quarter Inner Panel Removed Deduct 3.0

4 Reinf, Pan to Tank		20221896-7	30.75
5 Filler, Pan to Quarter			
	2 Door	20173880-1	16.05
	4 Door	20016474-5	16.05

WAGON

Refinish Pillar		1.0
Refinish Rear Bar		.8

1-1898

1 Bar, Rear Upper		20083652	#3.5	90.25
# w/Bumper Assembly Removed				
2 Bar, Compt Pan Cross		20116700		59.50
Bar, Compartment Side				
3 Upper Front	R	20006553		44.00
	L	20006554		70.25
4 Upper Rear	R	20006551		14.55
	L	20006552		8.55
5 Pan, Compartment		20365350		498.00
6 Pillar, Rear Lower		20113842-3		131.00
7 Pillar, Upper Outer		20115648-9	#4.0	44.75
¶w/Quarter & Glass Removed, Includes Inner w/Roof Removed 2.1				
8 Pillar, Upper Inner	R	20287592		39.00
	L	20287593		40.75
Moulding, Upper Opening¶		20398814		19.55
¶Paint to Match				
9 Extension, Pillar to Qtr		20115640-1		20.55
10 Extension, At Bmpr Cove		20024294-5		8.03

REAR LAMP

COMBINATION LAMP
COUPE

1-3948

1 Bezel	82-83 exc	5973308-7		46.00
	Calais-Hurst/Olds	16502058-7		33.25
	84-86	16501614-3		42.00
2 Lens & Housing	82-83	5972034-3	.3	50.50
	84-86	16502484-3	.3	50.50
Socket & Wire		8909517		10.15
Bulb	1157	9428902		■.40

SEDAN

1-3664

1 Bezel	82-83	5934078-7		43.75
	84-85	16501952-1		43.75
2 Lens	82-83	5971834-3	.2	32.75
	84-86	16501922-1	.2	27.75
3 Gasket		5931334		7.80
4 Filler, Closeout		5972416-5		4.80
5 Housing	82-83	5971854-3	#.4	39.25
	84-86	16502282-1	#.4	39.25
# Time is for Overhaul				

REAR LAMP Cont'd

SEDAN Cont'd

Socket & Wire		12003757	17.60
Bulb	Tail/Stop	9428902	■.40
	Back-Up	9417866	■.83

WAGON

1-1900

Lamp Assy (Sealed Unit) R		915930	.2	35.00
	L	915929	.2	35.00
Socket & Wire		8914822		8.85
Bulb	Tail/Stop	9428902		■.40
	Back-Up	9417866		■.83

STOP LAMP
HIGH MOUNTED

Lamp Assembly ¶	2 Door	5974464	36.00
	4 Door	5974460	36.00
¶ Package Tray Mounted on 2 & 4 Door Roof Mounted on Wagon			

BACK-UP/LICENSE LAMP
COUPE

Lamp Assembly (Sealed Unit)				
82-83	exc	915156-5	.3	61.75
	Calais-Hurst/Olds 83	918762-1	.3	61.75
	84-85	918366-5	.3	53.25
	86	5974350-49	.3	65.75
Socket & Wire		12006666		18.95
Bulb	Lic Lamp	9421330		■.40
	Back up Lamp	9417866		■.83

LICENSE LAMP
SEDAN/WAGON

Lamp Assy (Sealed)	Sedan	912822-1	.2	6.15
	Wagon R	913204	.2	6.20
Socket & Wire		12001470		13.70
Bulb		9421330		■.40

SIDE MARKER LAMP

Lamp Assy (Sealed) Coupe		915164-3	.2	8.05
	Sedan	915001	.2	10.65
	Wagon	913417	.2	10.35
Socket & Wire		6298886		3.85
Bulb		9421330		■.40

REAR BUMPER

COUPE

Refinish Cover		2.5
R&I Bumper Assembly		1.0
O/H Includes R&I		2.3
IOH - Included in Overhaul		

1-3950

1 Cover Assembly (Less Mldg)		5972519	2.0	183.60
Moulding, Cover				
Upper/Lower	(4) exc	22506627	IOH	13.63
	Hurst/Olds	22520086	IOH	28.50
Center Joint	(2) exc	22506606	IOH	6.05
	Hurst/Olds	22520087	IOH	6.89
2 Retainer, End	Use w/(a)	22506628-9	IOH	3.75
	Use w/o(a)	22512208-9	IOH	7.80
(a)Wide Lower Side Mouldings				
3 Bar, Impact		★22506424	2.3	207.00
4 Guard	exc	22508502-3	IOH	10.50
	Hurst/Olds	22514930-1	IOH	24.25
5 Reinft	Steel	22506343	IOH	149.40
	Aluminium	22506344	IOH	162.00
6 Reinforcement, Guard		22510182-3	IOH	2.15
7 Absorber, Impact		22016700	#.4	■50.66
8 Plate, Stud		10026908	IOH	8.93
9 Bracket, Absorber Mtg		10018503	#.4	1.47
#R&R Complete, w/Bumper Assy Removed				

SEDAN

Refinish Filler Panel	Complete		1.0
R&I Bumper Assembly			.8
O/H Includes R&I			1.8

FIGURE 3-7 Flat-rate times for removal and replacement of parts. (Courtesy of Mitchell Information Services, Inc.)

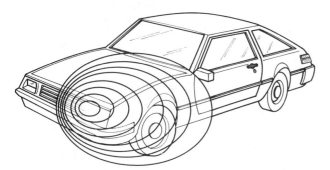

FIGURE 3-8 How the impact is absorbed as the sheet metal and body components collapse. (Courtesy of Inter-Industry Conference on Auto Collision Repair)

and greatly assists the technician to prevent the chances of overpulling an area.

Last In Is First Out

Pulling and repairing the indirect damage, which is "last in" but repaired first, and then the direct damage, which is "first in" but repaired last, is the most efficient way to repair a unibody vehicle. By careful measurement and by visual inspection, the indirect damage is easily identified.

After the inspection and recording all damages (Figs. 3-14, 3-15, and 3-16), the estimator and technician will know how far the indirect damage traveled into the structure of the unibody. With this information the proper damaged areas may be pulled and straightened; as this is being done,

some of the control points will be moved back toward their proper location. This will give the technician a greater amount of reference points where additional pulling may be done.

In a repair operation a sequence must be used, and the first pulls must be done from the impact point and in the opposite direction of the impact point. The technician must first give a gentle pull on the damaged area to see how the damaged metal reacts to the pulls as well as how securely the vehicle is tied down. An inspection of all clamps and fixtures or gauges should be done, and the location of control points should be examined to see if they have moved and if so in which direction. The technician should concentrate on repairing the damage the farthest away from the impact point and then progress toward the point of impact. Remember, first in is last out.

3-2 ANALYZING THE DAMAGE TO WRITE THE ESTIMATE

The estimator and adjuster should have some knowledge of what percentage of collisions occur at different angles or locations on the motor vehicle. A study made by the Mitek Collision Repair System has revealed the percentages of where vehicles are hit (Fig. 3-9).

In many areas the estimator adjuster must also apportion the blame for the collision. Figure 3-10 shows different diagrams of streets and collision examples and how the apportioning of the blame for the collision may be done.

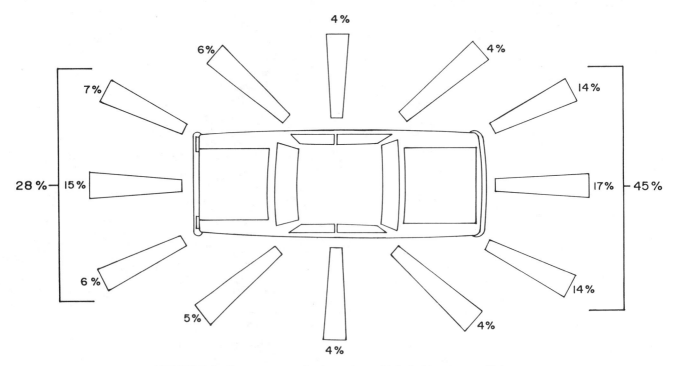

FIGURE 3-9 Percentages of where the vehicle is hit when collisions occur. (Courtesy of Applied Power of Canada Ltd.)

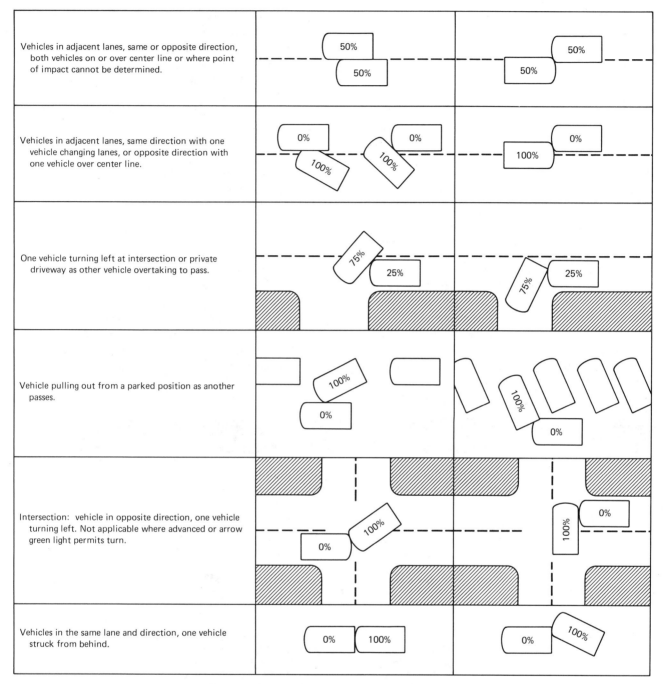

Vehicles in adjacent lanes, same or opposite direction, both vehicles on or over center line or where point of impact cannot be determined.	50% / 50%	50% / 50%
Vehicles in adjacent lanes, same direction with one vehicle changing lanes, or opposite direction with one vehicle over center line.	0% / 0% / 100% / 100%	0% / 100%
One vehicle turning left at intersection or private driveway as other vehicle overtaking to pass.	75% / 25%	75% / 25%
Vehicle pulling out from a parked position as another passes.	100% / 0%	100% / 0%
Intersection: vehicle in opposite direction, one vehicle turning left. Not applicable where advanced or arrow green light permits turn.	100% / 0%	100% / 0%
Vehicles in the same lane and direction, one vehicle struck from behind.	0% / 100%	0% / 100%

Intersection, no traffic lights, vehicles proceeding at right angles, vehicle on the right has the right of way. A driver who has failed to obey a traffic light, stop, or yield sign is a 100% liable. The driver is also 100% liable if the door of his or her parked vehicle, while being opened, causes any damage to another vehicle.

At a T intersection controlled by three-way stop signs or at a four-way intersection controlled by four-way stop signs, the vehicle that reaches the intersection first and having stopped usually has the right of way 100%.

The driver of a vehicle while proceeding the wrong way, backing up, making a U turn, and/or striking a parked vehicle is in each case liable 100%.

Liability may be apportioned as shown regardless of whether point of contact is front, center, or rear of the vehicle.

Some state or provincial regulations or laws may vary the liability amounts of percentage of fault.

FIGURE 3-10 Different examples which show how depending on the traffic law collision blame may be approportioned.

The estimator adjuster should have enough knowledge of traffic laws to be able to use good judgment in these cases.

Explanation of Procedures in Using the Flat-Rate Manual

When repairs are to be done to a vehicle, the estimator must know what the flat-rate time includes as repair operations. The flat-rate time given in manuals is for base line vehicles only; the fancier models will sometimes require more time to repair. Flat-rate manuals have pages that show the operation to be done and what is included for base-line models of a particular vehicle; the required time is given and also what is not included and must be added to the time as required. Figure 3-11 and 3-12 show sample pages from a collision estimating manual, which give the operations included and the additions, explanations, and what is not included. It is important that the estimator have a thorough knowledge of the estimating manual so as to be able to understand all the terms and explanations fully.

A ✓ beside an operation in the operations column means that the collision estimating guide time is believed to be adequate and reasonable for the particular operation. The letter × beside an operation in the additions and expla-

nations column in the text means that the time is not included for that particular operation. If some operation is listed as not included, a note is given to explain what must be done. If the required add-on time has been established, this time will be shown in the manual page or in the column of the procedures explanations. Some add-on time may be necessary because of the type of damage that has occurred and must therefore be estimated on its own.

The estimating manuals separate the different operations required to repair a damaged vehicle into separate sections to simplify using the manual. Figures 3-11 and 3-12 show two typical pages from an estimating manual.

Refinishing Guide Notes

A few more guidelines are required when refinishing operations are being done besides the regular paint work.

Base Coat/Clear Coat Paint.   This type of paint has a base coat with a high solid content of a nongloss acrylic lacquer or acrylic enamel, on which, after the required drying time of the base coat, a clear urethane or polyurethane top coat is sprayed. When looking at this type of finish, the base coat seems to be deep in the paint film

---

FRONT FENDER

	OPERATIONS INCLUDED	ADDITIONS/EXPLANATIONS NOT INCLUDED	

FRONT FENDER – R&R

	INCLUDED	NOT INCLUDED	
			See parts text
Refinish fender		X	See parts head notes
Replace or Transfer parts attached to fender	√		Except those listed below
Bumper assembly R&I		X	Unless noted otherwise in parts text
Antenna R&R		X	See parts head notes for drill and install allowance
Turn indicator lamp	√		See parts head notes for cut and install allowance
Cornering lamp	√		See parts head notes for cut and install allowance
Rocker moulding		X	See parts text for R&R allowance
R&R headlamps	√		If attached to panel
Aim headlamps		X	If lamps attached, see parts head notes
Mouldings/nameplates (clip type-new)	√		See parts head notes for drill and install allowance
Mouldings/nameplates (adhesive - new)		X	Use one-half allowance shown in parts text
Mouldings/nameplates (adhesive - transfer)		X	Add allowance to clean and retape
Stripes/decals/transfers/overlays-install		X	Use allowance in parts text

FIGURE 3-11 Items which show are included and excluded when removing and replacing a front fender. (Courtesy of Mitchell Information Services Inc.)

HOOD

	OPERATIONS INCLUDED	ADDITIONS/EXPLANATIONS NOT INCLUDED
HOOD – R&R		
Refinish hood		X See parts text
		See parts head notes
R&I hood assy	√	
Replace or Transfer parts attached to hood	√	Except those listed below
Mouldings/nameplates (clip type-new)	√	See parts head notes for drill and install allowance
Mouldings/nameplates (adhesive-new)		X Use one-half allowance shown in parts text
Mouldings/nameplates (adhesive-transfer)		X Add allowance to clean and retape
Stripes/decals/transfers/overlays-install		X Use allowance shown in parts text

FIGURE 3-12 Items which are included and excluded when a hood panel is removed and replaced.

and separate from the clear and the texture of the base coat will show. The clear applied to it will not only serve to accent the texture of the base coat but also will protect the paint film from the elements.

Clear Coat Paint Jobs. This type of finish uses either a lacquer or enamel base color with a clear, which may either be lacquer or enamel sprayed over it. This type of paint job uses standard exterior paint colors of either a lacquer or enamel composition, and a clear coat is sprayed over it when it is dry enough to receive the clear coat. The clear coat is applied as a finish coat for better gloss and protection from the elements for the color coat paint film. adherence and so that no separation is visible between each stage of the paint job.

The refinishing procedures in the estimating manual time allowances include the following operational steps: solvent wash, scuff panel, mask adjacent panels, prime as required, final sanding, and cleaning the vehicle or panels to be painted. It also includes mixing the materials, painting the panel or panels, cleaning the equipment, and a light polish on lacquer finishes if required. Refinish times will vary depending on the individual doing the work, procedures used, and weather conditions.

Figure 3-13 shows the items not given in the refinish procedures in the manual. When time is required to do any refinishing operations, the overlap should always be deducted before adding the additional time.

Analyzing the Damage

The estimator must be able to analyze the damage that occurred in the collision before any consideration of repairs,

as the estimate must show what needs repair and what does not. This assessment must begin by analyzing how the vehicle absorbed the energy of the damaging force. This is done by inspecting the areas of direct damage in great detail, noting in which direction the body parts shifted, such as fore or aft, vertically or laterally, which should show at what angle it was hit.

Then with great care the distortions that were caused by the direct damage must be followed and all indirect damage must be noted. The indirect damage results from the crushing of the sheet metal involved in the initial impact. Only with great attention to every detail will all the secondary damage be noted. A chart such as in Fig. 3-14 with its illustrations is used to show the direction of impact on both views and to label the direct damage.

Figure 3-15 shows a chart with diagrams to indicate specifically the areas that suffered secondary damage.

In many cases when a vehicle is hit hard enough, it is important to raise the vehicle (Fig. 3-16) to enable the estimator to check with gauges or a measuring tape where damage has occurred and how much damage is present. A structural damage chart such as in Figs. 3-17, 3-18, and 3-19 is very useful because the information is entered on a form that can be consulted later if any problems should arise.

Assessing Time for Frame and Structure Repair

The estimator must know how to correct frame and body damage to be able to determine the amount of time that should be given on the estimate for the required repairs.

ITEMS NOT INCLUDED IN REFINISH PROCEDURE

When additional time is required for any refinish operation, always deduct overlap before the additional time is added.

- **Clear Coat★**
  Add .4 per hour (after overlap if any is deducted)

- **Two Tone★**
  Add .4 per hour (after overlap if any is deducted)

- **Gravel Guard ★**
  Add .5 for the first major panel, .3 for each additional panel

- **Flex Coat★**
  Time is included in refinish operation

- **Jambs, Underside of Hood and Deck Lid★**
  Time is listed in text head notes

- **Color Match★**
  Add time if necessary to match paint

- **Blending★**
  Add time necessary to blend into adjacent panels or nearest breaking point

- **Cover Vehicle Completely★**
  Add time necessary to cover vehicle to prevent overspray damage

- **Removal of Protective Coating**
  Add time necessary to remove this material

- **Special Coating of Luggage Compartment★**
  Add time necessary for this operation

- **Welded Panel Refinish★**
  Add time necessary to prepare new and original panels that are joined by welding.

- **Overlap Refinish Time**
  Deduct .4 from guide time for each major adjacent panel
  Deduct .2 from guide time for each major non-adjacent panel

- **No Overlap Deductions**
  Pillars, door jambs, underside of hood or deck lid, inner panels, filler panels, soft bumper covers or bolt on finish panels

- ★ Add for materials as required

Additional refinish allowances if required, such as - featheredge, fill, sand and block a repaired area on existing or new panels, adhesive sealers or color sand and rub-out a surface, are not shown in this guide. These additions should be agreed upon among all parties and recorded on your damage report.

FIGURE 3-13   Refinishing procedure times not found in regular headings in estimating manual. (Courtesy of Mitchell Information Services.)

There are slightly different methods for estimating the time required when a frame is damaged, and with unitized construction both the frame and sheet metal are damaged, as well as the body structure, in many collisions. Many shops have a basic dollar rate for use of the equipment and the hookups required. The following are suggestions on how to put a time value on the various repair operations. A 1.4-hour time is used to put the vehicle on the frame machine multiplied by the necessary tie downs, which are usually 4. This would give $1.4 \times 4 = 5.6$ hours to put the vehicle on the equipment and tie it down. Then 1.4 hours is used for each condition; a sidesway will affect both rails

(two hookups) and if, for example, the vehicle has a sag and mash condition, another two tie downs will be required, giving a total of four more tie downs. The first four tie downs give $4 \times 1.4 = 5.6$ hours. The other four hookups will give $4 \times 1.4 = 5.6$ hours, for a total time of 11.2 hours. The estimator must deduct time if an overlap occurs and when the hook ups will help correct more than one damaged condition at the same time. Then the time for cosmetic repairs must be added to this total time; cosmetic repair is the repair of any dents or small wrinkles and the welding required to repair the damage and make it look like new.

ANALYSING DAMAGE

Before there can be any consideration of repairs, it is necessary to know what requires repairs and what does not. The starting point for this assessment begins with an evaluation of how the vehicle absorbed the damaging force. By inspecting the area of primary damage in detail, noting the direction of the shift of body parts - fore-aft, laterally or vertically - the angle of the impact can be determined.

Then, by systematically following through the vehicle along that line, taking note of all secondary damage resulting from the crushing of the metals involved in the initial impact, the full extent of the body damage may be ascertained.

Using the space and illustrations provided below show the direction of impact on both views.

Using the illustration (FIG. 1) label the extent of primary damage.

FIG. 1

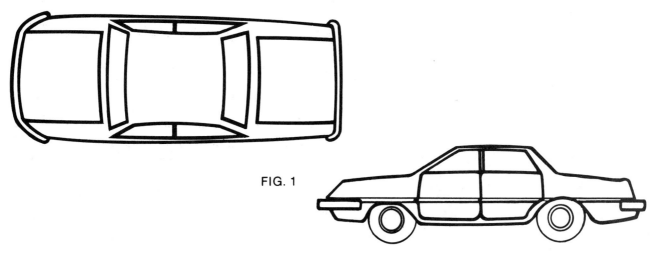

FIGURE 3-14 Chart used to label direct damage. (Courtesy of Chart Industries Ltd.)

Analysing Damage

Using the diagram below indicate specifically, the areas which suffered secondary damage.

Since some of the secondary damage cannot be marked out on the diagrams, describe those areas which have been affected.

_____

_____

_____

_____

_____

_____

_____

_____

FIGURE 3-15   Diagrams to show where secondary damage occurred
(Courtesy of Chart Industries Ltd.)

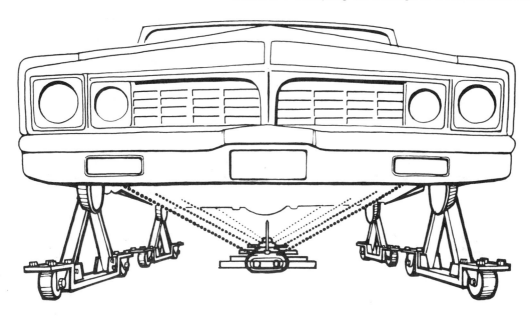

In certain types of damage situations it may be advantageous to set up four D.D.C. gauges on the underbody to quickly verify vertical and horizontal alignment.

FIGURE 3-16 Raising vehicle to analyze the damage. (Courtesy of Chart Industries Ltd.)

Some other companies will assess the time a bit differently based on the first $\frac{1}{2}$ inch or 13 millimeters for conventional frame and unibody damage, as per the following chart.

Frame Damages, $\frac{1}{2}$ inch (13 mm)	Regular Frame (hr)	Unitized (hr)
Horn sidesway	0.5	0.5
Front or rear sidesway	2.0	2.5
Front or rear side rail mash	1.5	1.5
Front or rear side rail sag	1.5	1.5
Diamond	2.0	N/A
Twist	2.0	N/A

N/a stands for not usually applicable

The estimator should add 0.5 hour of time for each additional $\frac{1}{2}$ inch (13 mm) of damage. The estimator must also give consideration to overlap when multiple pulls and types of damage are to be repaired. The estimator should reduce the time for each overlapping hookup by 0.5; these overlaps are usually found when pulling diamond, mash, and cowl hookups. The times used above do not include time for any required alignment hookups, cosmetic work, the removal and replacement of parts, or a wheel alignment check if required. Another method which can be used by the estimator is the repair time guide for unitized bodies.

Damage Conditions	Time (hr)
Rear or front rail sidesway	2.0 for each rail
Rear or front rail sag	2.0 for each rail
If both conditions are present	2.0 for each rail

The estimator should add 1.0 hour for a mash condition in each side rail and approximately 0.5 hour for each buckle in the rail. For vehicles that have strut towers, 1.0 to 1.5 hours is added depending on the damage present. Usually, 1.0 to 1.5 hours for each side is added when pulling the floor, quarter-panel, or cowl when the vehicle frame is being pulled for other damages. When replacing a rail, 1.5 to 2.0 hours should be given for roughing out operations, and then, depending on how much of the rail is to be sectioned, the R&R time in the manual should be changed accordingly. For example, changing approximately half of the outside rail on a 1982–87 Celebrity would be 5.0 hours for a full rail; for half the rail the time should be cut by one-third or one-half since only part of the rail is to be removed. This is a judgment call, which the estimator must be able to make and explain if necessary.

Whether a conventional frame rack or bench-type equipment is being used will vary the unitized setup or tie-down time. The time for conventional frame equipment could vary from 2.0 to 2.5 hours, and on bench-type equipment and universal measuring systems or a dedicated bench

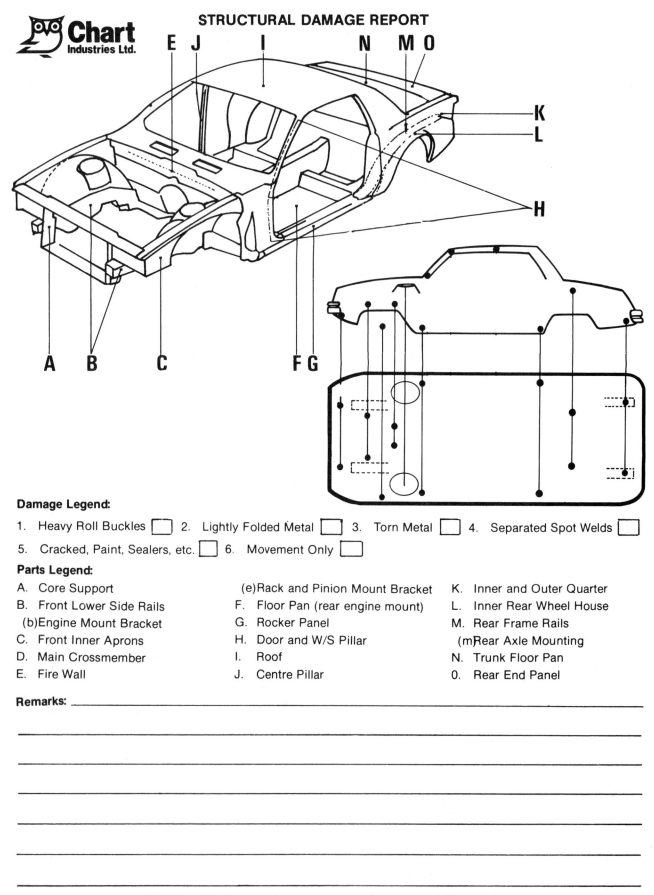

Damage Legend:

1. Heavy Roll Buckles ☐   2. Lightly Folded Metal ☐   3. Torn Metal ☐   4. Separated Spot Welds ☐

5. Cracked, Paint, Sealers, etc. ☐   6. Movement Only ☐

Parts Legend:

A. Core Support
B. Front Lower Side Rails
 (b)Engine Mount Bracket
C. Front Inner Aprons
D. Main Crossmember
E. Fire Wall

(e)Rack and Pinion Mount Bracket
F. Floor Pan (rear engine mount)
G. Rocker Panel
H. Door and W/S Pillar
I. Roof
J. Centre Pillar

K. Inner and Outer Quarter
L. Inner Rear Wheel House
M. Rear Frame Rails
 (m)Rear Axle Mounting
N. Trunk Floor Pan
0. Rear End Panel

Remarks: _____

_____

_____

_____

_____

_____

_____

FIGURE 3-17   Structural damage report. (Courtesy of Chart Industries Ltd.)

Body/Frame Damage Diagnosis Worksheet

Damage	Indication	Condition	
Twist: One corner of vehicle is higher than adjacent corner.	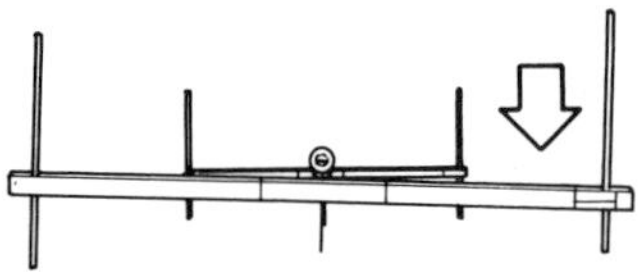	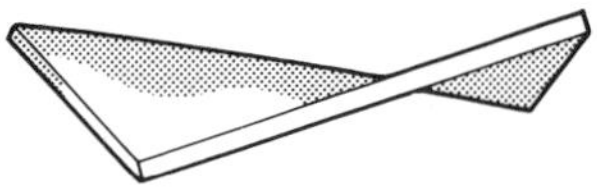	
Diamond: One side of vehicle is pushed back or forward.	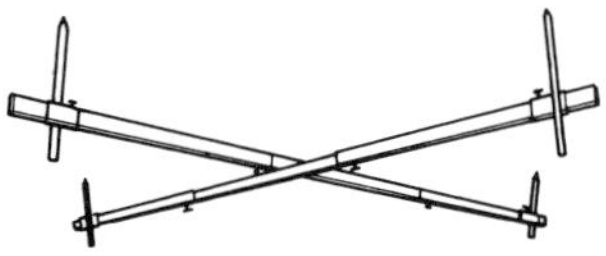	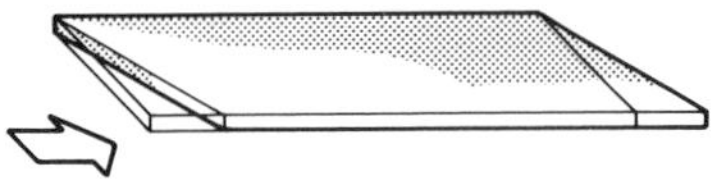	
Mash: Length of vehicle is shortened.	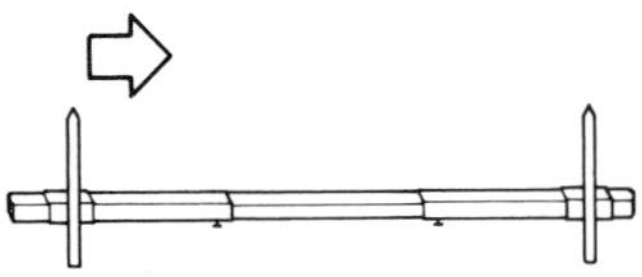	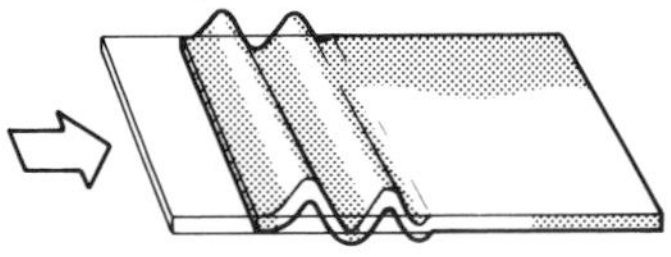	
Sag: Center is lower than normal.	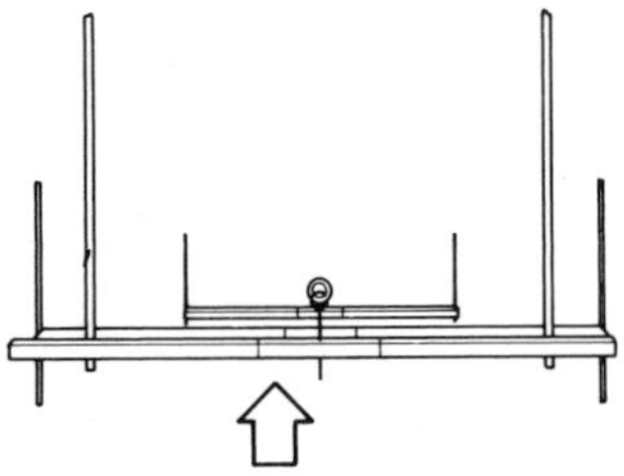	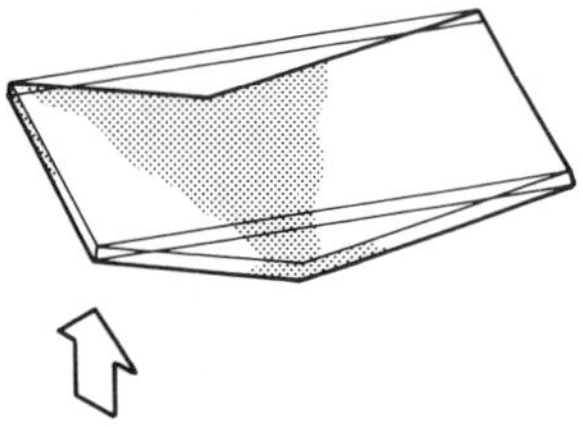	
Sidesway: Front, center, or rear is pushed sideways out of alignment	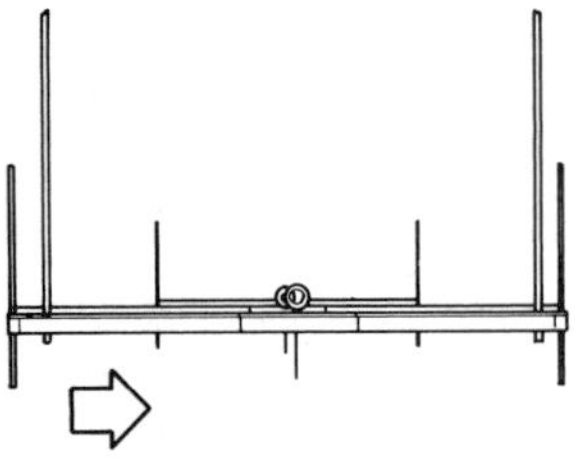	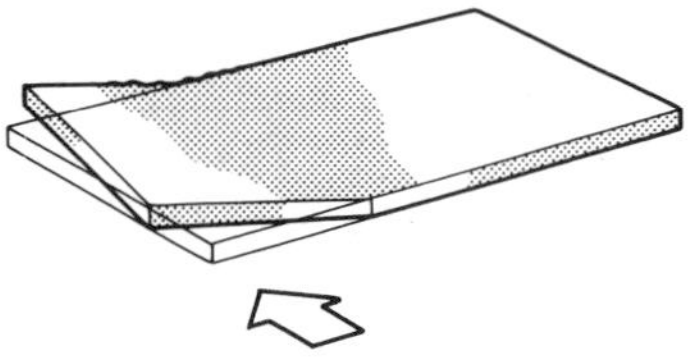	
Damage occurs in this order: (1) sidesway, (2) sag, (3) mash, (4) diamond, (5) twist	Make measurements and correction in this order: (1) twist, (2) diamond, (3) mash, (4) sag, (5) sidesway		

FIGURE 3-18 Chart showing gauges used and different types of damages. (Courtesy of Blackhawk, Division of Applied Power of Canada Ltd.)

BODY/FRAME DAMAGE ESTIMATING GUIDE

DAMAGE	AMOUNT (IN INCHES OR MILLIMETERS)	HOURS	
SIDEWAY			
SAG			
MASH			
DIAMOND			
TWIST			
COSMETIC (Welding, reinforcing, etc.)			
ADDITIONAL DAMAGE (Crossmember sag, McPherson tower correction, etc.)			
TOTAL			

FIGURE 3-19 Chart to be used to mark the amount of damage and time required for repairs. (Courtesy of Black Hawk, Division of Applied Power of Canada Ltd.)

with measuring jigs it could vary from 3.5 to 4.0 hours. The estimator must be able to use this knowledge because many of the decisions will have to be judgment calls for the time estimated.

3-3 ESTIMATING USING THE ZONE SYSTEM

The estimator must change the methods used slightly when estimating a front-wheel-drive vehicle; this is due to the change in location of the drive-train system and its components. The estimator must use a systematic method when estimating the damage; a checklist and evaluation sequences method should be used. The zone or area system should be used along with the checklist system to ensure that an accurate estimate is made. The vehicle is divided into five different zones or areas, and each of these contains a certain part of the body and or the power train. Figure 3-20 shows the direct damaged area caused by a collision, the first zone.

The second zone or area (Fig. 3-21) is the rest of the vehicle body; this includes the other damage resulting from the force of the collision being transmitted through the rest of the body and being dissipated as the affected area widens.

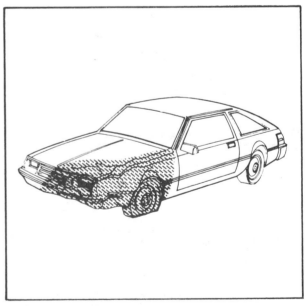

Zone 1

FIGURE 3-20 Direct damaged area. (Courtesy of Inter Industry Conference on Auto Collision Repair.)

Zone 2

FIGURE 3-21 Zone 2 includes the rest of the body. (Courtesy of Inter Industry Conference on Auto Collision Repair.)

Zone 4

FIGURE 3-23 Passenger compartment area. (Courtesy of Inter Industry Conference on Auto Collision Repair.)

This is usually referred to as the indirect damage, which was caused by the force of the impact.

The third zone (Fig. 3-22) covers all the mechanical components in the front area. If the vehicle is a front-wheel drive, then not only the engine, but also the transmission

Zone 3

FIGURE 3-22 Zone 3 includes all the mechanical components in the port area of the car. (Courtesy of Inter Industry Conference on Auto Collision Repair.)

and transaxle assemblies must be examined. If the vehicle is a rear-wheel drive, then the examination will also include the engine, transmission, drive shaft, and differential.

The fourth zone (Fig. 3-23) includes the components that are in the passenger area, such as the steering column, steering wheel, dash, and seats.

The fifth zone (Fig. 3-24) is the last to be checked. It includes all outer trim, lights, and moldings, in fact, all exterior items that were not checked off before on the checklist.

For the estimator to be able to write a valid estimate, equipment will have to be used to raise the vehicle off the ground. This equipment usually consists of safety stands and a jack or hoist to lift the vehicle high enough in the air so that underbody measurements may be performed. The estimator will need a tram rod with at least two adjustable pointers that are adjusted for the proper-length measurement by using a measuring tape with fractions in both inches and millimeters. Metric measurements are used on most of the newer passenger vehicles built since the early 1980s.

Some mechanical hand tools, pliers, screwdrivers, and an adjustable type of wrench should be available in case a component has to be disassembled or a few parts removed from the vehicle that may obstruct visual inspections or measurement checks. A collision estimating manual should be readily available to enable the estimator to identify required parts and obtain their prices; the frame manual is also used to obtain critical measurement dimensions. Equipment such as trouble lights, creepers, a stool or chair,

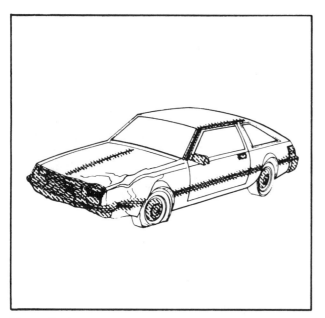

Zone 5

FIGURE 3-24 Exterior components used on vehicles. (Courtesy of Inter Industry Conference on Auto Collision Repair.)

and a desk should be available to assist the estimator in making and writing the estimate.

3-4 IDENTIFICATION AND ANALYSIS OF DAMAGE

The estimator must be very thorough when making his or her inspection. Many vehicles involved in collisions are front end damaged (Fig. 3-25).

Using a measuring tape, the estimator can obtain quick information on the damage if the collision has occurred in the front section of the vehicle. The measuring tape is used to measure the exact location of the McPherson strut towers (Fig. 3-26).

The measuring tape may also be used for underbody measurements, but sometimes certain components are in the way of an accurate measurement and the tram rod must be used as in Fig. 3-27, where it is used to measure a distance from underneath the axle.

The measurement obtained is then checked by finding the measurement specified on the frame specifications and then a measuring tape is used to check the accuracy of the measurement. A tram rod measurement may be used if the distance specified is measured on the tram rod pointers using a measuring tape (Fig. 3-28).

The estimator should use the checklist as the estimate is being done (see Table 3-1); the use of the checklist helps

FIGURE 3-26 Measuring location of strut towers. (Courtesy of Inter Industry Conference on Auto Collision Repair.)

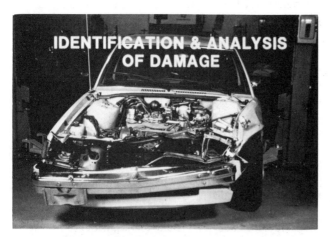

FIGURE 3-25 Typical front end collision. (Courtesy of Inter Industry Conference on Auto Collision Repair.)

FIGURE 3-27 Measuring with the tram rod. (Courtesy of Inter Industry Conference on Auto Collision Repair.)

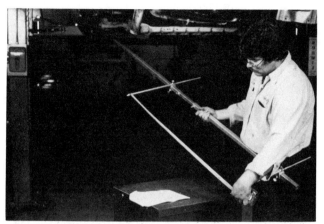

FIGURE 3-28 Measuring distance between pointers on tram rod. (Courtesy of Inter Industry Conference on Auto Collision Repair.)

to prevent missing certain items that are needed on an accurate estimate. Where the estimator starts checking off items on the checklist will depend upon where the vehicle was hit in the collision.

The first damage is, of course, the direct damage, that is, the area that was hit (Fig. 3-29). A system should be followed to ensure that no area or damaged part is missed, if at all possible, by using the checklist.

TABLE 3-1

Estimating checklist

Zone 1 Checklist

☐ Front bumper (energy-absorbing systems)	
☐ Licence plate bracket	☐ Rt & Lt fender
☐ Hood	☐ Rt & Lt fender molding
☐ Windshield or side glass	☐ Radiator support
☐ Grille	☐ Radiator
☐ Headlights	☐ Rt & Lt apron assembly
☐ Park lights	☐ Rt & Lt frame side
☐ Directional signal lights	member
☐ Air-conditioning	☐ Engine cradle assembly
condenser	☐ Front suspension
☐ Paint stress cracks	☐ Spot welds
☐ deck lid	☐ Welds
☐ spot welds	☐ Cracked sealer at seams
☐ Tail lights	☐ Rt & Lt quarter-panels
	☐ Door and center post
	assemblies
	☐ Large panels

Zone 2 Checklist

☐ Measurements of critical	☐ Measurements of chassis
assembly dimensions	☐ Suspension mounts
☐ Split or cracked sealer	☐ Floor pan distortion
☐ Large panel distortion	☐ Roof panel
☐ Sail panel	☐ Quarter-panel upper
☐ Broken welds	☐ Stressed cracked paint
☐ Underbody damage	

TABLE 3-1

(cont.)

Zone 3 Checklist

☐ Engine	☐ Engine mounts
☐ Compressor air	☐ Transmission or transaxle
conditioning	☐ Belt misalignment
☐ Fluid leaks	☐ Emission-control
☐ Engine linkage and	components
controls	☐ Front suspension
☐ Mechanical damage	☐ Steering assembly, lower
☐ Engine block,	☐ Steering assembly, upper
transmission	☐ McPherson struts
☐ Housing	☐ Power-steering pump
☐ Drive shaft	☐ Tie-rod ends
☐ Shock absorbers	☐ Alternator
☐ Suspension, rear	☐ Camber
☐ Steering linkage	☐ Caster
☐ Starter	☐ Toe in
☐ Electrical system	☐ Brake system
components	
☐ Heater parts	
☐ Brake hoses and lines	

Zone 4 Checklist

☐ Bent seat	☐ Steering wheel ignition
☐ Shift lever and linkage	☐ Switch lock
☐ Brake and clutch pedal	☐ Collapsed steering wheel
☐ Door controls	☐ Column
☐ Instrument panel	☐ Restraint system and
☐ Radio controls	anchors
☐ Air-conditioning controls	☐ Instrument panel pad
☐ Damaged trim panels	☐ Heater controls
☐ Doors	☐ Glove compartment door
☐ Mirror	☐ Inner door frames
	☐ Seat tracks and frames

Zone 5 Checklist

☐ Vinyl top and trim	☐ Moldings
☐ Lamp assemblies	☐ Striping paint or tape
☐ Windshield washer and	☐ Wiper arms and blades
nozzles	☐ Bumper systems
☐ Radio antenna	☐ Special paint finishes
☐ Exterior mirrors	

The parts required, plus the price, remove and replace time, or repair times are listed. Damage in newer cars affects the body in a different way than in the older cars. The damage will spread to a wider or longer zone than on older-style vehicles. A car hit on the rail hard enough will collapse, gradually absorbing the impact as it crumples (Fig. 3-30).

Depending on the force, the impact absorbed will probably distort the side engine shields or aprons (Fig. 3-31). The damage may also distort the floor, driving it up and back; this will bend the metal and pop some spots welds (Fig. 3-32).

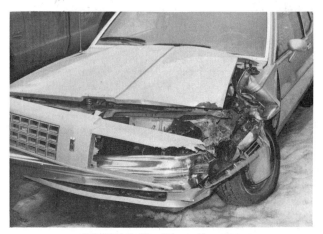

FIGURE 3-29   Direct Damage.

FIGURE 3-30   Collapsed rail and cradle

FIGURE 3-31   Damaged engine shield.

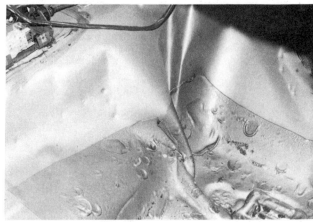

FIGURE 3-32   Distorted floor.

The sealer used at the joints by the manufacturer should be checked carefully to find out if it is cracked (Fig. 3-33).

The energy absorbers must also be checked to see if they have been damaged in the collision. The distance between the arrows on Fig. 3-34 shows the distance that the absorber was compressed and then returned to its original position.

Due to the amount of high-strength steel used in supporting members, the estimator will have to decide which parts can be repaired or replaced in whole or in part by sectioning and welding in new parts. The McPherson struts towers should be checked and measured to determine if they have moved (Fig. 3-35). The correct measurements are available from manufacturers' specifications drawings.

When making an estimate, it is imperative that a vehicle that has been in even a slightly serious accident be raised off the floor and put on safety stands or a hoist. The estimator must be able to get underneath to check for areas

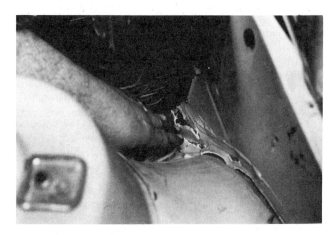

FIGURE 3-33   Cracked sealer at the joint. (Courtesy of Inter Industry conference on Auto Collision Repair)

FIGURE 3-34 Distance energy absorber was compressed. (Courtesy of Inter Industry Conference on Auto Collision Repair)

FIGURE 3-36 Bent brackets and damaged rack and pinion steering. (Courtesy Inter Industry Conference on Auto Collision Repair)

FIGURE 3-35 Measuring and checking McPherson strut towers.

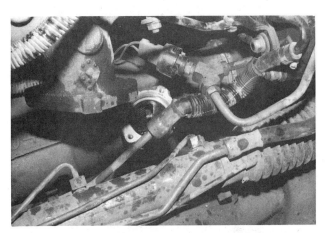

FIGURE 3-37 Broken speedometer gear housing.

that may be damaged, such as bent, distorted, or even broken parts (Figs. 3-36 and 3-37).

The estimator must check to see if some of the reinforcements have been damaged due to the force of the impact, as in Fig. 3-38. The estimator must also look carefully to see if the spot welds are still good welds or have been pulled, as in Fig. 3-39. The door-to-fender gap should be checked because the fender as well as the engine shield may have been driven back (Fig. 3-40).

The next area to examine is the door gaps, especially at the top of the windshield pillar (Fig. 3-41). This check will indicate if the cowl has moved back, thereby causing an uneven gap at the top front part of the door. It will also help to indicate if the frame has sagged at the cowl area. With a wide gap at the top of the pillar, it is very possible that the pressure exerted on the roof panel has warped it; this is due to the change of position of the pillar.

All direct damage is fairly easy to locate, but the indirect and hidden damage is harder to find. In this type

FIGURE 3-38 Bent reinforcement. (Courtesy Inter Industry Conference on Auto Collision Repair)

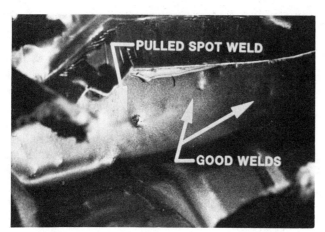

FIGURE 3-39 Showing good and damaged spot welds. (Courtesy of Inter Industry Conference on Auto Collision Repair)

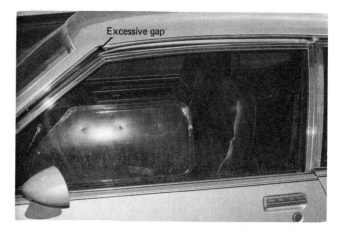

FIGURE 3-41 Gap between door and windshield pillar.

FIGURE 3-40 Fender-to-door distorted.

of construction, accuracy is very important; the maximum tolerance is $\frac{1}{8}$ inch (3 mm). Follow your checklist carefully each time a vehicle is evaluated; this will minimize chances for errors. If possible, all electrical systems should be operated and the engine started to check power equipment for damage.

A steering and suspension check should be conducted if possible. The rack-and-pinion steering and the McPherson struts are quite simple, but often misunderstood. These systems are based on a straight-line principle, and a simple bounce–rebound check will determine if there is any damage to the components of either system (see Chapter 6). The rest of the vehicle must be checked panel by panel to see

if the accident has distorted any panels. It is possible that the fuel tank may have been damaged or that the rear bumper gaps may have changed due to the impact or indirect damage traveling through the vehicle to the rear (Fig. 3-42).

The estimator must be very careful when checking the engine and its components because they are in the front, and if the collision is serious enough, a great amount of damage may be caused, such as breaking of the transmission bell housing part of the transaxle case (Fig. 3-43). In some cases the engine block may be cracked, and the alternator, air-conditioner compressor, and starter could be damaged beyond repair. It is at this time that the estimator must be very careful that the estimate be as accurate as possible; for extensive damage to the drive train, it will probably be necessary for technicians that specialize in the repair of these components to give an accurate figure for repairs. The estimator must also inspect the passenger compartment of the vehicle, as many parts may be damaged. In a front collision the steering column may be collapsed, the steering wheel bent, the instrument cluster broken, the dash crash pad broken, and interior trim broken or discolored. In a rear or side collision, the front seat is usually

FIGURE 3-42 Bumper showing uneven gap between the body lower line.

FIGURE 3-43 Broken Bell Housing on transmission case. (Courtesy of Inter Industry Conference on Auto Collision Repair)

FIGURE 3-45 Damaged door.

damaged as in Fig. 3-44. The seat frame will have to be straightened and repaired. The seat tracks may also be damaged.

The estimator must then check the collision manual and enter the part number, as well as the parts required, the labor time, the paint time, and any sublets to other firms. It is important that this be done well, with the least mistakes possible, as it could make a difference to the insurance company as well as the customer.

With all these figures gathered, the estimator can then write an accurate estimate for the repair of the vehicle and, if the cost of repair is too high, then write off the vehicle.

3-5 WRITING THE ESTIMATE

Exercise 3-1

To learn to write an estimate or a bid for a certain job, we will first start with a simple job, as shown in Fig. 3-45.

FIGURE 3-44 Damaged front seat. (Courtesy Inter Industry Conference on Auto Collision Repair)

The labor rate is $30.50/hour, body shop material is $4.50/hour, and paint material is $14.00/hour.

A damaged door is to be estimated for a bid on the job. The bid is to be prepared on the estimate form shown in Fig. 3-46. The vast majority of estimate bids are handwritten and should therefore be written legibly so as to be easy to understand. All information required at the top of the estimate form must be filled out as applicable. Then the appropriate information about the repairs must be filled in (Fig. 3-46). The vehicle is a 1986 Nissan with a damaged right rear door. The door has a dent in the lower section, and part of it is stretched where it is grooved; this will require 2.5 hours of labor. The molding must be removed and replaced and a new adhesive strip installed on it before replacing it (0.5 hour). Due to a scratch in the paint on the upper part, the whole door must be painted (2.3 hours). This information is entered on an estimate form, such as Fig. 3-46, which has been filled in as an example to help clarify the filling of these forms. All required information for time in hours is converted to dollars (see Appendix A) and entered, and the amount of money is totaled and the sales tax entered, if applicable; the estimate is then totaled for a final figure. There should always be at least two copies of the estimate form. The shop keeps one as a reference for later use, and the original is given either to the customer or the insurance company representative.

Exercise 3-2

Estimating Practice: Remove and Replace and Sheet metal Straightening
Study Figs. 3-47 through 3-50 and fill out the estimate form with the information given; most of the repairs required involve the remove and replace method, frame repair, and some slight sheet-metal repair. Additional write-in estimate forms are included in Appendix C for the student to use when doing the following exercises or other estimates.

ESTIMATOR'S REPORT

Insurance Company _____ | CLAIM NUMBER |

Estimate, Inspection and Location Date _____

ADJUSTER'S NAME	ESTIMATOR'S NAME	DATE OF COMPLETION	DATE OF LOSS

INSURED   VEHICLE

NAME·AND ADDRESS	LICENSE (POLICY) NUMBER	GVW	MILEAGE	AMOUNT OF DEDUCTIBLE
	YEAR, MAKE & MODEL		SERIAL NUMBER	

DESCRIPTION OF WORK TO BE DONE	RE-PAIR	REPLACE NEW	L.K.Q.	QTY.	PART NUMBER	PARTS COST	HRS.	LABOR COST
Right rear door	✓						2.5	76 ¦ 25
R + R Molding install new tape							.5	15 ¦ 25
Body shop material								
4.50 X 3 = $13.50								
Painting right rear door								
30.50 X 2.3 = $70.15								
Paint shop material								
14.00 X 2.3 = $32.20								

This is purely an estimate and not a definite contract price. Owing to the impossibility of determining damage of concealed parts, we reserve the right to submit a further estimate for approval or otherwise. Prices subject to change without notice.
Authorization to Repair _____

I _____ the registered owner of the above described vehicle authorize the repairs to proceed.

TOTAL PARTS COST ▶	nil ¦
TOTAL LABOR COST ▶	91 ¦ 50
SHOP MATERIAL	13 ¦ 50
PAINT LABOR	70 ¦ 15
PAINT MATERIAL	32 ¦ 20
SUB TOTAL	207 ¦ 95
TAX 6%	12 ¦ 47
TOTAL COST ▶	220 ¦ 42

ONLY APPROVED ADDITIONS PAID

FIGURE 3-46   Typical written in estimate form.

FIGURE 3-47 Front damaged automobile.

FIGURE 3-49 Mashed left frame rail.

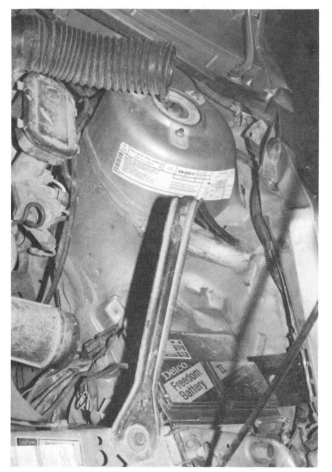

FIGURE 3-48 Damaged radiator support and panel assembly.

FIGURE 3-50 Mashed right frame rail.

information must be filled in on the estimating form (Fig. 3-62):

insurance company: A. B. C. Mutual Insurance, Inc.

claim number: 643CX53

estimate, inspection, and location: Grand Forks, 3/1/88

adjuster's name: John Smith

This job will be paid for by the insurance company (A.B.C. Mutual Insurance, Inc.), except for the deductible, and a competitive estimate will be made for this job.

Estimator's name: John LaRose

Date of estimate, inspection, and location: Grand Forks, 4/1/88

Date of completion: 4/1/88

Claim number: 27618

The estimating guide pages for this particular collision damage for parts and flat-rate time are given in Figs. 3-51 through 3-55, and the pages for the included operations are shown in Figs. 3-56 through 3-58. The following

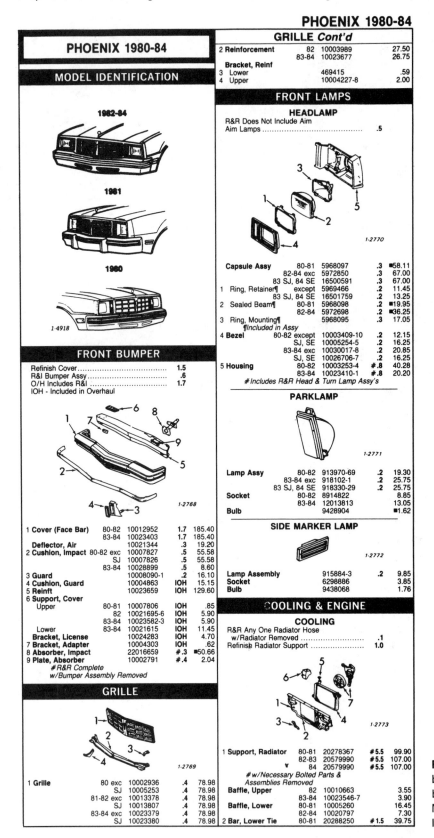

FIGURE 3-51 Esimated rates for bumper, grille, and lamp assembly. 1984 Phoenix. (Courtesy of Mitchell Information Services, Inc.)

PHOENIX 1980-84

COOLING & ENGINE *Cont'd*

COOLING *Cont'd*

	82-84	20292561	#1.5	39.75
3 Reinf, Bar	80-81 R	20300969	#.8	11.80
	L	20277465	#.8	11.80
	82-84 R	20291799	#.8	11.80
	L	20291800	#.8	11.80
#O/H Tie Bar & Reinforcements				
4 Radiator¶	Std	3039665	#1.0	197.00
	AC	3048001	#1.0	186.00
	HD	3039731	#1.0	268.00
#w/Auto Trans Add .2				
¶Order By Application				
5 Cap, Filler		6410427		■4.83
6 Tank, Coolant	80-81	14038591	.3	8.00
	82-84	14038591	.3	8.00
7 Motor, Fan		22035623	#.5	76.70
	w/AC	22035556	#.5	78.30
#Incl R&R Shroud, Fan & Motor Assy				
Fan	exc 80-83	22016679		28.50
	84	22040859		24.95
	w/AC or HD Cool	22035560		25.65
Shroud, Fan (W/Brkt)				
	w/o AC	22016678		25.10
	w/AC or HD Cool	22016680		45.25
	82-84	22035558		41.00
Guard, Fan	w/o AC	474448		2.15
Hose, Upper				
4 Cyl	80-81 exc	10008527	.4	10.10
	AC, HD	10008528	.4	7.60
	82 w/o AC	10019741	.4	10.10
	w/AC	10019742	.4	10.10
	83-84 exc	10026519	.4	10.10
	AC, HD	10027287	.4	10.10
V6	80-81 exc	472431	.4	10.10
	AC, HD	472433	.4	10.10
	82-84 w/o AC	14038539	.4	10.10
	w/AC	14038540	.4	10.10
Hose, Lower	4 Cyl 80-81	10004481	.5	11.95
	82-84	10020495	.5	14.40
	V6	472432	.5	10.10
Belt, Drive	4 Cyl	9433752		■7.18
	V6	9433736		■6.32
Pump, Water	4 Cyl	10004073	#1.1	■62.76
	V6 2.8X Eng	14033483	#1.1	61.50
	Hi-Output 2.8Z Eng	14054847	#1.1	d57.25
#Add w/PS V6 .3, w/AC 4 Cyl .8, V6 .3				
Pulley, Pump				
4 Cyl	1 Groove	10004814	.4	15.10
	2 Groove	10004815	.4	15.00
	3 Groove	10004816	.4	23.20
V6	3 Groove	14023192	.4	23.10

EMISSION SYSTEM

Pump, Air	80	7834420	.5	■148.74
	81 4 Cyl	7836599	.5	■192.49
	6 Cyl	7834488	.5	■148.74
	82	7834488	.5	■148.74
	83-84	7842076	.5	■148.74
Pulley, Pump¶		14085411		14.10
¶Order by Application				
Canister, Vapor				
80-82Federal 4 Cyl w/o (a)		17061008	.3	54.45
	w/(a)	17063014	.3	43.60
	6 Cyl w/o (a)	17061007	.3	54.45
	w/(a)	17063018	.3	50.35
	Calif 80-81 4 Cyl	17063015	.3	54.45
	V6	17061002	.3	54.45
	82 4 Cyl	17064625	.3	58.75
	6 Cyl	17063018	.3	50.35
83	4 Cyl	17063013	.3	39.00
	6 Cyl	17075831	.3	64.05
84		14075840	.3	
(a) Electronic Control Carb				

ELECTRICAL

Horn	Hi Note "A"	1892164	.3	■22.62
	"C"	1892246	.3	■26.95
	Lo Note "D"	1892162	.3	■24.65
	"F"	1892163	.3	■22.62
Relay, Horn	80	344813	.2	4.90
	81-84	25523703	.2	■8.00
Cap, Dist	4 Cyl 80-81	1974409	.4	19.80
	82-84	1978497	.4	■17.77
	6 Cyl	1894979	.4	■16.50
Module, Main Control (a)				
4 Cyl		1226156	1.0	110.00
V6		1226025	1.0	110.00
(a) Located Under Right Side of Dash, Order by Application				

ALTERNATOR & PARTS

Alternator Assy (a) 42 Amp		1105360	.6	205.70
	63 Amp	1105360	.6	205.70
	70 Amp	1101040	.6	256.70
	85 Amp	1105339	.6	326.10
Pulley (a)		1978067		9.35
Fan, Pulley (a)		1978057		14.20
(a) Order by Application				

COOLING & ENGINE *Cont'd*

ENGINE

R&I Engine Assembly	4 Cyl		5.0	
	V6		5.1	
Adjust Linkage Complete			1.0	
Pulley, Crankshaft				
4 Cyl	80-81	10004813	.6	19.15
	82-84	10021360	.6	17.45
V6	80-81 exc	14001809	.7	20.15
	AC, PS	14025544	.9	29.50
	82-83	14025544	.7	29.50
	84	14059347	.7	29.50
Damper, Vibration	V6 80	477234	#.8	42.75
	81	14024247	#.8	42.75
	82-83	14042537	#.8	45.50
	84	14083394	#.8	39.50
#Add w/PS .3, w/AC .3				
Hub, Pulley	4 Cyl	10028930	#.6	26.75
#Add w/PS, .3				
Mount, Frt Supt	80-81 ST	14000448	.7	28.50
	AT	14000451	.7	28.50
	82-84	14073097	.7	29.75
Strut, Eng Mtg	80-81 ST	14089581		■23.73
	AT	14089581		■23.73
	82-84	14089581		■23.73
Bracket, Eng Mtg				
4 Cyl	80-81	14000421	#.2	17.25
	82	10019214	#.2	17.25
	83-84	10023655	#.2	17.25
V6	80-81	14000422	#.2	10.40
	82-84	14036332	#.2	10.40
Mount, Trans Supt				
Front		10036062	.6	■17.85
Rear	80-81	14049343	.6	24.15
	82-84	14049343	.6	24.15
Bracket, Trans Mount				
Front	80-81 ST	14000423	#.2	3.05
	AT	14000424	#.2	3.55
	82-84 ST	14036335	#.2	5.40
	AT	14036336	#.2	5.75
Rear	80-81 ST	14000425	#.2	2.05
	AT	14000426	#.2	4.55
	82-84 ST	14036337	#.2	5.75
	AT	14065709	#.2	4.55
#w/Mount Removed				
Cover, Timing	4 Cyl 80-81	10007015	2.7	32.75
	82-84	547797	2.7	26.75
	V6, 80	14008860	2.2	85.00
	81-84	14033526	2.2	85.00
Pan, Oil	4 Cyl	10035817	2.7	47.50
	V6 80	14077873	2.2	53.50
	81-82	14046495	2.2	53.50
	83-84	14077873	2.2	53.50
Gasket, Pan	4 Cyl	10021749		■6.87
	V6 80-81	1260771		■3.17
	82-84 (a)	1052366		7.35
(a) Sealant Required				
Pump, Fuel				
4 Cyl	80-81	6471489	.8	30.65
	82-84 (a) w/o Fl	6471926	1.1	■59.96
	w/Fl	6472011	1.1	■86.53
V6	80-81	6471599	.8	■62.13
	82	6471929	.8	■58.81
	83-84	6472020	.8	■55.98
(a) Located in Fuel Tank				

EXHAUST

Manifold, Exhaust				
4 Cyl	80 exc	10003711	#1.0	91.00
	Calif	10007536	#1.0	94.25
	81	10007536	#1.0	94.25
	82	10018155	#1.0	94.25
	83-84	10023093	#1.0	94.25
V6	80 R	476514	#1.0	108.00
	L	14003973	#1.0	111.00
	81 R	14022622	#1.0	160.00
	L	14022622	#1.0	160.00
	82-84 R	14033209	#1.0	111.00
	L	14033208	#1.0	111.00
#4 Cyl w/Air Cond Add .6, V6 w/Cruise Control Add .3				
Pipe, Inlet¶		14032233	.7	77.25
Pipe, Intermediate¶		14026966	.5	36.50
Converter, Catalytic¶		8999652	.6	301.00
Muffler w/Pipe¶		14036322	.8	138.00
¶Order By Application				

AIR CONDITIONING

R&R Does Not Include
Evacuate & Recharge System 1.4

Condenser	80-83	3039923	1.0	160.25
	84	3055363	1.0	■152.59
Dehydrator & Receiver	80	2724243	.5	88.65
	81	2724250	.5	90.70
	82-84	2724239	.5	84.35
Compressor	exc 80	12300274	#1.3	■321.65
	81	12309223	#1.3	■321.65
	82-83	12309223	#1.3	■321.65
	84	12300307	#1.3	■321.65
	Hi-Output V6 Eng	12300307	1.3	■321.65

COOLING & ENGINE *Cont'd*

AIR CONDITIONING *Cont'd*
#4 Cyl Add .4

Pulley, Rim		6556715	#1.1	12.60
Clutch, Drive Assy		6551220	#.8	■35.63
Coil, w/Housing		6551217	#1.1	■49.25
#4 Cyl Add .2				
Core, Evaporator	80-81	3042836	2.0	234.70
	82 4 Cyl	3050557	2.0	259.00
	V6	3054167	2.0	247.40
	83-84	3054167	2.0	247.40
Case, Evaporator	80-81	3041348		33.75
	82-84	3049298		33.75
Motor, Blower	80-81	22048569	.5	47.30
	82-84	22020945	.5	■58.45

HEATER PARTS

Case, Blower		3041345		37.75
Core, Heater	exc	3042073	.5	51.10
	w/AC	3040837	2.0	■55.21
Motor, Blower		22048569	.3	47.30
Fan, Blower		3027031		■8.97

HOOD

Refinish Outside	2.8
Add for Underside	.8
Refinish Hinge	.2
R&I Hood Assy	.5

1 Panel, Hood		10023695	1.2	234.90
2 Moulding, Center		10013045	.2	26.00
Emblem	w/Sport Pkg	10004635	.2	10.35
Name	"Pontiac"	527216	.2	2.00
3 Hinge		20048554-5	#1.0	17.25
#w/Cowl Top Panel & Hood Removed				
4 Rod, Prop	80-81 Side	25506829		5.20
	82-84 Front	10020685		4.00
5 Latch		14070703	.3	16.15
6 Bracket, Latch		469444		3.95
7 Catch, Safety	80-82	10026129	.2	6.40
	83-84	10026129	.2	6.40
8 Spring, Pop Up		469445		.86
9 Cable, Release	80-81	20273472	.5	12.05
	82-84	20373950	.5	8.55
10 Support, Latch		10003990		8.41
11 Insulator		12306178	.3	35.25

FRONT UNIBODY DIMENSIONS

For Explanation of Measurements See Back of Guide

TOP VIEW *1-7000*

A	157cm	B	26cm	C	104cm
D	63.5cm	E	134cm	F	80cm
		G	133cm		

FRONT FENDER

Refinish Outside	2.2
Add to Edge Fender	.5
Add Inner Panel	1.0
Add to Fender R&R	
To Drill for & Install	One Mldg .3
	Each Add'l Mldg .2
R&I Fender Assy	2.5
HSLA – High Strength Low Alloy Steel	

FIGURE 3-52 Estimated rates for cooling, engine and hood. (Courtesy of Mitchell Information Services, Inc.)

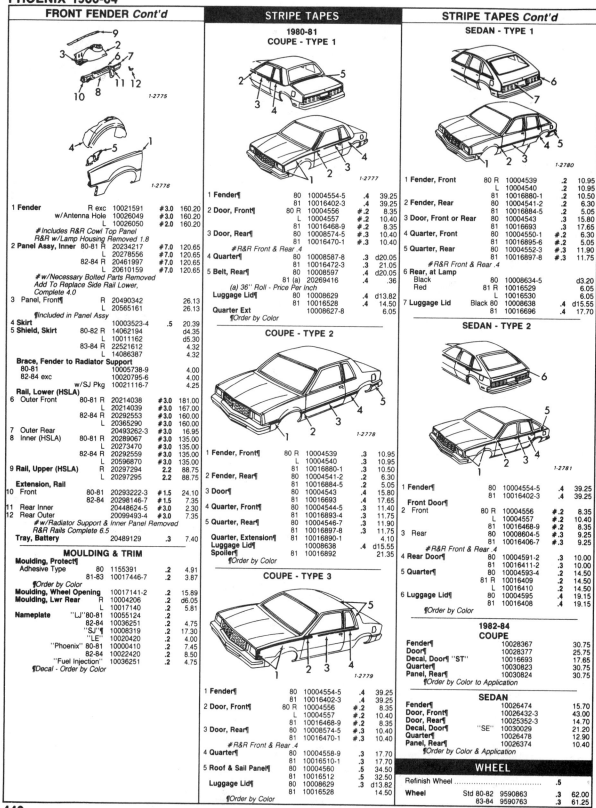

FIGURE 3-53 Estimated rates for fender and stripes. (Courtesy of Mitchell Information Services Inc.)

PHOENIX 1980-84

WHEEL Cont'd

Aluminum	80-81	10006394	.3	190.00
	82	10021755	.3	190.00
	83-84	10026818	.3	202.00
Styled Sport		10022440	.3	119.00
Spare	80-81	9590727		58.25
	82-84	9590727		58.25
Hub Cap Std Snap-On		10006464		6.90
Bolt-On¶		10012049		14.70
Alum Wheel	80-82	10004685		6.90
	83-84	10023934		10.50
Rally IV¶		10005651		7.30
¶Used w/Trim Ring				
Cover, Wheel Wire	80-81	10005386		112.00
	82	10013598		112.00
	83	10024143		112.00
	84	10032001		
Custom	80-82	10013677		61.50
	83	10023941		54.50
	84	10027126		54.50
Trim Ring		10007418		24.60

FRONT SUSPENSION

Check & Adjust Camber & Toe-In		1.3
Toe-In Only		.5

1-2782

1 Disc Brake		14046950	.7	64.25
2 Hub & Bearing Assy		7470002	#.9	■142.99
3 Seal, Inner		14084120	#.9	3.55
4 Shield, Splash		14009989	#.9	7.40
#R&R Complete				
5 Caliper, Brake	R	18011357	.8	d139.25
	L	18011667	.8	163.15
Hose, Brake	80-81	9767946-5	#.6	15.10
	82-84	9767946-5	#.6	15.10
#R&R One .6, Each Add'l .3, - Incl Bleed				
6 Shock Absorber w/Strut				
Standard	80-81	22008230	1.0	■63.50
	82-83	22035659	1.0	99.25
	84	22049969	1.0	56.90
Heavy Duty	80-81	22008231	1.0	■75.58
	82-83	22035660	1.0	■75.58
	84	22049970	1.0	56.90
7 Knuckle	80-83	14076994-3	1.1	86.25
	84 R	14076994	1.1	
	L	14076993	1.1	86.25
8 Spring¶		14003325	#1.0	34.25
¶Order by Application				
9 Mount, Abs & Strut	80-81 R	9763250	#1.0	49.00
	L	9763249	#1.0	49.00
	82-84	17980090-89	#1.0	49.00
10 Seat, Spring	80-81	468593	#1.0	3.55
	82-83	14077769	#1.0	3.55
	84	14065776	#1.0	3.55
11 Bmpr, Abs & Strut	80-81	9763510	#1.0	13.55
	82-83	14036459	#1.0	2.70
	84	14065773	#1.0	2.70
12 Shield, Dust	80-81	468594	#1.0	1.15
	82-83	14034677	#1.0	5.20
	84	14077313	#1.0	5.20
13 Insulator, Spring	80-83	14077726	#1.0	1.75
	84	14077726	#1.0	1.75
#R&R Complete				
14 Arm Assy, Lower	80-81	14082848-7	1.0	141.00
	82-84	14082848-7	1.0	141.00
15 Ball Joint¶	80-81	17983075	.7	40.25
	82-84	17983075	.7	40.25
16 Bushing¶	80-81	14026980		7.00
	82	14065721		7.00
	83-84	14065721		7.00
¶Included in Arm Assy				
17 Shaft, Stab exc	80-81	14038145	#.8	35.75
	82-84	14089551	#.8	43.50
HD Susp	80-81	14011793	#.8	49.25
	82-84	14089584	#.8	43.50
18 Bushing, Shaft		473525	#.8	.88
19 Bracket, Shaft		473524	#.8	1.85
20 Plate, Support		477054-3	#.8	1.85
#R&R Complete				

DRIVE AXLE

1-2783

Shaft Assembly					
w/ST	80-83 R		8740073	.8	
	L		7840074	.8	■495.81
	84 R		7844745	.8	■487.65
	L		7844748	.8	■487.65
w/AT	80-83		7840076-5	.8	■495.81
	84 R		7844754	.8	■487.65
	L		7844756	.8	■487.65
Joint Assy¶					
1 Inner	ST		7845171		■221.66
	AT R		7840071		■221.66
	L		7845019		■221.66
2 Outer	80-83		7845009		d175.00
	84		7544747		
Seal Kit¶					
3 Inner	80		7845016		■27.30
	81-84		7837828		■39.97
4 Outer			7844997		23.45
5 Shaft, Axle¶	ST R		7834181	1.2	70.70
	L		7834179	1.2	■43.16
	AT R		7834180	1.2	56.07
	L		7834179	1.2	■43.16
¶Included in Assy					

LINKAGE & GEAR

R&R Does Not Include Adjust Toe-In

Adjust Toe-In		.5

1-2784

Gear Assy				
Manual	80-81	7837400	#2.0	346.00
	82-84	7845436	#2.0	346.00
Power	exc 80-81	7837712	#2.1	481.00
	82	26003943	#2.1	214.30
	83	26003943	#2.1	214.30
HD Susp	80-81	7837713	#2.1	491.00
	82	26003943	#2.1	214.30
	83-84	26003943	#2.1	214.30
#Add To Gear R&R				
w/AT - Power 1.4, Manual 1.8				
1 Housing¶	80-81 Manual	7828525		134.00
	Power	7831187		183.00
	82-84 Manual	7837263		134.00
	Power	7846727		183.00
2 Rack, Strg¶	80-81 Manual	7834498		163.00
	Power	7828482		123.00
	82-84 Manual	7834080		163.00
	Power	7846698		123.00
3 Valve, Power Std	80-81	7837714		■260.64
	82	7842238		263.00
	83-84	7842238		263.00
HD Susp	80-81	7837715		222.00
	82-84	7842238		263.00
¶Included in Assy				
4 Grommet, Mounting		7828515-4		6.75
Bracket, Mtg	80-81	22501488-9		3.50
	82-84 R	22515805		3.50
	L	NA		
5 Tie Rod, Inner				
Manual	80-81	7832948		48.00
	82-84	7839153		49.50
Power	80	7843301		49.50
	81	7843301		49.50
	82-84	7839153		49.50
6 Tie Rod, Outer	80-81	7837439	.3	48.50
	82-84	7839154	.3	48.50
7 Boot Kit, Rack & Pinion				
Manual	80-81	7831122		23.95
	82-84	7839278		23.95
Power	80-81	7829879		23.95
	82-84	7839156		23.95
8 Line Kit, Fluid	80	7831189-8		14.30
	81 R	7834890		14.35

LINKAGE & GEAR Cont'd

		L	7834889	13.95
	82-84 R		7840455	15.65
		L	7843293	14.35

PUMP - POWER

Pump Assy, Less Pulley

4 Cyl	80	7830025	1.1	199.00
	81-84	7838471	1.1	199.00
V6	80	7830350	1.1	■198.93
	81-84	7838472	1.1	199.00
Pulley 4 Cyl	80	10009692	.5	14.80
	81	14023175	.5	15.65
	82-84	10009692	.5	14.80
V6	80-81 ST	14025546	.5	14.80
	AT	14025547	.5	14.80
	82-84 ST	14025546	.5	14.80
	AT	14025547	.5	14.80
Reservoir 4 Cyl	80	7833714		59.00
	81-84	7836806		60.50
V6	80	7832675		60.50
	81-84	7836823		60.50
Hose, Pressure 4 Cyl	80	7829942	.4	57.00
	81	7836878	.4	57.00
	82-84	7839955	.4	57.00
6 Cyl	80	7832439	.4	■51.71
	81	7839065	.4	50.50
	82	7839956	.4	57.00
83-84 exc		7842584	.4	57.00
	w/AC	7842705	.4	57.00
Hose, Return (a) 4 Cyl		7841122	.4	36.00
V6		26001782	.3	36.00

(a) Order by Application

STEERING COLUMN

WHEEL & TRIM

Wheel, Steering¶				
Standard	80-81	9763475	.5	86.75
	82	9765731	.5	87.25
	83	9769644	.5	87.25
	84	17980151	.5	87.25
Custom	80-81	10002246	.5	170.00
	82	10019134	.5	172.00
	83	17982059	.5	172.00
	84	17980192	.5	172.00
Sport		9768641	.5	247.00
Pad, Wheel¶ Standard		9762314		43.00
Custom	80-82	10013858		59.50
	83-84	9768652		30.50
Cap, Horn¶ Custom	80-82	10003383		7.45
	83-84	10023783		24.70
Sport		10018240		21.90
¶Order by Application				

COLUMN - STANDARD

Housing, Lock	ST	7837035		63.25
	AT	7837032		63.25
Lock, Ignition Coded		7830380	1.1	■9.50
Switch, Ignition	80-83	1990115	.6	■11.30
	84	1990115	.6	■11.30
Column Assy				
w/Column Shift				
w/o Pulse Wiper	80	7835255	2.0	230.00
	81	7836110	2.0	386.00
	82-83	7837295	2.0	230.00
	84	7842400	2.0	230.00
w/Pulse Wiper	81	7836219	2.0	230.00
	82	7837294	2.0	230.00
	83	7839885	2.0	237.00
	84	7842401	2.0	230.00
w/Floor Shift				
w/o Pulse Wiper	ST 80	7835256	2.0	230.00
	81	7836184	2.0	229.00
	83-83	7837297	2.0	230.00
	84	9842404	2.0	
	AT 81	7834491	2.0	230.00
	82-83	7837299	2.0	230.00
	84	7842402	2.0	230.00
w/Pulse Wiper	ST 81	7836220	2.0	230.00
	82-83	7837296	2.0	230.00
	84	7842405	2.0	230.00
	AT 81	7836221	2.0	230.00
	82-83	7842403	2.0	230.00
	84	7842403	2.0	230.00
Jacket¶				
w/Column Shift	80	7830196		d70.75
	81-84	7836130		74.25
w/Floor Shift	80-83	7830198		66.50
	84	7842998		74.25
Tube, Shift¶				
w/Column Shift AT	80-82	7830085		27.50
	83-84	7842055		27.50
w/Floor Shift	AT	7834520		27.50
Shaft, Steering¶				
Upper	80-81	7830192		71.25
	82-84	7841282		71.25
Lower	80-81 w/o PS	7830048		113.00
	w/PS	7837600		114.00
	82 w/o PS	7837320		113.00
	w/PS	7845147		114.00
	83-84 w/o PS	7844934		114.00

GM   **Procedure Explanation Pages Must Be Used With The Above Text for an Accurate Damage Report.**   **441**

FIGURE 3-54 Estimated rates for front suspension and steering (Courtesy of Mitchell Information Services, Inc.)

PHOENIX 1980-84

STEERING COLUMN Cont'd

COLUMN - STANDARD Cont'd

w/PS	7845147		114.00

¶ *Included in Column Assembly*

COLUMN - TILT WHEEL

Cover, Lock Housing		7837547		44.25
Housing, Lock		7827195		161.00
Lock, Ignition Coded		7830380	1.1	■9.50
Switch, Ignition	80-83	1990116	.6	■11.53
	84	7843451	.6	25.50

Column Assy
w/Column Shift

w/o Pulse Wiper		80	7835248	2.0	386.00
		81	7836191	2.0	386.00
		82	7837308	2.0	386.00
		83	7840171	2.0	386.00
		84	7842536	2.0	386.00
w/Pulse Wiper		81	7836190	2.0	386.00
		82	7837307	2.0	386.00
		83	7840170	2.0	386.00
		84	7842535	2.0	386.00

w/Floor Shift

w/o Pulse Wiper	ST	80	7835249	2.0	386.00
		81	7836193	2.0	386.00
		82-83	7837310	2.0	386.00
		84	7842538	2.0	386.00
	AT	81	7836223	2.0	386.00
		82-83	7837312	2.0	386.00
		84	7842540	2.0	386.00
w/Pulse Wiper	ST	81	7836192	2.0	386.00
		82-83	7837309	2.0	386.00
		84	7842537	2.0	386.00
	AT	81	7836224	2.0	386.00
		82-83	7837311	2.0	386.00
		84	7842539	2.0	386.00

Jacket¶

w/Column Shift	80	7836644		74.25
	81-83	7836644		74.25
	84	7843170		74.25
w/Floor Shift	80-82	7841616		74.25
	83	7841616		74.25
	84	7843171		74.25
Tube, Shift¶ AT exc	80-82	7830729		35.25
	83-84	7842079		35.25
w/Floor Shift		7836635		35.25
Shaft Assy, Col¶	80-81	7830721		174.00
	82-84	7841279		174.00
Upper w/Race(a)		7828404		72.00
Inter Lower	80-81	7830722		114.00
	82-84	7841280		114.00

(a)Included in Shaft Assembly
¶Included in Column Assy

Shaft, Lwr	Man 80-81	7830048		113.00
	82	7837320		113.00
	83-84	7844934		114.00
	Power 80-81	7837600		114.00
	82-84	7845147		114.00

FRAME

1-4516

1 Member Assembly

Side & Cross	80-81	14036303	#4.5	346.00
	82	14081979	#4.5	394.00
	83	14081979	#4.5	394.00
	84	14081979	#4.5	394.00

Does Not Include Alignment,
Includes Support Engine

Member, Front Cross¶		14044926		89.75

¶Incl in Member Assy

2 Damper, Trans	4 Cyl	14011736		1.10

WINDSHIELD

Glass, Windshield
w/o Antenna

	Clear	20037285	1.8	220.00
	NAGS C W904		1.8	231.30
	Shaded	20037287	1.8	251.00
	NAGS S W904		1.8	264.60
w/Antenna	Clear	20037286	2.0	252.00
	NAGS C W898		2.0	279.10
	Shaded	20037288	2.0	283.00
	NAGS S W898		2.0	315.50

Installation Material - Use as Required
Moulding, Reveal

Upper	Bright	20361586		16.85
	Black	20366636		18.10
Side	Bright	20361602-3		17.95
	Black	20366634-5		17.95

WINDSHIELD Cont'd

Lower	Bright	20130078-9		17.40
	Black	20161338-9		17.95

Moulding, Inside Garnish¶

Side	Lower R	20265184	.2	6.55
	L	20540641	.2	7.00
	Upper	20265196-7	.2	9.65
Upper	80-81	20384396	.2	17.80

¶*Paint to Match*

Mirror, Rear View		911582	.2	24.85
Visor, Sun¶	80	20305933	.2	32.75
	81	20305930	.2	32.75
	82	20357781	.2	32.75
	83	20393858	.2	31.25
	84	20467956	.2	31.25

¶*Order by Color*

Blade Assy	80-81 Trico	9664093	.2	■8.62
	Anco	20302535	.2	8.25
	82-84 Trico	20364747	.2	8.85
	Anco	20350040	.2	■8.50
Arm, Wiper	80-81	20349925	.2	26.00
	82-84	20343851	.2	26.00
Motor, Wiper		22020255	1.0	100.35
Pump, Washer		4961623	.4	■16.32
Reservoir, Washer	80-81	22048346	.3	7.85
	82-84	22029963	.3	8.25
Nozzle, Spray	80-81	25501882	.2	1.20
	82-84	25510958	.2	1.95

COWL & DASH

Refinish:	Cowl Top Panel	1.0
	Cowl Side	1.0
	Instrument Panel	1.0
	Glove Box Door	.5

1-2786

1 Pillar, Hinge	80	20128786-7	#6.5	91.50
	81-84 R	20306704	#6.5	90.50
	L	20541106	#6.5	90.50

#*w/Fender, Door & Windshield Removed*

2 Reinf, Inner	80-81 R R	20511456		27.50
	L	20303383		28.50
	82-84 R	20511456		27.50
	L	20303383		28.50

Panel, Cowl Trim¶

80-81	R	20154946		d3.05
	L	20127053		3.45
82-84	R	20382388		3.45
	L	20392978		3.45

¶*Paint to Match*

3 Pillar, Upper		20297548-9	#3.0	121.00

#*w/Fender, Door & Windshield Removed*
Moulding, Pillar Finish

w/Vinyl Roof	80-81	20194035		17.40

¶*Paint to Match*

4 Panel, Cowl Top	80-82	20326105	1.0	76.50
5 Panel, Dash		NA		
6 Panel, Upper Ext		NA		
Screen, Cowl Vent	80-81	20297844		2.90
	82-84	20326108		2.90
Moulding, Cowl		10004630		d5.40

INSTRUMENT PANEL

1-4365

1 Panel, Instrument (a) & (b)		10003101	#5.5	d237.00

#*Includes R&R Instrument Cluster*

2 Panel, Gauge Cluster (a)		25051240		200.42
3 Panel, Cluster Cover (a) & (b)		10012377		7.50
4 Shroud, Lower	R	25511785		19.55
5	L	25511810		19.55
6 Glovebox w/Door (b)		10009024	.3	17.10

(a) *Order by Application*
(b) *Paint to Match*

ROCKER PANEL & PILLAR

1-2787

ROCKER PANEL

Refinish Rocker			1.0	

HSLA – High Strength Low Alloy Steel

1 Panel, Rocker (HSLA)	R	★20365674	#4.5	38.25
	L	★20365675	#4.5	38.25

#*4 Door - Add 2.0*

2 Reinf, Rocker		20093078	.5	8.36

Moulding, Rocker
Wide Type

Except	80-82	10017628-9	.3	58.05
	83-84	10024512-3	.3	24.98
"LJ" Coupe		10017137-8	.3	90.90
Sedan		10017135-6	.3	90.90
"SJ"		10008545-6	.3	24.98
"LE"		25514528-9	.3	14.40

Scuff Plate

Coupe		20312881	.2	13.70
Sedan	80-81 Front	20312882	.2	13.70
	Rear	20312883	.2	10.25
	82-84 Front	20312882	.2	13.70
	Rear	20312883	.2	10.25

PILLAR

Refinsih Center Pillar		1.0

3 Pillar, Center Inner		★20164540-1	2.0	20.00
4 Pillar, Center Outer		★20506274-5	6.5	165.00

Moulding, Pillar

	80-82	20131768-9	.2	50.50
Black/Charcoal	83-84	20420880-1	.2	50.50
Bright/Charcoal		20420878-9	.2	50.50
Painted		20425306-7	.2	d45.00

Trim, Pillar Inside¶

	80-81	20129620-1		
	82-84 R	20529404		20.80
	L	20398207		20.80

¶*Paint to Match*

5 Pillar, Hinge - See Cowl & Dash
6 Pillar, Lock - See Quarter Panel

SEAT

Adjuster, Manual

Bench Seat	80-82 R	20121476	#.6	36.00
	L	20597677	#.6	36.00
	83-84 R	20308316	#.6	36.50
	L	20597678	#.6	36.50

Bucket Seat

Driver	80-81 Outer	20121479	#.6	36.00
	Inner	20121478	#.6	36.00
	82 Outer	20359922	#.6	36.00
	Inner	20359923	#.6	36.00
	83 Outer	20597680	#.6	36.50
	Inner	20243997	#.6	36.50
	84 Outer	20597680	#.6	36.50
	Inner	20243997	#.6	36.50
Pass	80-82 Outer	20121480	#.6	36.00
	Inner	20121481	#.6	36.00
	83 Outer	20243927	#.6	36.50
	Inner	20597679	#.6	36.50
	84 Outer	20597679	#.6	36.50
	Inner	20243927	#.6	36.50

Both One Seat .8
Adjuster, Power

Bench Seat	80-81 R	20170182	#.8	62.00
	L	20170185	#.8	60.00
	82 R	20327747	#.8	148.00
	L	20327746	#.8	148.00
	83-84 R	20411087	#.8	63.50
	L	20411084	#.8	63.50
Bucket Seat	80-81 Otr	20170196	#.8	60.00
	Inner	20170195	#.8	60.00
	82 Outer	20327749	#.8	148.00
	Inner	20327748	#.8	148.00
	83-84 Outer	20411096	#.8	62.00
	Inner	20429136	#.8	63.50

Both One Seat 1.0
Adjuster, Recline (a)

Driver	Outer	20130211		40.25
	Inner	20130217		35.50
Passenger	Outer	20130210		40.25
	Inner	20130216		35.50

(a) *Order by Application*

FIGURE 3-55 Estimated rates for frame and instrument panel. (Courtesy of Mitchell Information Services Inc.)

FRONT BUMPER

	OPERATIONS INCLUDED	ADDITIONS/EXPLANATIONS NOT INCLUDED

ASSEMBLY – R&I

Remove from frame	√	See parts head notes
Remove from impact absorber or mounting arm	√	Handle as a unit
Reinstall same assembly	√	Handle as a unit
Adjust alignment to vehicle	√	
Optional accessories		X Example: Auxiliary lights, brush guard, etc...

ASSEMBLY – O/H

		See parts head notes
Assembly R&I	√	
Disassemble & Replace damaged parts	√	Only parts attached to assembly
Assemble & Install	√	
Adjust alignment to vehicle	√	
Impact absorber or mounting arm		X See parts text for R&R time
Optional accessories		X Example: Auxiliary lights, brush guard, etc...

FIGURE 3-56 Procedure explanation front bumper. (Courtesy of Mitchell Information Services Inc.)

Insured name and address: David Hebert
1103 2nd Street North
Grand Forks, North Dakota

License number: VBC 374

Mileage: 3514 km

Deductible: $100.00

Year, make, and model: 1984 Pontiac Phoenix

Serial number: 1G2AX37B7ED 1341463

The vehicle is painted with acrylic lacquer (exterior code 20, interior code 20). The parts required are the following:

	Hours	Parts cost
1 Front bumper cover (face bar) 10023403	1.7	185.40
1 Deflector air 10021344	0.3	19.20
1 Cushion impact 10028899	0.5	8.60
1 Reinforcement (front bumper) 10023659	incl.	129.60
1 Impact absorber 220216659	4.3	50.66
1 Grille 10023379	0.4	79.98

	Hours	Parts cost
1 Grille reinforcement 10023677	incl.	26.75
1 Ring retainer 5969466	0.2	11.45
1 Sealed beam 55972698	0.2	36.25
1 Ring mounting 5968095	0.3	17.05
1 Bezel 10030018	0.2	20.85
1 Housing 10023411	0.8	20.20
1 Parklamp assy. 918101	0.2	19.30
1 Bulb 9428904	0.2	1.62
1 Left side marker lamp 915883	incl.	9.85
1 Support radiator 20579990	55.5	107.00
1 Baffle, lower 1002357	incl.	3.90
1 Bar lower tie 20292561	incl.	39.75
1 Reinf. bar R 20291799	incl.	11.80
1 Reinf. bar L 20291800	incl.	11.80
1 Radiator 3039665	incl.	197.00
1 Fan 22040859	incl.	24.85
1 Canister 17075831	0.3	64.05
1 Hood 10023695	1.2	234.90
1 Hood name Pontiac 527216	0.2	5.00
1 L Hood hinge (repair)	0.5	
1 Fender 10026050	2.5	160.20
1 Panel assy. inner 20610159	7.0	120.65
1 Panel front 20565161	incl.	26.13
1 Skirt 10003524	0.5	20.34
1 Rail outer front (HSLA) 20365290		

HOOD

	OPERATIONS INCLUDED ↓	ADDITIONS/EXPLANATIONS NOT INCLUDED ↓
HOOD – R&R		
Refinish hood		X See parts text
R&I hood assy	√	See parts head notes
Replace or Transfer parts attached to hood	√	Except those listed below
Mouldings/nameplates (clip type-new)	√	See parts head notes for drill and install allowance
Mouldings/nameplates (adhesive-new)		X Use one-half allowance shown in parts text
Mouldings/nameplates (adhesive-transfer)		X Add allowance to clean and retape
Stripes/decals/transfers/overlays-install		X Use allowance shown in parts text

FRONT FENDER

	OPERATIONS INCLUDED ↓	ADDITIONS/EXPLANATIONS NOT INCLUDED ↓
FRONT FENDER – R&R		
		See parts text
Refinish fender		X See parts head notes
Replace or Transfer parts attached to fender	√	Except those listed below
Bumper assembly R&I		X Unless noted otherwise in parts text
Antenna R&R		X See parts head notes for drill and install allowance
Turn indicator lamp	√	See parts head notes for cut and install allowance
Cornering lamp	√	See parts head notes for cut and install allowance
Rocker moulding		X See parts text for R&R allowance
R&R headlamps	√	If attached to panel
Aim headlamps		X If lamps attached, see parts head notes
Mouldings/nameplates (clip type-new)	√	See parts head notes for drill and install allowance
Mouldings/nameplates (adhesive - new)		X Use one-half allowance shown in parts text
Mouldings/nameplates (adhesive - transfer)		X Add allowance to clean and retape
Stripes/decals/transfers/overlays-install		X Use allowance in parts text

FIGURE 3-57   Procedure explanation hood and fender. (Courtesy of Mitchell Information Services Inc.)

FRONT INNER STRUCTURE (UNIBODY)

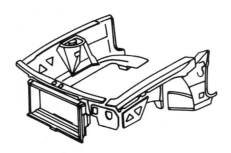

	OPERATIONS INCLUDED	ADDITIONS/EXPLANATIONS NOT INCLUDED	
RADIATOR SUPPORT – R&R			See parts text
Air Conditioning parts R&R		X	See parts text and AC Section below
Aim lamps		X	If lamps attached to support see Headlamps Section
Radiator assembly	√		Except when noted differently in the parts text
Impact absorber or mounting arm	√		If necessary to perform R&R operation
Bolted parts & assemblies		X	Example: Washer/coolant reservoir, cruise control, accessories, etc.
APRON PANEL – R&R			See parts text
Refinish panel		X	See parts head notes
R&I bumper assembly		X	See parts head notes
R&I sheet metal		X	See parts head notes
R&I engine		X	See parts head notes
R&I suspension assemblies		X	Unless stated otherwise in text labor notes
Carpet, insulation or cowl trim	√		If necessary to perform R&R operation unless stated otherwise in text labor notes.
R&I attached mechanical equipment		X	Estimate on sight
R&R upper reinforcement		X	Unless stated otherwise in text labor notes
Adjust alignment		X	See parts head notes
R&R impact absorber or mounting arm	√		If necessary to complete R&R operation
Bolted parts & assemblies		X	Example: Washer/coolant, reservoir, cruise control, accessories, etc.
STRUCTURAL RAILS – R&R			See parts text
Identify & Measure structural rails		X	Estimate on sight
R&I sheet metal		X	See parts text labor notes
R&I bumper assembly		X	
R&I engine		X	See parts head notes
R&I suspension assemblies		X	See parts head notes
R&I necessary mechanical assemblies		X	See parts text
R&I insulation or trim	√		If necessary to perform R&R operation unless stated otherwise in text labor notes
FRAME SET UP		X	Estimate necessary allowance required

FIGURE 3-58 Procedure explanation front inner structure (unibody).
(Courtesy Mitchell Information Services Inc.)

	Hours	Parts cost
(repair section 30 in. or 76 cm from rad. support location; time included in frame repair estimate)	incl.	160.00
1 Rail, upper (HSLA) 20297295	2.2	88.75
1 R Rail, inner (HSLA) 2029250		
(repair section 14 in. or 35 cm from rad. support location; time included in frame repair estimate)	incl.	135.00
1 R Front extension, rail 20298146	1.5	7.35
1 L Front extension, rail 20298147	1.5	7.35
1 Shock absorber w/strut 20049970	1.0	56.90
1 Wheel steering 1790151	0.5	87.25
1 Member assy. 14081979	4.5	394.00
1 Windshield tinted w/antenna 20037288	2.0	283.00
1 Windshield installation kit		15.00
1 Instrument panel 1003101	5.5	237.00
Undercoating time (repair)	0.5	
Undercoating material		12.50
Clean broken glass	1.0	
Wheel alignment	1.0	30.50

The impact area should be entered on Fig. 3-59, as well as the color of the vehicle. To be able to estimate for the damage that has occurred on the frame, a careful examination is required using a measuring tape or gauges and the blueprint of the particular frame. This information is written on a form such as in Fig. 3-60 and then the estimate may be written accurately on the form in Fig. 3-61.

This information can then be entered on the estimate form (Fig. 3-62). The inspection revealed that the frame had sideway in both rails in the front section. The front sections of both frame rails were mashed; the left rail was also sagged. The left inner skirt assembly and cowl had to be pulled ahead to stretch the skirt assembly, as well as to realign the door to the door frame. The right McPherson strut tower had to be pulled inward.

The left front outer frame rail had to be sectioned 30 inches (76 cm) from the position of the front of the radiator support. The right front inner rail had to be sectioned 14 inches (35 cm) from the position of the front of the radiator support. There must be a deduction of time from the flat-rate time as only part of the rails is being removed. The left rail time is reduced from 3.0 to 2.0; the right rail time is reduced from 3.0 to 1.5.

Incidental parts may have to be ordered as required when the job is done, but for this estimate they will not be considered. The painting time will cover all the panels involved, but not all the panels will be painted at the same time; therefore, there will not be overlap on every part. The underside and edge of the hood, hinge the inner panel

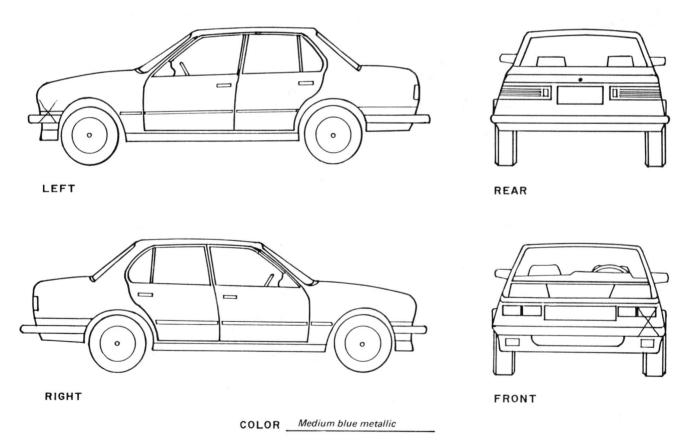

LEFT

REAR

RIGHT

FRONT

COLOR *Medium blue metallic*

FIGURE 3-59 Drawings of vehicles showing where collision damage occurred.

Body/Frame Damage Diagnosis Worksheet

Damage	Indication	Condition	
Twist: One corner of vehicle is higher than adjacent corner.	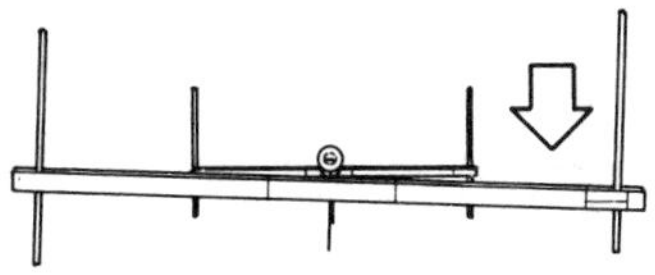	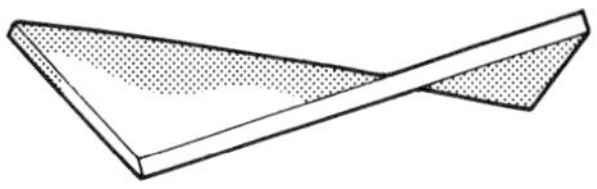	
Diamond: One side of vehicle is pushed back or forward.	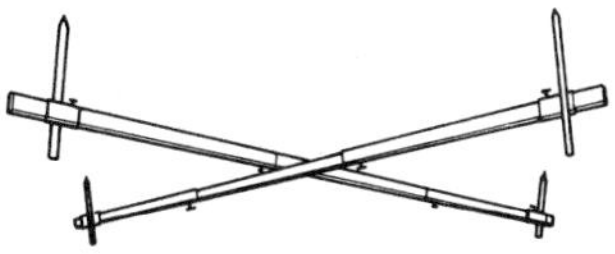	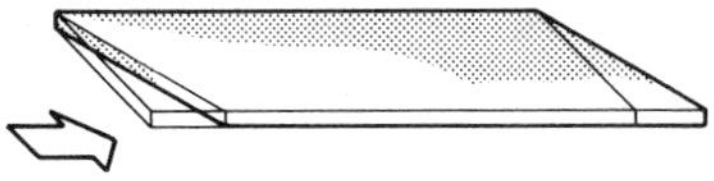	
Mash: Length of vehicle is shortened.	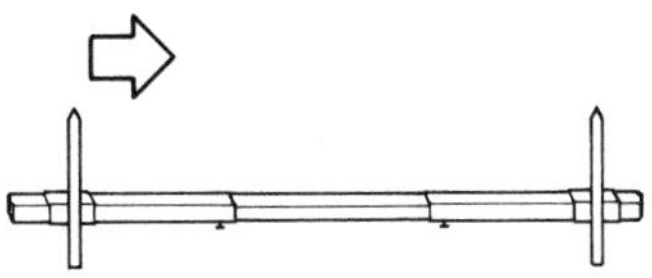	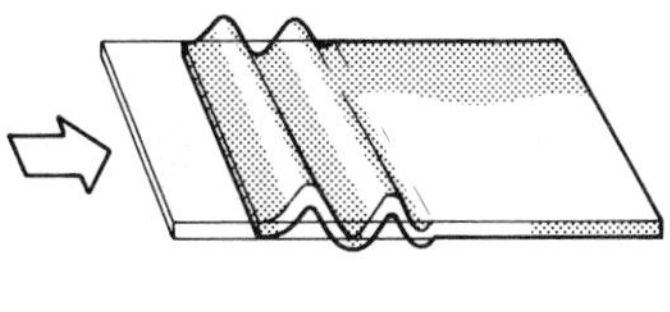	Right and left frame rail, top front, also left center of rail
Sag: Center is lower than normal.	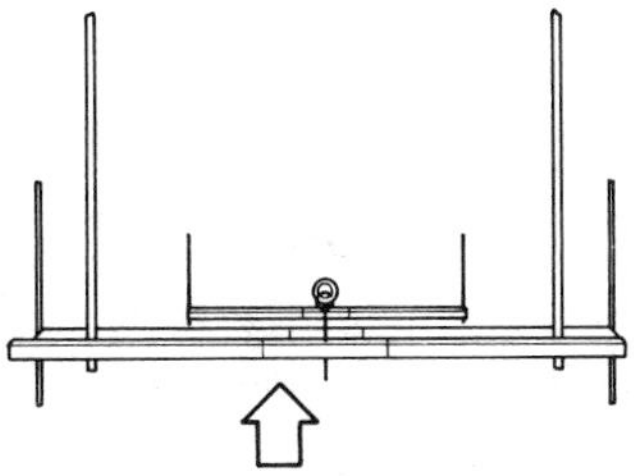	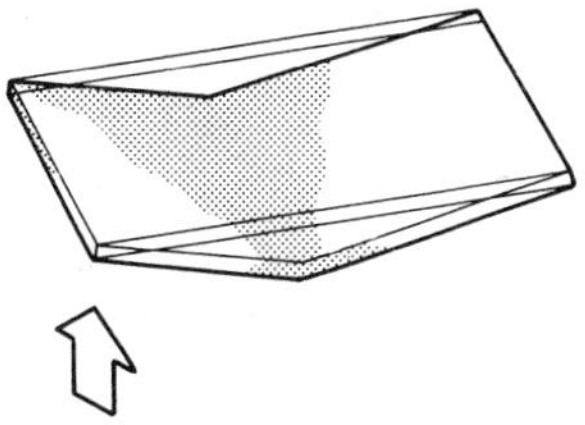	Left side, cowl area
Sideway: Front, center, or rear is pushed sideways out of alignment	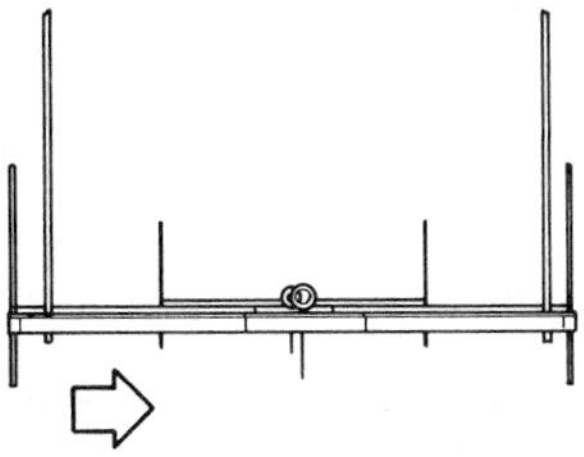	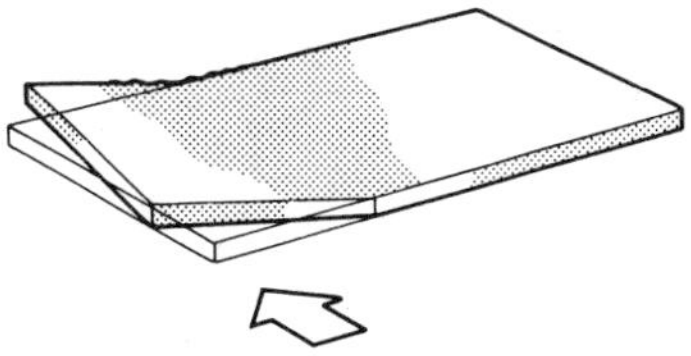	Front section, right McPherson tower
Damage occurs in this order: (1) sideway, (2) sag, (3) mash, (4) diamond, (5) twist		Make measurements and correction in this order: (1) twist, (2) diamond, (3) mash, (4) sag, (5) sideway	

FIGURE 3-60 Body/frame damage diagnosis worksheet. (Courtesy of Blackhawk, Division of Applied Power, Canada Ltd.)

Body/Frame Damage Estimating Guide

DAMAGE	AMOUNT (IN INCHES OR MILLIMETERS)	HOURS	
SIDEWAY	Sidesway both front frame rail, 1.5 in. or 38 mm.	4 anchors or tie-downs plus 2 hook-ups. 6 X 1.4 = 8.4 hours	$30.50 X 6 = $183.00
SAG	Sag left rail 1 in. or 25.4 mm pull cowl to align door	2 hook-ups 2 X 1.4 = 2.8 hours	$30.50 X 2.8 = 4 $85.40
MASH	Left and right frame rail	2 hook-ups 2 X 1.4 = 2.8 hours	$30.50 X 2.8 = $85.40
DIAMOND			
TWIST			
COSMETIC (Welding, reinforcing, etc.)	Metal repair on left and right frame rail, sectioning rails	2.5 hours 3.5 hours	$30.50 X 6 = $183.00
ADDITIONAL DAMAGE (Crossmember sag, McPherson tower correction, etc.)	Align right McPherson tower 0.5 in. or 13 mm.	1.4 hours	$30.50 X 1.4 = $42.70
TOTAL	Frame shop material	18.6 hours $4.50 X 18.6	$567.30 $ 83.70 ‾‾‾‾‾‾ $651.00

FIGURE 3-61 Body frame damage estimating guide. (Courtesy of Blackhawk, Division of Applied Power, Canada Ltd.)

assembly, and the fender edge must be painted separately, therefore there is no overlap.

Painting hood, underside and edge	0.8
Hood hinge	0.2
Front fender edge	0.5

There will be overlap when the inner panel assembly and the radiator support are painted together

Paint inner panel assembly	1.5	1.5
Radiator support	1.0	.6

There will also be overlap on some panels when the vehicle has been assembled as they are painted at the same time.

Paint time:	Bumper cover	1.5	Minus overlap:	1.5
	Bezel	0.3		0.0
	Hood outside	2.8		2.8 (major operation)
	Front fender	2.2		1.8
Spot repair left door		1.0		0.6
Cover vehicle		1.0		0.6

The instrument panel is painted as a separate operation with 25° gloss interior paint and the paint time is 1.0 hour.

Exercise 3-3

Fill in all necessary information on the estimate form concerning information as to insurance company, estimator name, adjuster name, and so on.

A bid for a 1985 Chevrolet Celebrity that was hit on the right rear corner is to be prepared. Repair will require a rear bumper, impact strip, center filler, right impact

ESTIMATOR'S REPORT

Insurance Company	A.B.C. Insurance Inc.	CLAIM NUMBER 27618

Estimate, Inspection and Location Date _____ 4/1/88 _____

ADJUSTER'S NAME	ESTIMATOR'S NAME John LaRose	DATE OF COMPLETION 4/1/88	DATE OF LOSS 2/1/88

INSURED   **VEHICLE**

NAME AND ADDRESS			
David Hebert 1103 2nd. Street N	LICENSE (POLICY) NUMBER VBC 374	GVW	MILEAGE 3514 Km.	AMOUNT OF DEDUCTIBLE $100.00
Grand Forks, North Dakota	YEAR, MAKE & MODEL 1984 Pontiac Phoenix		SERIAL NUMBER 1G2AX37B7ED 1341463

DESCRIPTION OF WORK TO BE DONE	RE-PAIR	REPLACE NEW	L.K.Q.	QTY.	PART NUMBER	PARTS COST		HRS.	LABOR COST	
Front bumper cover (Face Bar)		x		1	10023403	185	40	1.7	51	85
Deflector air		x		1	10021344	19	20	.3	9	15
Cushion impact		x		1	10028899	8	60	.5	15	25
Reinforcement (front bumper)		x		1	10023659	129	60	Inc		
Impact absorber		x		1	220216659	50	66	4.3	131	15
Grille		x		1	10023379	79	98	.4	12	20
Grille reinforcement		x		1	10023677	26	75	Inc		
Ring retainer		x		1	5969466	11	45	.2	6	10
Sealed beam		x		1	55972698	36	25	.2	6	10
Ring mounting		x		1	5968095	17	05	.3	19	20
Bezel		x		1	10030018	20	85	.2	6	10
Housing		x		1	10023411	20	20	.8	24	40
Parklamp assy		x		1	918101	19	30	.2	6	10
Bulb		x		1	9428904	1	62	.2	6	10
Left side marker lamp		x		1	915883	9	85	Inc		
Support radiator		x		1	20579990	107	00	5.5	167	75
Baffle lower		x		1	1002357	3	90	Inc		
Bar lower tie		x		1	202-2561	39	75	Inc		
Reinf. bar R		x		1	20291799	11	80	Inc		
Reinf. bar L		x		1	20291800	11	80	Inc		
Radiator		x		1	3039665	197	00	Inc		

This is purely an estimate and not a definite contract price. Owing to the impossibility of determining damage of concealed parts, we reserve the right to submit a further estimate for approval or otherwise. Prices subject to change without notice.
Authorization to Repair

I_____ the registered owner of the above described vehicle authorize the repairs to proceed.

TOTAL PARTS COST ▶	
TOTAL LABOR COST ▶	
SHOP MATERIAL	
PAINT LABOR	
PAINT MATERIAL	
SUB TOTAL	
TAX	
TOTAL COST ▶	

ONLY APPROVED ADDITIONS PAID

FIGURE 3-62 Write-in estimate forms used for Exercise 3-2.

ESTIMATOR'S REPORT

Insurance Company _____ | CLAIM NUMBER

Estimate, Inspection and Location Date _____

| ADJUSTER'S NAME | ESTIMATOR'S NAME | DATE OF COMPLETION | DATE OF LOSS |

INSURED | VEHICLE

| NAME AND ADDRESS | LICENSE (POLICY) NUMBER | GVW | MILEAGE | AMOUNT OF DEDUCTIBLE |
| | YEAR, MAKE & MODEL | | SERIAL NUMBER | |

DESCRIPTION OF WORK TO BE DONE	RE-PAIR	REPLACE NEW	REPLACE L.K.Q.	QTY.	PART NUMBER	PARTS COST		HRS.	LABOR COST	
Fan		X		1	22040859	24	85	Inc		
Canister		X		1	17075831	64	05	.3	9	15
Hood		X		1	10023695	234	90	1.2	36	60
Hood name Pontiac		X		1	527216	5	00	.2	6	10
L. hood hinge	X			1				.5	15	25
Fender		X		1	10026050	160	20	2.5	76	25
Panel assy inner		X		1	20610159	120	65	7.0	213	50
Panel front		X		1	20565161	26	13	Inc		
Skirt		X		1	10003524	20	34	.5	15	25
Rail outer front (HSLA)	X			1	20365290	160	00	Inc		
Section 30" or 76 cm. from rad support										
location, time included in frame										
Repair estimate										
Rail, upper (HSLA)		X		1	20297295	88	75	2.2	67	10
R. rail inner (HSLA)	X			1	20292550	135	00	Inc		
section 14" or 35 cm. from rad support										
Location time included in frame										
Repair estimate										
R. front extension, rail		X		1	20298146	7	35	1.5	45	75
L. front extension, rail		X		1	20298147	7	35	1.5	45	75
Shock absorber w/strut		X		1	10049970	56	90	1.0	30	50

This is purely an estimate and not a definite contract price. Owing to the impossibility of determining damage of concealed parts, we reserve the right to submit a further estimate for approval or otherwise. Prices subject to change without notice.
Authorization to Repair
_____

I_____ the registered owner of the above described vehicle authorize the repairs to proceed.

TOTAL PARTS COST ▶	
TOTAL LABOR COST ▶	
SHOP MATERIAL	
PAINT LABOR	
PAINT MATERIAL	
SUB TOTAL	
TAX	
TOTAL COST ▶	

ONLY APPROVED ADDITIONS PAID

FIGURE 3-62 (cont.)

ESTIMATOR'S REPORT

Insurance Company _____ | CLAIM NUMBER

Estimate, Inspection and Location Date _____

| ADJUSTER'S NAME | ESTIMATOR'S NAME | DATE OF COMPLETION | DATE OF LOSS |

INSURED VEHICLE

| NAME AND ADDRESS | LICENSE (POLICY) NUMBER | GVW | MILEAGE | AMOUNT OF DEDUCTIBLE |
| | YEAR, MAKE & MODEL | | SERIAL NUMBER | |

DESCRIPTION OF WORK TO BE DONE	RE-PAIR	REPLACE NEW	L.K.Q.	QTY.	PART NUMBER	PARTS COST	HRS.	LABOR COST
Wheel steering		X		1	1790151	87 25	.5	15 25
Member assy		X		1	14081979	394 00	4.5	137 25
Windshield tinted w/antenna		X		1	20037288	283 00	2.0	61 00
Windshield installation kit				1		15 00		
Instrument panel		X		1	1003101	237 00	5.5	167 75
Undercoating time	X						.5	15 25
Undercoating material						12 50		
Clean broken glass							1.0	30 50
SUBLET								
Frame repairs as per estimate						651 00		
Paint labor 11.9 hours								

This is purely an estimate and not a definite contract price. Owing to the impossibility of determining damage of concealed parts, we reserve the right to submit a further estimate for approval or otherwise. Prices subject to change without notice.
Authorization to Repair
_____

I_____ the registered owner of the above described vehicle authorize the repairs to proceed.

TOTAL PARTS COST ▶	3799 03
TOTAL LABOR COST ▶	1439 60
SHOP MATERIAL	212 40
PAINT LABOR	362 95
PAINT MATERIAL	166 60
SUB TOTAL	6027 78
TAX 6%	361 66
TOTAL COST ▶	6773 95

ONLY APPROVED ADDITIONS PAID

FIGURE 3-62 (cont.)

FIGURE 3-63 Picture shows a 1985 Celebrity hit on the right rear bumper and quarter panel.

FIGURE 3-64 Picture shows that the misalignment between quarter molding and door molding.

FIGURE 3-65 Picture shows the damage to the interior trunk floor and wheelhouse.

absorber, right lamp assembly, trunk lower panel, and panel lower finish. The rear floor pan must be straightened as well as the wheelhouse. The right frame rail is to be spliced close to the cross member over the rear axle (6.0 replace time). Replace the floor pan filler and the right quarter-panel. The damage is shown in Figs. 3-63, 3-64, and 3-65.

The student must study the pages that have the information on the parts required to obtain their numbers, the remove and replace time if applicable, the price, and any overlap (Figs. 3-66, 3-67, and 3-68). The included operations are shown on Figs. 3-69, 3-70, and 3-71; operations not included must be added on. The location of the collision must be marked on the form (Fig. 3-72).

The rear section of the vehicle has a double sidesway of $1\frac{3}{4}$ inches (82.6 mm). The time must be estimated to pull the floor, quarter-panel, and wheelhouse to proper alignment. Time must also be estimated for any welding and cosmetic repairs, plus the time allowed to remove and replace the right rear rail and to splice it on the remainder of the rail near the cross member over the rear axle. Extra time must be allowed for removal and replacement of undercoating, as well as any required painting. This specification information is entered on the form in Fig. 3-73. The estimated time is then worked out and entered in the form in Fig. 3-74A. It is also necessary to remove the gas tank to repair the frame to specifications.

The vehicle is painted with a base coat/clear coat paint system; the paint code is 22, and all replaced panels must be repainted, plus the luggage lid due to scratches on it. Figures 3-66, 3-67, and 3-68 should be consulted for the refinishing estimated time. All overlaps should be removed from the panels to be painted, but extra time must be added for clear coat time. All part numbers, estimated times, labor, and painting must be entered on the form in Fig. 3-74B.

Exercise 3-4

Prepare a bid on the vehicle in Fig. 3-75. This repair is to be paid for by the insurance company; the customer has a $200 deductible. The vehicle is a 1984 Omni that was hit on the side, causing a double sidesway, shortening of the wheel base by $3\frac{1}{2}$ inches (89 mm), and narrowing of the floor rocker to rocker panel measurement by $2\frac{1}{2}$ inches (64 mm). Some of the spot weld holding the rocker panel and the floor were broken at the area of the collision.

The right roof rail was pulled down $\frac{1}{2}$ inch (13 mm) and pushed in $\frac{3}{4}$ inch (19 mm). This caused the roof panel to be damaged at the point where the center pillar is spot welded to the roof rail. Time must be given to remove and

CELEBRITY 1982-87

QUARTER PANEL Cont'd
2 DOOR Cont'd

1-4251

1 Panel, Outer	82-85 R	20467106	**13.0**	318.60
	L	20467107	**13.5**	318.60
	86-87 R	20541130	**13.0**	318.60
	L	20541131	**13.5**	318.60
Door Fuel		20255389	**.3**	20.65
Filler, Fuel Door		20307650		19.45
Pocket, Fuel Filler		20275055		6.65
Extension, Panel				
2 to Rear Panel		20292792-3	**1.0**	16.63
3 to Back Window		20314418-9		6.13
4 Filler, Quarter Window		20255428-9		5.32
5 Panel, Wheelhouse				
Outer	R	20413552	**2.5**	67.25
	L	20255454	**2.5**	67.25
Inner	R	20447939	**2.0**	44.00
	L	20447941	**2.0**	44.00
6 Panel, Inner Lower		20307572-3	**3.5**	84.50
Pillar, Upper Lock				
7 Outer		20255385-6	**#2.5**	21.25
8 Inner		20298524-5	**#1.0**	22.20
#w/Outer Panel Removed				

INTERIOR TRIM
2 DOOR

1-4379

Panel, Trim Finish				
1 Pillar, Lock (a)	R	20539540	**.3**	42.00
	L	20539541	**.3**	45.50
2 Upper, Above Belt (a)	R	20546510	**.3**	21.50
	L	20546511	**.3**	20.48
3 Lower (a)	R	20539520	**#.4**	17.85
	L	20539521	**#.4**	23.80
#w/Rear Seat Removed				
4 Panel, Trim (b)				
82	Standard	20345416-7		d85.00
	Deluxe	20346216-7		101.00
	Custom	20346208-9		d91.00
83	Standard	20406328-9		66.50
	Custom	20385526-7		92.25
84	Standard	20406330-29		66.50
	Custom	20385526-7		92.25
85	Standard	20556838-9		64.00
	Custom	20556883-2		64.00
86-87	Standard	20589386-7		66.00
	Custom	26608652-3		
5 Arm Rest (a)	R	20539500		14.80
	L	20539501		11.80
Package Tray (b)	82	20389644		d30.50
	83-84	20410712		30.50
	85-87 exc	20546520		29.75
	w/4 Speaker Stereo	20590819		52.25
(a) Paint to Match				
(b) Order by Trim Code				

4 DOOR
SEDAN

Refinish Outside Including Pillar	**2.8**
Add to Quarter Panel R&R	
To Drill For & Install	
One Moulding	**.3**
Each Additional Moulding	**.2**
w/Vinyl Roof Cover	**2.0**
w/Tucked Vinyl Roof Cover	**5.0**

QUARTER PANEL Cont'd
4 DOOR Cont'd

1-4252

1 Panel, Outer	82-85 R	20467104	**11.5**	247.50
	L	20467105	**12.0**	247.50
	86-87 R	20541122	**11.5**	247.50
	L	20541123	**12.0**	247.50
Door, Fuel		20255389	**.3**	20.65
Filler, Fuel Door		20307650		19.45
Pocket, Fuel Filler		20275055		6.65
Extension, Panel				
2 to Rear Panel		20292792-3	**1.0**	16.63
3 to Back Window		20314418-9		6.13
4 Filler, Quarter Window		20255428-9		5.32
5 Panel, Wheelhouse				
Outer	R	20413552	**2.5**	67.25
	L	20255454	**2.5**	67.25
Inner	R	20447938	**2.0**	44.00
	L	20447940	**2.0**	44.00
6 Pillar, Upper Lock				
Inner		20433494-5	**#1.5**	39.75
#w/Outer Panel Removed				

INTERIOR TRIM
4 DOOR

1-4380

Panel, Trim				
1 Upper, Above Belt (a) (c)		20481232-3	**.3**	28.75
2 Lower (a)	R	20539510	**#.2**	11.60
	L	20398193	**#.2**	11.60
Package Tray (b)		20410712		30.50
(a) Paint to Match				
(b) Order by Trim Code				
(c) Order by Application				
#w/Rear Seat Removed				

STATION WAGON

Refinish Outside Including Pillar	**2.9**
R&R Quarter Panel	
Add to Quarter R&R	
To Drill For & Install	
One Moulding	**.3**
Each Additional Moulding	**.2**

1-4515

1 Panel, Outer	R	*20243537	**#10.0**	199.80
	L	*20243538	**#10.5**	199.80
# w/Glass Removed				
Door, Fuel		20255389	**.3**	20.65
Filler, Door		20307650		19.45
Pocket, Fuel Filler		20275055		6.65
Panel, Wheelhouse				
2 Outer		20563490-1	**2.5**	62.50
3 Inner	R	20324933	**2.0**	74.00
	L	20447940	**2.0**	44.00
Pillars Rear - See Rear Body				
Rail, Belt		20243547-8		36.50
Pillar, Lock				

QUARTER PANEL Cont'd
STATION WAGON Cont'd

4 Outer Upper		20243555-6	**#3.0**	67.00
5 Inner Upper		20243551-2	**#1.5**	35.25
#w/Outer Panels Removed				
6 Pocket, Tail Lamp		20265954-5		21.45

INTERIOR TRIM

Refinish	
Finish Panel .... Right	**.5**
Left	**.7**
Spare Cover Panel	**.5**
Pillar & Side Roof Panel	**.4**
Pillar Rear Panel	**.4**

1-4461

Panel, Finish (a)				
1 Right		20540993	**#.3**	33.75
2 Left		20541018	**#.4**	66.00
#w/Seat Cushion Removed				
3 Panel, Spare Cover (a)	R	20540768		47.75
4 Retainer, Trim Panel	exc	20540653	**#.2**	10.90
	w/Swing Out Glass	20540788-9	**#.2**	12.90
#w/Trim Panel Removed				
5 Panel, Pillar & Side Roof (a)		20540758-9	**.2**	9.15
6 Panel, Pillar Rear (a)	R	20467482	**.4**	30.50
	L	20541039	**.4**	30.50
(a) Paint to Match				
7 Panel, Pillar Finish		20541058-9		11.20

QUARTER MOULDING

1-4265

1 Moulding, Pillar Finish				
4 Door		20433490-1		5.70
Nameplate, Pillar	"CS"	14044267		4.00
	"CL"	14044268		3.00
2 Moulding, Wheel Opening				
Coupe/Sedan	82-83	20496086-7	**.3**	12.47
	84-87 Black	20499276-7	**.3**	15.35
Wagon	Black	20499280-1	**.3**	19.53
	Chrome	20499280-1	**.3**	19.53
3 Moulding, Side				
Front	2 Door 82-83¶	20410838	**.2**	28.80
	84-87 Black/Red¶	20499282-3	**.2**	28.80
	White/Red	20500223-4	**.2**	28.80
	White	52356556	**.2**	
	4 Door 82-83¶	20410839	**#.2**	18.86
	84-87 except	20499078-9	**.2**	18.86
	White/Red R	20500219	**.2**	18.86
	L	20500218	**.2**	
	Wagon except R R	20475412	**.2**	18.86
	L	20498913	**.2**	18.86
Rear	White/Red	20500221-2	**.2**	28.80
	82-83¶	20410838	**#.2**	28.80
84-86 - See Rear Bumper				
¶Adhesive - Cut to Fit				
# R&R Front and Rear .3				
Transfer, Woodgrain¶		12322035		79.25
Cut as Required				
Moulding, Woodgrain		20499306-7		27.90
Stripe Tape - See Front Fender				

QUARTER GLASS
2 DOOR

Refinish Outside Including Pillar	**3.1**
Add to Quarter Panel R&R	
To Drill for & Install	
One Moulding	**.3**
Each Additional Moulding	**.2**
w/Vinyl Roof Cover	**2.0**
w/Tucked Vinyl	**5.0**

FIGURE 3-66 Quarter panel time and price information. (Courtesy Mitchell Information Services Inc.)

CELEBRITY 1982-87

QUARTER GLASS Cont'd

Tinted	20264644-5		2.9	105.00
NAGS	T Q6661-2		2.9	353.65
w/Moveable Window				
Front	Clear	20369826-7	#2.5	108.00
	NAGS	C Q6663-4	#2.5	
	Tinted	20369828-9	#2.5	193.00
	NAGS	T Q6663-4	#2.5	663.05
Rear (Vent)	Clear 84	20370676-7	#2.5	29.25
	85-87	20598902-3	#2.5	67.75
	NAGS	C Q6665-6	#2.5	
	Tinted 84	20370678-9	#2.5	31.75
	85-87	20598904-5	#2.5	31.75
	NAGS	T Q6665-6	#2.5	663.05
#R&R Complete One Side				
Latch, Vent On Body	20541164			⁻8.10
Moulding, Reveal Lower				
2 Door	Bright	20294861-2		25.00
	Black	20434078-9		25.00
4 Door Sedan	Bright	20586444-5		11.05
	Black	20586446-7		25.00
Wagon		20314392-3		30.25
Retainer, Reveal Moulding				
2 Door		20294873-4		9.20
4 Door Sedan		20294875-6		3.80
Wagon		20312276-7		10.70
Hinge, Qtr Glass		20368120		10.85

LUGGAGE LID

Refinish Outside		2.7
Add For Underside		.8
Refinish Hinge		.2
R&I Lid Assembly		.5
Add To Lid R&R		
To Drill For & Install Luggage Rack		2.5

1-29

1 **Lid, Luggage**	82-84	20293094	1.2	263.70
	85-87	20565936	1.2	270.00
Name	"Chevrolet" Gray	20260428	.2	8.50
	Red	20481576	.2	8.50
	"Diesel" 82	20084367	.2	8.00
	83-85	20405712	.2	8.00
	"CL" Black/Gray	20429460	.2	4.00
	Red	20481580	.2	4.00
	"2.5 FI" Black/Red	20481578	.2	5.75
	Black/Chrome	20467622	.2	5.75
	"2.8 V6"	20465450	.2	6.00
	"2.8 Multi-Port FI" exc	20518965	.2	5.50
	Black/Red	20518994	.2	5.50
	"HO-V6" Black/Chrome	20474696	.2	6.00
	Black/Red	20515958	.2	6.00
Cylinder Kit - Uncoded 82		3981844	.3	4.70
	83-87	3910570	.3	■6.15
Latch	82-84	20166276	.3	13.60
	85	20513752	.3	11.15
	86-87	20513755	.3	11.15
Striker, Latch	82-84	20356039		2.75
	85-87	20564901		7.65
2 **Hinge**	(2)	20356018	#.8	13.60
#w/Lid & Upper Panel Removed				
R&R Both 1.2				
Box, Hinge		20356012-3		12.30
3 **Rod, Hinge Torque**		20356020-1		5.65
Weatherstrip		20490800	.6	28.00
Stripe Tape - See Front Fender				

REAR/LIFT GATE

Refinish Outside		2.9
Add For Underside		.8
Refinish Hinge		.2
R&I Gate Assembly		.8
Add to Gate Shell or Repair Panel R&R		
w/Wiper		.5
w/Electric Lock		.3

SHEET METAL

Gate Shell exc	20597664	#4.0	445.00
w/Quarter Vent ★	20622292	#4.0	471.00
#Includes R&R Glass			
Panel, Repair¶	20622290	#5.0	171.00
¶Included in Gate Shell			
#Includes R&I Gate & Glass			

EXTERIOR TRIM

Moulding, Window Frame			
Upper	w/o Wiper exc	20547552	18.20
	Eurosport	20547554	17.55
	w/Wiper exc	20444126	19.55
	Eurosport	20547553	18.20
Side	exc	20367744-5	46.25
	Eurosport	20491528-9	21.45
Lower	exc	20295449	17.85

REAR/LIFT GATE Cont'd

EXTERIOR TRIM Cont'd

	Eurosport	20491524		17.85
Transfer, Woodgrain¶		12322035		79.25
Cut as Required				
Moulding, Woodgrain		20499426-7		20.95
Name	"Chevrolet" Gray	20260428	.2	8.50
	Red	20481576	.2	8.50
	"2.5 FI" Black/Red	20481578	.2	5.75
	Black/Chrome	20467622	.2	5.75
	"HO-V6"	20474696	.2	6.00
Pocket, License Plate		20024280	.4	55.75

INTERIOR TRIM

Refinish	Lower Finish Panel	.8
	Upper Panel	.4

1-4465

1 **Panel, Lower Finish** (a) exc		20540833		.4	51.00
	w/Qtr Vent	20540773		.4	42.75
2 **Panel, Upper** (a)		20575056		.2	25.50
(a) Paint to Match					
3 **Moulding, Upper Finish**	R	20540878		.3	13.15
	L	20540879		.3	13.15

GLASS & PARTS

1-4466

1 **Glass, Rear Gate**					
w/o Wiper	Clear	20247730		1.2	347.00
	NAGS	C B6668		1.2	550.55
	Tinted	20247731		1.2	320.00
	NAGS	H TB6672		1.2	
	Heated	20247732		1.4	375.00
	NAGS	H B6668		1.4	
w/Wiper	Clear	20448434		1.2	225.00
	NAGS	C B6670		1.2	
	Tinted	20448435		1.2	241.00
	NAGS	T B6670		1.2	603.20
	Heated	20448436		1.4	458.00
	NAGS	H B6669		1.4	
2 **Hinge, Gate**					
Body Side		20298586		#1.2	2.65
w/Gate Removed					
3 **Strap, Hinge** Gate Side		20298588		#.4	4.85
# w/Gate Removed					
4 **Supt, Counter Balance¶**		20371024			18.30
¶Order by Application					
5 **Hinge, Glass** exc		20509466-7		#.2	6.55
	w/Air Deflector	20509468-9		#.2	6.85
# w/Glass Removed					
6 **Handle, Glass**		20295389		.2	2.20
7 **Striker, Glass**		20246943		.2	7.65
8 **Gasket, Handle**		20246960			.99
9 **Support, Glass¶**		20246958		.2	18.30
¶Order by Application					
10 **Lock, Glass & Cam**		20482218			28.50
11 **Latch, Gate**		20369896		.2	54.00
12 **Striker, Latch**		20547076		.2	8.30
13 **Actuator, Latch**		20246964			17.15
14 **Support, Actuator**		20482217			9.95
15 **Solenoid, Release**		20356657		#.3	34.50
w/Trim Panel Removed					
16 **Weatherstrip, Glass**		20524927			27.00

REAR/LIFT GATE Cont'd

GLASS & PARTS Cont'd

17 **Lace, Opening**		20480201		12.40
Weatherstrip, on Body		20510014		41.00
18 **Deflector, Air**		20446061	#1.2	52.25
# Included in R&R Glass				
Blade Assembly		20332648	.2	■8.50
Arm, Wiper	82-84	20360494	.2	17.45
	85-87	20580465	.2	16.80
Motor, Wiper		22039700	#.5	106.20
#w/Trim Panel Removed				
Pump, Washer		22049369		19.65
Reservoir	exc	25515684	.3	4.65
	w/Hi Perf V6	25523760	.3	8.60
Nozzle	82-84	20360490	.2	3.30
	85-87	20580464	.2	4.45

REAR SUSPENSION

R&I Axle Suspension Assembly	2.0

1-1398

1 **Drum, Brake**	Standard	25516196	.5	72.75
	HD	25516194	.5	69.25
	Wagon	25518892	.5	69.25
2 **Plate, Backing**	82-84	18011623-2	1.0	27.75
	85 R	18011964	1.0	27.75
	L	18011567	1.0	27.75
	86-87	18011568-7	1.0	27.75
Hose, Brake		9767287	#.6	7.30
#Includes Bleed Brakes, Ea Addtl .3				
3 **Spring, Coil** (a)		10019635	.8	36.25
(a) Order by Application				
4 **Insulator, Spring**	Upper	10019319		2.25
	Lower	10019321		2.15
5 **Shock Absorber**	exc	4993583	.5	33.90
	w/Special Performance	22046415	.5	25.50
	Air Lift	22046412-1	.6	79.50
6 **Support & Axle**		10017943	3.5	404.08
Hub & Bearing	exc	7466916	.6	170.25
	w/HD Brakes, Wagon 82-83	7466918	.6	171.15
	84-87	7466926	.6	■181.36
7 **Bracket, Arm Mounting** 82 R		10026571	#.3	13.95
	L	10022919	#.3	13.95
	83	10026571-2	#.3	13.95
	84-87	10029094-3	#.3	5.45
#w/Support Axle Removed				
8 **Bar & Bushings, Track**		10019317	.5	22.70

FUEL TANK

Tank Time Does Not Include Drain Fuel

Tank, Fuel	Gas	22515512	1.1	134.00
	Diesel	22515513	1.1	134.00
Cap, Filler	Gas	22525302		■6.98
	Diesel	22506731		7.70
Neck, Filler	Gas except	22514892		24.20
	Canada	22514893		25.75
	Diesel	22514893		25.75
Baffle, Neck		22512169		4.15
Hose, Filler		22511405		15.35
Gauge, Tank Unit				
Gas Eng	4 Cyl except	25003275	.9	■158.88
	Canada	25090481	.9	106.30
	V6	25003149	.9	77.85
Diesel	w/Filter	25003150	.9	135.70
	w/o Filter	25004275	.9	114.75
Label/Decal				
"Unleaded Fuel Only"		20337916	.2	.82
"Diesel Fuel Only"		NA		

REAR BODY

COUPE/SEDAN

Refinish	Lower Panel	1.5
	Lower Finish Panel	1.5

FIGURE 3-67 Luggage lid and fuel tank time and price information.
(Courtesy Mitchell Information Services Inc.)

CELEBRITY 1982-87

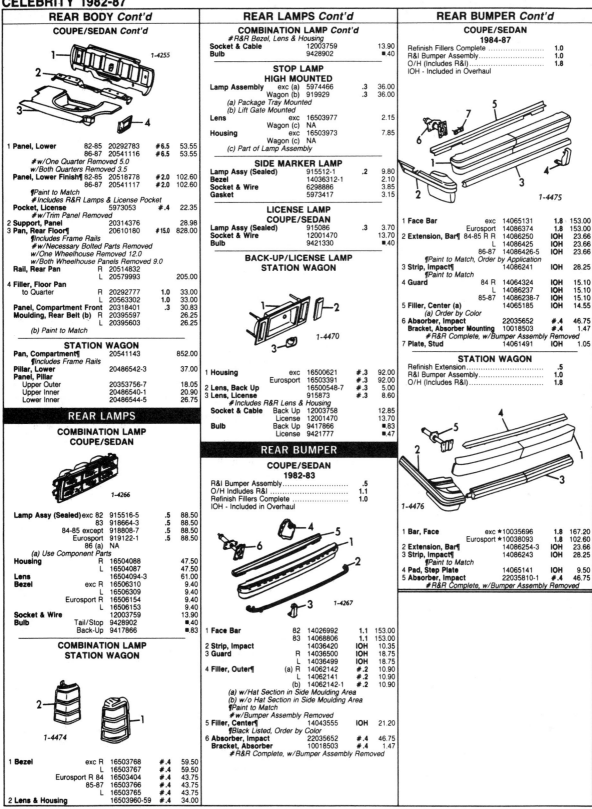

REAR BODY *Cont'd*			
COUPE/SEDAN *Cont'd*			

1-4255

1 Panel, Lower	82-85	20292783	#6.5	53.55
	86-87	20541116	#6.5	53.55
#w/One Quarter Removed 5.0				
w/Both Quarters Removed 3.5				
Panel, Lower Finish¶	82-85	20518778	#2.0	102.60
	86-87	20541117	#2.0	102.60
¶Paint to Match				
# Includes R&R Lamps & License Pocket				
Pocket, License		5973053	#.4	22.35
#w/Trim Panel Removed				
2 Support, Panel		20314376		28.98
3 Pan, Rear Floor¶		20610180	#15.0	828.00
¶Includes Frame Rails				
#w/Necessary Bolted Parts Removed				
w/One Wheelhouse Removed 12.0				
w/Both Wheelhouse Panels Removed 9.0				
Rail, Rear Pan	R	20514832		
	L	20579993		205.00
4 Filler, Floor Pan				
to Quarter	R	20292777	1.0	33.00
	L	20563302	1.0	33.00
Panel, Compartment Front		20318401	.3	30.83
Moulding, Rear Belt (b)	R	20395597		26.25
	L	20395603		26.25
(b) Paint to Match				

STATION WAGON			
Pan, Compartment¶	20541143		852.00
¶Includes Frame Rails			
Pillar, Lower	20486542-3		37.00
Panel, Pillar			
Upper Outer	20353756-7		18.05
Upper Inner	20486540-1		20.90
Lower Inner	20486544-1		26.75

REAR LAMPS

COMBINATION LAMP
COUPE/SEDAN

1-4266

Lamp Assy (Sealed)	exc 82	915516-5	.5	88.50
	83	918664-3	.5	88.50
	84-85 except	918808-7	.5	88.50
	Eurosport	919122-1	.5	88.50
	86 (a)	NA		
(a) Use Component Parts				
Housing	R	16504088		47.50
	L	16504087		47.50
Lens		16504094-3		61.00
Bezel	exc R	16506310		9.40
	L	16506309		9.40
	Eurosport R	16506154		9.40
	L	16506153		9.40
Socket & Wire		12003759		13.90
Bulb	Tail/Stop	9428902	■.40	
	Back-Up	9417866	■.83	

COMBINATION LAMP
STATION WAGON

1-4474

1 Bezel	exc R	16503768	#.4	59.50
	L	16503767	#.4	59.50
	Eurosport R 84	16503404	#.4	43.75
	85-87	16503766	#.4	43.75
	L	16503765	#.4	43.75
2 Lens & Housing		16503960-59	#.4	34.00

REAR LAMPS *Cont'd*			
COMBINATION LAMP *Cont'd*			
#R&R Bezel, Lens & Housing			
Socket & Cable	12003759		13.90
Bulb	9428902		■.40

STOP LAMP
HIGH MOUNTED

Lamp Assembly	exc (a)	5974466	.3	36.00
	Wagon (b)	919929	.3	36.00
(a) Package Tray Mounted				
(b) Lift Gate Mounted				
Lens	exc	16503977		2.15
	Wagon (c)	NA		
Housing	exc	16503973		7.85
	Wagon (c)	NA		
(c) Part of Lamp Assembly				

SIDE MARKER LAMP

Lamp Assy (Sealed)	915512-1	.2	9.80
Bezel	14036312-1		2.10
Socket & Wire	6298886		3.85
Gasket	5973417		3.15

LICENSE LAMP
COUPE/SEDAN

Lamp Assy (Sealed)	915086	.3	3.70
Socket & Wire	12001470		13.70
Bulb	9421330		■.40

BACK-UP/LICENSE LAMP
STATION WAGON

1-4470

1 Housing	exc	16500621	#.3	92.00
	Eurosport	16503391	#.3	92.00
2 Lens, Back Up		16500548-7	#.3	5.00
3 Lens, License		915873	#.3	8.60
# Includes R&R Lens & Housing				
Socket & Cable	Back Up	12003758		12.85
	License	12001470		13.70
Bulb	Back Up	9417866		■.83
	License	9421777		■.47

REAR BUMPER

COUPE/SEDAN
1982-83

R&I Bumper Assembly		.5
O/H Indludes R&I		1.1
Refinish Fillers Complete		1.0
IOH - Included in Overhaul		

1-4267

1 Face Bar	82	14026992	1.1	153.00
	83	14068806	1.1	153.00
2 Strip, Impact		14036420	IOH	10.35
3 Guard	R	14036500	IOH	18.75
	L	14036499	IOH	18.75
4 Filler, Outer¶	(a) R	14062142	#.2	10.90
	L	14062141	#.2	10.90
	(b)	14062142-1	#.2	10.90
(a) w/Hat Section in Side Moulding Area				
(b) w/o Hat Section in Side Moulding Area				
¶Paint to Match				
#w/Bumper Assembly Removed				
5 Filler, Center¶		14043555	IOH	21.20
¶Black Listed, Order by Color				
6 Absorber, Impact		22035652	#.4	46.75
Bracket, Absorber		10018503	#.4	1.47
#R&R Complete, w/Bumper Assembly Removed				

REAR BUMPER *Cont'd*		
COUPE/SEDAN		
1984-87		
Refinish Fillers Complete		1.0
R&I Bumper Assembly		1.0
O/H (Includes R&I)		1.8
IOH - Included in Overhaul		

1-4475

1 Face Bar	exc	14065131	1.8	153.00
	Eurosport	14086374	1.8	153.00
2 Extension, Bar¶	84-85 R R	14086250	IOH	23.66
	L	14086425	IOH	23.66
	86-87	14086426-5	IOH	23.66
¶Paint to Match, Order by Application				
3 Strip, Impact¶		14086241	IOH	28.25
¶Paint to Match				
4 Guard	84 R	14064324	IOH	15.10
	L	14086237	IOH	15.10
	85-87	14086238-7	IOH	15.10
5 Filler, Center (a)		14065185	IOH	14.55
(a) Order by Color				
6 Absorber, Impact		22035652	#.4	46.75
Bracket, Absorber Mounting		10018503	#.4	1.47
#R&R Complete, w/Bumper Assembly Removed				
7 Plate, Stud		14061491	IOH	1.05

STATION WAGON

Refinish Extension		.5
R&I Bumper Assembly		1.0
O/H (Includes R&I)		1.8

1-4476

1 Bar, Face	exc ★10035696		1.8	167.20
	Eurosport ★10038093		1.8	102.60
2 Extension, Bar¶		14086254-3	IOH	23.66
3 Strip, Impact¶		14086243	IOH	28.25
¶Paint to Match				
4 Pad, Step Plate		14065141	IOH	9.50
5 Absorber, Impact		22035810-1	#.4	46.75
#R&R Complete, w/Bumper Assembly Removed				

Allowances Shown Are for Replacement With New OEM Undamaged Parts on New Undamaged Vehicles.　　GM

FIGURE 3-68 Rear body and bumper time and price information. (Courtesy Mitchell Information Services Inc.)

QUARTER PANEL

	OPERATIONS INCLUDED	ADDITIONS/EXPLANATIONS NOT INCLUDED
QUARTER OUTER PANEL – R&R		
Refinish		X See parts text / See parts head notes
		If glass interferes with installation
Back window & moulding	√	
Headliner at quarter – loosen	√	
Convertible top at quarter	√	
Rear seat R&I	√	
Parcel shelf trim R&I	√	
Quarter trim R&I	√	
Luggage compartment trim R&I		X Add allowance necessary for R&I
		If close to weld
Sill plates R&I	√	
Door striker plate R&I	√	
Rear lamps R&I	√	If necessary to perform R&R operation
Fuel tank assembly R&I		X Except when noted differently in the parts text
Quarter inner panels R&R		X See parts text
Rear bumper assembly R&I	√	Except where noted differently in the parts text.
Bumper parts R&R		X Use allowance in parts text, or for O/H use O/H
		allowance less R&I allowance

	OPERATIONS INCLUDED	ADDITIONS/EXPLANATIONS NOT INCLUDED
QUARTER OUTER PANEL – R&I (Cont'd)		
Filler panel/stone deflector	√	Unless noted otherwise in text labor notes
Rear lower valance	√	Unless noted otherwise in text labor notes
Quarter glass or glass assembly R&I	√	Unless noted otherwise in text
Channels on glass R&I		X Add .2 for lower channel. Add .3 for lower and
		upper channel
Quarter panel with roof removed		X Use allowance in parts text less 3.0 hours
		unless noted otherwise
		See parts head notes for drill and install allowance
Mouldings/nameplates (clip type-new)	√	
Mouldings/nameplates (adhesive – new)		X Use one-half allowance shown in parts text
Mouldings/nameplates (adhesive – transfer)		X Add allowance to clean and retape
Stripes/decals/transfers/overlays – install		X Use allowance in parts text
QUARTER OUTER PANEL SECTION (NON-HSLA) – R&R		X See parts text for guide allowance and use same
Horizontal cut at belt and/or		Procedure Explanation as Quarter Outer
through quarter window opening		Panel R&R except as listed below
Back glass		X Cut below back window
Quarter glass or glass assembly		X See parts text labor notes

FIGURE 3-69 Quarter-panel, included operations (Courtesy of Mitchell Information Services Inc.)

REAR BODY

	OPERATIONS INCLUDED ⬇	ADDITIONS/EXPLANATIONS NOT INCLUDED ⬇
REAR BODY LOWER PANEL – R&R		See parts text
Refinish		X	See parts text notes
Rear bumper assembly R&I	√		
Bumper parts R&R		X	Use allowance in parts text except for O/H use O/H allowance less R&I allowance
Impact absorbers or mounting arm	√		If necessary to perform R&R operation
Filler panel/stone deflector	√		Except when stated otherwise in text
Rear lower valance	√		Except when noted otherwise in text
Rear lamps R&I	√		If necessary to perform R&R operation
Luggage compartment trim		X	Add allowance necessary to R&I
Rear gravel shield	√		If necessary to perform R&R operation
Weatherstrip in channel on lower panel	√		
Fuel tank R&I		X	Except when noted differently in the parts text
Rear body panel with quarter removed			See parts labor notes
Cylinder & key R&R	√		
Cylinder & key – Recode		X	Add local charge to recode
Latch	√		If attached to Rear Body Panel
Striker	√		If attached to Rear Body Panel
Mouldings/nameplates (clip type-new)	√		See parts head notes for drill and install allowance
Mouldings/nameplates (adhesive-new)		X	Use one-half allowance shown in parts text
Mouldings/nameplates (adhesive-transfer)		X	Add allowance to clean and retape
Stripes/decals/transfers/overlays – install		X	Use allowance in parts text
REAR FLOOR PAN – R&R			See parts text
Identify & measure		X	Estimate on sight
R&I Sheet metal		X	See parts text labor notes
R&I bumper assembly		X	
R&I engine (mid/rear)		X	See parts head notes
R&I suspension assemblies		X	See parts head notes
R&I necessary mechanical assemblies		X	See parts text
R&I insulation or trim		X	Unless noted otherwise in text
STRUCTURAL RAILS – R&R			See parts text
Identify & measure		X	Estimate on sight
R&I sheet metal		X	See parts text labor notes
R&I bumper assembly		X	
R&I engine (mid/rear)		X	See parts head notes
R&I suspension assemblies		X	See parts head notes
R&I necessary mechanical assemblies		X	See parts text
R&I insulation or trim		X	Unless noted otherwise in text
FRAME SET UP		X	Estimate necessary allowance required

FIGURE 3-70 Rear-body included operations (Courtesy of Mitchell Information Services Inc.)

	OPERATIONS INCLUDED	ADDITIONS/EXPLANATIONS NOT INCLUDED
ASSEMBLY – R&I		
Remove from frame	√	See parts head notes
Remove from impact absorber or mounting arm	√	Handle as a unit
Reinstall same assembly	√	Handle as a unit
Adjust alignment to vehicle	√	
ASSEMBLY – O/H		
Assembly R&I	√	See parts head notes
Disassemble & Replace damaged parts	√	Only parts attached to assembly
Assemble & Install	√	
Adjust alignment to vehicle	√	
Impact absorber or mounting arm		X	See parts text for R&R allowance

FIGURE 3-71 Rear-bumper included operations. (Courtesy of Mitchell Information Services Inc.)

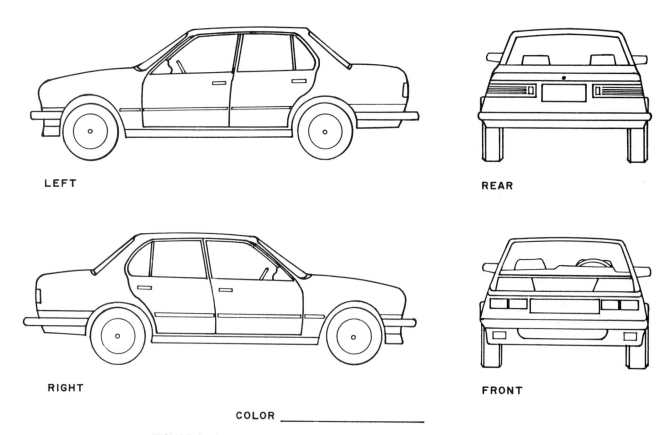

LEFT

REAR

RIGHT

FRONT

COLOR _____

FIGURE 3-72 Drawings of vehicles showing where collision damage occurred.

Body/Frame Damage Diagnosis Worksheet

Damage	Indication	Condition	
Twist: One corner of vehicle is higher than adjacent corner.	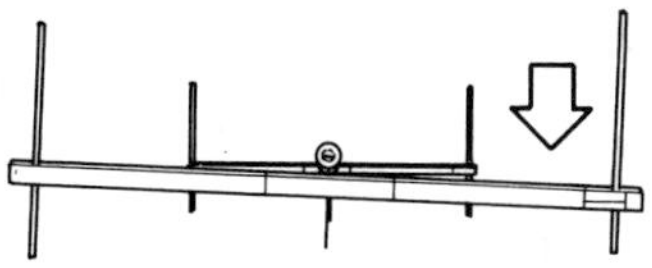	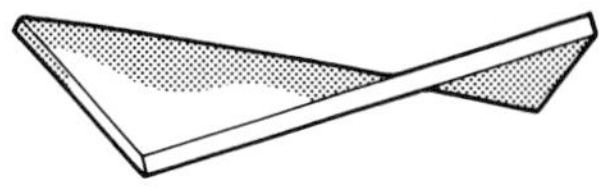	
Diamond: One side of vehicle is pushed back or forward.	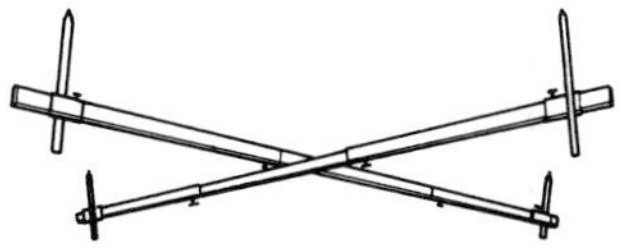	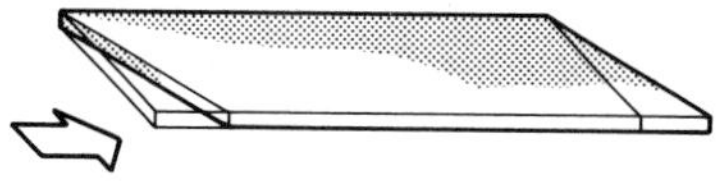	
Mash: Length of vehicle is shortened.	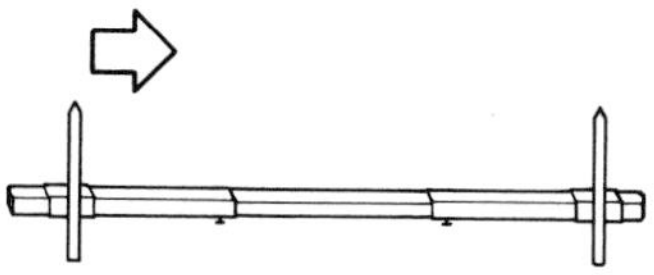	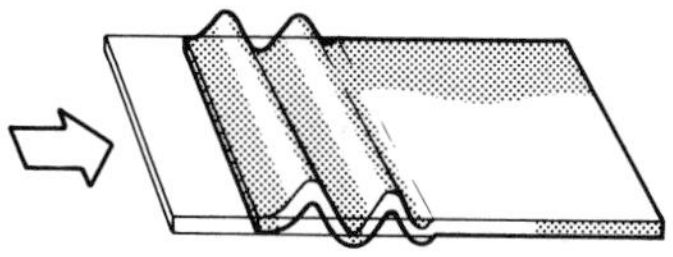	
Sag: Center is lower than normal.	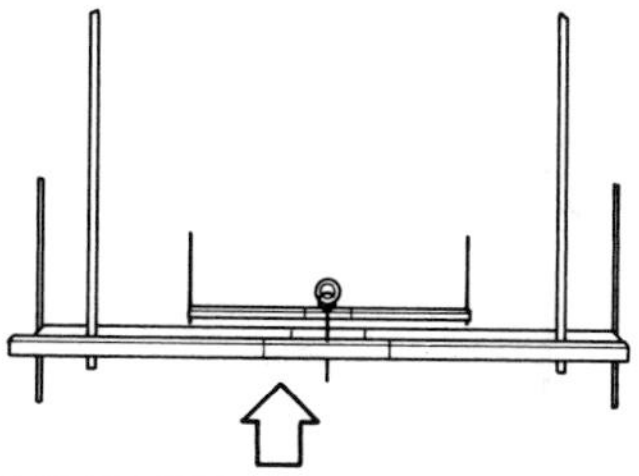	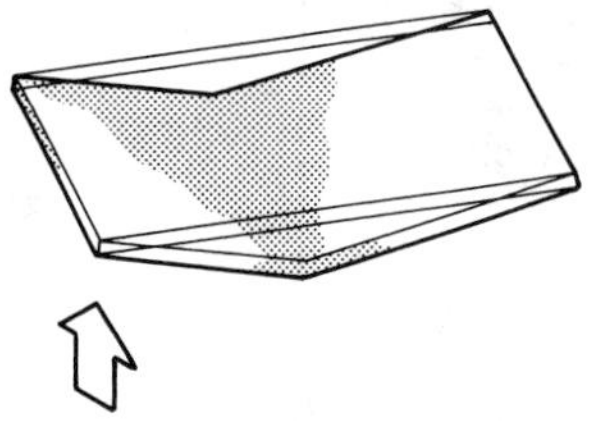	
Sidesway: Front, center, or rear is pushed sideways out of alignment	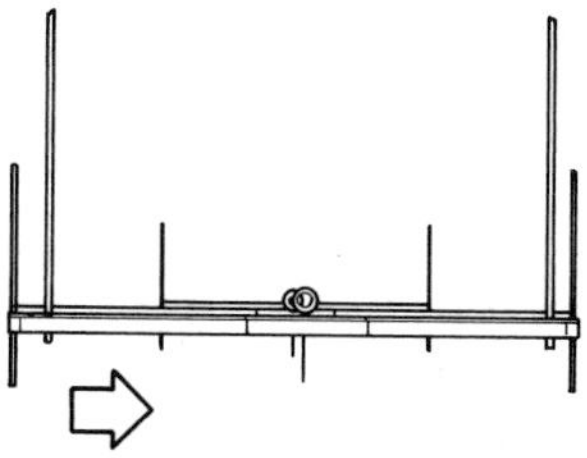	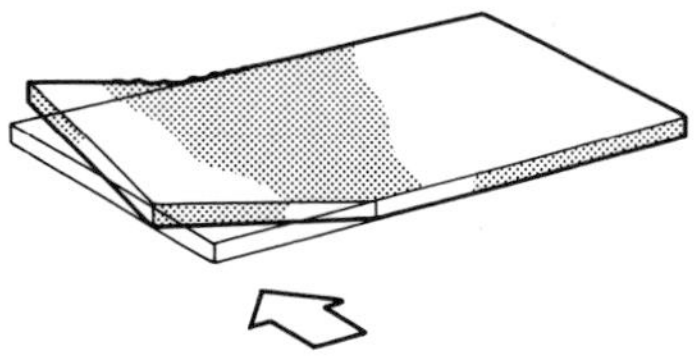	
Damage occurs in this order: (1) sidesway, (2) sag, (3) mash, (4) diamond, (5) twist	Make measurements and correction in this order: (1) twist, (2) diamond, (3) mash, (4) sag, (5) sidesway		

FIGURE 3-73 Body/frame damage diagnosis worksheet. (Courtesy of Black Hawk, Division of Applied Power, Canada Ltd.)

BODY/FRAME DAMAGE ESTIMATING GUIDE

DAMAGE	AMOUNT (IN INCHES OR MILLIMETERS)	HOURS	
SIDEWAY			
SAG			
MASH			
DIAMOND			
TWIST			
COSMETIC (Welding, reinforcing, etc.)			
ADDITIONAL DAMAGE (Crossmember sag, McPherson tower correction, etc.)			
TOTAL			

FIGURE 3-74a. Body frame damage estimating guide. (Courtesy of Blackhawk, Division of Applied Power, Canada Ltd.)

ESTIMATOR'S REPORT

Insurance Company _____

CLAIM NUMBER

Estimate, Inspection and Location Date _____

ADJUSTER'S NAME	ESTIMATOR'S NAME	DATE OF COMPLETION	DATE OF LOSS

INSURED   VEHICLE

NAME AND ADDRESS	LICENSE (POLICY) NUMBER	GVW	MILEAGE	AMOUNT OF DEDUCTIBLE
	YEAR, MAKE & MODEL		SERIAL NUMBER	

DESCRIPTION OF WORK TO BE DONE	RE-PAIR	REPLACE NEW	L.K.Q.	QTY.	PART NUMBER	PARTS COST	HRS.	LABOR COST

This is purely an estimate and not a definite contract price. Owing to the impossibility of determining damage of concealed parts, we reserve the right to submit a further estimate for approval or otherwise. Prices subject to change without notice.
Authorization to Repair _____

I_____ the registered owner of the above described vehicle authorize the repairs to proceed.

TOTAL PARTS COST ▶	
TOTAL LABOR COST ▶	
SHOP MATERIAL	
PAINT LABOR	
PAINT MATERIAL	
SUB TOTAL	
TAX	
TOTAL COST ▶	

ONLY APPROVED ADDITIONS PAID

FIGURE 3-74b. Write-in estimate form used for Exercise 3-3.

FIGURE 3-75 Picture of a vehicle involved in a side collision.

replace the seats, headliner, and any interior trim that would be in the way of the repair operations (3.5 hours).

Alignment of the roof panel and roof rail should be done at the same time that the other pulls are applied to the center post, rocker panel, and floor area. Estimate alignment time and also the metal repair time and enter on the estimate form.

The estimated time and prices in Figs. 3-76, 3-77, and 3-78 are given for information and comparison costs. The student should make two estimates, one estimate using new parts and the other to be with used parts, which will be the method of repair to be used.

To keep the price of repairs at a reasonable level, it was possible to locate a used rocker panel, center post assembly, and front door for the sum of $350; a 20% markup is to be added for the charge-out rate. The procedure explanation in Figs. 3-79 and 3-80 shows the included operations and additions for procedures not included that would apply if the vehicle were repaired with new parts. The rear door was not damaged extensively; a small dent and the window frame bent inward were all that had to be repaired.

Since used parts are to be used, the procedure will be as shown in Fig. 3-81. The form (Fig. 3-82) should be filled in as to impact point, and the color of the vehicle should be entered on the blank space provided for this information. The damage diagnosis provided information for the required repair of the damage to the frame side, the rail which in this case is the rocker panel in unitized construction, as well as other damages should be entered on (Fig. 3-83); from this the body/frame estimating form (Fig. 3-84) may be used to estimate the amount of time and money required to pull and align the damage. All required times, as well as the costs, are entered on the write-in estimate form (Fig. 3-85).

The two doors and rocker panel must have gravel guard applied to them, which will increase the time slightly. Time must be given for the removal and replacement of undercoating. Then the time must be added from the information provided on the amount of refinishing time required to paint the damaged parts. Be careful to remove any overlap that might be present.

Exercise 3-5

Prepare an estimate for a customer; the repairs will not be paid for by an insurance company but by the customer. The vehicle is a 1985 Jimmy 4 × 4 that was involved in a collision. Fill in the form (Fig. 3-96) that has the pictures of vehicles and show where the damage occurred. From Fig. 3-86, 3-87, and 3-88, prepare the estimate (Fig. 3-96); the remove and replacement time, the refinish time, and part numbers and prices are available in Figs. 3-89 through 3-95.

There is no frame damage; the hood edge and left quarter front edge must be repaired and the left front fender replaced, after market (see Appendix C). The front bumper is to be replaced with a recycled bumper (see Appendix B). The left front door is to be repaneled and the roof is to be repaired. Figure out the alignment and metal repair time. The windshield is to be changed; it is shaded. A replacement kit is required and 1.0 hour glass cleanup time is needed.

After replacing the door outer panel, it will have to be undercoated, as well as the front fender. All replaced or repaired parts are to be painted; check for time allowance and remove overlap as required.

OMNI 1978-86

WINDSHIELD Cont'd

	Lower	5209220		15.09
84-86	Upper	5209362-3		11.47
	Side	5209364-5		15.11
	Lower	5209339		16.23

Moudling, Inside Garnish (a)

Coupe	Upper	5231298	.2	11.32
	Side 79-81 R	F262AA3	.2	17.27
	L	F263SX9	.2	17.28
	82-86 R	F262AA3	.2	17.27
	L	F263AA3	.2	17.28
Sedan	Upper	5208508	.2	11.30
	Side 79-81 R	F260AA3	.2	20.91
	L	F261AA3	.2	20.91
	82-86 R	F260AA3	.2	20.91
	L	F261AA3	.2	20.91

(a) Black - Paint to Match

Band, WS Upper Tint w/Name

"De Tomaso"	4229372		28.89

Mirror, Rear View

Except		5207116	.2	20.38
Prismatic		5207117	.2	22.12
Visor, Sun¶	78-80	H597RX9	.2	37.73
	81	H597VX9	.2	40.88
82 except		H612VX9		54.14
w/Illuminated Mirror		H312AX9		117.60
	83-84	H612BX7		51.56
	85-86	H301DA2		40.91

¶Order by Color

Arm & Bracket, Visor

78-84 w/o Illuminated Mirror	5208539		11.83
w/Illuminated Mirror	4223513		12.68
85-86	5208714		11.83

Blade Assy, Wiper

78-85

Except	Anco	5211076	.2	5.70
	Trico	5211077	.2	5.70
Black	except	5211096	.2	5.08
	Plastic	5211128	.2	5.70
86	R	3799862	.2	18.09
	L	3799863	.2	22.66
Arm, Wiper	78-83 Brite	5211016	.2	14.26
	Black	3799861	.2	14.26
	84-86	3799861	.2	14.26
Pivot, Thru Cowl		5211008-9		14.72
Link, Mtr to Pivot	R	5211004	.6	14.01
	L	5211003	.6	6.51
Motor, Wiper	78-84	4205951	.8	106.69
	85-86	4339449	.8	106.68
Reservoir, Washer	78-82	5211084		18.35
	83-84	3799791		18.25
	85-86	4334190		18.24
Pump Assy, Washer		3799090	.4	21.36
Nozzle Assy, Spray		4176769		3.57

COWL & DASH

Refinish Cowl Top	....	1.0
Refinish Pillar	....	1.0

4-1438

1 Panel, Cowl Side 78-84 R

Panel, Cowl Side	78-84 R	4337658	#3.5	29.87
	L	5231777	#3.5	50.13
	85-86 R	4337658	#3.5	29.87
	L	5231777	#3.5	50.13

 # w/Hinge Pillar Removed

Panel, Cowl Inside Trim

Coupe (a)	79 R	F216SB5		13.72
	L	F217SB5		13.72
	80-86 R	F216TM6		14.14
	L	F217TM6		14.14
Sedan (b)	R	F266DT5		14.17
	L	F267DT5		14.17

(a) Order by Application
(b) Paint to Match

2 Pillar, Hinge

Coupe		5218462-3	#7.5	89.45
Sedan	78-80 R	5218452	#7.5	51.87
	L	5218039	#7.5	51.90
	81-82 to 9-81 R	5218452	#7.5	51.87
	L	4129875	#7.5	51.90
	82-86 From 9-81	5218452-3	#7.5	51.87

 # w/Fender, Door & Windshield Removed

3 Frame, Windshield Side

Coupe	Outer 79-83 to (c)	5231008-9	#2.5	24.46
	From (c) 83-86	4314782-3	#2.5	27.96
	Inner	5231004-5	1.5	23.94

COWL & DASH Cont'd

Sedan	Outer 79-83 to (d)	5200904-5	#2.5	21.22
	83-86 From (d)	4314780-1	#2.5	24.10
	Inner	5200900-1	1.5	16.58

(c) 1-25-83
(d) 1-19-83
 # w/Windshield Removed

4 Extension, Inner Frame

Coupe	Upper	5231614-5		7.83
	Lower	5231006-7		5.92
Sedan	Lower	5200902-3		3.09

Frame, Windshield Header

Coupe	4050977	#2.5	16.84
Sedan	4050529	#2.5	21.53

 # w/Roof Panel Removed

5 Panel, Cowl Top

Coupe	78-83	4129072	107.41
	84-86	5218481	107.37
Sedan	78-83	4050342	107.36
	84-86	5218480	107.37

6 Cover, Cowl Plenum Opening

except	5231168	7.37
w/Air Cond	5200988	13.57

Panel Cowl Plenum

w/o AC	78-82	5231583	141.55
	83	4278811	141.49
	84	4278813	141.50
	85-86	4314989	141.48
w/AC	78-82	5231584	141.55
	83	4278810	141.49
	84	4278812	141.50
	85-86	4314988	141.48

Panel, Dash

w/o AC	78-79	5231581	141.69
	80-81	4136327	158.70
	82	4278767	154.07
	83 to (e)	4278947	154.08
	From (e)	4314226	154.07
	84	4314751	158.67
	85-86	4337654	158.67
w/AC	78-79	5231582	133.30
	80-81	4136326	146.03
	82	4278766	158.69
	83 to (f)	4278946	154.08
	From (f)	4314224	158.69
	84	4314750	158.67
	85-86	4337655	158.67

(e) 11-1-82
(f) 10-7-82

INSTRUMENT PANEL

4-3017

1 Panel, Instrument (a)

w/Safety Pad (b)	76-83	P685BT8	#2.5	239.63
	84	P412DT5	#2.5	212.74
	85-86	P412DT5	#2.5	212.74

 # Includes R&I Instruments, w/AC Add 1.0

2 Cover, Panel Top

	5209707	19.07

Bezel, Panel Trim (a)

3	Left		5209661	7.74
4	Right	w/o AC	P611CC7	11.45
		w/AC	P610CC7	17.01

5 Glovebox & Door (a)

Except (b)	P639RX9	28.84
w/Woodgrain (c)	P669TX9	34.86

6 Housing Gauge Cluster (a)

w/o Rallye Pkg	5211395	16.71
w/Rallye Pkg	5209578	7.16

Lens & Mask, Cluster (a)

7	w/o Rallye Pkg	5211444	53.63
8	w/Rallye Pkg	5209579	45.32

(a) Order by Year & Model
(b) Paint to Match
(c) Order by Color

ROCKER PANEL & PILLARS

ROCKER PANEL

Refinish Outside	....	1.0

ROCKER PANEL & PILLARS Cont'd

ROCKER PANEL Cont'd

4-1439

1 Panel, Rocker

Coupe	R	4337530	#5.0	55.00
	L	4337531	#5.0	55.00
Sedan	R	4337528	#6.0	62.50
	L	4337529	#6.0	62.50

 # w/Bolted Parts & Trim Removed

2 Panel, Sill Lower(a)

Coupe	R	5230076	#3.0	32.81
	L	5230077	#3.0	32.81
Sedan	R	5200006	#3.5	32.89
	L	5200007	#3.5	32.89

 # Except w/Rocker Panel Removed 2.0

3 Extension, Lower Sill(a)

Front	5200004-5		10.56
Rear	5200162-3		10.56

(a)These Mount Under & Box in Area Below Rocker Panels

Panel, Sill Inner Rear	5200034-5		7.97

Moulding, Rocker

Coupe		5230514-5	.3	22.39
Sedan (R or L)	78-82	5209034	.3	23.85
	83-86	4293619	.3	16.20

Cover, Rocker Spoiler

Shelby	Blue R	X906BB6	.6	68.54
	L	X907BB6	.6	66.41
	Silver R	X906BA1	.6	68.54
	L	X907BA1	.6	68.54
	Gold R	X906DT4	.6	68.55
	L	X907DT4	.6	68.55
GLH		5209440-1	.6	60.00
Retainer, Spoiler	GLH	5209434		10.50
Bracket, Spoiler	GLH	5209439		.88
Decal, Cover	Pentastar	4270395		1.96

Plate, Sill Cover

Shelby	4319998-9	4.71

Plate, Sill Scuff

Coupe		5208814	.2	5.85
Sedan	Front	5208526	.2	11.60
	Rear	5208527	.2	7.37

PILLAR

Refinish Center Pillar	....	1.0

4 Pillar, Center

	78-79 R	★5218028	#7.0	d129.11
	L (a)	★5218141	#7.0	175.19
	80-82 R	★5218140	#7.0	186.76
	L	★5218141	#7.0	175.19
	83 R	★5218450	#7.0	181.30
	L	★5218317	#7.0	186.74
	84-86 R	★5218450	#7.0	181.30
	L	★5218451	#7.0	181.30

(a) 5231576 Check Strap Bracket Required
 # Except w/Roof or Rocker Removed 6.0

Moulding, Pillar		5209022-3	12.44

Panel, Pillar Inside Trim (b)

Upper	78 R	F196RX9	d3.86
	L	F197RX9	4.05
	79-86 R	F172AA3	4.27
	L	F173AA3	4.27
Lower	78 R	F168SX9	19.02
	L	F169SX9	18.11
	79-85 To 12-79 R	F168SX9	19.02
	L	F169SX9	18.11
	From 12-79 R	F202AA3	19.03
	L	F203AA3	19.03

(b) Paint to Match

5 Pillar, Hinge - See Cowl & Dash
6 Pillar, Lock - See Quarter Panel

SEAT

Adjuster, Track

Outer (a)		4277473	#.6	29.87
Inner (a)		5232143	#.6	29.87

 # R&R Both One Seat .9

Recliner, Back Rest (a)

	R	4239640	58.95
	L	4239641	58.95

(A)Order by Application

FRONT DOOR

Refinish Outside	........................2 Door	2.2
	4 Door	2.1
Add For Jambs	....	.5

Procedure Explanation Pages Must Be Used With The Above Text for an Accurate Damage Report.

CH   **133**

FIGURE 3-76 Estimated rates for rocker panel and doors. (Courtesy of Mitchell Information Services Inc.)

OMNI 1978-86

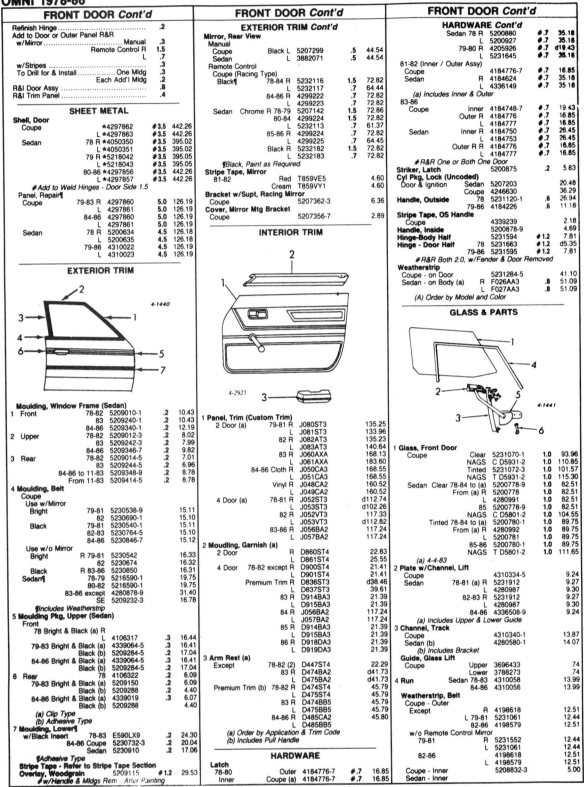

FRONT DOOR Cont'd

Refinish Hinge			.2
Add to Door or Outer Panel R&R			
w/Mirror		Manual	.3
		Remote Control R	1.5
		L	.7
w/Stripes			.3
To Drill for & Install		One Mldg	.3
		Each Add'l Mldg	.2
R&I Door Assy			.8
R&I Trim Panel			.4

SHEET METAL

Shell, Door

Coupe			*4297862	#3.5	442.26
		L	*4297863	#3.5	442.26
Sedan	78	R	*4050350	#3.5	395.02
		L	*4050351	#3.5	395.02
	79	R	*5218042	#3.5	395.05
		L	*5218043	#3.5	395.05
	80-86	R	*4297856	#3.5	442.26
		L	*4297857	#3.5	442.26

 # Add to Weld Hinges - Door Side 1.5

Panel, Repair¶

Coupe	79-83	R	4297860	5.0	126.19
		L	4297861	5.0	126.19
	84-86		4297860	5.0	126.19
		L	4297861	5.0	126.19
Sedan	78	R	5200634	4.5	126.18
		L	5200635	4.5	126.18
	79-86		4310022	4.5	126.19
		L	4310023	4.5	126.19

EXTERIOR TRIM

Moulding, Window Frame (Sedan)

1 Front	78-82	5209010-1		.2	10.43
	83	5209240-1		.2	10.43
	84-86	5209340-1		.2	12.19
2 Upper	78-82	5209012-3		.2	8.02
	83	5209242-3		.2	7.99
	84-86	5209346-7		.2	9.82
3 Rear	78-82	5209014-5		.2	7.01
	83	5209244-5		.2	6.96
	84-86 to 11-83	5209348-9		.2	8.78
	From 11-83	5209414-5		.2	8.78

4 Moulding, Belt

Coupe					
Use w/Mirror					
Bright	79-81		5230538-9		15.11
	82		5230690-1		15.10
Black	79-81		5230540-1		15.11
	82-83		5230764-5		15.10
	84-86		5230846-7		15.12
Use w/o Mirror					
Bright	R 79-81		5230542		16.33
	82		5230674		16.32
Black	R 83-86		5230850		16.31
Sedan¶	78-79		5216590-1		19.75
	80-82		5216590-1		19.75
	83-86 except		4280878-9		31.40
	SE		5209232-3		16.78

¶Includes Weatherstrip

5 Moulding Pkg, Upper (Sedan)

Front					
78 Bright & Black (a)	R				
	L	4106317		.3	16.44
79-83 Bright & Black (a)		4339064-5		.3	16.41
Black (b)		5209284-5		.2	17.04
84-86 Bright & Black (a)		4339064-5		.3	16.41
Black (b)		5209284-5		.2	17.04
6 Rear	78	4106322		.2	6.09
79-83 Bright & Black (a)		5209150		.2	6.09
Black (b)		5209288		.2	4.40
84-86 Bright & Black (a)		4339019		.3	6.07
Black (b)		5209288			4.40

(a) Clip Type
(b) Adhesive Type

7 Moulding, Lower¶

w/Black Insert	78-83	E590LX9		.2	24.30
84-86 Coupe		5230732-3		.2	20.04
Sedan		5230910		.2	17.06

¶Adhesive Type

Stripe Tape - Refer to Stripe Tape Section

Overlay, Woodgrain	5209115		#1.2	29.53

#w/Handle & Mldgs Rem. After Painting

FRONT DOOR Cont'd

EXTERIOR TRIM Cont'd

Mirror, Rear View

Manual					
Coupe	Black L	5207299		.5	44.54
Sedan	L	3882071		.5	44.54
Remote Control					
Coupe (Racing Type)					
Black¶	78-84 R	5232116		1.5	72.82
	L	5232117		.7	64.44
	84-86 R	4299222		.7	72.82
	L	4299223		.7	72.82
Sedan	Chrome R 78-79	5207142		1.5	72.86
	80-84	4299224		1.5	72.82
	L	5232113		.7	61.37
	85-86 R	4299224		.7	72.82
	L	4299225		.7	64.45
	Black R	5232182		1.5	72.82
	L	5232183		.7	72.82

¶Black, Paint as Required.

Stripe Tape, Mirror

81-82	Red	T859VE5		4.60
	Cream	T859VY1		4.60

Bracket w/Supt, Racing Mirror

Coupe	5207362-3		6.36

Cover, Mirror Mtg Bracket

Coupe	5207356-7		2.89

INTERIOR TRIM

1 Panel, Trim (Custom Trim)

2 Door (a)	79-81 R	J080ST3		135.25
	L	J081ST3		133.96
	82 R	J082AT3		135.23
	L	J083AT3		140.64
	83 R	J060AXA		168.13
	L	J061AXA		183.60
	84-86 Cloth R	J050CA3		168.55
	L	J051CA3		168.55
	Vinyl R	J048CA2		160.52
	L	J049CA2		160.52
4 Door (a)	78-81 R	J052ST3		d112.74
	L	J053ST3		d102.26
	82 R	J052VT3		117.33
	L	J053VT3		d112.82
	83-86 R	J056BA2		117.24
	L	J057BA2		117.24

2 Moudling, Garnish (a)

2 Door	R	D860ST4		22.83
	L	D861ST4		25.55
4 Door	78-82 except R	D900ST4		21.41
	L	D901ST4		21.41
Premium Trim	R	D836ST3		d38.46
	L	D837ST3		39.61
	83 R	D914BA3		21.39
	L	D915BA3		21.39
	84 R	J056BA2		117.24
	L	J057BA2		117.24
	85 R	D914BA3		21.39
	L	D915BA3		21.39
	86 R	D918DA3		21.39
	L	D919DA3		21.39

3 Arm Rest (a)

Except	78-82 (2)	D447ST4		22.29
	83 R	D474BA2		d41.73
	L	D475BA2		d41.73
Premium Trim (b)	78-82 R	D474ST4		45.79
	L	D475ST4		45.79
	83 R	D474BB5		45.79
	L	D475BB5		45.79
	84-86 R	D485CA2		45.80
	L	D485BB5		

(a) Order by Application & Trim Code
(b) Includes Pull Handle

HARDWARE

Latch				
78-80	Outer	4184776-7	#.7	16.85
Inner	Coupe (a)	4184776-7	#.7	16.85

FRONT DOOR Cont'd

HARDWARE Cont'd

Sedan 78	R	5200880		#.7	35.18
	L	5200927		#.7	35.18
79-80	R	4205926		#.7	d10.43
	L	5231645		#.7	35.18
81-82 (Inner / Outer Assy)					
Coupe		4184776-7		#.7	16.85
Sedan	R	4184624		#.7	35.18
	L	4336149		#.7	35.18

(a) Includes Inner & Outer

83-86					
Coupe	Inner	4184748-7		#.7	19.43
	Outer R	4184776		#.7	16.85
	L	4184777		#.7	16.85
Sedan	Inner R	4184750		#.7	26.45
	L	4184753		#.7	26.45
	Outer R R	4184776		#.7	16.85
	L	4184777		#.7	16.85

#R&R One or Both One Door

Striker, Latch	5200875		.2	5.83
Cyl Pkg, Lock (Uncoded)				
Door & Ignition	Sedan	5207203		20.48
	Coupe	4246630		36.29
Handle, Outside	78	5231120-1	.6	26.94
	79-86	4184226	.6	11.18
Stripe Tape, OS Handle				
Coupe		4339239		2.18
Handle, Inside		5200878-9		4.69
Hinge-Body Half		5231594	#1.2	7.81
Hinge - Door Half	78	5231663	#1.2	d5.35
	79-86	5231595	#1.2	7.81

#R&R Both 2.0, w/Fender & Door Removed

Weatherstrip

Coupe - on Door		5231284-5		41.10
Sedan - on Body (a)	R	F026AA3	.8	51.09
	L	F027AA3	.8	51.09

(A) Order by Model and Color

GLASS & PARTS

1 Glass, Front Door

Coupe	Clear	5231070-1		1.0	93.96
	NAGS C	D5931-2		1.0	110.85
	Tinted	5231072-3		1.0	101.57
	NAGS T	D5931-2		1.0	115.30
Sedan	Clear 78-84 to (a)	5200778-9		1.0	82.51
	From (a) R	5200778		1.0	82.51
	L	4280991		1.0	82.51
	85	5200778-9		1.0	82.51
	Tinted 78-84 to (a) R	5200780-1		1.0	89.75
	From (a) R	4280992		1.0	89.75
	L	5200781		1.0	89.75
	85-86	5200780-1		1.0	89.75
	NAGS T	D5801-2		1.0	111.65

(a) 4-4-83

2 Plate w/Channel, Lift

Coupe		4310334-5		9.24
Sedan	78-81 (a) R	5231912		9.27
	L	4280987		9.30
	82-83 R	5231912		9.27
	L	4280987		9.30
	84-86	4336508-9		9.24

(a) Includes Upper & Lower Guide

3 Channel, Track

Coupe	4310340-1		13.87
Sedan (b)	4280580-1		14.07

(b) Includes Bracket

Guide, Glass Lift

Coupe	Upper	3696433	.74
	Lower	3788273	.74
4 Run	Sedan 78-83	4310058	13.99
	84-86	4310058	13.99

Weatherstrip, Belt

Coupe - Outer			
Except	R	4198618	12.51
	L 79-81	5231061	12.44
	82-86	4198579	12.51
w/o Remote Control Mirror			
79-81	R	5231552	12.44
	L	5231061	12.44
82-86		4198618	12.51
	L	4198579	12.51
Coupe - Inner		5208832-3	5.00
Sedan - Inner			

FIGURE 3-77 Estimated rates for doors. (Courtesy of Mitchell Information Services Inc.)

OMNI 1978-86

FRONT DOOR Cont'd

GLASS & PARTS Cont'd

Except	to 2-81	5231886-7		5.90
	from 2-81	5231886-7		5.90
78 Custom	R	5208626		d8.35
	L	5208627		4.15

5 Regulator

Coupe		5231046-7	#1.1	48.89
Sedan		5231742-3	#1.1	48.93

 # Exc w/Glass Removed .2

6 Handle, Regulator

78-84	Except	3882764		14.07
	Black	5200983		14.07
85-86		4310824		14.07

REAR DOOR

Refinish Outside	2.0
Add for Jambs ..	.5
Refinish Hinge	.2
R&I Door Assy	.8
R&I Trim Panel	.4
Add to Door or Outer Panel R&R	
To Drill for & Install .... One Mldg	.3
Each Add'l Mldg	.2

SHEET METAL

Shell, Door				
78 R	*4050358	3.5	397.64	
L	*4050359	3.5	397.64	
79 R	*5218052	3.5	397.64	
L	*5218053	3.5	d397.64	
80 R	*5218096	#3.5	442.17	
L	*5218097	#3.5	442.17	
81-86 R	*4297850	#3.5	432.15	
L	*4297851	#3.5	432.15	

 # Add to Weld Hinges - Door Side 1.5

Panel, Repair				
78 R	5200648	4.5	120.17	
L	5200649	4.5	120.17	
79-86 R	4310024	4.5	126.19	
L	4310025	4.5	126.19	

EXTERIOR TRIM

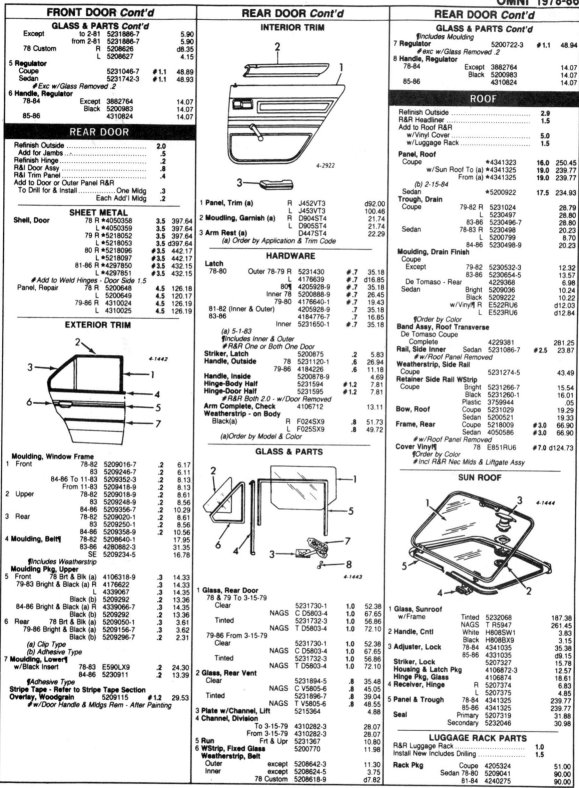

4-1442

Moulding, Window Frame

1 Front	78-82	5209016-7	.2	6.17
	83	5209246-7	.2	6.11
	84-86 To 11-83	5209352-3	.2	8.13
	From 11-83	5209418-9	.2	8.13
2 Upper	78-82	5209018-9	.2	8.61
	83	5209248-9	.2	8.56
	84-86	5209356-7	.2	10.29
3 Rear	78-82	5209020-1	.2	8.61
	83	5209250-1	.2	8.56
	84-86	5209358-9	.2	10.56
4 **Moulding, Belt**¶	78-82	5208640-1		17.95
	83-86	4280882-3		31.35
	SE	5209234-5		16.78

¶ Includes Weatherstrip

Moulding Pkg, Upper

5 Front	78 Brt & Blk (a)	4106318-9	.3	14.33
	79-83 Bright & Black (a) R	4176622	.3	14.33
	L	4339067	.3	14.35
	Black (b)	5209292	.2	13.36
	84-86 Bright & Black (a) R	4339066-7	.3	14.35
	Black (b)	5209292	.2	13.36
6 Rear	78 Brt & Blk (a)	5209050-1	.3	3.61
	79-86 Bright & Black (a)	5209156-7	.3	3.62
	Black (b)	5209296-7	.2	2.31

(a) Clip Type
(b) Adhesive Type

7 Moulding, Lower¶

w/Black Insert	78-83	E590LX9	.2	24.30
	84-86	5230911	.2	13.39

¶ Adhesive Type

Stripe Tape - Refer to Stripe Tape Section

Overlay, Woodgrain	5209115	#1.2	29.53

 # w/Door Handle & Mldgs Rem - After Painting

REAR DOOR Cont'd

INTERIOR TRIM

1 Panel, Trim (a)	R	J452VT3		d92.00
	L	J453VT3		100.46
2 Moudling, Garnish (a)	R	D904ST4		21.74
	L	D905ST4		21.74
3 Arm Rest (a)		D447ST4		22.29

(a) Order by Application & Trim Code

HARDWARE

Latch					
78-80	Outer 78-79 R	5231430	#.7	35.18	
	L	4176639	#.7	d16.85	
	80¶	4205928-9	#.7	35.18	
	Inner 78	5200888-9	#.7	26.45	
	79-80	4176640-1	#.7	19.43	
81-82 (Inner & Outer)		4205928-9	.7	35.18	
83-86		4184776-7	.7	16.85	
	Inner	5231650-1	#.7	35.18	

(a) 5-1-83
¶ Includes Inner & Outer
 # R&R One or Both One Door

Striker, Latch		5200875	.2	5.83
Handle, Outside	78	5231120-1	.6	26.94
	79-86	4184226	.6	11.18
Handle, Inside		5200878-9		4.69
Hinge-Body Half		5231594	#1.2	7.81
Hinge-Door Half		5231595	#1.2	7.81

 # R&R Both 2.0 - w/Door Removed

Arm Complete, Check		4106712		13.11
Weatherstrip - on Body				
Black(a)	R	F024SX9	.8	51.73
	L	F025SX9	.8	49.72

(a) Order by Model & Color

GLASS & PARTS

4-1443

1 Glass, Rear Door

78 & 79 To 3-15-79				
Clear		5231730-1	1.0	52.38
	NAGS	C D5803-4	1.0	67.65
Tinted		5231732-3	1.0	56.86
	NAGS	T D5803-4	1.0	72.10
79-86 From 3-15-79				
Clear		5231730-1	1.0	52.38
	NAGS	C D5803-4	1.0	67.65
Tinted		5231732-3	1.0	56.86
	NAGS	T D5803-4	1.0	72.10

2 Glass, Rear Vent

Clear		5231894-5	.8	35.48
	NAGS	C V5805-6	.8	45.05
Tinted		5231896-7	.8	39.04
	NAGS	T V5805-6	.8	48.55
3 Plate w/Channel, Lift		5215364		4.88
4 Channel, Division				
To 3-15-79		4310282-3		28.07
From 3-15-79		4310282-3		28.07
5 Run	Frt & Upr	5231367		10.80
6 WStrip, Fixed Glass		5200770		11.98
Weatherstrip, Belt				
Outer	except	5208642-3		11.30
Inner	except	5208624-5		3.75
	78 Custom	5208618-9		d7.82

REAR DOOR Cont'd

GLASS & PARTS Cont'd

¶ Includes Moulding

7 Regulator		5200722-3	#1.1	48.94

 # exc w/Glass Removed .2

8 Handle, Regulator

78-84	Except	3882764		14.07
	Black	5200983		14.07
85-86		4310824		14.07

ROOF

Refinish Outside	2.9
R&R Headliner	1.5
Add to Roof R&R	
w/Vinyl Cover	5.0
w/Luggage Rack	1.5

Panel, Roof

Coupe			*4341323	16.0	250.45
	w/Sun Roof To (a)		*4341325	19.0	239.77
	From (a)		*4341325	19.0	239.77
	(b) 2-15-84				
Sedan			*5200922	17.5	234.93

Trough, Drain

Coupe	79-82 R		5231024		28.79
	L		5230497		28.80
	83-86		5230496-7		28.80
Sedan	78-83 R		5230498		20.23
	L		5200799		8.70
	84-86		5230498-9		20.23

Moulding, Drain Finish

Coupe				
Except	79-82	5230532-3		12.32
	83-86	5230654-5		13.57
De Tomaso - Rear		4229368		6.98
Sedan	Bright	5209036		10.24
	Black	5209222		10.22
	w/Vinyl R	E522RU6		d12.03
	L	E523RU6		d12.84

¶ Order by Color

Band Assy, Roof Transverse

De Tomaso Coupe			
Complete		4229381	281.25

Rail, Side Inner	Sedan	5231086-7	#2.5	23.87

 # w/Roof Panel Removed

Weatherstrip, Side Rail

Coupe		5231274-5	43.49

Retainer Side Rail WStrip

Coupe	Bright	5231266-7	15.54
	Black	5231260-1	16.01
	Plastic	3759944	.05

Bow, Roof

Coupe	5231029		19.29
Sedan	5200521		19.33

Frame, Rear

Coupe	5218009	#3.0	66.90	
Sedan	4050586	#3.0	66.90	

 # w/Roof Panel Removed

Cover Vinyl¶	78	E851RU6	#7.0	d124.73

¶ Order by Color
 # Incl R&R Nec Mlds & Liftgate Assy

SUN ROOF

4-1444

1 Glass, Sunroof

w/Frame	Tinted	5232068		187.38
	NAGS	T R5947		261.45
2 Handle, Cntl	White	H808SW1		3.83
	Black	H808BX9		3.15
3 Adjuster, Lock	78-84	4341035		35.38
	85-86	4331035		d9.15
Striker, Lock		5207327		15.78
Housing & Latch Pkg		4106872-3		12.57
Hinge Pkg, Glass		4106874		18.61
4 Receiver, Hinge	R	5207374		6.83
	L	5207375		4.85
5 Panel & Trough	78-84	4341325		239.77
	85-86	4341325		239.77
Seal	Primary	5207319		31.88
	Secondary	5232046		30.98

LUGGAGE RACK PARTS

R&R Luggage Rack	1.0
Install New Includes Drilling	1.5

Rack Pkg

Coupe	4205324		51.00
Sedan 78-80	5209041		90.00
81-84	4240275		90.00

Procedure Explanation Pages Must Be Used With The Above Text for an Accurate Damage Report.   **135**

FIGURE 3-78 Estimated rates for doors and roof panels. (Courtesy of Mitchell Information Services Inc.)

ROCKER PANEL/PILLAR

	OPERATIONS INCLUDED	ADDITIONS/EXPLANATIONS NOT INCLUDED
ROCKER OUTER PANEL – R&R		See parts text
Refinish		X See parts head notes
Cowl trim R&I	√	Unless noted otherwise in text
Center pillar trim R&I	√	Unless noted otherwise in text
Sill plates R&I	√	Unless noted otherwise in text
Quarter trim at sill R&I	√	Unless noted otherwise in text
Rear seat cushion R&I	√	Unless noted otherwise in text
Floor mats	√	Turn back to avoid fire damage
Moulding		X Use allowance in parts text
Front fender R&I		X Add allowance if necessary to loosen edge of fender
Quarter panel R&R		X Add allowance necessary to gain access for complete R&R operation if HSLA steel is evident
Center pillar R&R		X Add allowance necessary to gain access for complete R&R operation if HSLA steel is evident
With center pillar removed		Use allowance in parts text less 1.0
With hinge pillar removed		Use allowance in parts text less 1.0
With lock pillar removed		Use allowance in parts text less 1.0
CENTER PILLAR – R&R		See parts text
Refinish		X See parts head notes
Pillar trim R&I	√	Unless noted otherwise in text
Rear door R&I	√	If door is replaced use door R&R allowance less R&I time unless noted otherwise in text
Front seat assembly R&I	√	Unless noted otherwise in text
Floor mats	√	Turn back to prevent fire unless noted otherwise in text
Door lock striker plate	√	Unless noted otherwise in text
Headliner (cloth type) loosen at pillar	√	Except pre-formed or moulded style unless noted otherwise in text
Pillar R&R w/roof removed	√	For full pillar only use pillar allowance less 1.0
Sill plates R&I	√	
Hinges R&I and/or R&R		X

FIGURE 3-79 Shows procedure explanation for rocker panel and center pillar replacement. (Courtesy of Mitchell Information Services Inc.)

FRONT OR REAR DOOR

	OPERATIONS INCLUDED	ADDITIONS/EXPLANATIONS NOT INCLUDED

FRONT OR REAR DOOR – R&R

Operation	Incl.	Not Incl.	Explanation
Refinish		X	See parts text
Replace or transfer parts attached to door	√	X	See parts text notes
			Except those listed below
Channels attached to glass		X	Add .2 for lower channel, add .3 for lower & upper channels
Transfer riveted type glass regulator		X	See parts text notes
Rivets (regulator)		X	
Broken glass – clean up		X	Estimate allowance on sight
Trim panel R&I	√		If panel is replaced, estimate & add to transfer or replace parts not included on new panel
Cylinder & key R&R	√		
Cylinder & key – Recode		X	Add local charge to recode
Power windows		X	See parts head notes
Mirror, rear view		X	See parts head notes
Weld on type hinges & regulators		X	See parts head notes
Hinge anchor plates		X	Check Hinge R&R for Anchor Plate R&R when rewelding is not recommended by the factory
Mouldings/nameplates (clip type-new)	√		See parts head notes for drill and install allowance
Mouldings/nameplates (adhesive - new)		X	Use one-half allowance shown in parts text
Mouldings/nameplates (adhesive - transfer)		X	Add allowance to clean and retape
Stripes/decals/transfers/overlays-install		X	Use allowance in parts text

DOOR REPAIR PANEL – FRONT OR REAR

Operation	Incl.	Not Incl.	Explanation
Refinish		X	See parts text
Door assembly R&I	√	X	See head notes
Trim panel R&I	√		
Glass, hardware, channels		X	See parts text
Cylinder & key R&R	√		
Cylinder & key – Recode		X	Add local charge to recode
Handle, door outside	√		
Weatherstrip on door edge	√		
Mouldings/nameplates	√		See parts head notes for drill & install allowance
Sound deadening		X	Estimate allowance on sight
Broken glass – clean up		X	Estimate allowance on sight
Stripes, decals, transfers or overlays – Install		X	Use allowance in parts text

FIGURE 3-80 Shows procedure explanations for the removal and replacement of doors. (Courtesy of Mitchell Information Services, Inc.)

	OPERATIONS INCLUDED	ADDITIONS/EXPLANATIONS NOT INCLUDED

ROOF PANEL – R&R

	INCLUDED	NOT INCLUDED	
Refinish		X	See parts text
Rear/Lift Gate R&I	√		See parts head notes
Windshield & mouldings R&R	√		See Windshield Section
Back glass & mouldings R&R	√		See Back Glass Section
Broken glass – clean up		X	Estimate allowance on sight
Sun Visors/dome lamps/coat hooks	√		
Front & rear seats	√		
Weathercords	√		
Weatherstrips & retainers	√		
Quarter trim	√		
Security cover	√		
Headliner assembly	√		
Stays etc., for new headliner R&I		X	Use local charge
Luggage rack R&I		X	See parts head notes
Roof rails & header panels		X	See parts text, allowance is after roof panel is removed
Roof cap and/or Vinyl cover		X	See parts head notes
Mouldings (clip type-new)	√		See parts head notes for drill and install allowance
Mouldings (adhesive-new)		X	Use one-half allowance shown in parts text
Mouldings (adhesive-transfer)		X	Add allowance to clean and retape
Stripes/decals/transfers/overlays-install		X	Use allowance in parts text

HEADLINER – R&R

			See parts head notes
Rear seat R&R	√		
Sun Visor/dome lamps/coat hooks	√		
Inside mouldings that interfere with R&I	√		

FIGURE 3-81 Procedure and times to be used when replacing or repairing roof panels. (Courtesy of Mitchell Information Services, Inc.)

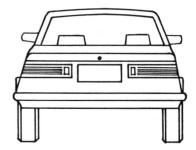

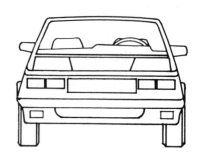

FIGURE 3-82 Drawings of vehicles.

Body/Frame Damage Diagnosis Worksheet

Damage	Indication	Condition	
Twist: One corner of vehicle is higher than adjacent corner.	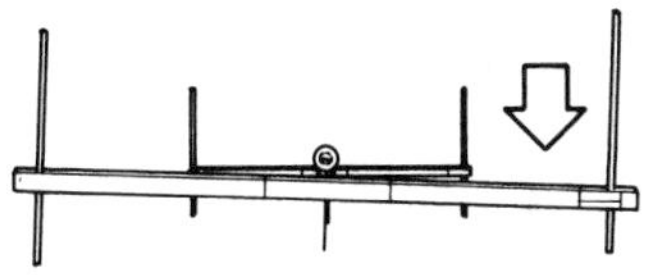	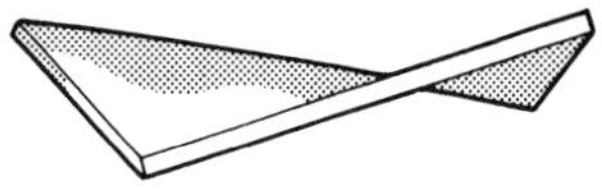	
Diamond: One side of vehicle is pushed back or forward.	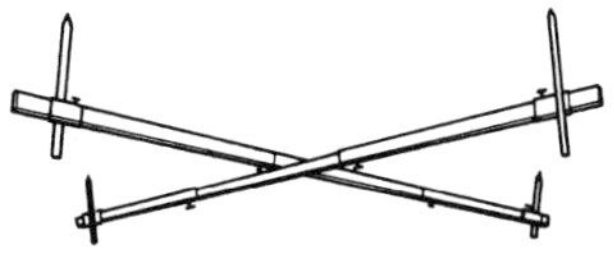	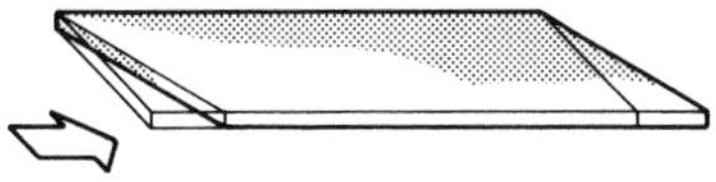	
Mash: Length of vehicle is shortened.	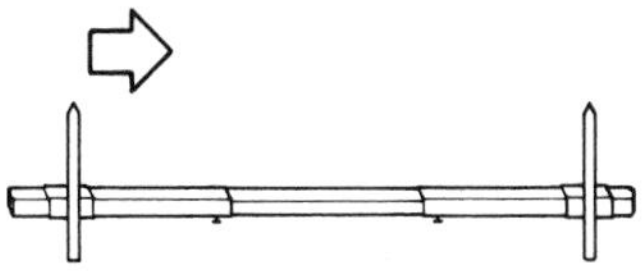	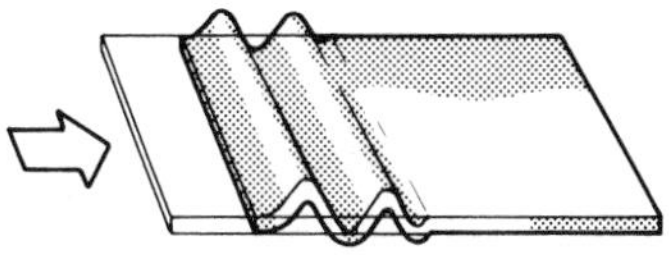	
Sag: Center is lower than normal.	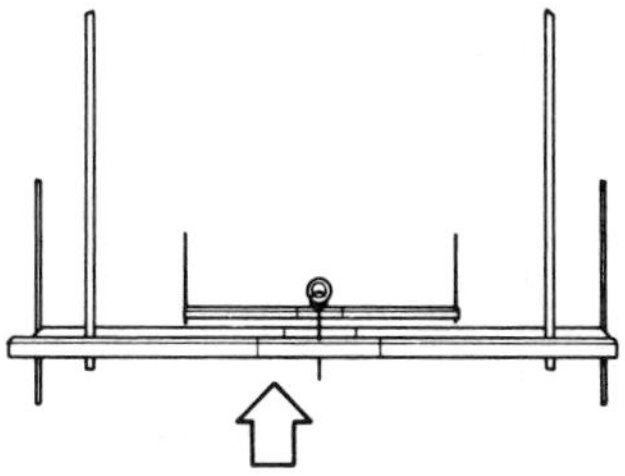	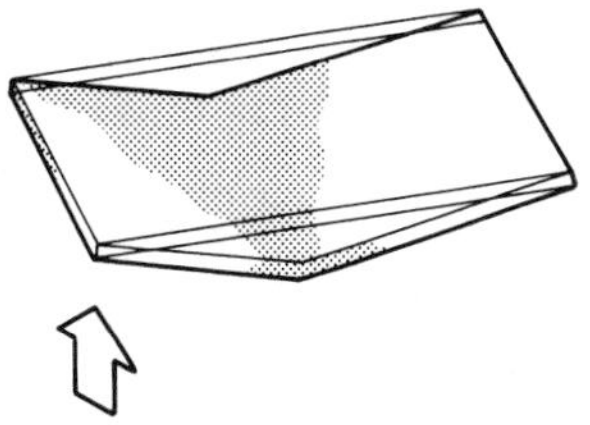	
Sideway: Front, center, or rear is pushed sideways out of alignment	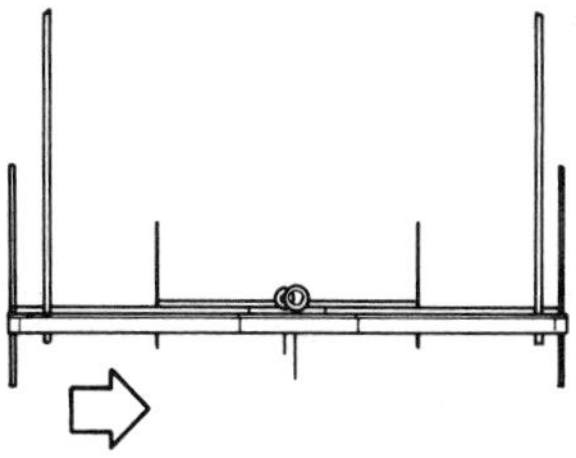	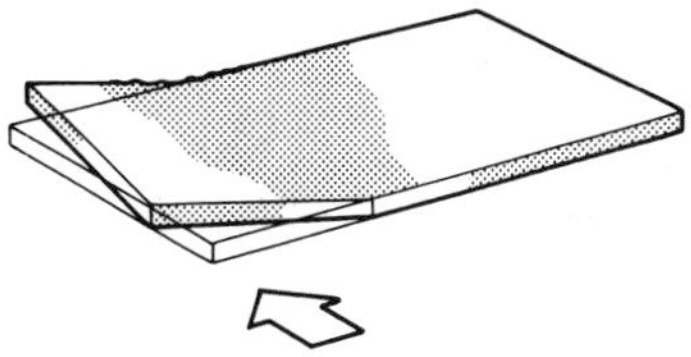	
Damage occurs in this order: (1) sideway, (2) sag, (3) mash, (4) diamond, (5) twist	Make measurements and correction in this order: (1) twist, (2) diamond, (3) mash, (4) sag, (5) sideway		

FIGURE 3-83 Body/frame damage diagnosis. (Courtesy of Black Hawk Division of Applied Power, Canada Ltd.)

BODY/FRAME DAMAGE
ESTIMATING GUIDE

DAMAGE	AMOUNT (IN INCHES OR MILLIMETERS)	HOURS	
SIDEWAY			
SAG			
MASH			
DIAMOND			
TWIST			
COSMETIC (Welding, reinforcing, etc.)			
ADDITIONAL DAMAGE (Crossmember sag, McPherson tower correction, etc.)			
TOTAL			

FIGURE 3-84 Body frame damage estimating guide. (Courtesy of Blackhawk, Division Applied Power, Canada Ltd.)

ESTIMATOR'S REPORT

	CLAIM NUMBER

Insurance Company _____

Estimate, Inspection and Location Date _____

ADJUSTER'S NAME	ESTIMATOR'S NAME	DATE OF COMPLETION	DATE OF LOSS

INSURED   VEHICLE

NAME AND ADDRESS	LICENSE (POLICY) NUMBER	GVW	MILEAGE	AMOUNT OF DEDUCTIBLE
	YEAR, MAKE & MODEL		SERIAL NUMBER	

DESCRIPTION OF WORK TO BE DONE	RE-PAIR	REPLACE NEW	L.K.Q.	QTY.	PART NUMBER	PARTS COST	HRS.	LABOR COST

This is purely an estimate and not a definite contract price. Owing to the impossibility of determining damage of concealed parts, we reserve the right to submit a further estimate for approval or otherwise. Prices subject to change without notice.

Authorization to Repair _____

I _____ the registered owner of the above described vehicle authorize the repairs to proceed.

TOTAL PARTS COST ▶	
TOTAL LABOR COST ▶	
SHOP MATERIAL	
PAINT LABOR	
PAINT MATERIAL	
SUB TOTAL	
TAX	
TOTAL COST ▶	

ONLY APPROVED ADDITIONS PAID

FIGURE 3-85 Write-in estimate form.

FIGURE 3-86 Side and front damage.

FIGURE 3-87 Side damage.

FIGURE 3-88 Front upper damage.

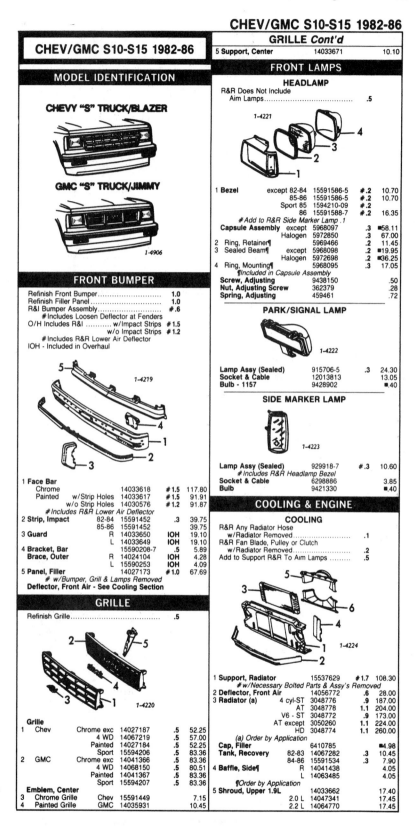

FIGURE 3-89 Estimated time rates and part prices. (Courtesy of Mitchell Information Services Inc.)

CHEV/GMC S10-S15 1982-86

COOLING & ENGINE Cont'd

COOLING Cont'd

	2.5 L 85	15538079		18.85
	86	15538079		18.85
	2.8L	14033664		19.10
6 Shroud, Lower	1.9L	14033663		19.10
	2.0 L	14047342		19.10
	2.2 L	14064771		17.45
	2.5 L	15597053		19.10
	2.8 L 82-85	14033665		9.20
	86	15590972		19.10

Hose, Upper

1.9 L	82	14024175	.5	9.65
	83-85	14060026	.5	10.10
2.0 L		14055718	.5	10.60
2.2 L		14063007	.5	10.10
2.5 L		15598533	.5	9.25
2.8 L	82	14024177	.5	9.65
	83-85	14060027	.5	9.25
	86	15530716	.5	9.25

Hose, Lower (b)

4 Cyl	14024172	.5	6.30
6 Cyl	14024176	.5	10.00

Pipe, Lower Outlet

4 Cyl w/AC	82	14024173		9.60
	83-86	14060052		13.40

Blade, Fan (b) w/o A/C 22008548 #.5 d44.80
  w/AC 14046528 #.5 ■32.50

Pulley, Fan (b)

1 Groove	14032386	#.5	16.60
2 Groove	14033108	#.5	22.00
3 Groove	14033109	#.5	30.75
4 Groove	14033110	#.5	40.00

(b) Order by Application

Clutch, Fan

Stamped KB	14076309	#.5	47.40
HF	22008970	#.5	76.00
HU	15530775	#.5	61.50
HH	22062564	#.5	58.88
CCN	14045253	#.5	76.00
AJC/CCR	14046527	#.5	72.30
ADC	14066205	#.5	76.00

#R&R Complete

Belt, Drive (b) 9433722 5.80
  (b) Order by Application

Pump, Water

1.9 L	94239153	#1.0	75.35
2.0 L	14063641	#1.0	78.25
2.2 L	94105354	#1.0	94.50
2.5 L	10032022	#1.0	59.50
2.8 L	14105921	#1.0	72.25

#w/Radiator Removed Deduct .5

EMISSION SYSTEM

Pump, Air

1.9 L		94230594	.5	258.00
2.0 L		7834488	.5	■148.74
2.5 L		NA		
2.8 L	82-85	7836061	.6	■148.74
	86	7834488	.6	■148.74

Pulley, Pump

1.9 L		94230592	.3	8.80
2.0 L		14081703	.3	4.65
2.5 L		NA		
2.8 L	82-84	14085411	.3	14.10
	85-86	14083354	.3	5.40

Fan, Pulley 7835231 5.70

Cannister, Vapor

except		17064627	.3	53.85
1.9 L		17075846	.3	57.15
2.0L w/50L Tank		17075833	.3	53.85
2.5 L		17075840	.3	29.95
2.8L w/50L Tank		17075832	.3	52.05

Manifold, Air 94109847 82.25
Sensor, Pressure 16054920 ■50.45

ELECTRICAL

Horn	"A" Note	1982164	.2	
	"F" Note	1892163	.2	■22.62
Relay, Horn	Federal	344813		4.90
	California 82-85	25523703		■8.00
	86	25523703		■8.00
Module, Main Computer (a)		1225950	1.0	110.00

(a) Located on Right Side of Dash
Order by Application

Cap, Distributor

1.9 L	94243347	.5	11.25
2.0 L	1978497	.5	■17.77
2.8 L	1979208	.5	■19.82

ALTERNATOR PARTS

Alternator Assembly

63 Amp	1105360	.6	205.70
78 Amp	1100250	.6	■224.89

Pulley

1.9 L	1978065	.3	8.80
2.0 L	1846787	.3	18.80
2.2 L	1978065	.3	8.80
2.5 L	1978065	.3	8.80
2.8 L	1984572	.3	23.10
Diesel	1978065	.3	8.80

Fan, Pulley 1984430 9.70
(a) Order by Application

COOLING & ENGINE Cont'd

ENGINE

R&I Engine Assembly .... 4 Cyl 5.3
                                          V6 5.7

Add To Engine R&I
  To Adjust Linkage Complete 1.0
  w/Standard Transmission 3
  w/Air Conditioning 5
  w/Power Steering 3
  AC Does Not Include Evacuate & Recharge System

Pulley, Crankshaft

1.9 L	w/o AC	94230056	.8	32.50
	w/AC	14032387	.8	16.00
2.0 L		14049766	.8	28.25
2.2 L	Federal	94105350	.8	121.00
	California	94133544	.8	99.50
2.5 L	w/o PS	10026575	.8	17.45
	w/P.S.	10016061	.8	14.75
2.8 L		14033107	.8	27.25

Balancer, Crankshaft

1.9 L	94233811	#1.0	25.00
2.0 L	14049767	#1.0	22.50
2.2 L	NA		
2.5 L	10028930	#1.0	26.75
2.8 L	14085401	#1.0	39.50

#Includes R&R Pulley

Mount, Engine Front

1.9 L		14027901	.8	26.75
2.0 L		14049682-1	.8	26.75
2.2 L	R	14063044	.8	26.75
	L	14063043	.8	28.25
2.5 L		15598556-5	.8	26.75
2.8 L		14062953	.7	30.25

Bracket, Front Mount

1.9 L 2 WD			14027906-5	#.2	6.85
4 WD			14049694-3	#.2	12.45
2.0 L					
To Engine	2 WD	R	15598538	#.2	8.35
		L	14049689	#.2	10.85
	4 WD	R	14049686	#.2	9.60
		L	14049687	#.2	10.85
To Frame	2 WD	R	14049684	#.2	10.85
		L	14049683	#.2	7.05
	4 WD	R	14049686	#.2	9.60
		L	14049687	#.2	10.85
2.2 L		R	94108329	#.2	18.25
		L	94108330	#.2	18.25
2.5 L		R	15598558	#.2	10.85
		L	15590289	#.2	12.90
2.8 L		R	15531862	#.2	10.85
	L 2 WD		14027913	#.2	10.85
	4 WD		14049679	#.2	17.25

#w/Mount Removed

Mount, Rear (Trans)

2 WD 82-83		14027910	.6	11.80
84-86		17980666	.6	15.25
4 WD		14049626	.6	13.25

Support, Rear Mount¶

AT

4 Spd	2 WD	14024012		32.00
	4 WD exc	14041697		30.75
	Blazer/Jimmy	14049561		37.75
5 Spd	2 WD 82	14041507		35.25
	83 exc	14063012		41.50
	4 WD exc	14041697		30.75
	Blazer/Jimmy	14049562		37.75

ST

3 Spd	2 WD	14024012		32.00
	4 WD exc	14041697		30.75
	Blazer Jimmy	14049561		37.75
4 Spd	2 WD	14063012		41.50
	4 WD exc	14041697		30.75
	Blazer/Jimmy	14049562		37.75

Brace, Auto Trans R 14011520 27.75
  L 14011519 27.75
¶Order by Application

Cover, Timing

1.9 L		94238338	#3.0	89.75
2.0 L		14069895	#3.0	73.75
2.2 L	Upper	94029804	#3.0	29.00
	Lower	94029805	#3.0	29.00
2.5 L		10036836	#3.0	25.00
2.8 L		14033526	#3.0	85.00

#w/Radiator Removed Deduct .5

Pan, Oil

2 WD	1.9 L	94227730	4.8	84.75
	2.0 L	14049780	4.8	55.25
	2.8 L 82-84 (a)	14033075	6.1	53.50
	(b)83-86	14077878	6.1	53.50

(a) Requires Sealer For Rear Seal
(b) Requires Rubber Seal For Rear Seal

4 WD	1.9 L	94253836	4.8	76.00
	2.0 L	14049784	4.8	55.25
	2.8 L 82-84	14077881	6.1	53.50
	85-86	14077881	6.1	53.50

Gasket, Pan

1.9 L	94204431		17.75
2.0 L¶			
2.2 L 2WD	94108336		14.60
2.8 L¶			

¶Requires Sealant #1052366 For Pan
Sealant 1052366 7.35

COOLING & ENGINE Cont'd

ENGINE Cont'd

Pump, Fuel¶

1.9 L		94228711	.6	76.00
2.0 L		6472030	.6	34.65
2.2 L		NA		
2.5 L		6472358	.6	58.90
2.8 L	2WD	6471963	.6	■58.43
	4WD	6471930	.6	■51.78

¶Order by Applicaton

EXHAUST

Manifold, Exhaust

1.9 L	Federal	94228998	.9	97.50
	Calif	94228997	.9	97.50
2.0 L		14054401	.9	97.50
2.2 L	Federal	94108327	.9	82.75
	California	94108328	.9	80.00
2.5 L		10037597	.9	93.75
2.8 L	82-85 R	14033087	.9	97.50
	L	14054859	.9	97.50
	86 R	14089850		70.00
	L	14059321	.9	94.75

Pipe, Front Exaust (a)

4 Cyl	14024122	.7	26.25
V6 (Crossover)	14024138	.7	49.75

Converter, Catalytic (a)

4 Cyl	except	8999365	.7	216.00
	Calif	25056089	.7	302.00
V6	except	8999917	.7	209.00
	Calif	8999919	.7	228.00

Pipe, Muffler Inlet (a)

w/6 Ft Box	14045064		25.00
w/7.5 Ft Box	14045062		25.00

Muffler (a) 14045068 #1.2 92.25
#Includes R&R Tail Pipe
Pipe, Tail (a) 14045067 .6 30.75
(a) Order by Application

AIR CONDITIONING

R&R Does Not Include
  Evacuate & Recharge System 1.4

Condenser 3048188 .8 138.20

Compressor (Radial)

1.9 L	ST	12300959	.9	■321.65
	AT	12300958	.9	■321.65
2.0 L	83	12300273	.9	■321.65
	84	12321359	.9	■321.65
2.2 L		12321365	.9	■321.65
2.5 L		12321362	.9	■395.82
2.8 L		12300959	.9	■321.65

Pulley		6556715	1.0	12.60
Clutch, Drive	except	6551220		■35.63
	2.5 L	6551996		40.80
Rotor & Bearing		6551216		■74.85
Drier/Accumulator	82	2724260	.5	89.50
	83-86	2724290	.5	80.05
Coil & Housing		6551217	1.0	■49.25

Case, Evaporator

Inlet	82	3049614		67.25
	83-86	3053801		67.25
Outlet		3053702		37.25

Core, Evaporator		3050414	2.0	209.45
Motor, Blower		22029915	.6	53.60
Fan, Motor	82	3037551		13.40
	83-86	3055691		17.10

Hose, Compressor
  to Condenser¶ 14074508 55.50
¶Order by Application

HEATER PARTS

Core, Heater	w/AC	3049486	1.3	54.90
	w/AC	3050142	1.3	66.00
Case, Blower		3053722		36.50

Motor, Blower

w/o AC	Standard	22048575	.4	43.25
w/AC	Heavy Duty	22048576	.4	43.25

Fan, Motor 3052244 17.95

HOOD

Refinish Outside	2.9
R&I Hood Assembly	.5
Refinish Hinge	.2

1-4225

1 Panel, Hood	82-84	14063458	1.0	142.50
	85-86	15591591	1.0	142.50
2 Hinge		14030524-3	#.8	5.20

FIGURE 3-90 Estimated time rates and parts prices. (Courtesy of Mitchell Information Services Inc.)

CHEV/GMC S10-S15 1982-86

HOOD *Cont'd*

#w/Hood & Cowl Vent Panel Removed

Latch¶	82-84	15530729	.2	4.10
	85-86	15530729		4.10
3 Catch Assy, Safety¶	82-84	15530728	.2	4.10
	85-86	15530728		4.10

¶Manufacturer Recommends Replacing Both Latch & Safety Catch as a Unit

Spring¶	14095649		1.95
Bolt¶	14058971		2.70

¶Included in Catch Assembly

Cable, Release	82-85	14033670	.5	13.25
	86	15390963	.5	
4 Rod, Prop		14027196		8.95
5 Insulator		12306178	#.3	35.25

 # Cut to Fit Add .7

Retainer	3977775		.44

STRIPE TAPES

TYPE 1
LOWER

1-4226

1-4387

Tape - Blue (Order by Color)

Hood		14039397	9.10
Fender	Front R	14035990	3.70
	L	14035989	3.70
	Rear	14039301-2	2.65
Door		14039314-3	14.60
Decal, Door "Super Sport"		15599885	55.50
Cab Corner	exc	14041314-3	2.50
	w/Extended Cab	14044772-1	14.90
Quarter			
Pickup			
6 FT Box	Front	14039356-5	10.50
	Rear	14039368-7	10.50
7.5 FT Box	Front	14039332-1	12.35
	Rear	14039344-3	12.35
Blazer/Jimmy	Front	14044784-3	16.10
	Rear	14044796-5	18.00
Decal, Quarter	"4x4" R	15597017	14.15
	L	15597012	

Tailgate - See Moulding & Trim
Under Pick-Up Bed

TYPE 2
UPPER-WIDE

1-4953

Tape-Black (Order by Color)

Hood		15592741	9.10
Fender		15592746-5	37.00
Door		15592842-1	37.00
Cab Corner	except R	15599820	47.00
	L	15599819	47.00
	w/Extended Cab	15599828-7	56.25
Quarter	R	15592780	60.75
	L	15592779	55.75
Fuel Door		15592787	7.85

STRIPE TAPES *Cont'd*

TYPE 3
UPPER-NARROW

1-4954

Tape-Black (Order by Color)

Fender	R	15530630	20.30
	L	15530629	20.30
Door¶		15530654-3	20.00
¶Includes Cab Corner on Pickup			
Quarter		15530690-89	24.45

FRONT FENDER

Refinish Outside		2.0
Add To Edge Fender		.5
R&I Fender Assembly		1.2

1-4227

1 Fender	82-84 R	15594252	#2.8	118.75
	L	14060415	#2.8	125.00
	85-86 R	15521746	#2.8	118.75
	L	15537959	#2.8	118.75

#w/Cowl Vent Panel Removed 1.8

2 Moulding, Side (Adhesive)¶

Front	12300649	.2	9.74
Rear	12300648	.2	2.99

¶Cut to Fit-Order by Application

3 Moulding, Wheel Opening

Bright		14033616-5	.3	8.12
Black		14047320-19	.3	10.12
Name	"V6"	1254540	.2	4.00
	"S10"	15592810	.2	5.70
	"S10 Tahoe" 82-84	15592814	.2	6.30
	85-86	15597018	.2	9.55
	"S10 Durango" 82-83	15592812	.2	5.70
	84	15592812	.2	5.70
	85-86	15592829	.2	6.55
	"S10 Sport" 82-84	15592816	.2	7.20
	85-86	15597019	.2	9.55
	"S10 Chevrolet"	15592828	.2	6.55
	"S15 Gypsy" 82-83	14041478	.2	7.20
	84	15592808	.2	7.20
	"S15 GMC Gypsy"	15597041	.2	10.20
	"S15 Sierra" 82-83	15592818	.2	7.20
	84	15592804	.2	5.70
	85-86	15592833	.2	7.50
	"S15 High Sierra" 82-83	14041477	.2	7.20
	84	15592806	.2	7.20
	85-86	15592834	.2	7.50
	"S15 Sierra Classic" 82-83	15592818	.2	7.20
	84	15592818	.2	7.20
	85-86	15597042	.2	10.20
	"Blazer" 83	14057638	.2	10.00
	84-86	15592824	.2	9.30
	"Jimmy" 83	14057637	.2	8.35
	84-86	15592822	.2	9.30
	"Jimmy 4x4" 83	15592820	.2	9.30
	84-86	15592820	.2	9.30
	"Blazer 4x4" 83	14057639	.2	10.00
	84-86	15592826	.2	9.30
4 Panel, Wheelhouse	R	15598114	.5	81.70
	L 82-84	15598114	.5	81.70
	85-86	15598113	.5	81.70
5 Shield, Splash		15592730-29	.3	2.76

FRONT FENDER *Cont'd*

Seal - to Cowl	R	14033610		21.15
	L	14033609		21.15
Antenna, Radio				
Mast	82-84	25510879		■6.15
	85-86	10023402		6.20
Body & Cable		14035170		7.25

WHEEL

Refinish Wheel			.5	
Wheel				
14X6.0		Std.	9590753	.3	62.25
		Rally	14077046	.3	86.25
		Styled 85-86	15598988	.3	87.75
15x6.0		2 WD	14042634	.3	82.25
		4 WD	14050322	.3	82.25
15x7.0		Rally	14077047	.3	84.25
		Styled 85-86	15598989	.3	91.25
		Aluminum	14063788	.3	211.00
16x4.0		2 WD	9590927	.3	66.00
		4 WD	9590942	.3	79.00
		TV, JJ	9590927	.3	66.00
Hub Cap				
Standard		Chev	14035559		16.15
		GMC	14035558		16.15
Rally/Styled w/o Insert			14035565		16.75
4 WD		w/Alum Whl	14047297		6.20
		w/o Alum Whl	15592299		14.05
Insert, Rally Cap		Chev	14035567		3.95
		GMC	14035568		3.95
		Deluxe	14074883		2.40
		4x4	14068909		4.95
Cover, Wheel		Chev	14035574		39.75
		GMC	14035575		39.75
		Deluxe	14074879		44.00
Ring, Wheel Trim		Standard	14035562		24.25
		Deluxe	3984524		32.25
		Blazer/Jimmy	471200		30.25

FRONT SUSPENSION

2 WHEEL DRIVE

O/H Suspension Assembly	One Side	4.4
	Both Sides	7.3
Check and Adjust		
Caster, Camper & Toe-In		1.2
Toe-In Only		.5

R&R Does Not Align
O/H Includes Align
IOH - Included in Overhaul

1-1172

1 Hub & Disc		14032431	.8	100.00
2 Bearing - Outer		14066918	#.9	11.50
3 Bearing - Inner		7450630	#.9	■9.43
4 Seal, Bearing		3965092	#.9	■3.45
#R&R Complete				
5 Shield, Splash		459758-7	1.1	7.40
6 Caliper, Brake	R	18010481	.8	148.45
	L	18010480	.8	137.00
Hose, Brake		9767269	#.6	27.00
#Each Additional .3, Includes Bleed				
7 Arm Assy Upper Control		14039012-1	IOH	97.75
8 Ball Joint, Upper¶		9767112	1.1	34.75
¶Included in Upper Arm Assembly				
9 Shaft, Upper Arm		474001	IOH	33.75
10 Spring, Coil (a)		14047217	1.0	46.75
11 Shock Absorber (a) Standard		4993590	.5	24.40
Heavy Duty		22046402	.5	■81.25
(a) Order by Application				
12 Knuckle, Steering		14012602-1	1.1	117.00
13 Arm Assy, Lower Control R		15599686	1.5	159.00
	L	15599683	1.5	159.00
14 Ball Joint, Lower¶		9767281	.7	■36.22
¶Included in Lower Arm Assy				
15 Shaft, Stabilizer¶	exc	14024115	.6	44.75

Allowances Shown Are for Replacement With New OEM Undamaged Parts on New Undamaged Vehicles.   GM

FIGURE 3-91 Estimated time rates and part prices. (Courtesy of Mitchell Information Services, Inc.)

CHEV/GMC S10-S15 1982-86

FRONT SUSPENSION Cont'd

2 WHEEL DRIVE Cont'd

Sport Package		14060076	.6	44.75
16 Bracket, Shaft¶	exc	334671		1.20
Sport Package		3978931		■1.37
17 Bushing, Shaft¶	exc	3927019		■1.93
Sport Package		14062929		2.35

¶Order by Application

FRONT SUSPENSION

4 WHEEL DRIVE

Check & Adjust
Caster, Camber & Tow-In 1.2
Toe-In Only 5
R&R Does Not Include Align
O/H Includes Align

1-4388

1 Hub & Bearing		7466920	1.0	■190.76
2 Disc		14056179	.5	70.10
3 Shield, Splash		14047282-1	1.2	4.90
4 Caliper, Brake		18008846-5	.8	137.00
Hose, Brake		9768950-49	#.6	27.00

 # Each Additional .3 Includes Bleed

5 Arm, Upper Control	82-83	14067522-1	.9	129.00
	84-86	15596694-3		129.00
6 Ball Joint, Upper	82-83	9767781		52.00
	84-86	17980952		52.00
Shaft, Upper Arm		NA		
7 Shock Absorber (a)	exc	4993732	.5	26.43
	HD	4993733	.5	40.63
8 Bar, Front Torsion (a)		14034277	.8	103.00

(a) Order by Application

9 Knuckle, Steering	83	22522938-7	1.2	158.00
	84-86	14070360-59	1.2	158.00
10 Seat, Knuckle Inner		560680		4.65
11 Arm Assy, Lower Control				
1982-83		14067524-3	1.1	213.00
1984-86	R	15596696	1.1	213.00
	L	15537757	1.1	213.00
12 Ball Joint, Lower¶		17980954		52.00

¶Included in Lower Arm Assy

Bushing, Lower Control Arm			
Front	14041609		4.40
Rear	14049624		4.40
13 Shaft, Stabilizer (a) Standard	14078615	.8	90.50
Off Road	15598514	.8	90.50
14 Bracket, Shaft(a) 82-83	14073310		2.55
84-86	15598515		2.45
15 Bushing, Shaft(a)	14062929		2.35

(a) Order by Application

STEERING LINKAGE

R&R Does Not Include Set Toe-In
Check and Adjust Toe-In 5

1-1173

End Assy, Tie Rod				
1 Outer	2 WD	14050634	#.3	31.75
	4 WD	14067619	#.3	31.75
2 Inner	2 WD	7837183	#.3	40.25
	4 WD	7833122	#.3	51.00

#R&R Both on One Side .5

3 Tube Kit, Adjusting	2 WD	7829465		15.70
	4 WD	12309226		15.90
4 Arm, Pitman				
2 WD	Manual 82	7837644	.6	44.00
	183-86	14067621	.6	44.00
	Power	14067622	.6	44.00
4 WD	Manual	14070268		44.00

STEERING LINKAGE Cont'd

	Power	14067525	.6	44.00
5 Rod, Relay	2 WD	14067587	.7	44.00
	4 WD	14067618	.7	44.00
6 Arm, Idler	2 WD	7837635	.6	■52.68
	4 WD	7830667	.6	■72.13
Absorber, Steering	2WD	4993598		67.72
	4WD	4993599		46.32

STEERING COLUMN

STEERING WHEEL

Wheel & Trim (a)

w/Round Center Cap				
Wheel	Black	9766231	.5	95.25
	Almond	9766233	.5	95.25
Shroud	Black	9766777		24.70
Cap	Black	9765458		16.40
	Almond	9765459		16.40
Lens		9765455		14.95
w/Oblong Center Cap				
Wheel	Blue	9766282	.5	95.25
Shroud	Blue	17983910		24.70
Cap	Blue	9766859		26.00
Lens		9766862		11.40

(a) Order by Color & Application

COLUMN - STANDARD

O/H Column Assembly 2.5

Housing, Lock	ST 82	7837379		57.25
	83-86	7837035		63.25
	AT	7837032		63.25
Lock, Ignition (Coded)				
Chrome		7830380		■9.50
Black		7840574		23.35
Switch, Ignition	82-84	1990115	.8	■11.30
	85-86	1990116	.8	■11.53
Column Assembly ST	82-83	7842415	1.5	226.00
	84-86	7842415	1.5	226.00
AT	82-83	7836974	1.5	226.00
	84-86	7842414	1.5	226.00
85-86 w/o Pulse Wiper		7843380	1.5	226.00
w/Pulse Wiper		7843381	1.5	226.00
Jacket, Column ST	82-85	7837528		78.00
	86	7847143		78.00
AT	82-85	7837524		78.00
	86	7847142		78.00
Tube, Shift¶ AT	82-85	7837531		69.00
	86	7847148		69.00
Shaft, Strg-Upper¶	82-85	7833429		79.00
	86	7847146		79.00

¶Included in Column Assembly

Shaft, Strg Intermediate			
Upper	82	7838309	67.50
	83-86	7842219	72.25
Lower		7843340	80.25

COLUMN - TILT

O/H Column Assembly 2.8

Cover, Lock Housing		7837547		44.25
Housing, Lock		7843690		161.00
Lock, Ignition (coded)				
Chrome		7830380	1.1	■9.50
Black		7840574	1.1	23.35
Switch, Ignition	82-83	19900110		
	84-86	1990116	.8	■11.53
Column Assembly ST	82-83	7836980	1.5	448.00
	84	7842459	1.5	448.00
85 w/o Pulse Wiper		7842459	1.5	448.00
w/Pulse Wiper		7844958	1.5	448.00
86 w/o Pulse Wiper		7847442		448.00
w/Pulse Wiper		7847441		448.00
AT	82-83	7836978	1.5	448.00
	84	7842458	1.5	448.00
	85	7844957	1.5	448.00
86 w/o Pulse Wiper		7843380		226.00
w/Pulse Wiper		7843381		226.00
Jacket, Column¶ ST	82-85	7837565		78.00
	86	7844432		78.25
AT	82-85	7837533		78.00
	86	7847668		78.00
Tube, Shift¶ AT	82-85	7837537		77.75
	86	7847672		69.00
Shaft Assy, Steering Upper¶				
1982-85		7837536		135.00
1986		7847670		135.00
Shaft, Yoke (a)	Upper	7828404		72.00
	Lower	7831105		79.00

¶Included in Column Assembly
(a) Included in Upper Shaft Assembly

Shaft, Strg Intermediate			
Upper	82	7838309	67.50
	83-86	7842219	72.25
Lower		7830094	74.00

STEERING GEAR

GEAR - MANUAL

Gear Assembly	82-84	7841893	.9	266.00
	85-86	7845260	.9	266.00
Shaft, Worm¶	82-84	7816558		86.25
	85-86	7845597		125.00
Shaft, Pitman¶	82-84	7841897		63.25
	85-86	7843970		94.75
Housing, Gear¶	82-84	7840889		127.00
	85-86	7843960		127.00

¶Included in Gear Assembly

GEAR - POWER

Gear Assembly	82	7837376	1.1	412.00
	83-85 2 WD	7848138	1.1	441.00
	4 WD	7840241	1.1	412.00
Rack & Piston	2WD	7817526		151.00
	4 WD	7817528		162.00
Shaft, Pitman¶	2 WD	7815885		87.50
	4 WD	7813631		87.50
Housing, Gear¶		7834139		183.00

¶Included in Gear Assembly

PUMP - POWER

Pump Assy (Less Pulley)				
1.9 L	w/AC	7838617	.9	199.00
	w/o AC	7839085	.9	199.00
2.0 L		7841430	.9	199.00
2.2 L		7843045	.9	199.00
2.5 L		7843045	.9	199.00
2.8 L		7841780	.9	199.00
Pulley, Pump				
1.9 L		14023172	.3	10.45
2.0 L		14030019	.3	14.85
2.2 L		14066222	.3	16.60
2.5 L		10024304	.3	10.45
2.8 L		14088278	.3	10.45
Reservoir				
1.9 L	w/AC	7839493		65.50
	w/o AC	7839495		65.50
2.0 L		7842088		65.50
2.2 L	84	14063083		21.35
	85	15595981		21.35
2.5 L		15595981		21.35
2.8 L		7837332		60.50
Hose, Pressure				
1.9 L	w/AC	7838618	.5	55.75
	w/o AC	7839031	.5	46.00
2.0 L		7841354	.5	35.00
2.2 L		7843030	.5	35.00
2.5 L		7846465	.5	55.75
2.8 L		7842169	.5	36.75

FRAME

Frame Assembly¶				
Pickup				
	6' Box	14024030	22.0	581.00
	7.5' Box	14024031	23.5	631.00
	2 WD	14070070	22.0	601.00
	4 WD	14070067	24.5	601.00
	w/Extended Cab	14070068	25.5	631.00
Mbr, Drive Shaft Cross¶		14024139		33.25

¶Order by Application

WINDSHIELD

Glass, Windshield	Clear	14020303	2.2	308.00
	NAGS C W943		2.2	324.70
	Shaded	14020343	2.2	381.00
	NAGS S W943		2.2	369.15
Installation Material - Use as Required				
Moulding, Reveal		14030581		7.55
Mirror, Rear View		914293	.2	24.85
Visor, Sun (a)		15590357	.2	11.20
(a) Blue Listed - Order by Color				
Blade w/Insert, Wiper		14031240	.2	8.55
Arm, Wiper		14031236	.2	11.15
Motor, Wiper	except	22030809	.6	105.00
	w/Pulse Wiper	22049813	.6	132.65
Pump, Washer		4961623	.5	■16.32
Jar, Washer		22048355	.3	8.25
Nozzle, Washer		14033659	.2	3.20

CAB SHEET METAL

PICKUP

Refinish Cab:
Outside 8.7
Cowl Vent Panel 1.0
Windshield Frame 1.2
Door Frame 1.5
Side Panel 2.2
Roof Panel 2.5
Rear Panel 2.3

FIGURE 3-92 Estimated time rates and part prices. (Courtesy of Mitchell Information Services Inc.)

CHEV/GMC S10-S15 1982-86

CAB SHEET METAL *Cont'd*

PICKUP *Cont'd*

1-4389

1 Panel, Cowl & Dash	82	14050608		185.00
	83-85	15536531		199.00
	86	15536531		199.00
2 Panel, Plenum Side	82 R	14067426		49.50
	L	14062353		56.50
	83-84 R	15593304		51.25
	L	14062353		56.50
	85-86 R	15593304		51.25
	L	15594265		33.25
3 Panel, Cowl Vent	82-84	15594250	1.0	28.75
	85-86	15594250	1.0	28.75
4 Screen, Cowl Vent		14033669		9.75
5 Panel, Windshield		15594261	#6.0	199.00
#w/Front Sheet Metal, Doors & Glass Removed				
6 Reinforcement¶		14027198-7		24.50
¶Included in Windshield Panel				
7 Frame Assy, Door Opening		14063678-7	#12.0	177.00
#w/Door, Windshield, Seat & Trim Removed				
8 Panel, Rocker¶		NSS		
9 Reinforcement, Hinge¶		NSS		
¶Included in Opening Frame Assy				
Plate, Sill Scuff				2.05
10 Panel, Floor	2 WD exc	14056741		301.00
	w/Extended Cab	14035935		321.00
	4 WD exc	14035968		292.00
	w/Extended Cab	14035958		321.00
11 Extension, Floor Rear	exc	14027134-3		28.50
	w/Extended Cab	15530800-799		19.20
12 Panel, Roof	exc	14020322	8.0	80.99
	w/Extended Cab	14035958	9.0	76.95
Moulding, Drip Scalp		15594240		7.85
Panel, Side (Extended Cab)				
13 Outer		14035956-5	#7.5	193.80
#Add To Loosen Bed for Access 2.0				
14 Inner		14063964-3	2.5	59.14
15 Panel, Rear Outer	exc	14020306	#11.0	309.00
	w/Extended Cab	14035957	#11.0	296.00
# Except w/Roof Panel Removed 7.5				
Includes R&R Back Window				
w/Each Door Frame Removed Deduct 1.0				
w/Each Side Panel Removed Deduct 2.0				
Suggested Times Are w/Bed Removed				
Moulding, Rear Panel				
Adhesive Type (a)		12300650		15.44
(a) Cut to Fit				
16 Panel, Rear Inner	exc	14020305	5.0	97.00
	w/Extended Cab	15598179	5.0	60.75

BLAZER/JIMMY

Refinish	
Cowl Top Panel	1.0
Windshield Frame	1.2
Door Frame	1.5
Roof Panel	3.6

CAB SHEET METAL *Cont'd*

BLAZER/JIMMY *Cont'd*

1-4390

1 Panel, Cowl & Dash	83-85	15536531		199.00
	86	15536531		199.00
2 Panel, Plenum Side	R	15593304		51.25
	L	14062353		56.50
Panel, Cowl Vent	83-85	15594250	1.0	28.75
	86	15594250	1.0	28.75
4 Screen, Cowl Vent		14033669		9.75
5 Panel, Windshield		15594261	#6.0	199.00
#w/Front Sheet Metal, Doors & Glass Removed				
6 Reinforcement, Frame¶		14027198-7		24.50
¶Included In Windshield Panel				
7 Frame Assy, Door Opening	R	14063678	#12.0	177.00
	L	14063677	#12.0	177.00
#w/Door, Windshield, Seat & Trim Removed				
8 Panel, Rocker¶-NSS				
9 Reinforcement, Hinge¶-NSS				
¶Included In Opening Frame Assembly				
10 Panel, Floor (Front)		14039376	#22.0	232.00
#w/Rocker Panel Removed 18.0				
Panel, Floor (Rear)-See Rear Body				
11 Panel, Roof		15591515	14.5	102.60
Bow, Roof Panel				
Front		14041397		12.73
Center/Rear		14041354		12.73

LUGGAGE RACK

R&I Luggage Rack		1.0
Carrier Package	997890	#1.8	95.00
# Includes Drilling			
Rail¶	Front & Rear	14057682	47.75
	Side	14057679	98.75
Support¶		14044197-8	21.90
Slat¶		14056788	4.55
¶Included in Assembly			

INSTRUMENT PANEL

Refinish Instrument	1.0

1-4391

1 Panel, Instrument (a)		15599685	#6.5	239.00
# Includes R&I Guages				
2 Panel, Cluster (b)	w/AC	14042835		24.00
	w/o AC	14042836		15.10
3 Housing, Gauge (b)	w/Tach	25046198		36.25
	w/o Tach	25045506		33.50
Lens, Instrument	exc	25053995		27.55
	w/Trip Odometer	25053996		27.50
4 Panel, Center Trim (b)		14057729		13.60
5 Cover, Panel Lower				
1982-85 (a)		4028763		
1986 (b)		15588189		16.65
6 Glovebox	82	14028771		6.00
	83-84	15588186		4.60
	85-86	15588186		4.60
7 Stop Glovebox Door		14042826		.63
8 Door, Glovebox (b)				
Standard		14042822	.3	8.85
Deluxe		14042821	.3	9.60
9 Nameplate, Glovebox (b)				

CAB SHEET METAL *Cont'd*

INSTRUMENT PANEL *Cont'd*

82			
Chevrolet	"Tahoe"	14044346	3.55
GMC	"High Sierra"	14044345	3.45
	"Sierra Classic"	14044349	3.45
	"Gypsy"	14044347	3.45
83-86			
Chevrolet	"Tahoe"	14059870	3.60
	"Sport"	14059872	3.60
GMC	"Gypsy"	14059871	3.60
	"Sierra Classic"	14059873	3.60
10 Insert, Panel Rt (b)		14059825	4.85
11 Grille, Speaker (a)		14028756-5	2.93
(a) Paint to Match			
(b) Order by Application			

BACK WINDOW

PICKUP

Glass, Back Window	Clear	14020302	1.0	69.25
	NAGS	C B6425	1.0	84.85
	Tinted	14020332	1.0	73.50
	NAGS	T B6425	1.0	101.65
	Privacy	14062324	1.0	181.00
	NAGS	P B6425	1.0	258.65
Window Assy, Sliding		998277	1.0	83.05
Glass-Stationary¶	Tinted R	NA		
	L	NA		
	NAGS	T B6426-7		51.35
Glass-Moveable¶	Tinted	NA		
	NAGS	T B6428		49.50
¶Included in Window Assy				
Moulding, Reveal				
Upper/Lower		14062321		8.20
Cap, Moulding Joint		14031298		1.30
Weatherstrip, Moulding				
Use w/Reveal Mldgs	82	15598163		28.25
	83-86	15598163		28.25

SEAT

Adjuster, Seat				
Bench Seat		14063464-3	#.4	21.65
Bucket Seat				
exc				
Driver	Outer	14063462	#.4	21.65
	Inner	14063461	#.4	21.65
Passenger	Outer	14056728	#.4	18.25
	Inner	14056758	#.4	20.00
Easy Entry	83-84 Outer	20480431	#.4	72.75
	Inner	20547093	#.4	20.95
	85-86 Outer	20547093	#.4	20.95
	Inner	20547092	#.4	72.75
#R&R Both on One Seat .6				

FRONT DOOR

Refinish Outside		2.2
Add for Jambs & Interior		1.0
Refinish Hinge		.2
R&I Door Assembly	Manual Window	.8
	Power Window	1.2
R&I Trim Panel		.4
Add to Door Shell R&R		
w/Power Windows		.4

SHEET METAL

Shell, Door	82-84 R	14071846	4.5	382.00
	L	15589933	4.5	382.00
	85-86 R	15536654	4.5	382.00
	L	15536653	4.5	382.00
Panel, Repair	R	14020326	5.5	101.65
	L	14020325	5.5	101.65
¶Included in Door Shell				

EXTERIOR TRIM

1-4230

1 Moulding, Side		12300650	.2	15.44
2 Moulding, Edge Guard				
Black		14051640-39	.2	3.85
Bright		14033688-7	.2	2.70
Stripe Tape - See Hood				
Mirror, Rear View				
Standard	82-84 R	14058008	.5	39.75
	L	14058007	.5	34.50
	85-86 R	15592884	.5	38.00
	L	15592883	.5	33.00
Below Eyeline				
Chrome		14031250-49		51.50

---

514 **Allowances Shown Are for Replacement With New OEM Undamaged Parts on New Undamaged Vehicles.** GM

FIGURE 3-93 Estimated time rates and part prices. (Courtesy of Mitchell Information Services Inc.)

CHEV/GMC S10-S15 1982-86

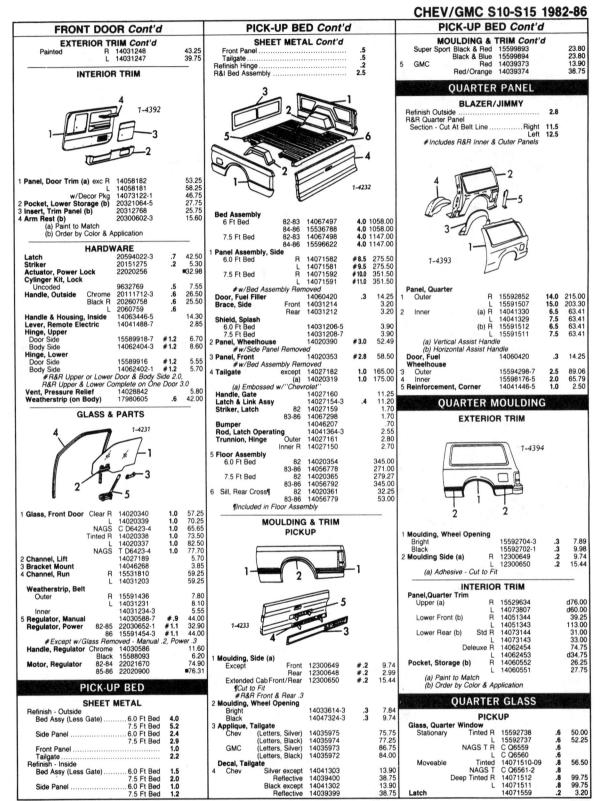

FRONT DOOR *Cont'd*

EXTERIOR TRIM *Cont'd*
Painted	R	14031248	43.25
	L	14031247	39.75

INTERIOR TRIM

1-4392

1 Panel, Door Trim (a) exc R		14058182	53.25
	L	14058181	58.25
w/Decor Pkg		14073122-1	46.75
2 Pocket, Lower Storage (b)		20321064-5	27.75
3 Insert, Trim Panel (b)		20312768	25.75
4 Arm Rest (b)		20300602-3	15.60
(a) Paint to Match			
(b) Order by Color & Application			

HARDWARE
Latch		20594022-3	.7	42.50
Striker		20151275	.2	5.30
Actuator, Power Lock		22020256	■	32.98
Cylinder Kit, Lock				
Uncoded		9632769	.5	7.55
Handle, Outside	Chrome	20111712-3	.6	26.50
	Black R	20260758	.6	25.50
	L	2060759	.6	
Handle & Housing, Inside		14063446-5		14.30
Lever, Remote Electric		14041488-7		2.85
Hinge, Upper				
Door Side		15589918-7	#1.2	6.70
Body Side		14062404-3	#1.2	8.60
Hinge, Lower				
Door Side		15589916	#1.2	5.55
Body Side		14062402-1	#1.2	5.70
#R&R Upper or Lower Door & Body Side 2.0,				
R&R Upper & Lower Complete on One Door 3.0				
Vent, Pressure Relief		14028842		5.80
Weatherstrip (on Body)		17980605	.6	42.00

GLASS & PARTS

1-4231

1 Glass, Front Door	Clear R	14020340	1.0	57.25
	L	14020339	1.0	70.25
	NAGS	C D6423-4	1.0	65.65
	Tinted R	14020338	1.0	73.50
	L	14020337	1.0	82.50
	NAGS	T D6423-4	1.0	77.70
2 Channel, Lift		14027189		5.70
3 Bracket Mount		14046268		3.85
4 Channel, Run	R	15531810		59.25
	L	14031203		59.25
Weatherstrip, Belt				
Outer	R	15591436		7.80
	L	14031231		8.10
Inner		14031234-3		5.55
5 Regulator, Manual		14030588-7	#.9	44.00
Regulator, Power	82-85	22030652-1	#1.1	32.90
	86	15591454-3	#1.1	44.00
#Except w/Glass Removed - Manual .2, Power .3				
Handle, Regulator	Chrome	14030586		11.60
	Black	15588093		6.20
Motor, Regulator	82-84	22021670		74.90
	85-86	22020900	■	76.31

PICK-UP BED

SHEET METAL
Refinish - Outside		
Bed Assy (Less Gate) ....6.0 Ft Bed		4.0
	7.5 Ft Bed	5.2
Side Panel ....6.0 Ft Bed		2.4
	7.5 Ft Bed	2.9
Front Panel		1.0
Tailgate		2.2
Refinish - Inside		
Bed Assy (Less Gate) ....6.0 Ft Bed		1.5
	7.5 Ft Bed	2.0
Side Panel ....6.0 Ft Bed		1.0
	7.5 Ft Bed	1.2

PICK-UP BED *Cont'd*

SHEET METAL *Cont'd*
Front Panel	.5
Tailgate	.5
Refinish Hinge	.2
R&I Bed Assembly	2.5

1-4232

Bed Assembly				
6 Ft Bed	82-83	14067497	4.0	1058.00
	84-86	15536788	4.0	1058.00
7.5 Ft Bed	82-83	14067498	4.0	1147.00
	84-86	15596622	4.0	1147.00
1 Panel Assembly, Side				
6.0 Ft Bed	R	14071582	#8.5	275.50
	L	14071581	#9.5	275.50
7.5 Ft Bed	R	14071592	#10.0	351.50
	L	14071591	#11.0	351.50
# w/Bed Assembly Removed				
Door, Fuel Filler		14060420	.3	14.25
Brace, Side	Front	14031214		3.20
	Rear	14031212		3.20
Shield, Splash				
6.0 Ft Bed		14031206-5		3.90
7.5 Ft Bed		14031208-7		3.90
2 Panel, Wheelhouse		14020390	#3.0	52.49
# w/Side Panel Removed				
3 Panel, Front		14020353	#2.8	58.50
# w/Bed Assembly Removed				
4 Tailgate	except	14027182	1.0	165.00
	(a)	14020319	1.0	175.00
(a) Embossed w/"Chevrolet"				
Handle, Gate		14027160		11.25
Latch & Link Assy		14027154-3	.4	11.20
Striker, Latch	82	14027159		1.70
	83-86	14067298		1.70
Bumper		14046207		.70
Rod, Latch Operating		14041364-3		2.55
Trunnion, Hinge	Outer	14027161		2.80
	Inner R	14027150		2.70
5 Floor Assembly				
6.0 Ft Bed	82	14020354		345.00
	83-86	14056778		271.00
7.5 Ft Bed	82	14020365		279.27
	83-86	14056792		345.00
6 Sill, Rear Cross¶	82	14020361		32.25
	83-86	14056779		53.00
¶Included in Floor Assembly				

MOULDING & TRIM PICKUP

1-4233

1 Moulding, Side (a)				
Except	Front	12300649	#.2	9.74
	Rear	12300648	#.2	2.99
Extended Cab Front/Rear		12300650	#.2	15.44
¶Cut to Fit				
#R&R Front & Rear .3				
2 Moulding, Wheel Opening				
Bright		14033614-3	.3	7.84
Black		14047324-3	.3	9.74
3 Applique, Tailgate				
Chev	(Letters, Silver)	14035975		75.75
	(Letters, Black)	14035974		77.25
GMC	(Letters, Silver)	14035973		86.75
	(Letters, Black)	14035972		84.00
Decal, Tailgate				
4 Chev	Silver except	14041303		13.90
	Reflective	14039400		38.75
	Black except	14041302		13.90
	Reflective	14039399		38.75

PICK-UP BED *Cont'd*

MOULDING & TRIM *Cont'd*
Super Sport Black & Red		15599893	23.80
	Black & Blue	15599894	23.80
5 GMC	Red	14039373	13.90
	Red/Orange	14039374	38.75

QUARTER PANEL

BLAZER/JIMMY
Refinish Outside		2.8
R&R Quarter Panel		
Section - Cut At Belt Line ....Right		11.5
Left		12.5
#Includes R&R Inner & Outer Panels		

1-4393

Panel, Quarter				
1 Outer	R	15592852	14.0	215.00
	L	15591507	15.0	203.30
2 Inner	(a) R	14041330	6.5	63.41
	L	14041329	7.5	63.41
	(b) R	15591512	6.5	63.41
	L	15591511	7.5	63.41
(a) Vertical Assist Handle				
(b) Horizontal Assist Handle				
Door, Fuel		14060420	.3	14.25
Wheelhouse				
3 Outer		15594298-7	2.5	89.06
4 Inner		15598176-5	2.0	65.79
5 Reinforcement, Corner		14041446-5	1.0	2.50

QUARTER MOULDING

EXTERIOR TRIM

1-4394

1 Moulding, Wheel Opening				
Bright		15592704-3	.3	7.89
Black		15592702-1	.3	9.98
2 Moulding Side (a)	R	12300649	.2	9.74
	L	12300650	.2	15.44
(a) Adhesive - Cut to Fit				

INTERIOR TRIM
Panel, Quarter Trim				
Upper (a)	R	15529634		d76.00
	L	14073807		d60.00
Lower Front (b)	R	14051344		39.25
	L	14051343		113.00
Lower Rear (b)	Std R	14073144		31.00
	L	14073143		33.00
	Deluxe R	14062454		74.75
	L	14062453		d34.75
Pocket, Storage (b)	R	14060552		26.25
	L	14060551		27.75
(a) Paint to Match				
(b) Order by Color & Application				

QUARTER GLASS

PICKUP
Glass, Quarter Window				
Stationary	Tinted R	15592738	.6	50.00
	L	15592737	.6	52.25
	NAGS T R	C Q6559	.6	
	L	C Q6560	.6	
Moveable	Tinted	14071510-09	.8	56.50
	NAGS T	C Q6561-2	.8	
	Deep Tinted R	14071512	.8	99.75
	L	14071511	.8	99.75
Latch		14071559	.2	3.20

FIGURE 3-94 Estimated time rates and parts prices. (Courtesy of Mitchell Information Services Inc.)

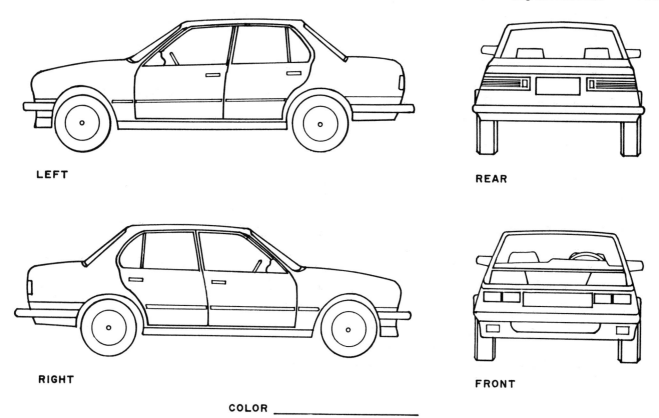

LEFT

REAR

RIGHT

FRONT

COLOR _____

FIGURE 3-95 Drawing of vehicles.

ESTIMATOR'S REPORT

Insurance Company _____

CLAIM NUMBER

Estimate, Inspection and Location Date _____

ADJUSTER'S NAME	ESTIMATOR'S NAME	DATE OF COMPLETION	DATE OF LOSS

INSURED

VEHICLE

NAME AND ADDRESS	LICENSE (POLICY) NUMBER	GVW	MILEAGE	AMOUNT OF DEDUCTIBLE
	YEAR, MAKE & MODEL		SERIAL NUMBER	

DESCRIPTION OF WORK TO BE DONE	RE-PAIR	REPLACE NEW	REPLACE L.K.Q.	QTY.	PART NUMBER	PARTS COST	HRS.	LABOR COST

This is purely an estimate and not a definite contract price. Owing to the impossibility of determining damage of concealed parts, we reserve the right to submit a further estimate for approval or otherwise. Prices subject to change without notice.
Authorization to Repair _____

I_____ the registered owner of the above described vehicle authorize the repairs to proceed.

TOTAL PARTS COST ▶	
TOTAL LABOR COST ▶	
SHOP MATERIAL	
PAINT LABOR	
PAINT MATERIAL	
SUB TOTAL	
TAX	
TOTAL COST ▶	

ONLY APPROVED ADDITIONS PAID

FIGURE 3-96 Write-in estimate.

QUESTIONS

3-1. What is meant by the term remove and install (R&I)?

3-2. What is meant by the term overhaul (O/H)?

3-3. What is meant by the term overlap/additional time?

3-4. How much time is added per panel for spraying a clear coat?

3-5. Explain how overlap is taken off and why when painting several panels on a vehicle.

3-6. Explain the system which is used to differentiate between right and left part numbers.

3-7. Explain how overlap on body repairs may be deducted.

3-8. What is meant by direct damage?

3-9. What is meant by indirect damage?

3-10. What sequence should be followed when pulling damage out?

3-11. Where are the times for repair procedures found?

3-12. What is meant by the terms "not included" or "included" when an operation method of remove and replace is described?

3-13. Explain what is meant by the zone system of estimating.

3-14. Why should a checklist be used when estimating?

## CHAPTER FOUR

Repairing Plastics

4-1 USES OF PLASTICS AND THEIR IDENTIFICATION

The use of plastic, when first introduced, was very limited; it was used mainly in the manufacturing of lenses on dash instruments, tail lamps, clearance lights, dome lights, window regulator handles, and various other small parts. However, over the years, its use has constantly increased, and today, as a result of automobile engineers' efforts to reduce the weight of their models, thereby enhancing fuel economy, more and more auto parts, such as dashboards, interior trim panels, filler panels, fender liners (wheel housings), fan blades, fan shrouds, bumper covers and impact strips, grilles, and headlamp and tail lamp bodies and lenses, are being made of plastic.

More than 15 different kinds of plastics are used in manufacturing auto parts (Fig. 4-1). There are two types:

- *Thermoplastic:* can be softened with the application of heat, can be reshaped, and can be welded.
- *Thermosetting:* permanently set; cannot be softened with the application of heat, cannot be reshaped, and cannot be welded. However, minor damage can often be repaired with a structural adhesive.

To determine if a material is thermoplastic, hold a heated welder 1 inch (25.4 mm) from the material for approximately 10 seconds. If the material begins softening, it is thermoplastic and can in most instances be welded.

To repair plastic, the repair person must first identify the material. This can be done by looking for a set of letters on the back or underside of the part and matching the letters to the manufacturer's identification chart (Fig. 4-1). If no letters can be found on the part, consult the manufacturer's plastic identification guide (Fig. 4-2).

The following tests will also help the repair person to identify five of the more common plastics used.

ABS and Polypropylene (PP) Test

Using a sharp knife, remove a sliver of plastic from the hidden back side of the part. Hold the sliver of plastic with tweezers or lay it on a clean, noncombustible surface. Ignite the plastic and observe the burning closely. ABS plastic burns with a readily visible black smoke residue that will hang temporarily in the air. Polypropylene burns with no visible smoke, has its own distinguishing smell, will continue to burn when removed from flame, and will float in water.

Symbol	Plastic material
ABS	ABS
ABS/PVC	ABS/Vinyl
PA	Nylon
PC	Lexan
PE	Polyethylene
PP	Polypropylene
PPO	Noryl
PUR	Thermoset polyurethane
PVC	Polyvinyl chloride (vinyl)
SAN	SAN
TPUR	Thermoplastic polyurethane
UP	Polyester (Fiberglass)
TPR	Thermoplastic rubber
EPDM	Ethylene propylene diene monomer

FIGURE 4-1   Types of plastics.

Polyvinyl Chloride (PVC) Test

With a propane or similar torch, heat a copper wire until it begins to glow or turns red. Touch the heated wire to the hidden or back side of the plastic material so that some of the plastic adheres to the wire. Move the wire back into the flame. If the plastic on the wire burns, giving off a greenish-turquoise blue flame, it is polyvinyl chloride.

Polyethylene (PE) Test

This material will melt, swell, and drip when a flame is directed on it. Drippings may burn and will continue burning when the flame is removed, giving off a burning wax odor. It will also float in water.

Thermoplastic Polyurethane (TPUR) Test

This plastic is very flexible. When set on fire, it burns with a yellow orange flame, gives off black smoke, and continues to burn with a sputter when the flame is removed.

4-2 REPAIR METHODS

Thermoplastic Welding

The welding of plastics is done with a special torch equipped with three tips and with a 115-volt, 300 to 500-watt element that heats low-pressure compressed air to a temperature of 400° to 700°F (260° to 371°C), hot enough to melt most thermoplastic materials (Fig. 4-3). Each manufacturer supplies its own operational instructions, and these should be carefully followed.

CAUTION: The barrel of the torch, heated by the electric element, gets hot enough that skin contact could cause a burn.

Plastic Welding Rod.   Plastic welding requires a welding rod made from the same material as the plastic being repaired. Welding rods are available from local plastics suppliers or can be made from clean scrap materials of the same type as that being repaired, provided that the material has not been stressed.

Preparing the Damaged Area for Welding.   The break or tear should be trimmed to a V shape using a sharp knife or by sanding (Fig. 4-4). The reason for sanding the tear to a V shape is to expose a larger surface area to heat and provide a void to fill with the softened welding rod, resulting in complete bonding or fusion. Any dust or shaving should be wiped from the joint with a dry, clean rag. Do not use solvents for cleaning, because these tend to soften the edges, causing poor welds. Figure 4-5 shows the various types of V butt welds.

Start-up Procedure.   Before starting the welding torch, make sure that you use clean compressed air and that the air is flowing through the torch before the electricity is turned on.

1. Turn on the compressed air and adjust the pressure to approximately $2\frac{1}{2}$ psi (17.2 kPa). The pressure setting may vary depending on the type and thickness of the plastic being welded.
2. Plug in the torch to the power supply (115 volts) and allow it to preheat for 5 to 10 minutes.
3. Check the temperature by holding a thermometer $\frac{1}{4}$ inch (6 mm) from the hot-air end of the torch tip. The temperature should be in the range from 400° to 750°F (204.4° to 399°C) for most thermoplastic welding.

Shutting-off Procedure

1. Disconnect the torch from the 115-volt power supply.
2. Allow compressed air to cool off the heating element before disconnecting the air supply.

Aligning the Tear or Break.   Align the edges to be joined as necessary. If the tear is long and back-up difficult, small tack welds can be made along its entire length to hold the two sides in place while finish welding is carried out. Tack welding is done:

1. By holding the damaged area in its correct shape and position, using clamps, fixtures, and so on.
2. Using the torch equipped with either the tack welding or round freehand welding tip and applying hot air evenly to both sides of the break or tear until the material melts together. Adding

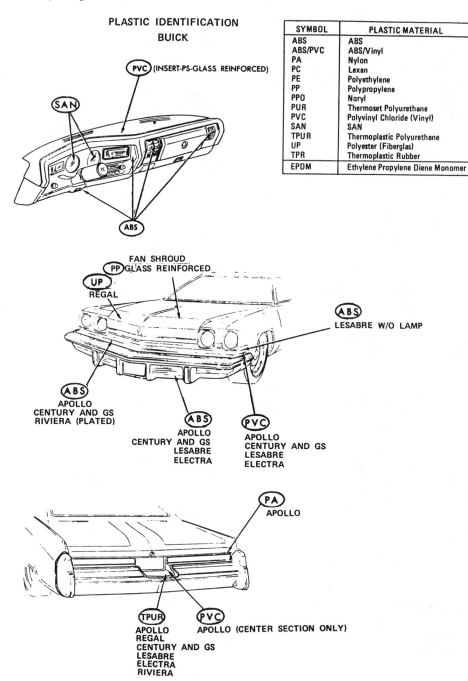

SYMBOL	PLASTIC MATERIAL
ABS	ABS
ABS/PVC	ABS/Vinyl
PA	Nylon
PC	Lexan
PE	Polyethylene
PP	Polypropylene
PPO	Noryl
PUR	Thermoset Polyurethane
PVC	Polyvinyl Chloride (Vinyl)
SAN	SAN
TPUR	Thermoplastic Polyurethane
UP	Polyester (Fiberglas)
TPR	Thermoplastic Rubber
EPDM	Ethylene Propylene Diene Monomer

FIGURE 4-2   Plastic identification for the Oldsmobile. (Courtesy of General Motors of Canada, Ltd.)

additional material (welding rod) should not be attempted at this time.

Starting the Weld Bead.   Hold the torch $\frac{1}{2}$ inch (12 mm) from the work end tip of the welding rod, which is held at 90° to the base material (Fig. 4-6). Play the torch between the rod and base material, evenly preheating both until shiny and tacky. Now move the rod to barely touch the base material. If preheated sufficiently, the rod will

stick. Keep moving the torch between the material and rod, simultaneously pressing the rod into the V weld area, with a light pressure of about 3 psi (20.7 kPa). When enough heat has been applied, a molten wave will form in the area where the welding rod and base material meet, and the rod will begin to bend and move forward (Fig. 4-7).

NOTE: In plastic welding, a good start is essential in running a strong bead, because it is at the outer edges of

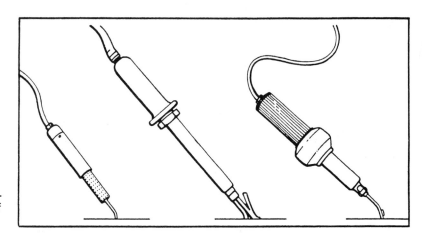

FIGURE 4-3 Types of torches. (Courtesy of General Motors of Canada, Ltd.)

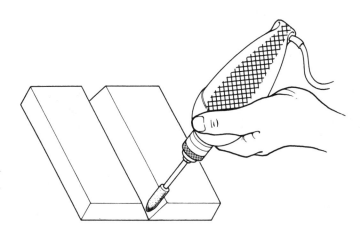

FIGURE 4-4 V shaping a tear or break using a power drill. (Courtesy General Motors of Canada, Ltd.)

Single-V
single bead
butt weld

Double-V
butt weld

Multiple bead
single-V
butt weld

Multiple bead
double-V
butt weld

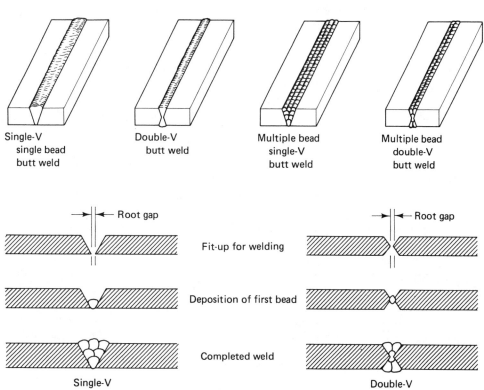

Root gap — Fit-up for welding — Root gap

Deposition of first bead

Completed weld

Single-V

Double-V

FIGURE 4-5 Different types of joints. (Courtesy of General Motors of Canada, Ltd.)

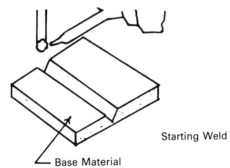

FIGURE 4-6   Starting the weld. (Courtesy of
General Motors of Canada Ltd.)

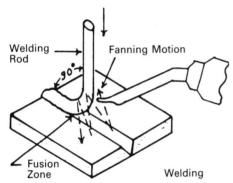

FIGURE 4-7   Welding motion. (Courtesy of
General Motors of Canada, Ltd.)

the base material where most weld failures begin. Therefore, wherever possible, the starting points on multiple-
bead welds should be staggered.

Running of the bead is continued by moving the torch
between the rod and the base material, with a sort of fanning
motion. However, because the rod is much lighter and less
bulky than the base material, it is important that more heat
be directed on the base material if overheating and charring
of the welding rod are to be prevented.

Feeding the Welding Rod.   A constant pressure
must be applied on the rod as it is being fed into the material.
A release of this pressure may cause the rod to lift away
from the weld bead and air to become trapped under the
weld, resulting in a poor weld. The welder must therefore
develop skill at applying a constant pressure on the rod,
while repositioning the fingers. This can be done by
applying pressure on the rod with the third and fourth fingers
while the thumb and first fingers are repositioned higher up
on the rod (Fig. 4-8). To do this, the rod must be kept cool
enough. This is accomplished by careful aiming of the torch
and by applying heat only to the bottom end of the rod.

Completing the Weld.   When reaching the end of
a weld, stop the fanning forward motion with the torch and

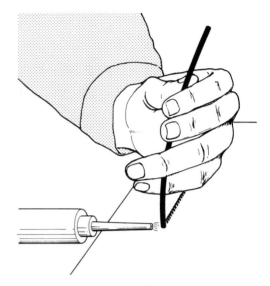

Completing the Weld

FIGURE 4-8   Holding the rod and torch. (Courtesy of General Motors of Canada, Ltd.)

direct it at the intersection of rod and base material. Remove
the torch but maintain a constant downward pressure on the
rod for a few more seconds. This will allow the rod to cool
and prevent it from being pulled from the base material.
The unused rod can then be cut from the weld.

A weld does not develop its full strength until it has
completely cooled, which generally takes about 15 to 20
minutes. Cooling can be speeded by applying cold water
or compressed air.

CAUTION: Any attempt to test a thermoplastic weld by
bending it before it has completely cooled may result in
weld separation.

Grinding Down the Weld.   Excess plastic on rough
welds can be removed with a sharp knife before grinding
down of excessive buildup on large beads is attempted.
Grinding can best be done with a 9-inch (229-mm) variable-
speed polisher (5000 rpm), equipped with a No. 36 or P36
grit sanding disk. Care must be exercised not to overheat
the weld area or it will become soft. Periodic cooling with
water will speed up the grinding process and prevent damage
to the weld.

Checking the Strength of the Weld.   After the
weld has been ground level and smooth, it should be
examined for defects. Any pores or cracks visible before
or after bend testing of the welded material will make the
weld unacceptable. The weld should be just as strong as
the part itself.

Finish Sanding of the Welded Area.   Welded
areas found acceptable are finish-sanded with either an

orbital or a belt sander, or by hand-sanding with a sanding block using No. 220 or P220 grit sandpaper, followed with No. 320 or P400 grit. The welded part is now ready for refinishing.

Semiautomatic Speed Welding. Long, straight breaks or tears can be welded much faster with the torch equipped with a speed welding tip than with a round, freehand welding tip. This tip makes it possible for the repair person to apply heat, pressure, and the feeding of the welding rod with only one hand, once the weld has been started (Fig. 4-9).

In starting the weld, hold the torch at 90° to the base material; insert the rod into the preheating tube, and place the pointed shoe immediately on the base material on the base material at the starting point (Fig. 4-10).

Holding the torch perpendicular to the base material with one hand, push the welding rod down with the other hand until it makes contact with the base material. Applying a slight pressure on the rod and with only the weight of the torch on the shoe, slowly begin pulling the torch forward. The rod should be helped along by pushing it into the tube for the first 1 to 2 inches (25.4 or 50.8 mm) of travel. Once the weld has been started, the torch should be brought to an approximate 70° angle. The rod will then feed automatically, or hand-feeding can be continued.

The quality of the weld can be visually inspected as the torch is moved along. If the welding rod has been softened too much due to overheating, it will cause the rod to stretch, break, or flatten out, and the fusion lines on each side of the bead will be oversized. If no fusion lines are visible, not enough pressure is being applied on the base material or the welding speed (forward movement of the torch) is too fast.

The angle between the torch and base material determines the welding speed. Since the preheater hole in the speed tip precedes the shoe, the angle of the torch to the material determines how close the preheater hole is to the base material and how much preheating occurs. For this reason, the torch is held at a 90° angle when starting the weld (bead) and changed to approximately 45° as welding is continued (Fig. 4-11).

If inspection of the bead indicates too fast a welding speed, the torch should be brought back temporarily to a 90° angle to slow down the welding speed, and then gradually adjusted to the proper angle for the welding speed desired.

NOTE: It is very important that the torch be held so that both the preheater hole and shoe of the speed welding tip are always kept in line with the direction of the weld and that only the base material in front of the shoe is preheated. The heat pattern on the base material clearly indicates the

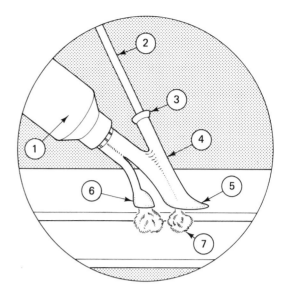

1. Electric torch
2. Welding rod
3. Speed tip
4. Rod is preheated in tube
5. Shoe provides pressure
6. Orifice preheats area to be welded
7. Heat

FIGURE 4-9 Electric torch with speed welding tip. (Courtesy of General Motors of Canada, Ltd.)

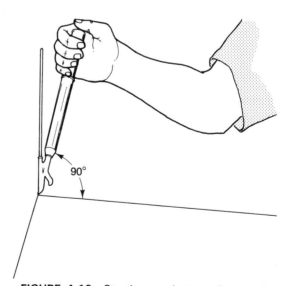

FIGURE 4-10 Starting semiautomatic speed weld. (Courtesy of General Motors of Canada Ltd.)

area being preheated, and the rod should always be solidly fused in the center of that pattern.

Completing the Speed Weld. Speed welding, once started, must be continued at a relatively constant

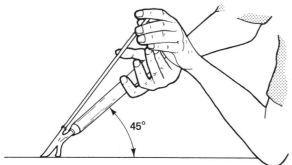

FIGURE 4-11 Continuing the semiautomatic speed weld. (Courtesy of General Motors of Canada Ltd.)

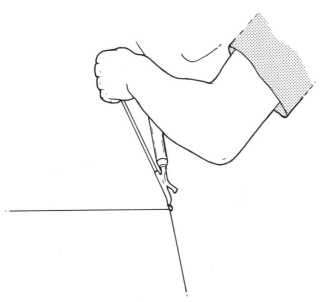

FIGURE 4-12 Finishing the semiautomatic speed weld. (Courtesy of General Motors of Canada Ltd.)

speed. When welding is to be stopped before the rod has been used up, the torch is brought back past the 90° angle, and the rod is cut off with the shoe (Fig. 4-12). The cut-off rod must be removed immediately from the preheater tube or it will melt and char, plugging the tube and making its cleaning necessary. Welding can also be stopped by pulling the speed tip off the remaining rod, which is allowed to cool before it is cut off with a sharp knife.

The bead on a good weld will have a slightly higher crown and more uniformity than is possible in freehand welding. It will appear shiny and smooth. For best results, the speed tip must be kept perfectly clean by occasionally cleaning it with a wire brush.

Repairing Flexible Exterior Plastic Parts

Soft plastic parts used for exterior and cosmetic application are made of resins that have flexible characteristics, enabling them to absorb minor impact without sustaining damage. Front and rear bumper filler panels, valance and end panels, quarter-panel extensions, front and rear bumper upper and lower covers, and bumper center moldings are typical examples. These parts, usually fabricated of thermosetting plastic, cannot be welded, but minor damage such as punctures, gouges, and tears (Fig. 4-13) can be repaired successfully with structural adhesive.

Structural Adhesive Repair Procedure. The damaged area is cleaned with a general-purpose adhesive cleaner and wax remover. Clean both sides of the part if damage extends through the entire thickness of the part. Using a No. 36 or P36 grit disk, grind away all damaged material and, for best adhesion, feather-edge a large area around the damage with a No. 180 or P180 grit desk (Fig. 4-14). Lightly singe the repair area with a gas torch for approximately 15 seconds (Fig. 4-15).

Apply either body tape or a new or clean used adhesive-backed disk to the back side of the damage, so as to keep the patch material from falling through (Fig. 4-16). Remove all dust and any loose particles from the repair area.

Take the 3M No. 8101 Structural Adhesive Tube Kit, or equivalent, and thoroughly mix the two-component adhesive according to the manufacturer's instructions, using a putty knife or the stick enclosed in the package (Fig. 4-17). The mixing board should be made of nonporous material, such as metal, glass, or plastic, onto which equal-length beads of each component are deposited.

In mixing, do not lift the adhesive from the mixing board. Scrape the two components together, and with downward pressure on the putty knife or stick provided, continue spreading the components out thinly on the mixing board until a uniform color and consistency is achieved. This procedure will prevent the trapping of air (bubbles) in the adhesive.

Scrape the mixed adhesive from the mixing board and apply a thin coat over the damaged area with a soft squeegee. Mix and apply a second heavy, filling coat of adhesive (Fig. 4-18). Allow the filled area to cure 20 to 30 minutes at 60° to 80°F (16° to 27°C).

Sand the filling adhesive level with the surrounding area, using a flat, curved-tooth body file to establish a rough contour (Fig. 4-19), followed by disk sanding with a No. 240 or P280 grit disk, and then wet sanding with No. 320 or P400 grit sandpaper (Fig. 4-20). Check the area for voids and low areas and, if necessary, apply more adhesive to these areas.

Bake the repaired area for about 15 minutes at 180°F (83°C) using heat lamps (Fig. 4-21). Allow to cool before sanding down (rechecking the contour and simultaneously feather-edging) the area to its final shape and finish, using

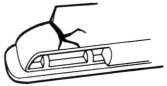

FIGURE 4-13 Types of damage. (Courtesy of Ford Motor Company of Canada, Ltd.)

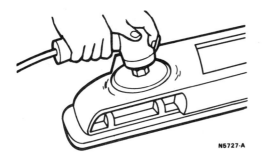

FIGURE 4-14 Grinding and feather-edging damaged areas. (Courtesy of Ford Motor Company of Canada, Ltd.)

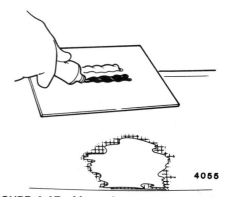

FIGURE 4-15 Lightly singeing repair area. (Courtesy of Ford Motor Company of Canada, Ltd.)

FIGURE 4-17 Measuring two component repair material. (Courtesy of General Motors of Canada, Ltd.)

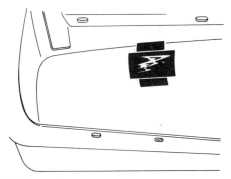

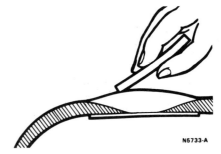

FIGURE 4-16 Tape applied for support of repair material. (Courtesy of General Motors of Canada, Ltd.)

FIGURE 4-18 Applying structural adhesive material. (Courtesy of Ford Motor Company of Canada, Ltd.)

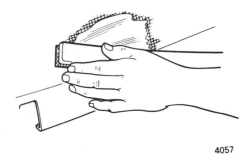

4057

FIGURE 4-19 Establishing rough contour. (Courtesy of General Motors of Canada, Ltd.)

4058

FIGURE 4-20 Block sanding for accurate contour. (Courtesy of General Motors of Canada, Ltd.)

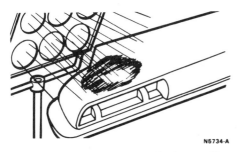

N5734-A

FIGURE 4-21 Baking the repaired area. (Courtesy of Ford Motor Company of Canada, Ltd.)

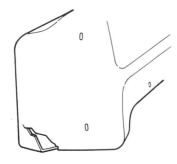

4059

FIGURE 4-22 Damaged attaching surface. (Courtesy of General Motors of Canada, Ltd.)

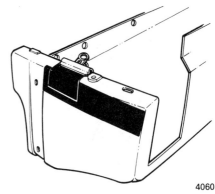

4060

FIGURE 4-23 Aligning break with tape and clamp. (Courtesy of General Motors of Canada, Ltd.)

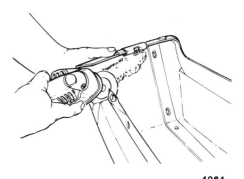

4061

FIGURE 4-24 Disksanding back side of damaged area. (Courtesy of General Motors of Canada, Ltd.)

No. 320 or P400 and No. 400 or P800 grit wet sandpaper, respectively. The repaired part is then refinished as required.

Structural-type Repair. The structural strength of the attaching surface (flange) of a part that is cracked or has broken away (Fig. 4-22) can be successfully repaired as follows.

Align and securely position the piece on the face side with body tape and a clamp (Fig. 4-23). Clean the underside of the repair area with a general-purpose adhesive cleaner and wax remover before sanding each side of the break with a No. 50 or P50 grit sanding disk (Fig. 4-24).

Cut a piece of fiberglass cloth large enough to overlap the break $1\frac{1}{2}$ inches (38 mm) (Fig. 4-25).

Mix a quantity of structural adhesive and apply a layer of the mixture, about $\frac{1}{8}$ inch (3 mm) thick, on the back side of the part, overlapping the break at least $1\frac{1}{2}$ inch (38 mm) (Fig. 4-26).

Apply the precut fiberglass cloth over the adhesive, and immediately cover the cloth with enough additional adhesive to completely fill and cover the weave (Figs. 4-27 and 4-28).

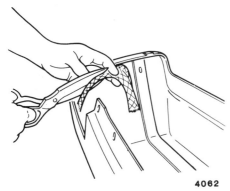

FIGURE 4-25 Cutting fiberglass cloth to size. (Courtesy of General Motors of Canada, Ltd.)

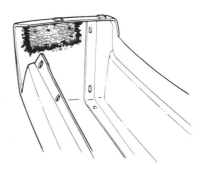

FIGURE 4-27 Applying fiberglass cloth. (Courtesy of General Motors of Canada, Ltd.)

FIGURE 4-26 Applying structural adhesive material. (Courtesy of General Motors of Canada, Ltd.)

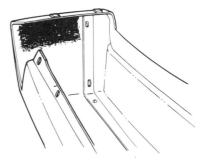

FIGURE 4-28 Filling fiberglass cloth. (Courtesy of General Motors of Canada, Ltd.)

Allow the area 20 to 30 minutes curing time at 60° to 80°F (16° to 27°C) before trimming off any excess material from the edge, if necessary.

The clamp and body tape are then removed, and the face side of the part is now repaired following the same repair procedure as that employed in repairing a puncture, gouge, or tear, and described earlier in this unit.

QUESTIONS

4-1. Name the two types of plastic used in manufacturing automobile parts and how they differ.

4-2. How can a repair person identify the material to be repaired?

4-3. Describe the test used in identifying ABS and polypropylene (PP) plastic.

4-4. How can polyvinyl chloride (PVC) be identified?

4-5. How can polyethylene (PE) and thermoplastic polyurethane (TPUR) be identified when ignited?

4-6. What type of torch is used for welding plastics?

4-7. What can be used as a welding rod when a particular kind of rod is not readily available?

4-8. How and why should a break or tear be trimmed to a V shape?

4-9. Briefly describe the procedure used in starting up and shutting down a welding torch.

4-10. How is the tack welding of a tear or break carried out?

4-11. At what distance from the work should the torch be held when starting the weld bead?

4-12. In plastic welding, why is a good start essential in the running of a strong bead?

4-13. How is the torch manipulated in welding once the bead has been started?

4-14. Why must more heat be directed on the base metal than on the rod?

4-15. How is a constant pressure kept on the rod as it is fed into the material?

4-16. Once a weld has been completed, how can cooling off be speeded?

4-17. How and with what is excessive buildup on large beads ground down?

4-18. What special tip makes welding of long, straight breaks much faster?

4-19. When using the speed welding tip, how is the torch held once the bead has been started?

4-20. What appearance will a good speed-welded bead have?

4-21. What material is used in repairing minor damage on parts made of thermosetting plastic?

4-22. Describe how the surface of a damaged area is prepared for the structural adhesive.

4-23. How and on what are the two components of structural adhesive mixed?

4-24. How is the mixed structural adhesive applied?

4-25. Explain the procedure used in repairing the attaching surface or flange on a thermosetting plastic panel.

## CHAPTER FIVE

Metal Inert Gas Welding and Sectioning of Body Components

SAFETY TIPS

When any grinding is done, a face mask or goggles that cover the eyes should be worn at all times. A body grinder can be a very dangerous tool if not used properly; the disk can disintegrate and hurt the operator or any other person in the vicinity. Compressed air is a very useful tool. If used improperly, however, it could cause serious injury to a person if some particles of dust are blown into the eyes.

A basic rule of safety is that staff should not horse around, run, or play practical jokes, because the jokes and tricks get worse and worse until somebody gets hurt. A first-aid kit should be available at all times; it should be stocked with all basic items required to render first aid for simple injuries.

Welding Tips

1. Never convert an acetylene regulator to oxygen use, or vice versa.
2. Never use cylinder gas without a regulator.
3. Always stand to the side of an oxygen regulator when the valve is opened.
4. Always open the oxygen valve slowly until the pressure reaches the maximum; then finish opening the valve.
5. Always check to see that the pressure-adjusting screw is released before opening the cylinder valve.
6. Never use a hose that is dirty or that has talc inside; blow it out with oxygen. Dirt or talc could clog the torch.
7. Never use more than hand pressure to open cylinder valves. If the valve is too tight, the cylinder should be replaced.
8. Heating a cylinder with a flame could cause it to explode.
9. Never try to fill a small cylinder from a large one.
10. Observe all fire-prevention practices. Have water and a fire extinguisher handy for use if necessary.
11. Always wear welding goggles when welding or cutting.
12. Never try to repair regulators or torches unless you know how to do so. A poor job could cause a serious explosion.
13. Always protect the hose from fire, slag, or sharp edges. It is made of rubber and burns or can be cut easily.
14. Always take good care of your welding equipment. It is a good servant if used properly.
15. When a welding torch is not being used, it should be shut off because it could set a fire or seriously burn a fellow worker if he should come in contact with it. One of the most dangerous things to weld is a gas tank that has not been

steamed properly, for there is a good chance that it will explode on contact with the flame. One of the best methods to repair a gas tank is to use a soldering iron and do a solder repair instead; it is much safer.

16. Always use proper clothing and safety helmet when MIG welding.

17. Always shut the MIG welder switch and C25 cylinder valve off when the welding is finished.

5-1 METAL INERT GAS WELDING

Metal inert gas (MIG) welding, also called gas metal arc welding (GMAW), uses a continuous, consumable, bare wire that is automatically fed through the torch into the work at a constant preset speed. As the wire makes contact with the work, it short-circuits; an arc is established and a small portion of the end of the wire melts, drops down on the work (forming a puddle), and the arc goes out. However, while the arc is out, the molten metal (puddle) begins cooling and flattening out; the wire continues to be fed, contacting the work and short-circuiting out again. This procedure of heating and cooling is repeated time after time, an average of up to 90 times per second, and each time a small amount of molten metal is transferred to the work (Fig. 5-1). The molten metal or puddle is protected from atmospheric contamination by a shielding gas, such as carbon dioxide (CO_2), or a mixture of 75% argon and 25% carbon dioxide. The latter, although more costly, has been found most suitable for welding mild- and high-strength steel, because argon produces a much more stable arc than CO_2, resulting in a neater bead, with less spatter and burn-through, especially when welding very thin sheet metal.

Most MIG welders, as shown in Fig. 5-2A, come set up from the factory for 0.023 or 0.030 inch (0.6 and 0.8 mm) wire, available in 8- to 12-inch (203 to 305 mm) spools at most welding supply outlets. They require a constant voltage power source to operate with optimum efficiency, and should be used employing a direct-current reverse polarity (DCRP) circuit (Fig. 5-2B) in order to get the maximum penetration possible, with a minimum of heat transfer to the base metal or work.

However, it is possible, and sometimes desirable, to reverse the direction of electron flow by changing from a direct-current reverse polarity (DCRP) circuit to a direct-current straight-polarity (DCSP) circuit. Each circuit has its advantages.

When a DCRP circuit is used, one-third of the heat generated in the arc is released at the base metal and two-thirds is released on the wire-electrode metal and the surrounding shielding gas, causing them to be superheated. As a result, the molten metal in the arc travels at a far higher rate of speed across the arc to the base metal. Deep penetration, with little or no warping of the base metal, results.

When a DCSP circuit is used, just the opposite occurs. One-third of the heat generated in the arc is released on the wire electrode and two-thirds is released on the base metal. A weld with less penetration, greater heat buildup in the weld zone, and more warping of the base metal results.

Advantages of MIG Welding

MIG welding has the following advantages compared to other methods of welding:

1. It makes faster high-speed welding possible.

2. Because welding can be done at a higher speed, distortion and warping are greatly reduced.

3. It provides a narrower, more concentrated, and controlled heat, making it ideal for mild-steel, high-strength steel (HSS), and aluminum welding.

4. It is much easier to learn, making possible faster operator training.

5. Less waste of welding wire (filler rod) is realized.

6. No slag or flux has to be removed from welds, resulting in considerable saving in labor costs.

7. Perfect penetration in fusion and spot welding of sheet metal is obtained.

8. Less dismantling is required for the prevention of fire.

Using the MIG Welder

Setting up the Welding Gun. The welder must first select the proper liner for the gun. The type of liner used in the gun is determined by the wire being used. A Teflon liner is used for aluminum wire and a steel liner for all other types of wire (Fig. 5-3).

Selecting the Contact Tip. The size of contact tip required in the gun is determined by the size of wire used. A contact tip that is too small will hinder wire feed, and a contact tip that is too large will not provide sufficient electrical contact for the weld wire (Fig. 5-4). For easy identification, each contact tip is stamped with its proper size. To install the tip, just screw it clockwise into the end of gun and tighten.

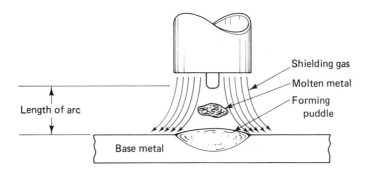

Length of arc

Shielding gas
Molten metal
Forming puddle

Base metal

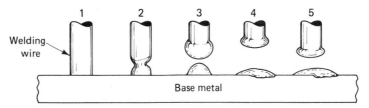

Welding wire

Base metal

(A)

FIGURE 5-1 Transfer of welding wire to work.

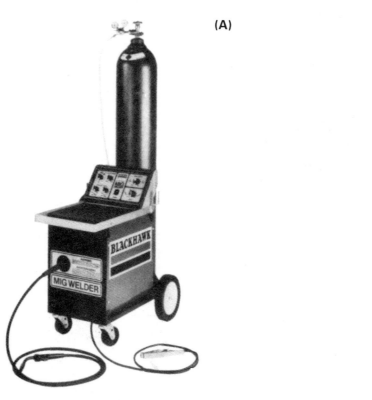

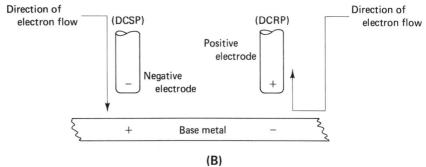

Direction of electron flow   (DCSP)

Negative electrode

Positive electrode

(DCRP)   Direction of electron flow

+   Base metal   —

(B)

FIGURE 5-2A Typical MIG welder. (B) Direct-current straight-polarity and direct-current reverse-polarity circuits. [(A) Courtesy of Blackhawk, Division of Applied Power of Canada Ltd.]

Selecting the Gas Nozzle. Two gas nozzles are provided with each machine: a standard welding nozzle and a spot welding nozzle (Fig. 5-5). The standard nozzle is used for applications other than spot welding.

NOTE: Gas nozzles should be kept clean. Use a small piece of wood to remove spatter buildup. Antispatter spray on the gas nozzle and contact tip before operation will make

the removal of spatter easy. Nozzles thread on and off and should only be hand-tightened.

Selecting the Welding Wire. The type and size of welding wire required are determined by the type and thickness of the metal to be welded (Fig. 5-6). Many welding machines come set up from the factory for 0.023-

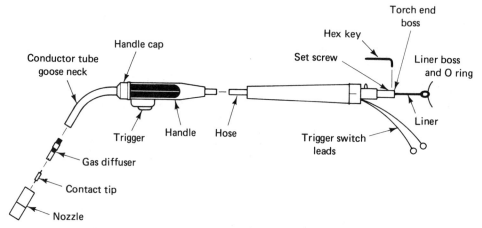

FIGURE 5-3 Liner change installation. (Courtesy of Blackhawk, Division of Applied Power of Canada Ltd.)

Wire size (in.)	Contact tip size [(in.) mm]
0.023	0.023 (0.6)
0.030	0.030 (0.8)
0.035	0.035 (1.0)

FIGURE 5-4 Contact tip-size chart. (Courtesy of Blackhawk, Division of Applied Power of Canada Ltd.)

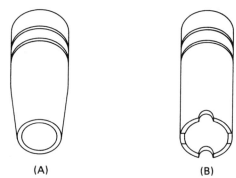

(A)   (B)

FIGURE 5-5 Gas nozzles: (A) standard; (B) spot weld.

Material thickness		Gage No.	28	22	16	10	4	0
		Fractional (in.)	1/64	1/32	1/16	1/8	1/4	3/8
		Decimal (in.)	0.015	0.030	0.062	0.125	0.250	0.340
		Metric (mm)	0.4	0.8	1	3	6	9
Recommended wire size	Steel	0.023 in. (0.6 mm) 0.030 in. (0.8 mm) 0.035 in. (1.0 mm)						
	Aluminum	0.030 in. (0.8 mm) 0.035 in. (1.0 mm)						

FIGURE 5-6 Wire size selection chart. (Courtesy of Blackhawk, Division of Applied Power of Canada Ltd.)

inch (0.6 mm) wire, and with only minor modifications will also accept 0.030- and 0.035-inch (0.8 and 0.9 mm) wire.

Only premium wire meeting AWS Spec. A5.18, electrode classification E70-S6, should be used for all automotive steel welding, including high-strength steel (HSS) and high-strength low-alloy steel (HSLA). The electrode classification number E70-S6 conveys the following information:

- E identifies the wire to be used as an electrode.
- 70 stands for 70,000 psi (483,000 kPa) tensile strength.
- S denotes a solid, bare steel welding wire.
- 6 specifies the chemical composition of the welding wire in accordance with American Welding Society specifications.

Two common filler wires are recommended for aluminum welding: type 5356 and type 4043. Either type should be compatible with automotive applications of aluminum, but filler wire 0.035 inch (1 mm) in diameter is recommended for heavy applications.

Installing the Welding Wire

1. The power switch should be flipped to *off* before the door on the left side of the cabinet is opened.
2. The wire tension lever is then flipped out, and the spool hub flange nut is removed (Fig. 5-7).
3. Unpack the wire very carefully. If narrow spools are used, put wire on first; then install the spool spacer. Make sure that the wire unwinds from the top in a clockwise direction and that the guide pin on the wire spindle lines up with the hole in the back side of the wire spool. To verify that the guide pin is in position, rock the wire spool back and forth on the spindle.
4. Reinstall the spool hub flange nut to hold the spool on the hub.
5. Adjust the spool hub brake tension by turning

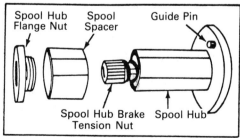

FIGURE 5-7 Wire spool installation. (Courtesy of Blackhawk, Division of Applied Power of Canada Ltd.)

the nut clockwise to increase, or counterclockwise to decrease, braking.

6. Carefully loosen the wire from the spool so that it does not unravel, keeping a firm grip on the wire throughout the cutting and threading operation. Straighten the wire and cut the end off straight.
7. Check the drive wheel groove for proper size. The small groove is used for wire 0.023 inch (0.6 mm) in diameter and the large groove for wire 0.030 and 0.035 inch (0.8 and 0.9 mm) in diameter.
8. Thread the wire through the brass guide tube of the drive assembly, past the drive and idler rollers into the torch end, making sure that the wire is properly started in the liner of the torch assembly.

NOTE: Check that the correct gun liner and contact tip are being used for the wire size selected.

9. Close the wire drive pressure wheel assembly by moving the tension lever.
10. Remove the gas nozzle and contact tip from the end of the welding gun to prevent an obstruction to the welding wire end to be fed through the torch assembly (Fig. 5-8).
11. Push the power switch into the *on* position. Set the wire feed control to number 4 and, pointing the gun away from the welding machine and yourself, press the gun control trigger until the welding wire emerges from the torch.
12. Check the wire spool brake tension by holding the spool with your hand. While turning the spool, you should feel a slight amount of resistance, just enough tension to prevent unraveling of the wire when drive is stopped. Spool brake tension should be checked frequently, not only when changing wire, but also as the spool is used.
13. Install the proper contact tip (the size is marked on its side) and the desired gas nozzle. Antispatter should now be applied to help keep the spatter from sticking.
14. Cut off the extra wire protruding so that the end of the welding wire extends about $\frac{1}{4}$ inch (6 mm) from the tip of the gun (Fig. 5-9).

Selecting the Shielding Gas. The type of gas to be used is determined by the type of metal to be welded. Be sure to use a welding-grade gas. Local welding suppliers can advise you as to the shielding gas for auto body welding (Fig. 5-10).

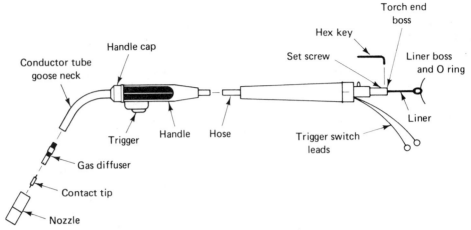

FIGURE 5-8 MIG welding torch assembly. (Courtesy of Blackhawk, Division of Applied Power of Canada Ltd.)

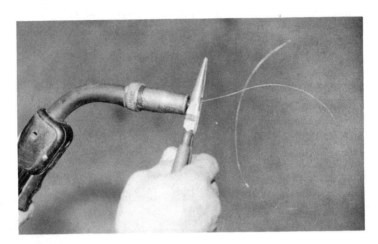

FIGURE 5-9 Cutting off welding wire.

Material	Gas	Flow rate with gun control trigger depressed
All steels	75% Argon 25% CO₂	12–20 cfh*
	Stargon 100% CO₂	12–20 cfh*
		16–24 cfh*
Aluminum	100% Argon	16–24 cfh*

FIGURE 5-10 Shielding gases and flow rates. (Courtesy of Blackhawk, Division of Applied Power of Canada Ltd.)

NOTE: Pure carbon dioxide (CO_2) shielding gas is not recommended for autobody welding. Shielding gas does not produce heat.

Connecting the Gas Regulator to the Shielding Gas Cylinder. Basically the same procedure is followed in connecting a gas regulator to a shielding gas cylinder as in oxyacetylene welding.

Connecting the Ground Clamp. All paint, rust, scale, oil, and other nonconductive or flammable material must be removed from the welding area and the area where the ground connection is to be made. Clamp the ground cable as close to the weld area as possible.

A good, clean ground clamp connection is very important in all arc welding. A poor connection not only wastes power but results in poor welder performance.

Steps To Be Followed before Welding Is Attempted

1. Place power switch in the *on* position.
2. Open the shielding gas cylinder very slowly but fully.
3. Adjust the heat and wire speed control.

4. Move the weld selector switch to the manual weld position.

5. Adjust the regulator flow rate.

6. Clamp the ground cable to the work.

7. Extend the welding wire about $\frac{1}{4}$ inch (6 mm) beyond the contact tip.

8. Follow all necessary safety precautions. Place the torch in position; wear gloves and proper clothing; lower the helmet or use a shield; press the trigger and proceed to weld.

Welding Positions. As in oxyacetylene welding, MIG welding can be done in all four positions: flat, horizontal, vertical, and overhead. Welding in the flat position is usually the easiest and fastest and allows for better penetration; overhead welding is the most difficult, requiring many hours of practice to perfect. Wherever possible, position the work so that welding can be done in the flat position, especially if the operator has little or no MIG welding experience.

Clamp workpieces firmly in position to prevent them from shifting or moving around while tack welding and running of a bead is carried out.

Holding the Gun. The gun should be held with the nozzle at an angle of 45° to 60° to the work (Fig. 5-11) and since the wire is not energized until the gun control trigger is pressed, the wire can be positioned on target before the helmet or face shield is brought over or up to the face. The gun should be held so that the contact tip is about $\frac{1}{4}$ inch (6 mm) from the work. To enable the operator to maintain this distance, the wire must be extended to be about $\frac{1}{4}$ inch (6 mm) beyond the gas nozzle before striking the arc. Holding the gun too close or too far from the work will result in poor welds and increased spatter and will cause the torch to operate with an erratic sound (Fig. 5-12).

Travel Methods and Travel Speed. Two different methods of travel, in the running of beads, are employed in MIG welding: the pulling method and the pushing method. The gun is held at an angle of about 60°

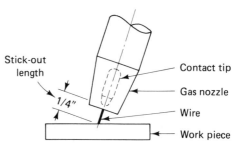

FIGURE 5-12 Initiating the arc. (Courtesy of Blackhawk, Division of Applied Power of Canada Ltd.)

to the work (Fig. 5-13) and moved with little or no weaving motion, except in the welding of poorly fitted edge joints, where some weaving is desirable. Wherever possible, the pulling method is used for welding light-gauge metal; the pushing method is used for heavy metal and all-aluminum welding because of the greater shielding gas protection required in combating contamination.

The speed of travel is regulated by the type of weld bead required. While learning, travel at a speed that allows you to maintain a bead of uniform width. Never allow the bead width to be less than the thickness of the metal or to become too wide. Too wide a bead, especially when welding high-strength steel, may cause overheating of the metal and result in the destruction of the base metal properties.

A good bead requires steady gun movement along the weld seam. Moving the gun too rapidly or straying off the seam will result in improper metal-to-metal fusion and an uneven, poor-looking, and generally weaker weld bead.

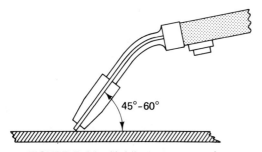

FIGURE 5-11 Holding gun to work.

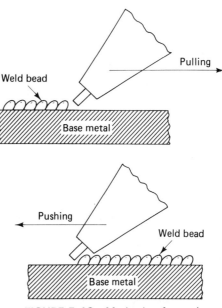

FIGURE 5-13 Methods of travel.

Continuous Welding. In continuous welding, as in other MIG welding, the heat-selector switch, having nine positions, must be accurately set for the job on hand. Generally, the thicker the metal to be welded, the higher the heat setting is (Fig. 5-14).

Wire speed control is used for fine-tuning the welding operation. An increase in heat will require an increase in wire speed. The chart (Fig. 5-15) will help with the basic settings of the machine, but fine tuning of the operation, using similar metal, will be required until the correct "sizzling" sound is obtained. It is similar to the sound of tearing a linen sheet or the frying of eggs. If the wire speed setting is too low, the torch will develop a "hiss" and the wire will burn, forming a ball; if too high, the wire will push the torch away from the work, accompanied by a loud, crackling arc.

Continuous welding is used mostly for welding thicker metal. For thinner metals, such as sheet metal, stitch or spot welding is recommended. However, continuous welding should be used in welding aluminum, because a continuous weld is more likely to have fewer contamination imperfections than a stitch-welded weld.

Preparing the Metal for MIG Welding. Clean the area to be welded. Using either a power wire brush or a disk grinder, remove any nonconductive or flammable

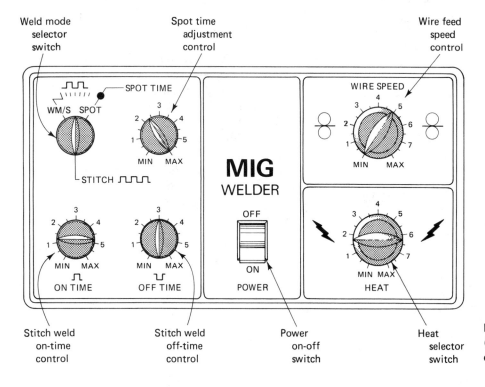

FIGURE 5-14 Control panel. (Courtesy of Blackhawk, Division of Applied Power of Canada Ltd.)

Material thickness	Gage No.	28	22	16	10	4	0
	Fractional (in.)	1/64	1/32	1/16	1/8	1/4	3/8
	Decimal (in.)	0.015	0.030	0.062	0.125	0.250	0.340
	Metric (mm)	0.4	0.8	1	3	6	9
Settings* — 0.023 in. Wire	Heat / wire	2–3 / 2–4	3–4 / 2–5	5–7 / 3–5	7–8 / 4–6	Not recommended; use 0.030 in. wire	
Settings* — 0.030 in. Wire	Heat / wire	Not recommended; use 0.023 in. wire	3–5 / 1–3	5–6 / 4–5	6–7 / 3–5	8 / 3–6	8 / 3–6
Aluminum 0.030	Heat / wire	Not recommended	3–4 / 4–5	4–5 / 5–7	5–6 / 7-Max	Not recommended	

FIGURE 5-15 Base setting chart for wire speed control. (Courtesy of Blackhawk, Division of Applied Power of Canada Ltd.)

*Your settings may vary depending on the input voltage, material used and operator preference.

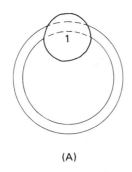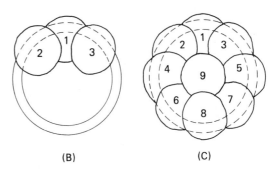

(A)   (B)   (C)

FIGURE 5-16 Steps used in filling holes. (Courtesy of Blackhawk, Division of Applied Power of Canada Ltd.)

materials, such as rust, undercoating, primer, paint, putty, plastic filler, solder, galvanized or zinc coatings, oil, grease, or dirt.

WARNING: Exposure to the welding arc is extremely dangerous and harmful to the eyes and skin and prolonged exposure can cause blindness and severe burns. Never start arc welding unless you are adequately protected by wearing flameproof welding gloves, a heavy long-sleeved shirt, cuffless trousers, high-top shoes, and a welding helmet or shield. Never bring a butane lighter with you into the weld area.

Using a perfectly clean piece of sheet metal or body panel, firmly clamped in a flat position, practice running beads about 3 inch (76 mm) in length. Holding the gun at the correct angle and on target and using the pulling method of travel, strike the arc and move along at a uniform speed. On reaching the end of the bead, release the gun control trigger, which cuts off the welding current and stops the wire feed, but keep the gun over the weld bead until the shielding gas stops flowing. This protects the puddle from contamination. Practice welding by repeating the operation, frequently examining specimens for defects, until you are able to make reasonably good weld beads, before attempting longer beads.

Filling Holes in Body Panels.   Small holes in body panels can easily be filled by reducing the heat setting one or two steps lower than for continuous welding. Make a short tack weld on the outer edge of the hole and allow it to cool until the orange color disappears. Proceed, making short tack welds, alternating from side to side, until the hole is filled (Fig. 5-16).

Seam-welding Tears and Gaps.   In seam-welding tears and gaps, the heat setting is also reduced one or two steps lower than for continuous welding. Bridge the gap at intervals about $\frac{1}{2}$ inch (12 mm) apart by making short tack welds on each side of the gap, and let each cool before proceeding with the next weld (Fig. 5-17). Fill in the remaining gaps using the hole-filling technique. If required,

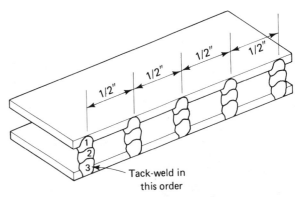

FIGURE 5-17 Seam welding tears and gaps. (Courtesy of Blackhawk, Division of Applied Power of Canada Ltd.)

the appearance of the filled tear or gap can be improved (smoothed out) by stitch welding over the area, using the normal heat setting.

Spot and Plug Welding.   Spot/plug welding is used extensively on unitized body cars, because welds can be made at the identical factory locations and through two different thicknesses of metal. It is recommended that whenever possible, the lighter metal be welded to the heavier metal, that both pieces make good contact with each other, and that the overlapping surfaces be clean.

A spot weld is a small, round, localized weld that penetrates through one piece of metal into the other (Fig. 5-18).

A plug weld is similar to a spot weld, except that holes are first punched into the top piece of metal with a hole-punching tool before the two pieces of metal are spot-welded together (Fig. 5-19 A and B). It produces the strongest spot weld possible, requiring a minimum amount of heat. When more then two panels have to be spot-welded together, the holes for the plug welds must be made larger in the top layers; this allows the plug weld to penetrate and have a large enough nugget at the top surface (Fig. 5-19 A and B).

Spot and plug welding can be done either manually or automatically, with or without the spot weld gas nozzle.

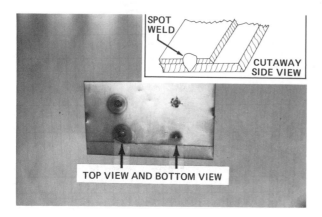

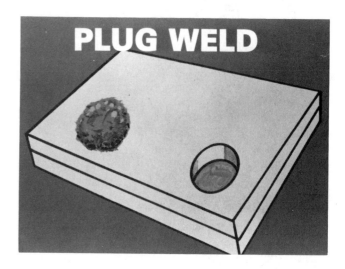

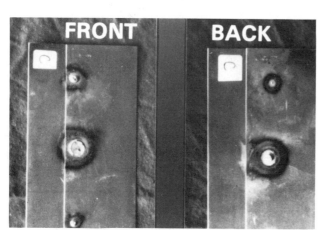

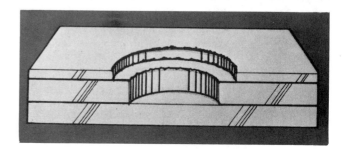

FIGURE 5-18   Sheet-metal spot welds. (Courtesy of Inter-Industry Conference on Auto Collision Repair)

Spot welding should be done manually when only a few welds have to be made or when the metals to be welded vary in thickness. Automatic welding should be used when making many welds on metals of equal thickness.

Automatic Spot and Plug Welding Procedure

1. Remove the standard nozzle, attach a spot weld nozzle to the gun, and apply antispatter spray to the gun nozzle and contact tip.
2. Adjust the heat and wire speed control base settings, as shown in Fig. 5-15. Settings should be based on combined metal thicknesses.
3. Fine-tuning of control settings is done by making welds manually on pieces of similar scrap metal.
4. Move the weld selector switch to the spot weld position (Fig. 5-14), adjust the spot time adjustment control, and fine-tune the setting using similar scrap metal. An ideal spot weld is small in diameter, with penetration clearly visible on the back side of the metal.

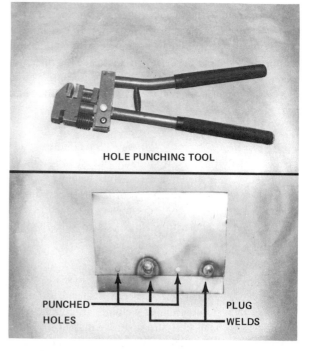

FIGURE 5-19   Plug welds. (Courtesy of Inter-Industry Conference on Auto Collision Repair)

5. Extend and then cut the wire so that it is flush or within the end of the spot weld nozzle (Fig. 5-20).

6. Hold the nozzle perpendicular to the work, allowing the nozzle to rest on the work. If spot welding using a punched hole, aim the wire at the center of the hole before dropping the helmet over the face and pressing the gun control trigger. The welding machine will stop automatically when the spot weld has been completed. Then move to the next area and continue spot welding.

Another type of spot welder used in autobody repairing is the resistance spot welder (Fig. 5-21), which

will make two spot welds at the same time. This machine has two cables, each having its own electrode holder; different types of electrodes are supplied to perform welds in different locations. The two electrodes are held one in each hand and pressed against the area to be spot-welded (Fig. 5-22). One electrode has a push button that is pressed whenever spot welds are to be performed. There is a variable timer on the machine to provide and to select the desired heat to complete the spot welds. Figure 5-23 shows a drawing of the typical spot weld done by this machine.

Stitch Welding. Stitch welding is used in welding thin or rusty metal, where warpage and burn-through are a problem. Basically, it consists of a series of overlapping spot welds, each being allowed time to cool before the next weld is made (Fig. 5-24). Stitch welding is comparable in quality and penetration to a continuous weld, with less heating of the metal. It can be done either manually or automatically. Stitch welding should be done manually when only a few welds are to be made or when welds must be made on metals varying in thickness.

Automatic stitch welding should be used when many welds are to be made on metal of the same thickness. The operating techniques followed are very similar to those used in automatic spot welding, except that the weld selector switch is moved to the stitch weld position. Start spot welding with a time base setting of 2 on both stitch *on* time

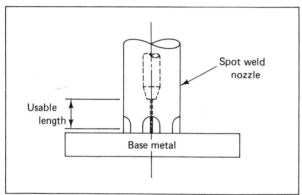

FIGURE 5-20 Wire cut flush with end of spot weld nozzle. (Courtesy of Blackhawk, Division of Applied Power of Canada Ltd.)

FIGURE 5-21 Resistance spot welder.

FIGURE 5-22 Electrodes positioned on panel for spot welding.

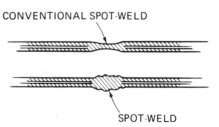

FIGURE 5-23 Different types of spot welds.

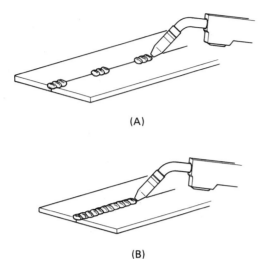

(A)

(B)

FIGURE 5-24A Manual stitch and (B) skip welding. (Courtesy of Blackhawk, Division of Applied Power of Canada Ltd.)

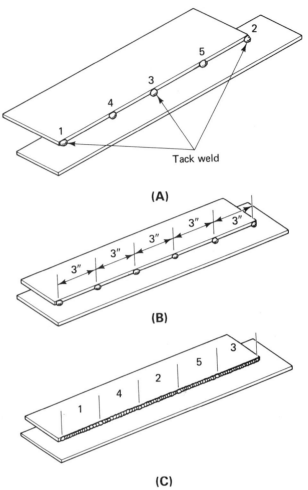

(A)

(B)

(C)

FIGURE 5-25A Procedure of tack welding; (B) tack welds should be 3 inches or less apart; (C) alternate welding: stitch, skip, or spot in the order indicated. (Courtesy of Blackhawk, Division of Applied Power of Canada Ltd.)

Carbon rod

FIGURE 5-26 Heat-shrinking attachment. (Courtesy of Blackhawk, Division of Applied Power of Canada Ltd.)

and stitch *off* time controls. Then test the weld. The orange color of the weld should disappear completely before the next cycle begins. Fine-tuning of the operation is done on similar metal by adjusting the weld *on* time control to get the desired puddle size and the weld *off* time control for the proper cooling-off time.

Skip Welding. Skip welding is employed to further reduce distortion problems. It requires the running of very short beads, about $\frac{1}{2}$ inch (12 mm) in length, stopping, and restarting another short bead about $\frac{1}{4}$ inch (6 mm) farther up the seam (Fig. 5-24). It is used primarily where spot welding is not enough and distortion is a major problem.

Controlling Overheating and Burn-through. Overheating will cause large, thin autobody panels to warp, and if the heat is concentrated on a very small area, as it is in welding, it will often cause burn-through.

To minimize burn-through, stop the running of the bead occasionally, as in stitch welding, and before starting again, allow the weld to cool until it loses its orange color. If burn-through continues, adjust to a lower heat setting.

Burn-through and warping can also be controlled by properly tack-welding the metal (Fig. 5-25), followed by alternate welding, using the same procedural steps as in oxyacetylene welding.

Heat-shrinking Attachment. This attachment is used in shrinking stretched areas on thin-gauge body panels and is done without the use of shielding gas or weld wire. The gas nozzle must be removed from the gun and a carbon rod attached by means of a special attachment (Fig. 5-26). The heat control is set between 1 and 4, depending on the

thickness of the panel, and the weld selector switch is moved to the manual weld position.

The tip of the carbon rod is then placed on the outer edge of the stretched area, the face is covered with the helmet or shield, and the trigger is pressed. Moving in a circular pattern, work your way round and round, in a slow but steady manner, to the center of the stretched area, and stop when the area starts changing color. Then quench the area with a cold, water-soaked rag. Do only a small area at a time. However, there is a limit to the amount of shrinking possible with this attachment.

Maintenance of the MIG Welder. Regular maintenance and adjustments are needed to keep the MIG welder in top operating condition and to provide years of trouble-free service. The gun and torch assembly is the most important part of a MIG welder and must be properly cared for and maintained by observing the following general rules:

1. Never make sharp bends with the gun hose and frequently check it for signs of abrasion and other defects or damage.

2. Keep the gun nozzle and contact tip free of spatter using a wooden stick to remove spatter deposits. Use antispatter spray, as recommended, after each operating period.

3. Always replace the contact tip when the hole is abraded too large or when there is excessive dirt buildup, generally after one-third of the spool of wire has been used.

4. The gas nozzle should be replaced with a new one when the insulator begins to get brittle or when it does not provide even shielding.

5. Check the wire conduit or liner occasionally for free wire movement. To clean it, remove and soak the liner in solvent and blow it dry with compressed air.

6. Clean the inside of the cabinet regularly with a vacuum cleaner and a soft-haired brush.

7. Check the wire spool brake tension and adjust, if necessary, at least every time one-third of a spool of wire has been used.

Aluminum Welding. The setup for aluminum welding is similar to that for steel welding, with the following exceptions:

1. Suitable aluminum wire must be used; type 5356 and type 4043 are recommended (see the wire selection chart, Fig. 5-6).

2. A Teflon liner should be used in the torch assembly, which allows the aluminum wire to slide easily through the torch assembly and will not have any steel particles on it to contaminate the aluminum weld.

3. Only pure argon shielding gas should be used, at 16 to 24 cubic feet/hour (38 to 56 liters/hour).

NOTE: When welding aluminum, surface preparation is extremely important. The weld area should be cleaned with a suitable solvent, such as lacquer thinner or enamel reducer, and brushed vigorously, just before welding, with a clean stainless steel brush to remove any surface oxidation.

Contamination from dirt, grease, oil, water, and other foreign material is the biggest enemy of aluminum welding. For this reason it is best to use a new, unopened spool of aluminum wire, and because it cannot be kept from contamination very long, the smallest spool possible should be purchased from the supplier.

Aluminum Welding Technique. The basic operating techniques are the same as those for steel welding, with the following differences:

1. The stick-out length of the aluminum wire is increased to $\frac{5}{16}$ inch (8 mm).

2. The travel speed will be much faster for aluminum welding.

3. The base setting of the wire feed speed will be higher per heat setting than for steel (see the base setting chart, Fig. 5-15).

4. While welding aluminum, it is recommended that the work area be free of drafts.

After the aluminum welding project is completed, the MIG welder is shut off following the same procedure as that used in steel MIG welding.

Different Types of Joints Used

Several types of joints are used to weld sheet metal on autobodies. The most common are the butt joint, the recessed lap joint, the lap joint, and the offset butt joint.

5-2 PREPARATION FOR SECTIONING OF BODY COMPONENTS

Major automobile manufacturers, insurance companies and nonprofit societies have all been involved in developing safe methods to repair the new types of vehicles that use HSS or HSLA components. It is important that the technician remain up to date on these methods of repairing damaged automobiles. The information may come from articles published by the manufacturers or courses given by societies, such as I-Car.

Methods and proper procedures for sectioning of unibody structural components have been developed. These components include rocker panels, floor pans, front and rear rails, trunk floors, and A and B pillars. Check for C pillars. Two basic types of construction design are used in the basic types of unibody structural components. One type is the closed section, which is usually found on body frame rails, rocker panels, and A and B pillars (Fig. 5-27). These closed sections are the most widely used in the unibody as they provide the main strength due to their shape and construction. The other type of construction is usually of the open-surface or single-layer type, such as used in floor pans, trunk floors, and similar components (Fig. 5-28).

Closed sections are made from an open C channel with flanges, which is spot-welded to another open channel with flanges or a flat piece of metal. This type of channel is stronger than a flat piece of metal, but it is still easy to bend or compress under load. When the C channel is closed by spot welding its flanges to another piece of metal, its load-bearing strength is maximized (Fig. 5-29).

To retain the strength of a closed section when it is necessary to cut it for repair purposes, care must be taken

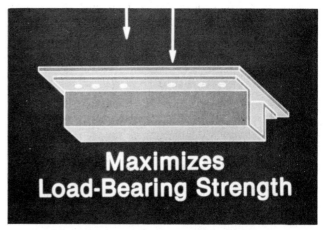

FIGURE 5-29   C-channel spot welded to another piece of metal. (Courtesy of Inter-Industry Conference on Auto Collision Repair)

as to where the cut and weld operation is carried out. The location chosen must allow the technician not only to cut off the damaged panel in a very accessible area, but also allow enough room for the total rewelding of the section that is to be cut. If the area is not totally accessible and too awkward to allow proper welding, then another area should be chosen, as only a completely closed section will retain the strength of the panel and joint (Fig. 5-30).

Any area that is not welded will decrease the load-carrying capacity of the particular load-bearing member. This gap in the weld may cause the panel in time to crack due to too much flexing and could cause the joint to break. Therefore, when it is required to make a joint, the technician must plan where it will be done so that it will be possible to close the section properly.

Many structural components have crush zones or buckling points built into their design so that the component will be able to absorb the impact energy from a collision.

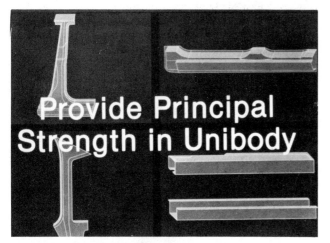

FIGURE 5-27   Typical closed structures in a unibody. (Courtesy of Inter-Industry Conference on Auto Collision Repair)

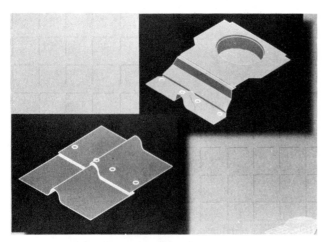

FIGURE 5-28   Floor pans. (Courtesy of Inter-Industry Conference on Auto Collision Repair)

FIGURE 5-30   Closed section. (Courtesy of Inter-Industry Conference on Auto Collision Repair)

These crush zones are found particularly in the components used in front and rear rails, because the greater percentage of collisions occurs at these areas. Crush zones can usually be identified by convoluted or crinkled areas in part of their construction. Other components use dents or dimples, and still others use slots or holes (Fig. 5-31). These different methods in the design and construction allow the rails to collapse and absorb energy.

Crush zones are usually located ahead of the front suspension components and behind the rear suspension components. Whenever sectioning of a panel is to be done, crush zones must be avoided as much as possible because any sectioning in these areas could change the designed collapsibility of the section if the sectioning is improperly located.

When a vehicle has been damaged in a major collision, the crush zones will be easy to locate; but if the vehicle was involved in only a moderate collision, examination must be made to see if the collision has used up the crush zone completely or not. It may be necessary to compare one side to the other side of the vehicle or examine another vehicle using the same components.

Areas to avoid cutting when sectioning are any holes in the component, any reinforcement, such as double layers of metal, or any anchor point.

Joints

The sectioning of unibodies involves three basic types of joints, with certain variations or combinations of them. These are the butt joint, offset butt joint, and lap joint. When done properly, these joints will retain the integrity of the components (Fig. 5-32).

The most common type of welding done is the butt weld, a joint which is used frequently to join two pieces of metal together. The two pieces of metal are aligned closely edge to edge, but a gap of one thickness of metal is allowed

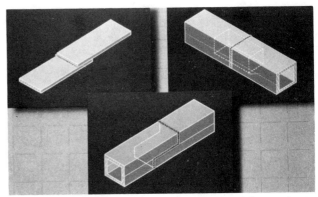

FIGURE 5-32 Butt joint, offset butt joint, and lap joint. (Courtesy of Inter-Industry Conferences on Auto Collision Repair)

to counteract expansion and contraction. The joint is tack welded at one end of the slit, and then the other end of the joint is also tack welded, if the joint is not too long. If it should be a long joint, the panels must be kept in alignment using tack welds which are done alternating from one side to the other on the top of the joint. This procedure will help control distortion from the welding effects. Weld metal from the rod is used to fill the gap between the spot welds to provide a smooth even weld bead and a strong joint.

A variation of the butt joint is to use an insert with it; the insert is made of the same metal and shaped to fit the area to be welded (Fig. 5-33). This type of joint is mainly used when sectioning body rails, rocker panels, and A and B pillars. The insert makes it easier to fit and align the joint to be welded and also helps the technician to achieve a good weld.

Another type of joint that can also be used is the offset butt joint without an insert (Fig. 5-34). This type of joint may be used on A and B pillars and front frame rails.

The last type of joint is the lap joint which can also

FIGURE 5-31 Different types of crush zones in panel. (Courtesy of Inter-Industry Conference on Auto Collision Repair)

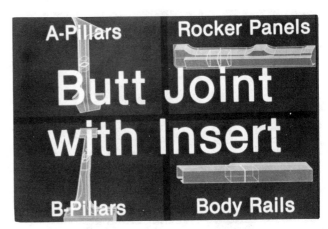

FIGURE 5-33 Butt joint with insert. (Courtesy of Inter-Industry Conference on Auto Collision Repair)

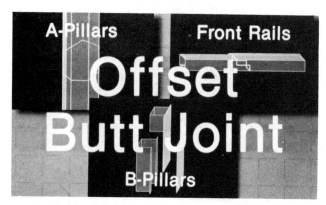

FIGURE 5-34 Offset butt joint without insert. (Courtesy of Inter-Industry Conference on Auto Collision Repair)

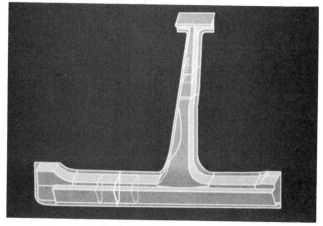

FIGURE 5-36 Rocker panel sectioning with pillar. (Courtesy of Inter-Industry Conference on Auto Collision Repair)

be called an overlap joint (Fig. 5-35). This type of joint is used mainly on floor pans, trunk floors, rear rails, and the B pillar.

A butt joint with an insert could be the preferred method when using a recycled part such as a rocker panel and B pillar. But the type of section and shape of the part may require that the three methods be used. The butt joint with insert would be used on the rocker panel (Fig. 5-36). On the B pillar, sectioning could require an offset cut with a butt joint for the outside piece and a lap joint used on the inside part (Fig. 5-37).

Recycled Parts

Recycled parts are often used in the repair of automobiles, and it is of the utmost importance that the recycler be told where the part to be used should be cut because, when the parts are cut off with an oxyacetylene torch, enough material must be present so that at least 2 inches (50 mm) may be

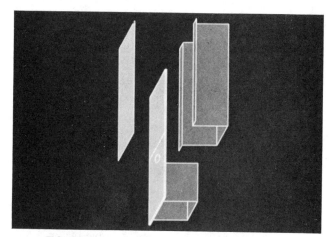

FIGURE 5-37 B pillar sectioning. (Courtesy of Inter-Industry Conference on Auto Collision Repair)

FIGURE 5-35 Lap or overlap joint. (Courtesy of Inter-Industry Conference on Auto Collision Repair)

trimmed off, using a metal saw or panel cutter, to remove the area of heat dispersion on the panel. This area must never invade the area where the joint is to be made.

A plasma cutting system may be used to cut both new panels and recycled panels, as the heat from the plasma cutting system (Fig. 5-38) does not create as large a heat zone as an oxyacetylene torch and is very fast.

The recycler should also be instructed not be cut through reinforcements that are welded in the component. When the part is received, it should be checked for corrosion; if it is rusty, it should not be used. The recycled part should also be checked for damage and to see that its measurements are accurate. It must always be remembered that quality materials and proper methods are required to achieve a quality repair.

FIGURE 5-38 Plasma cutting system.

MIG Welding

On unibodies it is also mandatory that a MIG welder be used to weld the sections, and the technician must possess the skills required to achieve quality welds. The steel wire used must meet or exceed the requirements of the American Welding Society Standard (AWS-EX-705-6) when using 75% argon and 25% carbon dioxide gas or other, comparable argon-based mixes.

The technician must observe all safety practices toward himself, the shop, and the vehicle so as not to cause any damage. The technician must also clean all surfaces to be welded by removing heavy undercoats, rust proofing, tars, caulking, sealants, road dirt, primers, paint, and oil if present. For the primary removal, an oxyacetylene torch with carburizing flame, if required, along with a scraper may be used. The wire brush and low controlled heat on the torch are used to do the final cleanup; just enough heat should be used to do the job. If the area is rusted, it should be sandblasted or machine- or hand-sanded until the metal surfaces are clean. This will also help provide the MIG welder with a good circuit for the ground cable to give trouble-free welding.

When joints that are to be welded on galvanized or zinc-metallized steels, this protection should never be removed. Any grinding of these surfaces would reduce the thickness of the metal and weaken it. It would also create a zinc-free area around the weld zone, which would become a prime target for corrosion.

Figure 5-39 shows a well-prepared butt joint that is cleaned and aligned ready for the MIG welding to proceed.

To achieve high quality in sectioning, the MIG welder must be precisely adjusted for the welding job that is to be done. The welder is adjusted as in Fig. 5-10 for gas flow and Fig. 5-15 for wire speed; also, the heat setting is adjusted to receive the proper weld arc voltage. A test weld using the same metal 22 gauge and a typical joint should be welded together to find out if the machine is adjusted properly and the joint is welded properly with enough penetration. By using these methods, it can be assured that the repairs being done will restore the vehicle to its original strength, integrity, and alignment.

5-3 SECTIONING OF BODY COMPONENTS

Frame Rails

As mentioned in Section 5-2, body frame rails are of two distinct types of construction. One type, sometimes called a box section or closed section, comes from the recycler or the factory with its four sides intact. The other type comes as an open C channel with flanges and is closed on the open side by being spot-welded to some other part or parts in the structure of the body. The technician should at all times use a butt joint with an insert to repair a closed section rail (Fig. 5-40).

Most frame rails in the rear portion of the vehicle are of the open C channel type with flanges, as are the frame rails used in the front of some vehicles. Some C channel with flange closures are used vertically as a front rail joined to a side apron. This type of channel is also used horizontally, for example the rear frame rail used under and spot-welded to the trunk floor. When repairing this type of channel, it is usually sectioned using a lap joint with $\frac{5}{16}$-

FIGURE 5-39 Prepared butt joint. (Courtesy of Inter-Industry Conference on Auto Collision Repair)

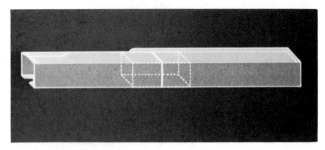

FIGURE 5-40 Butt joint with insert used to repair closed section rail. (Courtesy of Inter-Industry Conference on Auto Collision Repair)

inch (8 mm) holes punched or drilled in another section of the lap joint (Fig. 5-41). The section is aligned and fitted, and the holes are plug welded first and then a continuous lap weld is used on the edge of the overlap. Remember when sectioning frame rails that they all contain crush zones, holes, and reinforcements and that no joint should ever be made in these areas.

Rocker Panels

Rocker panels are supplied in two- or three-piece designs depending on the type and manufacturer of the unibody vehicle. Some rocker panels contain reinforcements, which could be continuous or intermittent. Depending on the severity of the collision damage, the rocker panel may be repaired with a B pillar or without it. Different methods are used to repair the rocker panel, such as using a straight-cut butt joint with an insert or cutting only the outside piece of the rocker panel and adding the replacement part with overlap joints.

Usually, a butt joint with insert is used when a recycled rocker panel with a B pillar is attached or if a recycled quarter-panel is installed. When a butt joint with an insert is to be done, the panel should be cut straight

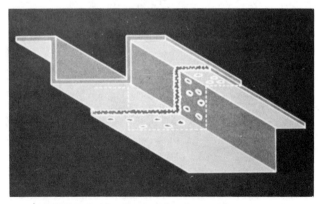

FIGURE 5-41 Typical lap joint. (Courtesy of Inter-Industry Conference on Auto Collision Repair)

across. The insert is made from pieces that were cut from the excess length of the repair panel or from the end of the damaged panel. The insert must be shaped to fit the repair panel, which must have $\frac{5}{16}$ inch (8 mm) holes punched or drilled for the plug welds (Fig. 5-42). Plug-weld holes of an adequate size are required for structural sectioning, and the plug weld must have an adequate nugget and proper penetration and weld strength. The insert is held in place by using a few plug welds in the section.

When an insert is used in a closed section such as an A or B pillar, body rail, or rocker panel, it is of the utmost importance, after the plug welds are done, that the weld that closes the joint fully penetrate the metal of the insert. A gap the thickness of the metal but no less than $\frac{1}{16}$ inch (2 mm) and up to $\frac{1}{8}$ inch (4 mm) must be left between the two sections of the joint that is being sectioned (Fig. 5-43).

The sections of the joint must always be cleaned to

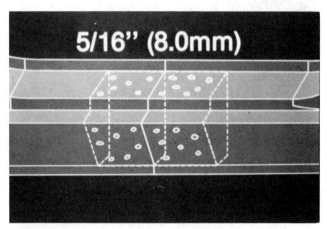

FIGURE 5-42 Rocker panel sectioned and plug welded. (Courtesy of Inter-Industry Conference on Auto Collision Repair)

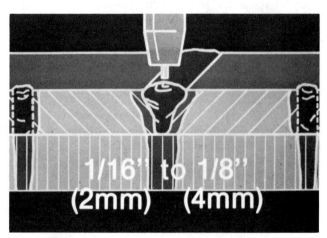

FIGURE 5-43 Proper gap between sectioned panels before applying closing weld. (Courtesy of Inter-Industry Conference on Auto Collision Repair)

remove any burrs. If the burr is left it could cause the weld metal to travel around and up under the burr. A flawed weld and resulting stress concentration could possibly cause cracks and damage the sectioned joint.

The overlap procedure is used when an outer rocker panel or a portion of it is installed and the inner panel is not damaged and is therefore left intact; only the outer rocker panel is cut. This procedure can be varied according to the requirements of the job; it can be cut in the front door opening, but enough material must be left for the overlap. The cut must be made several inches away from the base of the B and C pillars so as not to damage or cut any reinforcements that might be inside the rocker panel assembly (Fig. 5-44). The new outer rocker panel is measured and cut neatly to allow the proper amount of overlap, which is at the bases of the pillars. The new outer rocker panel is drilled or punched so that the factory spot welds may be duplicated as required, as well the overlap areas around the base of the B and C pillars. The plug welds around the pillars should be approximately the same as the spot weld used in the pinch weld flange. The overlap edge at the base of the B and C pillars is welded intermittently using $\frac{1}{2}$ inch (13 mm) of weld per $1\frac{1}{2}$ inches (38 mm) of the overlap edge. The overlap area at the door opening is plug welded, and a lap weld is then used to close the joint (Fig. 5-45).

This procedure may be varied to suit the damaged area to be repaired on the rocker panel. The overlap cut may be done in the rear door opening and the A and B pillars, or the whole outer rocker panel may be replaced by cutting around the bases of the three pillars and then overlapping them with the new rocker panel. These different procedures may be used with success and integrity as long as the welds and the joints are done properly.

A and B Pillars

A and B pillars may be replaced by sectioning, using either the butt weld joint or an offset butt joint. A pillars are

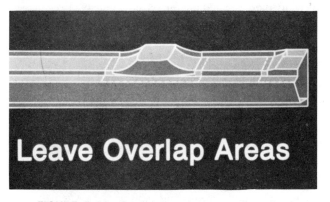

FIGURE 5-44   Rocker panel cut to allow for overlap. (Courtesy of Inter-Industry Conference on Auto Collision Repair)

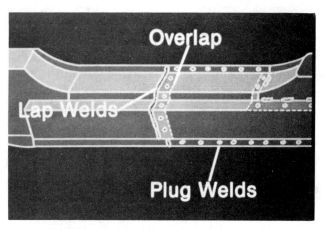

FIGURE 5-45   Rocker panel with new outer panel lapped over. (Courtesy of Inter-Industry Conference on Auto Collision Repair)

usually made from two to three pieces and may be reinforced at the bottom and upper end, or both, but not usually in the middle. Therefore, the cut should be made in the middle; the only difference in the cut made is the type of joint that will be used to section the pillar.

If the butt joint with an insert (Fig. 5-46A) is to be used, the same method as for the rocker panel is used. The insert is fitted and plug welded leaving the proper gap between the two sections to facilitate the closing of the pillar using a continuous butt weld (Fig. 5-46B). When the offset butt joint is used, the inner piece of the pillar is cut at a different point than the outer piece. The cuts should always be made between factory welds to make it easier to drill them out. The offset cuts should be no closer to each other than 2 to 4 inches (50 to 100 mm). The sections should be fitted together and then butt welded and spot welded as required (Fig. 5-47).

The B pillar may be sectioned using two different types of joints, a butt joint with an insert or a combination of an offset cut with an overlap joint (Fig. 5-48). It is usually easier to fit and align the two parts when using the butt joint with an insert as a guide. When a simple two-piece cross section is used, it usually has very little internal reinforcements, and will be weaker than when additional strength is provided by the insert. The pillar should always be cut below the seat belt D ring mount, as most B pillars have them; this is to avoid the cutting of any reinforcements. The insert is only used in the inside of the outer piece of the B pillar, as the reinforcements for the seat belt anchor are usually welded to the inside of the inner part of the pillar. The new inside piece is overlapped on the existing piece on the inside and lap welded, instead of butt welding them together. The sectioned joint is welded using plug welds, butt welds around the pillar, and a lap weld on the inside (Fig. 5-49).

On some occasions it is more economical or expedient

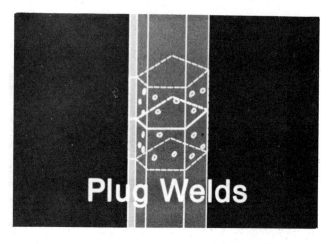

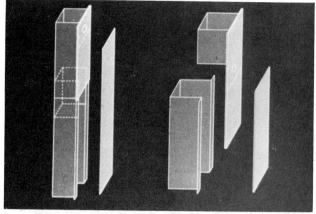

FIGURE 5-48 Different types of joints used when sectioning the B pillar. (Courtesy of Inter-Industry Conference on Auto Collision Repair)

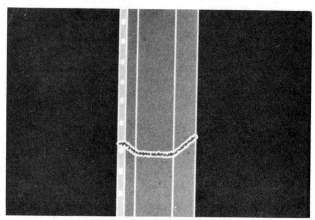

FIGURE 5-46 A pillar sectioned using an insert and butt weld. (Courtesy of Inter-Industry Conference on Auto Collision Repair)

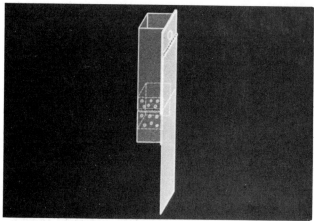

FIGURE 5-49 Completed B pillar sectioned joint. (Courtesy of Inter-Industry Conference on Auto Collision Repair)

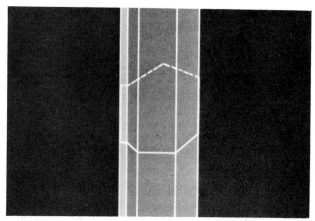

FIGURE 5-47 Offset butt joint used on A pillar.

to use a recycled rocker panel and B pillar assembly and to replace them as a single unit. This is done when the B pillar is badly damaged and the force of the impact also damaged the rocker panel. The upper part of the B pillar is installed using either of two recommended methods. The rocker panel assembly is changed according to the methods described before with a butt joint and insert. The location of the damage will govern where the butt joint is made; for example, if the damage is in the rear door lower opening, the butt joint with insert is done in the front door opening and the rest of the rocker is installed in its entirety as required. If the damage is in the front door area, the procedure on the rocker panel is reversed (Fig. 5-50).

A combination offset and overlap joint (Fig. 5-48) is more often used when using new parts, as two separate parts are used for the joint. The butt joint is used on the

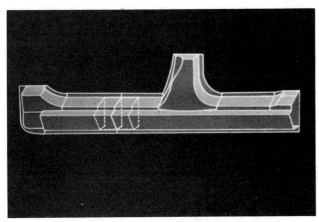

FIGURE 5-50 Sectioned rocker panel assembly, front or rear door. (Courtesy of Inter-Industry Conference on Auto Collision Repair)

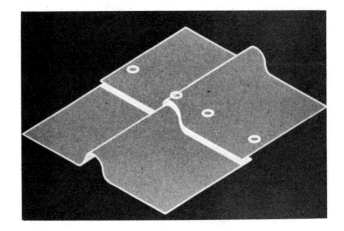

outside piece, usually above the seat belt anchor reinforcement, and the lap cut on the inside is made below the reinforcement. The inside part should be installed first, with the new part overlapping the existing part, and it is lap welded once it fits properly. The outside pieces are fitted and the flanges are plug welded; then a continuous weld is used at the butt joint to close the section. It is usually advantageous to use an offset and overlap joint if the B pillar has three or more pieces where the joint is made. In some cases the offset and overlap procedure is the only one that can be used as it is impossible to have an insert in the joint due to lack of room.

Floor Pans

When a floor pan is to be sectioned, it should always be cut to avoid any reinforcements, such as the anchor for the seat belts. The floor pan sections should always be joined with an overlap joint. The rear section of the joint should overlap the front section by being on top of the front section so that the edge of the bottom piece is always pointing rearward (Fig. 5-51). This type of joint allows the road splash to move past the bottom edge of the joint and not hit it head on (Fig. 5-52). The plug welds are done from the top once the joint is fitted properly. The bottom rear edge is welded to the other panel from the bottom. A continuous weld is done, but the welding should preferably be staggered from one part of the section to another to prevent warping and less weld draw. The topside edge is caulked; then the lap weld is cleaned and primed and seam sealer is applied to the joint before the top coat paint is applied to the joint (Fig. 5-53). This will give corrosion protection to the joint and also seal it to prevent carbon monoxide from penetrating into the passenger compartment.

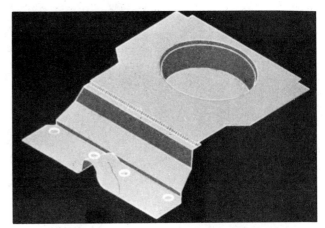

FIGURE 5-51 Typical overlap joint used when sectioning floor pans. (Courtesy of Inter-Industry Conference on Auto Collision Repair)

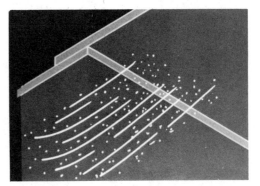

FIGURE 5-52 Road splash streaming past bottom edge. (Courtesy of Inter-Industry Conference on Auto Collision Repair)

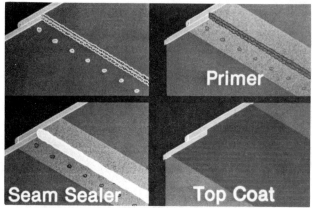

FIGURE 5-53 Protecting the joint from corrosion. (Courtesy of Inter-Industry Conference on Auto Collision Repair)

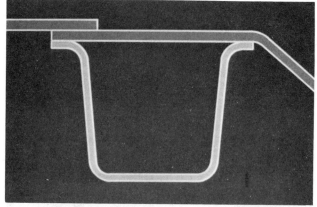

FIGURE 5-54 Sectioned trunk floor joint. (Courtesy of Inter-Industry Conference on Auto Collision Repair)

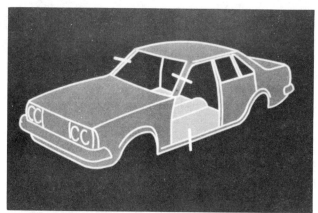

FIGURE 5-55 Full body section. (Courtesy of Inter-Industry Conference on Auto Collision Repair).

Trunk Floors

When sectioning a trunk floor, the same basic procedures used for the floor pans are used with a few variations. Usually, when sectioning a trunk floor is required, it is due to damage that results from a collision, which will make it necessary to change the frame rail also. As there is usually a cross member under the trunk floor near the rear suspension, the floor should be sectioned above the rear cross member's rear flange (Fig. 5-54).

The damaged frame rail is sectioned at an appropriate distance from the cross member. The section of new floor pan is overlapped on the rear part of the flange of the cross member and plug welded from the top. The top forward edge is caulked as on the floor pan; but if the joint was done on a cross member, due to its strength it is not necessary to weld the top section to the bottom section. But if no cross member is present, then the welding, corrosion, and carbon monoxide prevention methods given for floor pans are used on this section.

Having learned the different sectioning procedures, and by using careful methods in measuring, it is easy to apply these methods to sectioning a full-body section of a vehicle (Fig. 5-55). By using approved methods, the vehicle will retain its integrity and strength as designed into the body by the manufacturer.

QUESTIONS

5-1. Briefly explain how a MIG welder works.

5-2. What shielding gas is most suitable for welding mild- and high-strength steel?

5-3. For what size of welding wire are most MIG welders set up at the factory?

5-4. What type of electrical circuit should be used to get maximum penetration?

5-5. Why is deeper penetration of the base metal achieved when a direct-current, reverse-polarity circuit is used in MIG welding?

5-6. State the advantages of MIG welding over other methods of welding.

5-7. What different types of liners are used in MIG welders?

5-8. What determines the size of contact tip to be used, and how is tip size identified?

5-9. What gas nozzles are provided with every welding machine?

5-10. How are gas nozzles cleaned and maintained?

5-11. What information does the electrode classification number convey?

5-12. How is the spool hub brake tension adjusted?

5-13. Why should the gun liner and contact tip be checked for size before attempting to install the welding wire?

5-14. Once the spool of wire has been installed, how is the wire spool brake tension checked?

5-15. How is a good ground connection made, and why is it necessary?

5-16. In what position, whenever possible, should MIG welding be done to make it easier?

5-17. How is the gun held in striking the arc?

5-18. What two methods of travel are used in MIG welding, and for what welding is each method most suitable?

5-19. What regulates the speed of travel in MIG welding?

5-20. How is the wire speed control used in fine-tuning the welding operation?

5-21. What sound should the MIG welder make when in operation and fine-tuned?

5-22. What different types of welding are used in welding thicker and thinner metals?

5-23. What safety precautions must be taken before any MIG welding is attempted?

5-24. How are holes in body panels filled?

5-25. What is the difference between a spot weld and a plug weld?

5-26. When should spot and plug welding be done manually and when automatically?

5-27. What type of spot-welder makes two spot welds at the same time?

5-28. What is stitch welding, and where is it used?

5-29. Where is skip welding employed?

5-30. What attachment makes shrinking of stretched areas with a MIG welder possible, and how is it carried out?

5-31. What general rules must be observed in maintaining a MIG welder?

5-32. What surface preparation is required in welding aluminum?

5-33. Name the organization that organized and developed the method of repairing unitized bodies?

5-34. How is a frame rail reinforced?

5-35. What tool and attachments are used in cutting sheet metal and in breaking spot welds?

5-36. Explain why a closed box section joint must be totally butt welded.

5-37. Explain what makes a C channel with flanges stronger.

5-38. Explain what is meant by a crush zone and what its purpose is.

5-39. What types of joints are used when sectioning is done?

5-40. What is the purpose of the insert in a butt joint?

5-41. Explain how a B pillar is sectioned.

5-42. How is a recycled part prepared for sectioning?

5-43. What type of welding equipment is used when welding is done when sectioning?

5-44. Describe how a butt joint with insert is prepared and where it is used.

5-45. Describe how an offset butt joint is prepared and where it is used.

5-46. Where and how is a lap weld used in sectioning components?

## CHAPTER SIX

Frame Alignment

6-1 FRAME ALIGNMENT AND STRAIGHTENING

Frame alignment is the procedure by which the frame of a car, truck, or bus that has been damaged in an accident or from wear is restored to the manufacturer's specifications. This procedure is usually done without removing the body (engine, etc.) on a machine that provides for the proper positioning of the vehicle and can hold, push, or pull the frame back into alignment.

All automobiles have a frame, either the conventional frame design or the unitized body-frame construction. In the conventional type, the frame is bolted to the body and its members extend the full length of the body. The conventional frames are divided into two types: the perimeter frame and the ladder frame.

The perimeter frame is separate from the body and it forms a border that reinforces and surrounds the passenger compartment. Its front section supports the power train, front suspension assemblies, and front body mounts. The side rails extend to the back where the body and rear suspension are bolted. It is usually constructed of box or channel-type rails that are joined to torque boxes at the four corners. The primary load is transferred to the frame by the torque boxes, but the complete frame to a great extent relies on the body structure for its rigidity (Fig. 6-1).

The ladder frame is self-descriptive and was the forerunner of the various types of frames found on newer vehicles. It is similar to the perimeter frame, but its side rails do not surround the passenger compartment. Its rails are built with less offset and are constructed in a more direct line from the front to the rear wheels. This frame is constructed with several cross-members and by itself is quite rigid, forming a strong support on which the body is mounted (Fig. 6-2).

In unitized construction, the frame members are shorter and usually welded to the body. The underbody section is reinforced to provide the floor with enough structural strength to replace the side rail on conventional frames. There are several variations of unitized construction. In the first type (Fig. 6-3) every member is related one to the other so that all sections carry part of the load. The rocker panels, floor pans, and so on, of the lower portion of the body are welded together to form a basic structure. The front of the structure where the engine and suspension are mounted is heavily reinforced and has the appearance of a separate frame except that the rails are not bolted but welded to the body structure.

In the construction of the newer type of automobiles, the vehicle has been totally redesigned (Fig. 6-4). This is due to the emphasis that has been placed on increasing the miles per gallon or liters per 100 kilometers that a particular vehicle will achieve. Manufacturers have downsized the

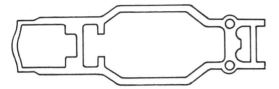

FIGURE 6-1 Perimeter frame.

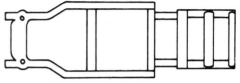

FIGURE 6-2 Ladder frame.

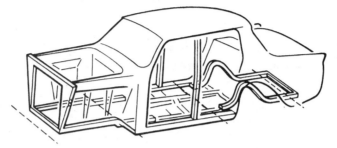

FIGURE 6-3 Unitized construction.

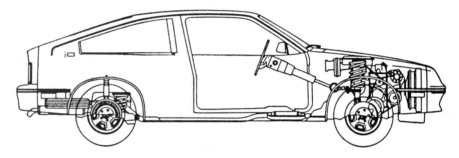

FIGURE 6-4 Unitized body design. (Courtesy of Chart Industries Ltd.)

automobile and reduced its weight by using more plastics, HSS and HSLA steel, and aluminum (Fig. 6-5). Moving the total power train to the front of the vehicle and using front-wheel-drive systems have greatly reduced the weight of the automobile.

This new design in automobiles required total changes in engineering and styling. The new design had to be engineered to meet many safety aspects, such as the protection of passengers when involved in a collision. These vehicles are designed with what is called a passive safety design (Fig. 6-6). This means that the vehicle is designed to absorb an impact as it crushes or bends. Manufacturers design areas in the vehicle that are meant to bend and crush to absorb the energy of the impact. The vehicle is designed in such a way that all panels are used to reinforce the basic structure when it is involved in collision. The forces of the impact are spread out in an ever-widening area or in a cone-shaped effect (Fig. 6-7).

The lighter-gauge metals used throughout the structural members require finesse rather than force to correct the damage. Excessive force will only cause tearing and stretching of the members instead of correcting and straightening the damage.

The technician must learn the proper technique so as to be able to repair and replace the damaged section or panels in order to be competitive in the marketplace. The technician will also have to acquire a general mechanical knowledge of wheel alignment and the mechanical disassembly of its components.

The newer vehicles have more control points, so very accurate measurement is required to bring them back to factory specifications. In the repair process, great care must be used so as not to ruin or destroy the integrity of the passive safety design of these vehicles.

The fundamental approach to a basic understanding of frame construction as it relates to body-frame straightening is known as *the four controlling points*. The controlling points of any car frame are the front cross member, the cross member at the cowl, the cross member at the rear door, and the rear cross member (Figs. 6-8 and 6-9).

A frame or unitized body is divided into three sections: the front section, the center section, and the rear section. This is done to simplify the location of the damaged areas and the misaligned controlled points in the vehicle body (Fig. 6-10). Each is bordered by a cross member or a controlling point. This establishes the basis for all frame-

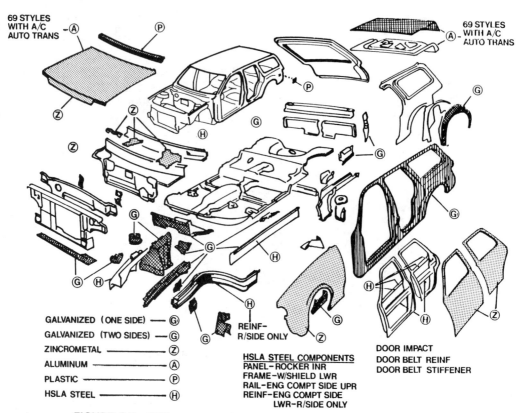

GALVANIZED (ONE SIDE) ⎯⎯ Ⓖ
GALVANIZED (TWO SIDES) ⎯⎯ Ⓖ
ZINCROMETAL ⎯⎯⎯⎯⎯⎯ Ⓩ
ALUMINUM ⎯⎯⎯⎯⎯⎯ Ⓐ
PLASTIC ⎯⎯⎯⎯⎯⎯ Ⓟ
HSLA STEEL ⎯⎯⎯⎯⎯ Ⓗ

REINF-
R/SIDE ONLY

HSLA STEEL COMPONENTS
PANEL-ROCKER INR
FRAME-W/SHIELD LWR
RAIL-ENG COMPT SIDE UPR
REINF-ENG COMPT SIDE
LWR-R/SIDE ONLY

DOOR IMPACT
DOOR BELT REINF
DOOR BELT STIFFENER

FIGURE 6-5 Different materials used in automobile body construction. (Courtesy of Chart Industries Ltd.)

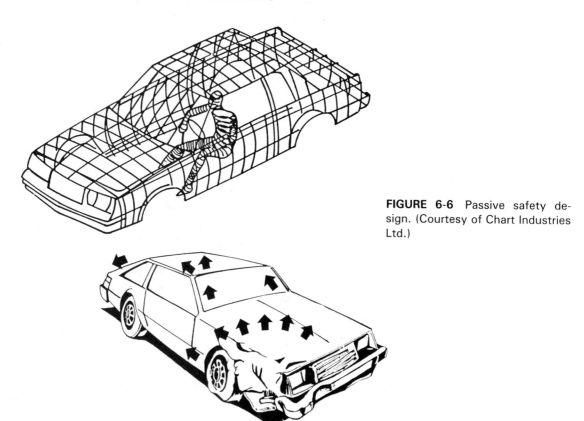

FIGURE 6-6 Passive safety design. (Courtesy of Chart Industries Ltd.)

FIGURE 6-7 Absorption of impact. (Courtesy of Chart Industries Ltd.)

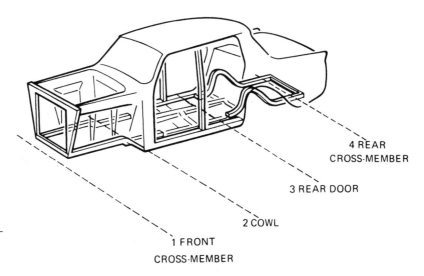

FIGURE 6-8 Concept of four controlling points in utilized body-frame design. (Courtesy of Bear Manufacturing Co.)

4 REAR
CROSS-MEMBER

3 REAR DOOR

2 COWL

1 FRONT
CROSS-MEMBER

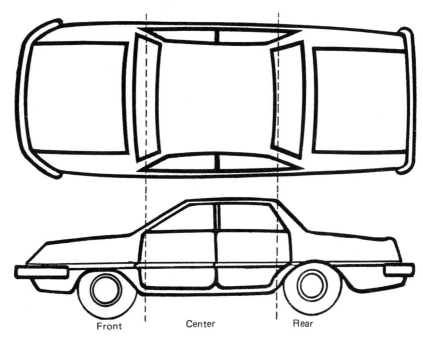

FIGURE 6-9 Fundamentals of body-frame straightening. Concepts of three sections: (1) front section, (2) center section (3) rear section. (Courtesy of Chart Industries Ltd.)

Front   Center   Rear

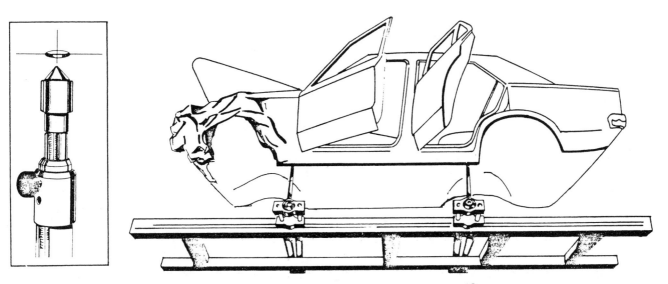

FIGURE 6-10 Measuring with universal measuring gauge. (Courtesy of Chart Industries Ltd.)

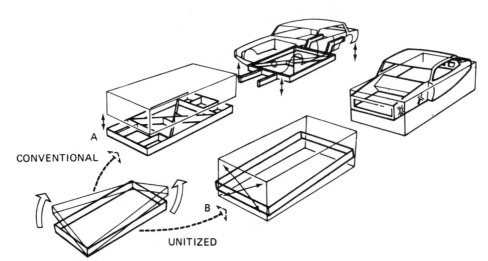

FIGURE 6-11   Lower half of unit must be stiff and strong if a frame structure is to be used to support body and running gear. Unitized bottom section B can be kept light, as it depends on upper half of body to complete box section structure. Welding, instead of nuts and bolts reduces the rattles. (Courtesy of Bear Manufacturing Co.)

straightening procedures. Figure 6-11 is an example of unitized construction.

First a level plane is found, usually in the center section, if possible, four control points that are not damaged, and, which will indicate an area that is not damaged either in length, width, or height. If four undamaged control points cannot be located there, alternative control points either rearward or forward must be found and selected by measuring until four controlling points meet manufacturer's specifications (Fig. 6-10).

6-2 GAUGES

Collision damage almost always occurs at the controlling points. Upon impact, both frame side rails will move together. One possible exception is the direct impact incurred in the side of the vehicle. When there is no cross member at the controlling points, these points are then called *areas,* such as the cowl area or the rear door area. Frame-centering gauges are positioned at the controlling points. They are used to diagnose the damage that may be present in the frame.

Each frame-centering gauge is a self-centering unit that has sliding dowel pins at the tip of each leg to provide a simple means of attaching it to either the inside or outside of box- or channel-type side rails (Fig. 6-12A). On certain types of frames, it is necessary to use magnetic holders to hold the gauges, for certain holes or flanges may not be

accessible. At times it is also necessary to use extensions to provide clearance and ease of sighting.

When checking for sidesway, sag, mash, and twist frame damage, the gauges may have to be installed as in Fig. 6-12B. The four locations are the front cross member, the cowl area, the rear door area, and the rear cross member. For easier sighting, the gauges with short legs should be attached at the cowl and rear door areas. It is important that the gauges be mounted in identical holes or areas on each side rail and that they be in contact with the side rails. This condition will allow the sighting pins to align and center themselves in the center of the gauge.

McPherson Strut Gauge

The new automobiles have what is called a McPherson strut type of suspension. To be able to check the center line and position of the different parts in the front section, a centering gauge was developed to enable the technicians to diagnose any problems in this section. If used properly, it is a very accurate way to measure strut tower position as well as other front-end components (Fig. 6-13A).

The strut gauge is installed on the vehicle's McPherson strut towers with the required hanger pins when repairs have progressed enough for it to be used. The gauge horizontal upper bar is calibrated from its center line, but it must be read adjusted to a total width dimension for each side. The lower horizontal bar also has a definite center line and uses the hanger scales to adjust for level and datum

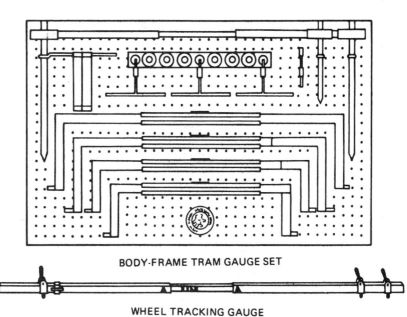

BODY-FRAME TRAM GAUGE SET

WHEEL TRACKING GAUGE

FIGURE 6-12A Step 1: Diagnosis, tools, and gauges. (Courtesy of Bear Manufacturing Co.)

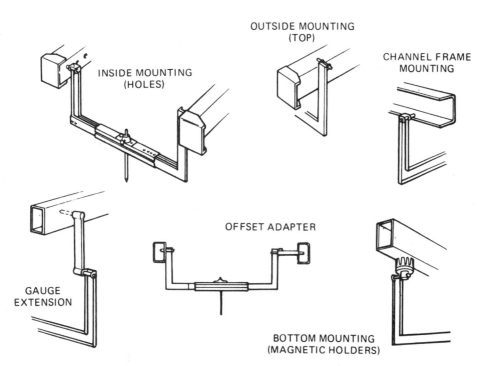

INSIDE MOUNTING (HOLES)

OUTSIDE MOUNTING (TOP)

CHANNEL FRAME MOUNTING

GAUGE EXTENSION

OFFSET ADAPTER

BOTTOM MOUNTING (MAGNETIC HOLDERS)

FIGURE 6-12B Methods used to hang gauges. (Courtesy of Bear Manufacturing Co.)

heights. When setting the datum line, it is required that the distance from the reference point to the upper horizontal bar be added to the given dimensions.

The gauge is used to read the level in two ways, by sighting the upper bar into the cowl area or by sighting the lower bar into the number 2 datum gauge. For the width measurements, gauges are set on the upper bar and tram and then the lower bar center line sighting pin is sighted as in Fig. 6-13B with the number 2 and 3 gauge center sighting pins. This will assure the technician that the strut towers are the proper width apart and that they are centered properly if all three sighting pins are in a straight line. With the datum measurements set properly, the gauge will show if the strut towers are too high or too low. Depending on the

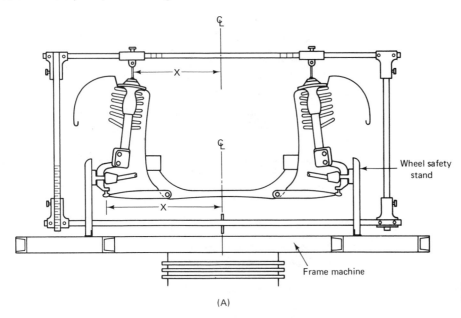

Wheel safety stand

Frame machine

(A)

FIGURE 6-13A Unistrut tower gauge. (Courtesy of Chief Automotive System, Inc.)

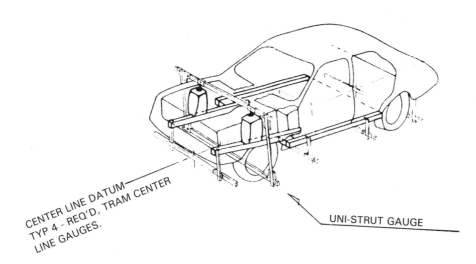

CENTER LINE DATUM — TYP 4 - REQ'D, TRAM CENTER LINE GAUGES.

UNI-STRUT GAUGE

FIGURE 6-13B Unistrut tower gauge. (Courtesy of Chief Automotive Systems, Inc.)

type of strut gauge used, other components may be checked for proper alignment.

Tram Gauges

Tram gauges are used to measure car bodies and frames to help pinpoint the damage. In this case the proper measurements from blueprints must be available (Fig. 6-14). With the accurate measurements, it is easy to find where the damage in a particular area is and to repair it to specifications.

The tram gauge and measuring tape may be used to measure many types of damage if used properly. It must be remembered that all vehicles have a center line, and this is the base for using centering gauges. The vehicle also has a lot of diagonal measurements, and this is where a tram gauge is very useful, to measure a diagonal measurement from point to point and then compare this measurement with the corresponding opposite points within a control area or length (Fig. 6-15).

The tram gauge may also be used for linear measurements on the datum line. To do this, the tram gauge is adjusted for the proper length required and then the measurements from the datum line to the area being measured must be applied to the pointers or measuring rods on the tram gauge (Fig. 6-16). When doing these measurements, the specifications must be checked carefully, as some of the locations or control points are symmetrical and some are asymmetrical. Check Fig. 6-34 from the strut tower to cowl; the measurements are not the same, so they are asymmetrical.

A datum line is an imaginary horizontal line that

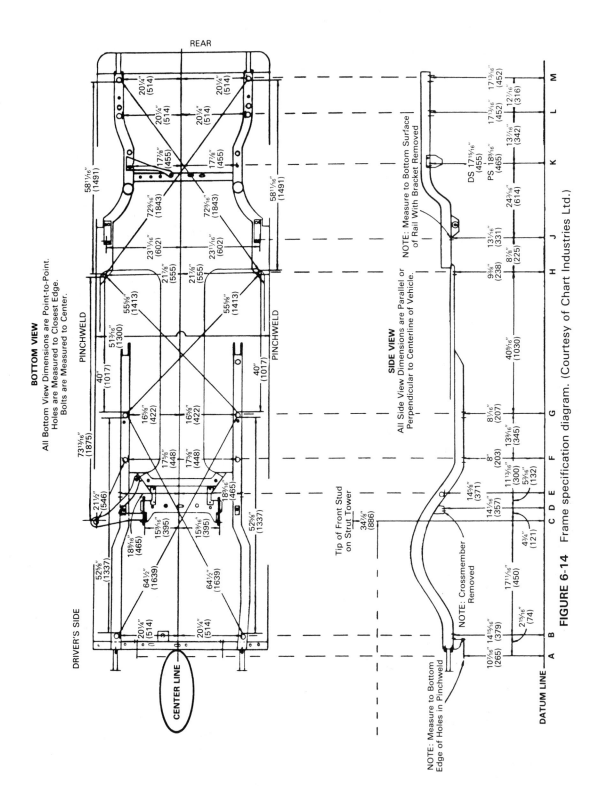

FIGURE 6-14 Frame specification diagram. (Courtesy of Chart Industries Ltd.)

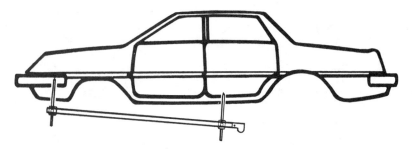

FIGURE 6-15   Point-to-point measuring. (Courtesy of Chart Industries Ltd.)

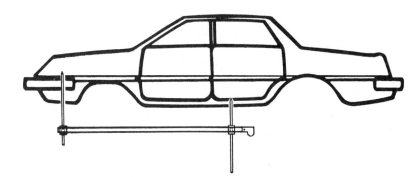

FIGURE 6-16   Linear measurement on datum line. (Courtesy of Chart Industries Ltd.)

appears on frame blueprints or charts to help determine correct frame heights. Vertical measurements from specific points on the frame to the imaginary line are given on the blueprints (Fig. 6-14). When checking the datum line, the gauges should be attached to or hung from the frame at the vertical measurement locations indicated on the blueprint (Fig. 6-17).

The crossbars should be adjusted for the specified vertical measurement for that location. If the frame is at the correct height, the crossbars will all be in line when they are sighted, indicating that the datum line is correct.

When the technician is doing the different operations required to straighten a frame, he or she must keep in mind that the frame has to be brought back to the manufacturer's

specifications (Table 6-1). If the frame is not returned to specifications, the vehicle may not drive properly or it may be impossible to fit the sheet metal on the body. Frames that have torque boxes must be returned to within $\frac{1}{16}$ inch ($1\frac{1}{2}$ mm) of the specifications in the location to the rails and length from one torque box to the other.

Tracking

After the frame has been repaired and the wheels aligned, the vehicle should be checked to see if the wheels are tracking properly. Tracking means that the rear wheels follow the front wheels in a parallel position. To check tracking, the gauge is adjusted to the distance between the front and rear wheels on one side of the vehicle and compared with the other side (Figs. 6-18 and 6-19). The proper procedure to follow is to split the toe-in; the gauge is set to the approximate length of the wheelbase. The pointers are aligned, one at the front and two at the rear. The pointers are adjusted to make contact between the tire

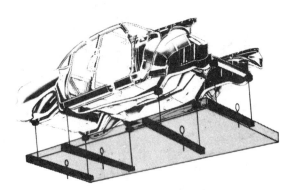

FIGURE 6-17   Datum line checking. (Courtesy of Blackhawk, Division of Applied Power of Canada Ltd.)

TABLE 6-1

Factory tolerances for frame adjustment

Passenger Cars	*Trucks*
Sidesway, $\frac{1}{8}$ in. (3 mm)	Sidesway, $\frac{1}{4}$ in. (6 mm)
Sag, $\frac{1}{8}$ in. (3 mm)	Sag, $\frac{1}{4}$ in. (6 mm)
Mash, $\frac{1}{16}$ in. ($1\frac{1}{2}$ mm)	Diamond, $\frac{1}{4}$ in. (6 mm)
Diamond, $\frac{1}{8}$ in. (3 mm)	Twist, $\frac{1}{4}$ in. (6 mm)
Twist, $\frac{1}{8}$ in. (3 mm)	

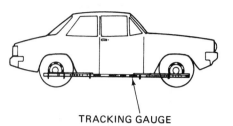

TO CHECK TRACKING: ADJUST GAUGE TO THE DIS-
TANCE BETWEEN THE FRONT AND THE REAR WHEELS ON
ONE SIDE OF THE VEHICLE AND COMPARE WITH THE
OTHER SIDE. MANUFACTURER'S SPECS. ON FRONT
POINTER ONLY:

$\frac{1}{8}$'' (3 mm) TOLERANCE FOR PASSENGER CARS

$\frac{1}{4}$'' (6 mm) TOLERANCE FOR TRUCKS

NO OPEN POINTERS AT THE REAR

TRACKING GAUGE

FIGURE 6-18 Using the tracking gauge. (Courtesy of Bear Manufacturing Co.)

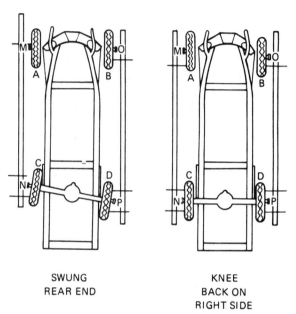

SWUNG
REAR END

KNEE
BACK ON
RIGHT SIDE

FIGURE 6-19 Tracking examples. (Courtesy of Bear Manufacturing Co.)

and rim at axle height; the setting is then compared with the other side. Hookups, hold-downs, and corrective pressures are usually applied at the controlling points, very rarely in between.

From a technician's point of view, the basic difference between conventional frame and unitized construction vehicles is the difference in the correction procedure. Vehicles with unitized construction require that the body and frame be straightened and aligned together. This also applies for conventional frames, especially for rear-end and side collisions.

When repairing unitized construction vehicles, the body technician must be able to measure accurately when the body or the body panels have been realigned to their proper position. This measuring is usually done via the X-checking method, which provides fast and accurate measurements (Fig. 6-20).

Dimensions covering frames, door openings, trunk openings, and floor panels are available from manufacturers. If required, measurements can also be taken from a similar model that is not damaged.

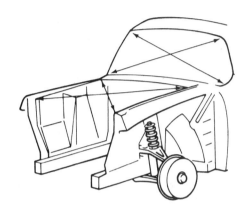

WHEELHOUSE PANEL MEASURING

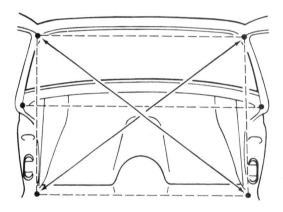

TRUNK OPENING MEASURING

FIGURE 6-20 Typical body-measuring points. (Courtesy of Bear Manufacturing Co.)

6-3 TYPES OF BODY-FRAME MISALIGNMENT

Five different types of frame damage can occur, depending on the type of collision: sidesway, sag, mash, diamond, and twist. Each condition is described next, and each applies to both conventional frame and unitized construction vehicles.

Sidesway is found when the front, center, or rear section side rails are bent to the right or left (Fig. 6-21). Side-rail sag misalignment of the frame is caused by the

Sidesway

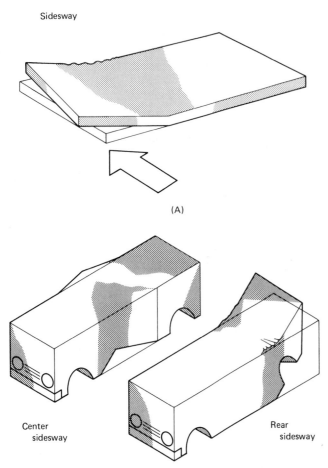

(A)

Center
sidesway

Rear
sidesway

FIGURE 6-21A and B   Sidesway condition examples (Courtesy of Blackhawk, Division of Applied Power of Canada Ltd.)

another area or controlling point. Mash will occur behind the front cross member or over the rear axle. In a mash, the side rail buckles underneath; the sag has the buckles on top (Fig. 6-23).

Diamond damage results from a heavy impact, sufficient to push the side rail back, on the corner of either side rail of the frame. As a result, the cross members are pushed out of a right angle with the side rail (Fig. 6-24).

A twisted frame usually results from a collision on a frame carrying a heavy load that causes it to turn over and twist the side rails out of horizontal alignment (Fig. 6-25).

When a vehicle is involved in an accident, it should always have a body-frame alignment checkup to determine the amount of damage. When a vehicle has been struck in the front, whether it is a conventional frame or unitized, the order of damage that will result in the frame will generally be as follows: The first condition will be sidesway,

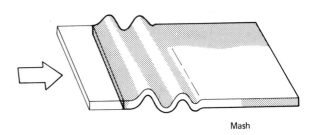

Mash

FIGURE 6-23   Mash condition. (Courtesy of Blackhawk, Division of Applied Power of Canada Ltd.)

buckling of the left or right side rail, or both, upon impact (Fig. 6-22). The weight of the motor or the body usually forces the side rail to drop. The buckles in the side rail are always on the top when sag is present. When the frame receives a heavy impact, the side rail will also bend in

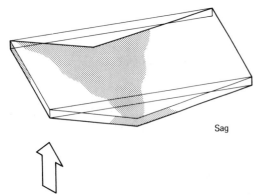

Sag

FIGURE 6-22   Sag condition. (Courtesy of Blackhawk, Division of Applied Power of Canada Ltd.)

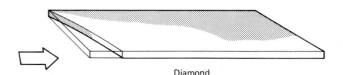

Diamond

FIGURE 6-24   Diamond frame. (Courtesy of Blackhawk, Division of Applied Power of Canada Ltd.)

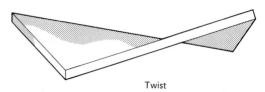

Twist

FIGURE 6-25   Twisted frame. (Courtesy of Blackhawk, Division of Applied Power of Canada Ltd.)

then sag, mash, diamond, and twist, depending on the impact.

Regardless of the severity of the impact, a certain amount of sidesway can be expected when the frame is hit. When the vehicle is struck in a more severe collision, sag will occur. Mash will occur if sidesway exceeds $\frac{1}{2}$ inch (13 mm) or if sag exceeds $\frac{3}{8}$ inch (9 mm). Diamond and twist will occur in severe collisions with certain types of frames. Unitized construction is especially resistant to diamond and twist damage.

Vehicles with conventional frames when struck in the rear will probably have the following conditions: mash, sidesway, and sag. Twist could be present, but as the mash, sag, and sidesway are removed, the twist will also be corrected. Since the rear part of the frame is very elastic, it will absorb a severe impact and not diamond the center section of the frame.

Vehicles with unitized construction, when struck in the rear, will follow the same order of frame damage as when struck in the front section. These are sidesway, sag, and mash.

Advanced Body-Frame Measuring and Straightening Equipment

With all the changes taking place in the automobile industry, it is inevitable that a lot of updating of equipment will have to be done in order to repair the newer unitized high-strength steel (HSS) constructed automobiles competitively and properly. Equipment manufacturers have introduced a lot of new equipment on the market. The dedicated bench body and frame straightener with fixtures manufactured to fit the numerous types of automobiles built (Fig. 6-26) was introduced from Europe. The dedicated bench body and frame straightener is equipped with fixtures made to fit jig holes and reference points on the underbody of an automobile; these are adjusted according to blueprints supplied by the manufacturer and employed in restoring the damaged automobile to factory specifications.

All the new body and frame straighteners have one feature in common. They are all designed and constructed using the pinch-weld flanges on the rocker or sill panels on

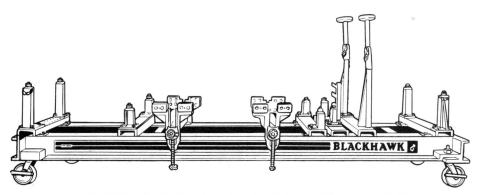

FIGURE 6-26 Dedicated bench with fixtures. (Courtesy of Blackhawk, Division of Applied Power of Canada, Ltd.)

FIGURE 6-27 Underbody clamping system.

FIGURE 6-28 P4 anchoring clamps. (Courtesy of Chart Industries Ltd.)

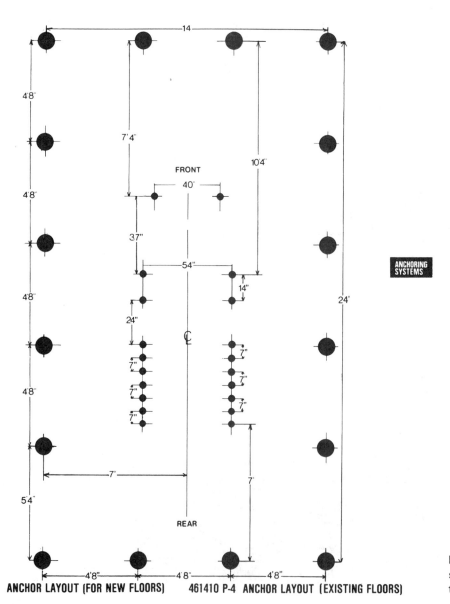

ANCHORING SYSTEMS

ANCHOR LAYOUT (FOR NEW FLOORS)   461410 P-4 ANCHOR LAYOUT (EXISTING FLOORS)

FIGURE 6-29 Floor anchoring system. (Courtesy of Chart Industries Ltd.)

the automobile to tie it down and hold the vehicle on the straightener.

The rocker or sill panels are the backbone of an automobile, and when exerting or applying corrective pulls, care must be taken that the multiclamp sets are properly positioned (on perfectly clean and straight areas of the rocker or sill panel flanges) and tightened securely, to prevent tearing or damaging the rocker or sill panels (Fig. 6-27). A variety of other hold-down, anchoring, and clamping systems are illustrated in Figs. 6-28 and 6-29.

One manufacturer of body and frame straighteners also has available universal measuring devices, as shown in Fig. 6-30. The universal measuring gauges, once set up under the automobile in their proper positions and height according to specifications, eliminate the need for repeated

tape measuring during the straightening process and monitor all control points simultaneously. They also provide continuous information on the movement and position of body members and sheet metal as the corrective pulls are applied in the desired areas of correction. They monitor all control points desired, even the location or position of strut towers and spindles.

The Tri-Scan Universal Laser Gauge Measuring system (Fig. 6-31), one of the latest, more sophisticated systems, will verify an automobile's underbody in three dimensions simultaneously, such as height, width, and length. It also has side body dimension monitoring capabilities, enabling the repairer to check the alignment of strategic areas on the body, such as door hinges, cowls, and bumpers.

FIGURE 6-30 Exacto 3D measuring gauge and Porta Bench. (Courtesy of Chart Industries Ltd.)

FIGURE 6-31 Porta Bench system with tri-scan laser gauge. (Courtesy of Chart Industires Ltd.)

BODY/FRAME DAMAGE DIAGNOSIS WORKSHEET

DAMAGE	INDICATION	CONDITION	
TWIST One corner of vehicle is higher than adjacent corner.			
DIAMOND One side of vehicle is pushed back or forward.			
MASH Length of vehicle is shortened.			
SAG Center is lower than normal.			
SIDESWAY Front, center or rear is pushed sideways out of alignment.			
DAMAGE OCCURS IN THIS ORDER (1) Sidesway (2) Sag (3) Mash (4) Diamond (5) Twist	**MAKE MEASUREMENT AND CORRECTION IN THIS ORDER** (1) Twist (2) Diamond (3) Mash (4) Sag (5) Sidesway		

FIGURE 6-32 Diagnosis sheet. (Courtesy of Blackhawk, Division of Applied Power of Canada Ltd.)

There are so many different types of body and frame straighteners on the market today that it is impossible to describe and illustrate them all. When contemplating what type of body and frame straightener to purchase, it is advisable to get all the information possible from the manufacturers' representatives about every type of straightener on the market and then to select the straightener with the features that makes it most suitable for the type of work that a particular body shop will handle.

The technician should have a diagnosis sheet such as that in Fig. 6-32 before starting to do the measuring and the installation of gauges on the vehicle. With this type of worksheet, the data obtained while doing the diagnosis can be recorded and retained for both the estimating and repairing procedures.

When doing a diagnosis, the vehicle should be raised and supported with safety stands, which are placed under the front and rear torque boxes; for unitized bodies, these general locations are used except underbody clamps are attached to the pinchweld flange at both ends of the rocker panel. Then a cross tube is placed through the safety stands and under body clamps as shown in Fig. 6-33.

But due to overhang deflection from the weight of the section, for the final check for twist, sidesway, and datum, the vehicle should only be supported by a hydraulic jack under the front cross member, lifting the front torque boxes or section slightly off the safety stands.

Sidesway

Three centering gauges are used to check the frame for sidesway. When the vehicle has been struck from the front, the gauges are attached at the front cross member, the cowl

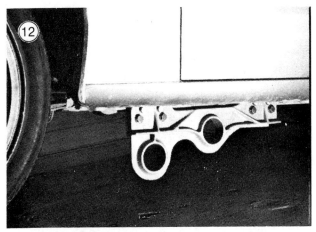

FIGURE 6-33 Supporting vehicle on safety stands. (Courtesy of Blackhawk, Division of Applied Power of Canada Ltd.)

area, and the rear door area. Since the sighting pins are self-centering, the pins are always in the center of the gauge. The best method to check the frame is to align the sighting pins on gauges 2 and 3. If the sighting pin on gauge 1 does not line up with the pins on the other gauges, the frame has sidesway (Fig. 6-34); if it lines up, it has no sidesway.

When the frame has been struck in the rear and sag is present at the rear door area, one gauge is attached at the cowl area, one is at the rear door area, and the gauge at the rear is installed in front of the mash condition. When checking the sag at the rear, the centering gauge is never installed at the rear cross member. A mash in the frame over the rear housing will interfere with a true sag measurement or reading. Sighting from the rear of the vehicle, the bottom bars of the first two centering gauges should be

SIDESWAY DIAGNOSIS (FRONT)

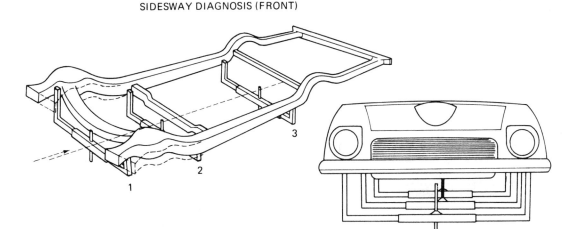

FIGURE 6-34 To check sidesway misalignment, place three frame-centering gauges at the controlling points and sight gauge pointers. The direction and amount of front sidesway are determined from the position of gauge pointer 1. (Courtesy of Bear Manufacturing Co.)

horizontally in line with each other. The sag is located on the side behind the high corner of the gauge.

Sag

Three centering gauges are used to check for a sag condition; it is a condition that can usually be noticed since the top of the front door and front fender usually overlap one another. One gauge is placed at the front cross member, the next one at the cowl area, and the third one at the rear door area.

To find the side of the vehicle and the amount of sag present at the cowl area, the bottom bars of the first two frame-centering gauges are sighted to determine if they are horizontally in line with one another. If they are, there is no sag. If sag is present, it will be found on the side behind the high corner of the front gauge. The bars of the gauge are usually 1 inch (25 mm) wide; this helps to determine the amount of sag (Fig. 6-35).

Very often a vehicle will have both sidesway and sag. To determine the amount of sag present, the low corner of the front gauge is raised until the pointer is perpendicular; then by sighting along the centering pins the amount of sidesway will be determined when a frame also has sag.

Mash

A mash occurs directly behind the front cross member or above the rear housing. Buckles appear on the underside of the rail; this bending will cause the rail to become shorter in length. To find the amount of mash in the front frame, it is measured from the cowl area to the front cross member. The measurements are taken from holes or rivet heads and then compared to the other side rail. The difference in the measurement between the two rails is the amount of mash present (Fig. 6-36). A frame that has been struck in the rear is measured for mash from the rear door area to the end of the frame.

If the frame has been struck head on and both rails

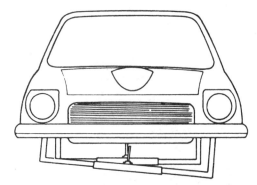

FIGURE 6-35 Sag condition. (Courtesy of Bear Manufacturing Co.)

FIGURE 6-36 Mashed frame diagnosis. To check mash misalignments, measure from a point at the front cross member to a point on the side rail at the cowl area. Compare length measurement to that of opposite side rail and car blueprint specifications. (Courtesy of Blackhawk, Division of Applied Power of Canada Ltd.)

are mashed, it is necessary to refer to the manufacturer's blueprints or a similar, undamaged model for the correct specifications.

Diamond

A diamond condition in a frame always occurs in the center section between the cowl area and the rear-door area. A diagonal or X-ing measurement is used through the center section of the frame. The side rail that has been pushed back will have a longer diagonal measurement than the other. The frame is always measured in the center; this eliminates interference from other collision damage that could make it impossible to obtain an accurate measurement (Fig. 6-37A and B).

Twist

A twisted frame is checked by attaching two centering gauges on the center section of the frame, one at the cowl area and one at the rear-door area. To check the direction and amount of twist, sight along the bottom bars of the frame-centering gauges. If the gauges are parallel, the frame is not damaged; but if they are not parallel, the frame is twisted (Fig. 6-38).

Therefore, when a vehicle is repaired, the passive safety or integrity of the design of the body shell and passenger compartment must not be compromised. The key to successful repairs will depend on an accurate diagnosis of the damage that has occurred in the collision.

In diagnosing the damage, a visual inspection is

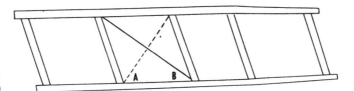

FIGURE 6-37 Diamond frame. (Courtesy of Blackhawk, Division of Applied Power of Canada Ltd.)

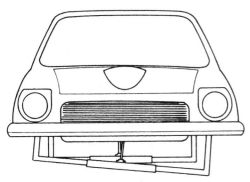

FIGURE 6-38 Twist. (Courtesy of Bear Manufacturing Co.)

(I) **LIGHTER GAUGE METAL THROUGHOUT STRUCTURAL MEMBERS.**

(II) **EXTENSIVE USE OF COATED STEELS, HIGH STRENGTH STEEL, ALLUMINUM, PLASTICS.**

(III) **STRUCTURAL PARTS OF BODY USED FOR ATTACHMENT OF MECHANICAL COMPONENTS.**

(iv) **MORE CONTROL POINTS TO MONITOR IN DAMAGE ANALYSIS.**

(v) **CLOSE TOLERANCE CONSTRUCTION - LESS THE 3mm.**

(vi) **MORE PASSIVE SAFETY DESIGN.**

(vii) **FRONT WHEEL DRIVE, RACK AND PINION STEERING, MACPERSON STRUT SUSPENSION.**

(viii) **IMPACT FORCES TRANSFERRED INTO LARGER ADJACENT PANELS.**

(Ix) **PASSENGER COMPARTMENT DESIGNED TO STAY INTACT UNDER SEVERE IMPACT.**

FIGURE 6-39 Features of unitized body construction. (Courtesy of Chart Industries Ltd.)

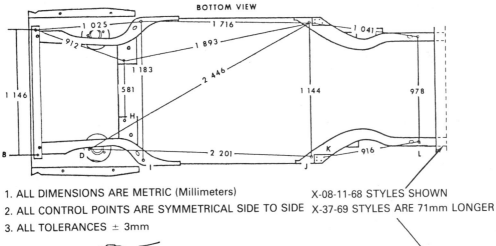

BOTTOM VIEW

1. ALL DIMENSIONS ARE METRIC (Millimeters)
2. ALL CONTROL POINTS ARE SYMMETRICAL SIDE TO SIDE
3. ALL TOLERANCES ± 3mm

X-08-11-68 STYLES SHOWN
X-37-69 STYLES ARE 71mm LONGER

SIDE VIEW

(A)

FIGURE 6-40 Frame measurements. Horizontal and vertical dimensions. (Courtesy of General Motors of Canada Ltd.)

usually done first, such as checking the overall body lines, the relationship of one panel to the other, the riding height of the vehicle at all four corners, and the impact angle.

The direct damage is then checked, such as buckled or wrinkled sheet metal, paint and sealer splits, and stretched and split spot welds. The indirect damage, including cracked glass, tension or pressure spots, sagged doors, uneven gaps, and poor fit on trunk lid or hood, is checked next.

On the inside, the steering column and steering operation must be checked. The dash and lower panels, the space between the weather stripping and door panels, buckled floor sections, deformed parcel shelf, and pulled spot welds must all be inspected for damage.

To determine all the damage that has occurred to the underbody, the vehicle must be checked for datum line, center line, and all required linear references.

After completing this inspection and measurements, specific facts about the vehicle should be revealed. The inspection should show how much of the vehicle is damaged, as well as the underbody and the angle of the impact and how the forces have entered the vehicle. All pertinent information should be entered on the diagnosis worksheet.

It must be realized that the damage in this type of vehicle will not be the same as in the conventional frame and body, as they respond differently to an impact to a certain degree. This is why such a careful diagnosis and inspection with a systematic approach must be carried out, so as not to miss any area of damage. Some of the most important points to remember as the diagnosis is done are the features listed in Fig. 6-39.

The information obtained by the diagnosis will determine the specific nature and type of damage, the area or location, and the extent of it in inches or millimeters. This is accomplished with complete and careful measurements of the underbody and by comparing these to the factory specifications (Figs. 6-40, 6-41, and 6-42).

Remember that these structures are designed to transfer the damaging force of the impact into the larger adjacent panels to absorb and dissipate the collision forces. In cases where primary damages seem quite light, the possibility of severe extensive damage may exist. Never be fooled by the first appearance and restrict the measurements to the damaged area, rather than measuring the whole vehicle, and be sure of the facts as they are gathered. This is done to determine how much of the vehicle is damaged and how much of it is free of damage. The principles of body-frame straightening have not really changed except that the repairs have to be done with greater care and precision on the new unitized HSS-constructed vehicles. Multiple hookups provide a fast and efficient method for the realignment of damaged parts. The body and frame structures must be straightened and aligned. On unitized vehicles, whenever possible, standard or conventional body panels are not

1. ALL DIMENSIONS ARE METRIC (Millimeters)
2. ALL CONTROL POINTS ARE SYMMETRICAL SIDE TO SIDE
3. ALL TOLERANCES ± 3mm

TOP VIEW

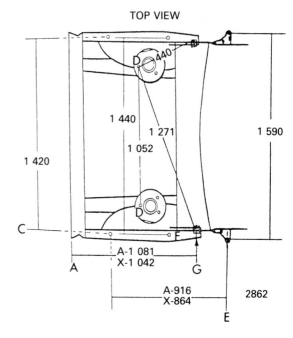

BOTTOM VIEW

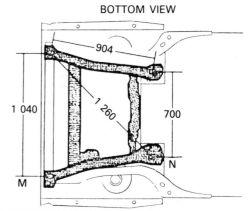

1. ALL DIMENSIONS ARE METRIC (Millimeters)
2. ALL CONTROL POINTS ARE SYMMETRICAL SIDE TO SIDE
3. ALL TOLERANCES ± 3mm

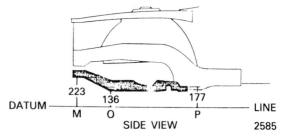

FIGURE 6-41A Engine cradle horizontal and vertical dimensions. (B) Suspension strut tower dimensions, front door and hood hinge locations. (Courtesy of General Motors of Canada Ltd.)

Ref.	Horizontal	Vertical	Location
A	Leading edge	Upper surface at corner	Engine compartment bar upper rail
B	Center of 16 mm (5/8 in.) gauge hole	Lower surface at gauge hole	Lower engine compartment front panel, outboard of cradle attaching hole
C	A: Center of 18 mm (11/16 in.) gauge hole X: Center of 9 mm (23/64 in.) gauge hole	None	A: Engine compartment side rail X: Engine compartment side rail in depression
D	Center of strut shock tower, front attaching hole	Upper surface at strut shock tower, front attaching hole	Strut shock tower
E	Center of front upper hinge pin hole	Upper surface at hinge pin hole	Front upper door hinge, body side
F	Center of 9 mm (23/64 in.) gauge hole	None	A: Engine compartment side rail X: Engine compartment side rail in depression
G	Top surface of hood hinge, centered with rivet	None	Hood hinge
H	Center of 16 mm (5/8 in.) gauge hole	Lower surface at gauge hole	Reinforcement No. 1 floor pan bar, inboard of cradle attachment hole
I	Center of 16 mm (5/8 in.) gauge hole	Lower surface at gauge hole	Engine compartment side rail, rearward and outboard of slot in rail
J	Front edge of 20 mm (13/16 in.) gauge hole	Lower surface at gauge hole	Compartment pan longitudinal rail, forward of control arm reinforcement
K	Center of control arm rear inboard attaching hole	Lower surface at rear inboard attaching hole	Compartment pan longitudinal rail control arm reinforcement
L	Front edge of 20 mm (13/16 in.) gauge hole	Lower surface at gauge hole	Compartment pan longitudinal rail, rearward of slot in rail
M	Center of front cradle attaching hole	Lower surface at front attaching hole	Engine cradle
N	Center of rear cradle attaching hole	None	Engine cradle
O	None	Lower surface of cradle at cross-member	Engine cradle
P	None	Upper surface of cradle at rear edge	Engine cradle

FIGURE 6-42 Horizontal and vertical locations. (Courtesy of General Motors of Canada Ltd.)

removed or replaced until the body and frame have been aligned.

Because of the design of the new automobiles, they tend to have more control points built into the vehicle, and many of them are contained within the body shell itself. A good definition of control points is reference points on each side rail, usually jig holes that allow the repairer to determine, by measurement, if the structure meets its designed specifications (Figs. 6-43 and 6-44).

All reference points must meet specifications to all other designated points by measuring within tolerance from the vehicle center line out, from the datum line up to the member, and the jig holes from each other linearly. By using this method the repairer will know that the correct alignment of the body shell is accurate when specifications are within tolerance.

Many of these control points will affect the wheel alignment and steering geometry. When the repairer does this type of correction, he or she must be mindful of the caster and camber, as these angles will change simultaneously when aligning the damaged sections. The repairer must be careful not to overcorrect one set of control points

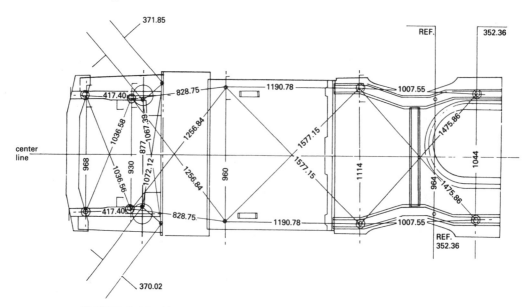

FIGURE 6-43   Underbody dimensions. (Courtesy of Ford Motor Company of Canada Ltd.)

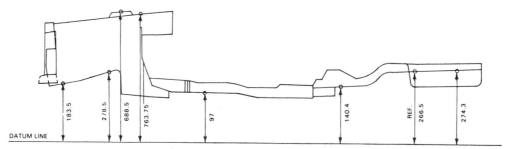

FIGURE 6-44   Datum line measurements. (Courtesy of Ford Motor Company of Canada Ltd.)

when trying to achieve dimensions in another area. Such situations can be controlled by constantly monitoring all the major control points to recognize any movement and its direction in the undamaged areas.

Because of the close tolerances of the all-welded construction, the measurements must be taken with great accuracy, within $\frac{1}{8}$ inch (3 mm) of factory specifications. Failure to achieve proper measurements may produce a vehicle that has poor panel alignment and may handle and drive poorly.

6-4 STRAIGHTENING THE BODY AND FRAME

Depending on the type of equipment available, the shop will vary some of the hookup techniques. A manual should be obtained from the manufacturer of the equipment to obtain the proper methods to be used to correct the damage in the vehicle. The following steps and concepts will apply in most cases to the job of straightening unitized vehicles (Fig. 6-45A and B).

Unitized Vehicles

1. Sheet metal and the bumper are removed only if absolutely required; when straightening unitized vehicles, it is required that all component parts

Body-Frame Correction Hook-ups

1. **Diamond**
2. **Mash**
3. **Sag**   4-Way Hook-up
4. **Sidesway**
5. **Twist**

FIGURE 6-45A   Correction sequence for a collision occurring at front of vehicle. (Courtesy of Bear Manufacturing Co.)

retch and pull hookup is first attached on the vehicle having the most damage. This hookup basic hookup that is used to remove all other me misalignment except twist.

a collision of any consequence occurs, damage ture will seldom be in a single direction (Fig. damage from the collision will usually affect the everal directions simultaneously and will occur ly fashion. When a vehicle is hit in the front , it will cause a shortness of length first, then th, side movement, and so on. Visualize the it occurs because the repair will logically have he sequence. Therefore, the hookups will have the damage in the proper sequence, either alone other damage, in the reverse order in which it To avoid problems with overpulling some areas ulling others, this method should be followed le still trying to achieve overall dimensions.

ype of equipment available in the shop will vary e hookups, but the new unitized vehicles must d with four pinch-weld clamp systems on the els. It may be necessary to have additional tie-ontrol height and side movement.

er alignment of the sheet metal will not occur ternal stresses from the impact are relieved. This the dimensions to remain when the corrective re released. The stress relief may be done cold ses, and in other cases heat must be applied.

e corrective forces are applied, movement will e areas where secondary damage has occurred. econdary damaged areas move, work the ridges s slowly while raising low metal (Fig. 6-49).

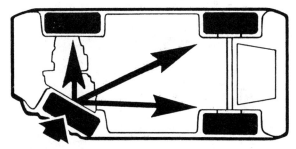

FIGURE 6-49 Relieving stresses using a block of wood and hammer. (Courtesy of Chart Industries Ltd.)

If the metal should tear, it should be rewelded as realignment occurs. This type of construction and metal must be worked slowly to allow time for the metal to reposition itself in its proper shape or space.

Since HSS is used in most structural members, care must be used when applying heat. Heat-stress relief will work best at the critical temperature of approximately 900°F (371°C). The structured member being heated turns blue in color. Some manufacturers may recommend slightly higher heat, but never more than 1400°F (760°C). These ranges are acceptable for most HSS specifications depending on the domestic manufacturer, as long as the area is not heated for more than a total of 3 minutes. A heat crayon (Fig. 6-50) should be used to guide the repairer for higher-temperature exposure of panel.

Heat should be applied along the edges of the damaged members, around spot welds, because this is where

FIGURE 6-47 Direction that damage travels. (Courtesy of Chart Industries Ltd.)

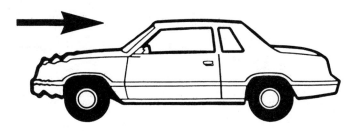

-48 Crushing due to collision. (Courtesy of ustries Ltd.)

Unitized Body-Frame Construction

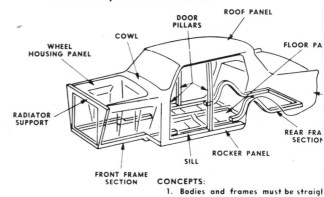

ROOF PANEL

DOOR
PILLARS

COWL

FLOOR PA

WHEEL
HOUSING PANEL

RADIATOR
SUPPORT

REAR FRA
SECTION

RABBER PANEL

SILL

ROCKER PANEL

FRONT FRAME
SECTION

CONCEPTS:

1. Bodies and frames must be straigh
   together.
2. Body panels must not be removed
   after the body and frame have be
3. Multiple hook-ups are the secret to
   rection work.
4. More power is needed to straighten
   than for conventional frames.

FIGURE 6-45B Unitized body-frame construction. (Courtesy of Bear Manufacturing Co.)

be straightened on the vehicle as much as possible. This is to increase or gain as much support as possible when pressure is applied when straightening the body and reinforcing structures.

2. The power train and suspension assemblies on older unitized and newer unitized HSS-constructed vehicles are removed as required.

3. A wire brush is used to clean the buckled or cracked areas.

4. All breaks in the frame and body panels are welded to avoid further tearing of the metal while the frame and body are being straightened.

5. After all welding is completed, HSS welded areas are primed with a zinc primer.

Body-frame damage is always removed in the opposite direction from that of the impact. In most cases, the damage

is removed by pulling instead o
is minimized; as much of the w
cold-working. The work can be
or a movable straightening syste

With the unlimited power a
be careful not to tear body pan
they are being pulled out. Thus
the buckles until a silver streak
buckle; then and only then is h
tip and a neutral or slightly ca
technician heats the area to th
more pressure is applied to the f

When a frame is being
necessary to overcorrect to allo
construction does not require as
conventional type of frame. As t
ened, the body panels should als
time and helps to relieve strains o

side
serve
type

to th
6-47
vehic
in ar
(Fig.
heigh
dama
to re
to pu
or wi
happe
and u
strictl

some
be an
rocke
downs

until t
will a
hooku
in son

occur
As the
and bu

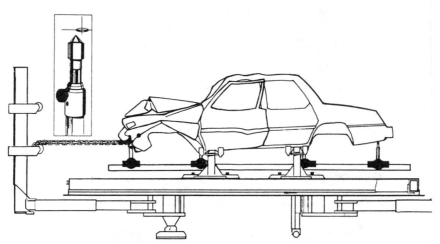

FIGURE 6-46 Accu-rack and Exacto gauge. (Courtesy of Chart In-dustries Ltd.)

FIGUR
front-e
Chart I

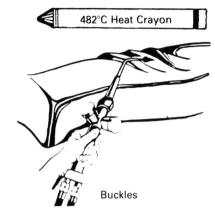

FIGURE 6-50   Heat crayon. (Courtesy of Chart Industries Ltd.)

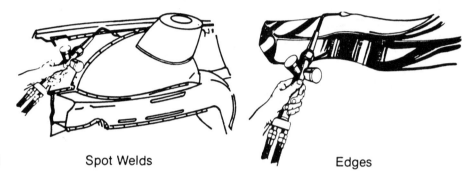

FIGURE 6-51   Heat application. (Courtesy of Chart Industries Ltd.)

Spot Welds   Edges

compression occurs (Fig. 6-51). Heat should never be applied to the side surfaces of any box-shaped members.

The first type of frame damage that must be removed is the diamond (Fig. 6-52). During the straightening procedure, a careful diagonal measurement must be taken at the center section to ensure that the cross members are brought back to right angles and that the diagonal measurements are equal. This condition is not usually present in unitized construction (Fig. 6-52).

Mash is the next frame condition that has to be corrected. The proper hookup is installed and the side rail is then stretched back to meet the specifications from the manufacturer's blueprint. As mash is removed, it is important to check the distance from the center of the lower ball joint to the specified area on the frame. If the distance is not correct to within $\frac{1}{8}$ inch (3 mm), one or both wheels will not be in their proper location. This could cause the car to pull to the short side of the vehicle and could make a proper alignment almost impossible; this condition is often referred to as a *knee-back*. Therefore, careful measurements must be taken to assure that the proper distance from the center of the lower ball joint to the specified point on the frame is reached.

A mash at the rear requires the same type of hookup except that it is reversed; when removing mash on unitized vehicles, refer to sag corrections. When removing sag, the

rail is held as in Figs. 6-53 and 6-54, and the sagged rail is jacked up a bit past the correct height and then normalized and released to see if it is at the proper height. If the rail is not at the proper height, it must be jacked higher until proper alignment is achieved. Wood or steel plates must always be used when padding is required; otherwise, crushing of the panels can occur (Fig. 6-55A).

When diamond, sag, and mash conditions have been repaired, the next condition to repair is sidesway or double sidesway (Fig. 6-56). The proper hookup is attached and the frame is pulled back until the sighting pins on the centering gauges remain in line. On unitized vehicles, it is necessary to correct the body or wheelhouse section at the same time (Fig. 6-57).

The strut towers should be checked during these repair operations, and at the proper time the strut tower gauge is used to check both the progress and accuracy of the ongoing repairs (Fig. 6-55B).

The last condition of frame damage to be corrected is the twist, and again the equipment available will determine the hookup. The two high points are attached to the frame machine to hold them when hydraulic pressure is applied to the two low corners. Figure 6-58 shows a typical hookup on a frame rack. On many occasions the twist condition may have been corrected as other conditions were repaired.

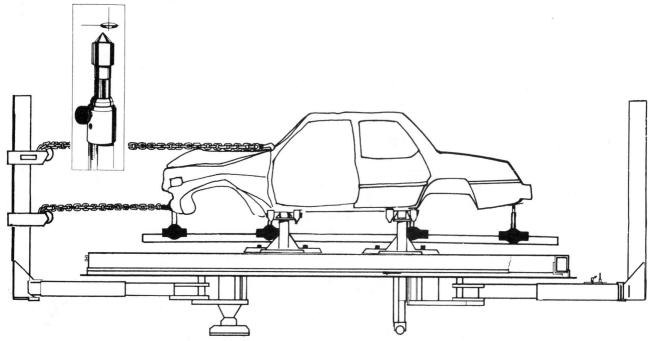

FIGURE 6-52 Mash and sag correction hookup on frame rack. (Courtesy of Chart Industries Ltd.)

Unitized Body-Frame

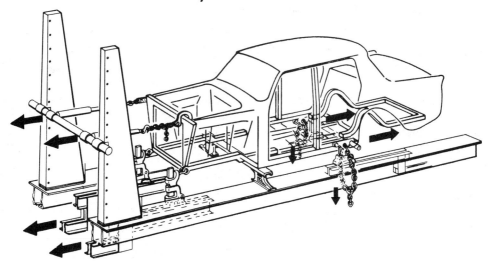

**Double Mash, Sag and Front Body
Correction Hook-up
(Both sides)**

FIGURE 6-53 Double mash, sag, and front body correction hookup on both sides. (Courtesy of Bear Manufacturing Co.)

The low corners will have to be raised equally high enough and the body and frame normalized as in all other conditions; if twist returns after the first push, the operation must be repeated until the gauges at the cowl and rear door are parallel horizontally.

The last damage to repair is the finishing of the frame horns that were roughly aligned to facilitate the hookups necessary to start the repair of the frame. Whether the horns are repaired or replaced, they have to be returned to their proper place in relation to the frame center line and datum

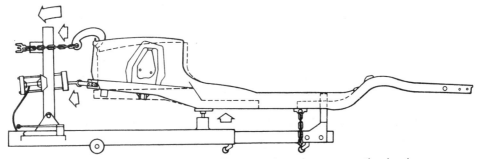

FIGURE 6-54 Damage dozer. Front mash and sag correction hookup on unitized body. (Courtesy of Bear Manufacturing Co.)

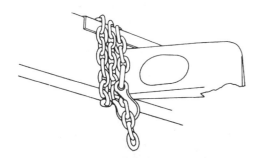

FIGURE 6-55A Padded section.

FIGURE 6-55B Dataliner strut gauge being used to check progress of repairs.

Unitized Body-Frame

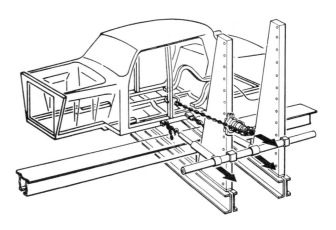

SIDE ROCKER PANEL, FLOOR PANEL AND DOOR POST CORRECTION HOOK-UP

FIGURE 6-56 Basic correction hookup for sidesway. Whenever sidesway exceeds $\frac{1}{2}$ inch (13 mm), use stretch and hookup pull. Sidesway has been corrected when the three pointers of the frame centering gauges are in line. (Courtesy of Bear Manufacturing Co.)

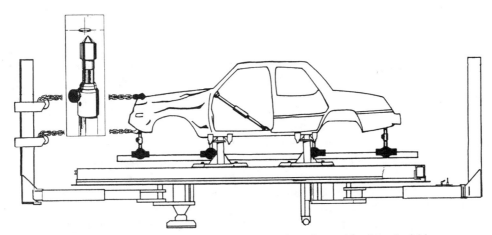

FIGURE 6-57 Sidesway correction hookup for unitized body (side view). (Courtesy of Chart Industries Ltd.)

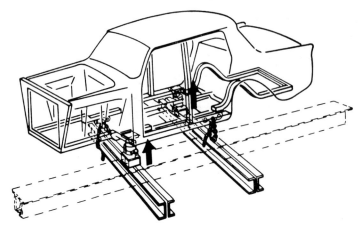

FIGURE 6-58 Unitized body frame. (Courtesy of Bear Manufacturing Co.)

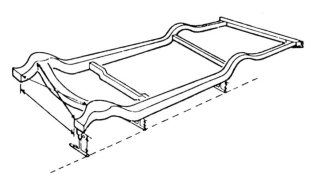

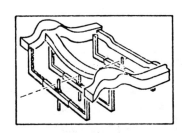

FIGURE 6-59A Frame-horn alignment is the final step in the body-frame straightening operation. To assure correct alignment, frame-centering gauges, datum-line gauges, X-ing measurements, and car factory blueprints are used.

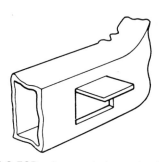

FIGURE 6-59B Access hole cut in side rail.

line. If they are not in their proper location, it will be impossible to install the front end on the car and make it fit to the body. Figure 6-59A shows the methods used to align the horns properly using a tape measure and the centering gauges.

When the rails have been brought back to their proper location, it may be necessary to do metal work on some sections. Doors are sometimes cut in the rail (Fig. 6-59B) to enable the straightening of the member; these are welded shut after the repair is completed. Bars forged with different curvatures and hooks are very handy to pull or push existing damage through holes on side rails so that the members or rails are returned to their proper shape for maximum strength.

6-5 WHEEL ALIGNMENT

When a vehicle is involved in an accident in which the frame is bent and the tires or wheels are damaged, it should receive a complete wheel-alignment check. A vehicle that has poor or hard steering after an accident will certainly not please the owner. See Table 6-2 for different conditions.

When all the major controlling points on the body have been correctly aligned, the wheels must be checked for their position in relation to the body. The rear wheels should be parallel to the center line of the vehicle. Since some of the new vehicles have solid rear axles and some have independent suspension, it is imperative that they be checked for toe and camber according to manufacturers' specifications. The lower ball joints must be in linear alignment to the specifications and the wheel base in proper

TABLE 6-2

Wheel alignment trouble chart

Trouble	Camber	Caster	Turning Radius	Toe-In	Steering Gear	Wheels
				Probable Causes*		
Cuppy tire wear						Bent or out of balance
Excessive tire wear	Incorrect		Incorrect	Incorrect		
Pulling to one side	Unequal	Unequal				
Wander or weave		Not enough		Incorrect	Loose or tight	
Hard steering		Too much	Incorrect		Tight	
Excessive road shock		Too much			Loose or worn	Bent or out of balance
Low-speed shimmy		Too much			Loose or worn	
High-speed shimmy						

*Other factors that cause steering trouble and excessive tire wear are faulty brakes and brake drums, bent frame, improperly adjusted front wheel bearings, improper tire inflation, faulty shock absorbers, loose spring shackles, weak springs, and out-of-round tires.

dimensions (Fig. 6-60). Some of these checks can be done by using a tracking gauge (see Fig. 6-19).

The new unibodies employ inner fender aprons that have strut towers to which the upper part of the McPherson strut assembly is bolted. Rack-and-pinion steering is used on this type of suspension on most new vehicles. The strut towers have to be placed within specifications to assure that the vehicle will have the proper steering angles (Fig. 6-61). The camber adjustments are on the bottom part of the strut, which is a slotted hole. This slot in the bracket will allow the required adjustments.

Because of the variety of wheel-alignment equipment, it is impossible to describe the use of all available types. The student should receive instruction on and operating manuals for the particular type of equipment that he or she will use.

The main purpose of wheel alignment is to make the wheels roll without scuffing, dragging, or slipping under all road-operating conditions. The result is greater safety in driving, easier steering, longer tire wear, and less strain on the parts that make up the front end of the automobile. Five simple angles are the foundation of wheel alignment. These angles are designed by the manufacturer to locate the weight on moving parts properly and to facilitate steering.

Car manufacturers' specifications provide a range that serves as a guide for what each angle should be. Good wheel-alignment service maintains the five simple angles within the range of the manufacturer's specifications.

Camber

Camber is the inward or outward tilt of the wheel at the top. It is the tire-wearing angle measured in degrees and is the amount of center line of the wheel is tilted from true vertical.

Outward tilt of the wheel at the top from true vertical is positive camber (Fig. 6-62). Inward tilt of the wheel at the top from true vertical is negative camber. Manufacturers' specifications indicate negative and positive camber by the letters N and P. Where a letter is not given, it is to be regarded as positive camber.

The purpose of camber is to bring the road contact of the tire more nearly under the point of load, to provide

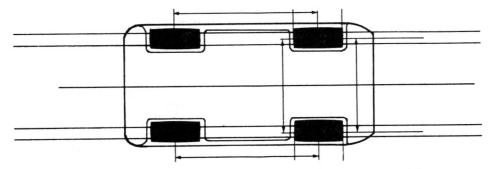

FIGURE 6-60 Wheel alignment to body. (1) Rear wheel parallel to centerline of vehicle. (2) Rear wheels properly toed. (3) Lower ball joints in linear alignment to specification. (4) Wheel base in dimension. (Courtesy of Chart Industries Ltd.)

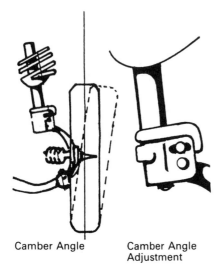

Camber Angle   Camber Angle
Adjustment

FIGURE 6-61 McPherson strut camber adjustment. (Courtesy of Chart Industries Ltd.)

shown, both wheels should be within $\frac{1}{2}°$ of each other. Generally, zero to positive camber should be maintained.

The harmful effects of incorrect camber are excessive wear to ball joints, to wheel bearings, and to one side of the tire tread (negative camber, inside wear; positive camber, outside wear). Excessive unequal camber will cause the vehicle to pull to one side.

Steering-axis Inclination

Steering-axis inclination is the inward tilt of the king pin or spindle support arm (ball joint) at the top. Steering-axis inclination is a directional control angle measured in degrees and is the amount the spindle support center line is tilted from true vertical (Fig. 6-63). This angle is not adjustable.

Figure 6-64 shows the relation of camber to steering-axis inclination. This relationship does not change except when the spindle or spindle support arm (ball joint) becomes

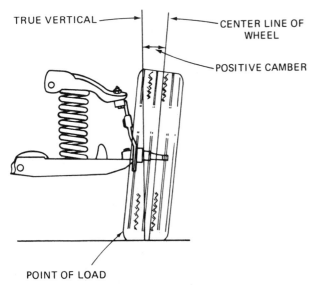

FIGURE 6-62 When the wheel is tilted outward at the top from true vertical, it is known as positive camber. (Courtesy of Bear Manufacturing Co.)

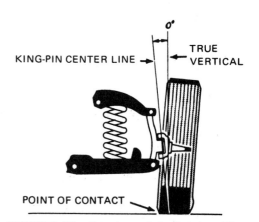

FIGURE 6-63 Steering axis inclination. (Courtesy of Bear Manufacturing Co.)

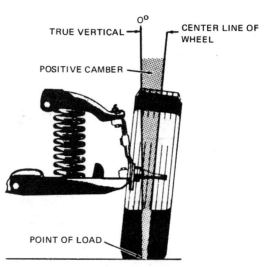

FIGURE 6-64 Camber and steering axis inclination. (Courtesy of Bear Manufacturing Co.)

easy steering by having the weight of the vehicle borne by the inner wheelbearing and spindle, and to prevent tire wear.

When camber is within the range of the manufacturer's specifications, the weight of the vehicle is positioned on the spindle and wheel bearings in accordance with the design. Camber will change under weight (passengers and load) to varying degrees because of independent front-end construction. The top of the wheel is allowed to move in and out while the bottom remains stationary. When preferred specifications are given, the camber should be adjusted to the preferred setting. When preferred specifications are not

bent. The purposes of steering-axis inclination are to reduce the need for excessive camber, to distribute the weight of the vehicle more nearly under the road contact point of the tire, to provide a pivot point about which the wheel will turn (thereby producing easy steering), and to aid in steering stability.

Caster

Caster is the backward or forward tilt of the king pin or spindle support arm at the top. Caster is a directional control angle measured in degrees and is the amount the center line of the spindle support arm is tilted from true vertical. Backward tilt of the spindle support arm at the top (Fig. 6-65) is positive caster. Forward tilt of the spindle arm at the top from true vertical is negative caster. Manufacturers' specifications indicate negative and positive caster by the letters N and P. Where a letter is not given, it is to be regarded as positive caster.

The purposes of caster are to gain directional control of the vehicle by causing the front wheels to maintain a straight-ahead position or return to a straight-ahead position out of a turn and to offset road crown.

Tilting the spindle support arm gives front wheels the tendency to maintain straight-ahead position by projecting the center line of the support arm ahead, and establishing a lead point ahead of the point of contact of the wheel, as shown in Fig. 6-66. Proof that the wheels tend to run straight is the fact that bicycles can be ridden without touching the handlebars.

Recently, car manufacturers have designed negative caster into the front wheels of their automobiles. Through wider-tread tires and the influence of another angle, steering-axis inclination, directional control tendencies are maintained.

Caster is not a tire-wearing angle. Some manufacturers recommend that the right front wheel have more caster toward positive, approximately $\frac{1}{2}°$, than the left front wheel to offset road crown. This spread in caster must stay within the range of the car manufacturers' specifications.

The harmful effects of incorrect caster are as follows: Unequal caster will cause the vehicle to pull toward the side of least caster. Too little caster causes wander and weave and instability at high speeds. Too much caster causes hard steering and excessive road shock and shimmy.

In the new unibodies, caster is a built-in feature of

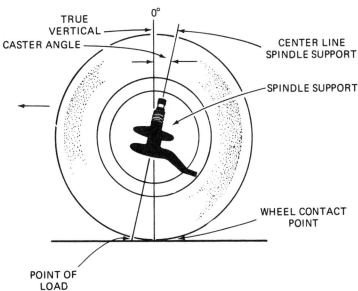

FIGURE 6-65 Principle of caster is identical in whether ball joint, McPherson strut, or king-pin suspension arrangement is used.

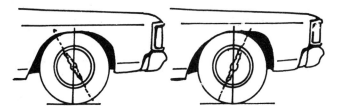

FIGURE 6-66A Positive caster. (B) Negative caster. (Courtesy of Chart Industries Ltd.)

most strut suspension-type vehicles. Therefore, the position of the lower control arm and strut assembly in respect to the specifications becomes extremely important. Figure 6-67 shows a typical strut assembly.

If it is impossible to obtain the proper caster and camber angles and the mounting positions are not damaged and are at their proper location, it is an indication of bent suspension parts. It is then imperative that a diagnostic angle and dimension check be made to the suspension and any damaged parts should be identified and replaced as required (Fig. 6-68).

Turning Radius

Turning radius means toe-out on turns. The inner front wheel travels a shorter path than the outer front wheel, creating a toe-out condition when the vehicle is turned either to the right or to the left. The design of the steering arms in relation to the wheelbase of the vehicle provides this toe-out on turns.

Turning radius is a tire-wearing angle measured in degrees and is the amount by which one front wheel turns sharper than the other on a turn. The car manufacturer usually allows a difference of 1° between the inner front wheels when measured on each turn.

Correct turning radius allows the front tires to roll free on turns. For that reason, turning radius will be correct when the other alignment angles are correct, except when a steering arm is bent. Incorrect turning angles will give excessive wear of tires on turns and squealing even at low speeds (Fig. 6-69).

Toe-in

Toe-in is the distance that the front of the front wheels (line B) are closer together than the rear of the front wheels (line A, Fig. 6-70). Toe-out is the distance that the front wheels are farther apart than the rear of the front wheels.

Toe-in is considered the most serious tire-wearing angle of the five, and it is measured in inches (millimeters). Its purpose is to compensate for widened tolerances in the steering linkage. Its characteristic tire wear appears as a feather-edged scuff across the face of both tires. It has been found, however, that a little too much toe-in will result in wearing on the outside of the right front tire only. Conversely, a little too much toe-out will result in wear appearing on the inside of the left front tire only.

Toe-in is the last of the alignment angles to be set in any wheel alignment operation. It is adjusted by turning the tie-rod adjusting sleeves until the measurement taken at the front of the wheels complies with the car manufacturer's specifications.

When adjusting toe, the steering wheel should be centered and held in position so it cannot move. This will

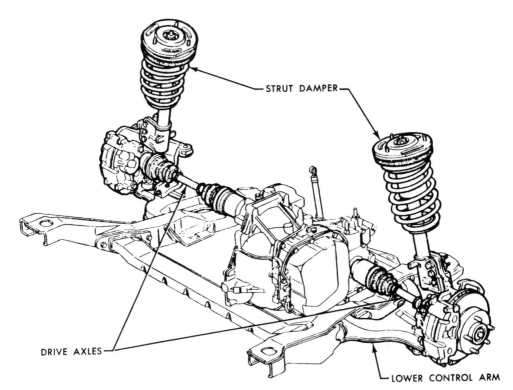

FIGURE 6-67 Side and cross-member assembly. (Courtesy of General Motors of Canada Ltd.)

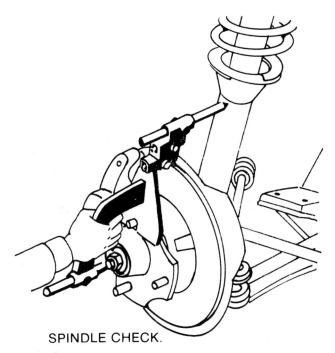

SPINDLE CHECK.

FIGURE 6-68 Checking the spindle. (Courtesy of Chart Industries Ltd.)

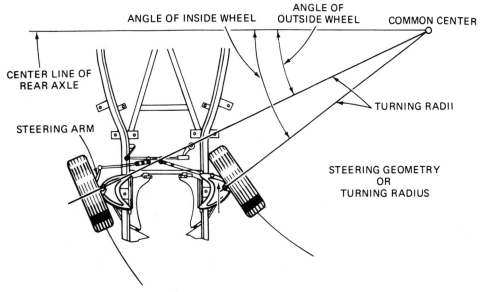

FIGURE 6-69 The wheels turn about a common center determined by the wheelbase of the vehicle. Note that, with respect to the common point, the inside wheel is ahead of the outside wheel and makes a sharper angle than the outer one. (Courtesy of Bear Manufacturing Co.)

center the rack and pinion; then the adjustments on the tie-rod ends must be done evenly on both sides of the rack-and-pinion gear (Fig. 6-71).

If the adjustments are not evenly made, the rack assembly will be off center in the gear. The driver will feel a pull on the wheel as the car is driven due to the off centering of the gear in the rack. This pull condition is especially prevalent with power-assisted rack-and-pinion assemblies. If it should be adjusted off center, the power assist will power the gear into a corner, causing a pull effect

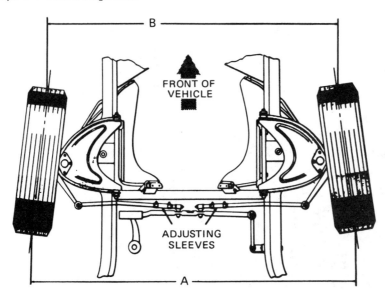

FIGURE 6-70   When the fronts of the wheels (line B) are closer together than the rears of the wheels (line A), they are said to have toe-in. (Courtesy of Bear Manufacturing Co.)

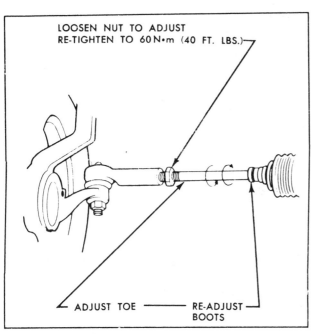

FIGURE 6-71   Adjusting the tie-rod ends. (Courtesy of General Motors of Canada Ltd.)

to be felt by the driver. This pull effect must be corrected by readjusting the tie rods so that the adjustment is equal on both sides of the gear.

Rear toe refers to the in or out angle of the rear wheel at the front of the tire when viewed from the top. This angle has an important effect on the handling characteristics of the vehicle; some have toe adjustments and some do not. Some vehicles that have independent rear suspension will also have an at-rest toe setting; this compensates for play and wear in the rear suspension components. Vehicles that have improper toe settings at the rear can possibly dog-track or a wheel could have a slight drag or cause the

vehicle to slip sideways due to wet or icy road conditions. Any out-of-adjustment condition will cause the tires to wear unevenly if improper adjustments are made.

When the toe adjustment is completed, it would be prudent for the repairer to do one more check on the front end. This could possibly pick up a condition known in the trade as toe change, bump steer, or orbital steer. This condition can be caused by several components, such as bent steering knuckle arms or arm, a damaged or out-of-position engine cradle, or bent rack-and-pinion steering gear clamps or brackets. This condition can cause the driver to lose control of the vehicle if it is severe enough.

The simplest way to check for this condition is with a tram gauge unless the equipment available for front-end alignment is capable of measuring the toe of each front wheel separately. If a tram gauge is used, Fig. 6-72 shows how to set up the gauge and scribe the tires in the center of the tread.

What is known as a jounce/rebound test is used to

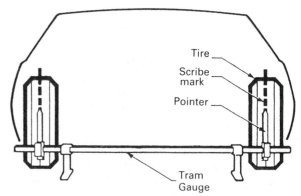

FIGURE 6-72   Using tram to check for bump steering condition. (Courtesy of Blackhawk, Division of Applied Power of Canada Ltd.)

check the toe deflection of each front wheel. The tram gauge is set up to the proper width with the pointers on the scribe mark. The car should be pulled down 3 inches (7.5 cm); then the toe deflection is measured and registered on a chart as right wheel and left wheel.

The car should then be raised at least 3 inches (7.5 cm) above its normal riding height, and after making sure that each side of the car has been lifted equally, the amount of toe deflection is measured. The reading for each wheel is added to the chart. Unless the reading for each wheel is the same as they move in and out in opposing directions, the car has a bump steer condition that must be corrected immediately by checking out what is causing the problem. Always check the manufacturer's specifications for the amount of deflection built into the steering of the vehicle.

6-6 WHEEL BALANCING

When an unbalanced wheel and tire assembly is jacked up, it will turn backward and forward until the heaviest part rests at the bottom. When it is revolved, the centrifugal force that acts on the heavy part will tend to lift and slam the tire down on the road with each revolution. This condition will cause wheel *hop* or bounce, which will transmit uncomfortable vibrations to the vehicle. This condition is called *static unbalance;* if uncorrected, it will wear rubber from the tread of the tire in flat spots or cups (Fig. 6-73). The vibration also wears out ball joints and tie-rod ends; in fact, all parts of the steering are subjected to extreme stress and strain (Fig. 6-74).

To eliminate this condition of tire hop, weights are

EXCESS TOE-IN

DYNAMIC UNBALANCE

STATIC UNBALANCE

WORN-LOOSE PARTS

UNDER INFLATION

EXCESS CAMBER

FIGURE 6-73 Effects of misalignment and unbalanced wear. (Courtesy of Bear Manufacturing Co.)

FIGURE 6-74 Static unbalance results in vertical oscillations or hop of the wheel assembly. (Courtesy of Bear Manufacturing Co.)

STATIC BALANCE
CORRECTION

ADD COMPENSATING
WEIGHT HERE

ADD COMPENSATING WEIGHT

HEAVY SECTION

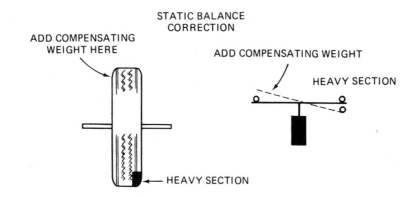

HEAVY SECTION

FIGURE 6-75 A wheel that has an unbalanced condition due to a heavy spot will tend to rotate by itself until the heavy portion of the assembly is down. Add compensating weight at the top. (Courtesy of Bear Manufacturing Co.)

DYNAMIC BALANCE   BALANCING A WHEEL IN MOTION

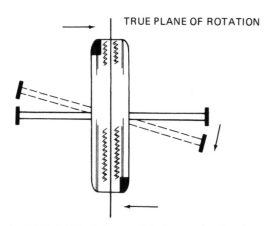

FIGURE 6-76 A wheel that is dynamically unbalanced results in horizontal oscillations or wiggle of the wheel assembly. (Courtesy of Bear Manufacturing Co.)

DYNAMIC UNBALANCE

TRUE PLANE OF ROTATION

FIGURE 6-77 It is possible for a wheel to be in balance statically and be out of balance dynamically. Once a wheel is in motion, the static weights try to reach a point that is exactly perpendicular to the true plane of rotation due to the action of centrifugal force. (Courtesy of Bear Manufacturing Co.)

DYNAMIC UNBALANCE

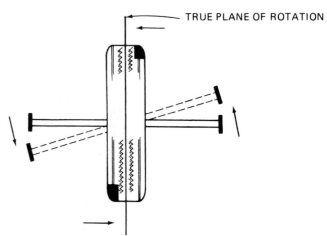

TRUE PLANE OF ROTATION

FIGURE 6-78 At 180° of wheel rotation, static weights, in attempting to reach the true plane of rotation, kick the spindle in the opposite direction. Severe vibration and shimmy result. (Courtesy of Bear Manufacturing Co.)

DYNAMIC BALANCE

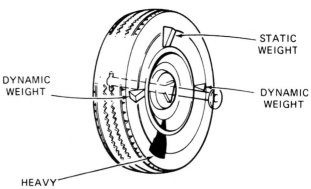

STATIC WEIGHT

DYNAMIC WEIGHT

DYNAMIC WEIGHT

HEAVY PART OF WHEEL

FIGURE 6-79 To eliminate this coupling action, compensating weights (dynamic) are placed at 180° opposite each other. Dynamic balance is obtained, while static balance remains unaffected. (Courtesy of Bear Manufacturing Co.)

installed on the light side of the tire to balance the wheel; this is called *static balance* (Fig. 6-75). A wheel and tire may have static balance but still not be balanced properly if the weight of the wheel is not distributed on each side of the tire's center line. It will have a wiggle (Fig. 6-76). A wheel and tire with this condition are dynamically unbalanced. A dynamically unbalanced wheel will not be discovered and corrected unless the wheel is revolved to simulate the conditions of being on a vehicle. The wheel assembly is spun on a machine that will help to locate the heavy spots (Fig. 6-77 and 6-78). The necessary weights can then be installed on the opposite side of the wheel in the desired location. Locating these weights at the proper area of the wheel will make it dynamically balanced (Fig. 6-79). Wheel balancing is the proper distribution of weight around a tire and wheel assembly to counteract centrifugal forces acting on the heavy areas. The purpose of this is to maintain a true-running wheel perpendicular to its rotating axis.

QUESTIONS

6-1. What are the five frame misalignments?

6-2. In what order would the frame misalignments occur in a severe front collision?

6-3. What are the three frame misalignments that can occur in the rear of the car because of a severe collision?

6-4. Name the four controlling points in a frame.

6-5. Explain passive safety design.

6-6. Explain how collision damage is absorbed in a unitized vehicle.

6-7. Explain how a good analysis is done on a collision-damaged vehicle.

6-8. How is it determined what hookups are necessary to repair frame damage?

6-9. When checking sag with frame-centering gauges, what is used to sight from the first gauge to the second gauge: pointers, bars, or the legs of the gauge?

6-10. Where are the gauges located when checking for sag and twist?

6-11. When both side rails of the frame have been bent in a head-on collision, how is the amount of damage determined?

6-12. To check for a mash in the front sections of a frame, the measurement is taken from what section?

6-13. What is a datum line?

6-14. When the metal in a buckle starts looking silvery, what kind of heat is used: spot heat, controlled heat, or the heat of the blowtorch?

6-15. What is the maximum heat that can be used on HSS?

6-16. What can be used to relax stresses as metal sections are pulled back to specifications?

6-17. What type of flame is used when heating areas in a frame?

6-18. Name the five angles that are used for steering alignment.

6-19. What is *steering axis inclination*?

6-20. What is the purpose of caster in wheel alignment?

6-21. What is toe-in?

6-22. What is *dynamic balancing*?

6-23. What is *static balancing*?

6-24. What is the allowable tolerance for mash in a car frame?

CHAPTER SEVEN

Repairing Collision Damage

SAFETY TIPS

When a vehicle with collision damage is brought into the shop, the first thing that should be done is to disconnect the battery in case of shorts in the wiring. When the vehicle is jacked up, it should always be supported with safety stands so that the car will not fall on any employee that might be working on it. The floor should always be as clean and clear of obstructions as possible, because numerous accidents occur in shops that have a poor cleaning attitude.

With the frequent use of torches in the body shop, the dangers of a fire are always present unless precautions are taken to avert such occurrences. The owner should make sure that the proper fire extinguishers are on hand and that all staff know where they are and how they should be used. All rags that are soaked with oil, grease, or paint should be stored in proper containers and not in a corner where they could cause spontaneous combustion. Grease, oil, or any slippery substance should be cleaned off the floor regularly, because in addition to being a fire hazard the substance can also be a safety hazard. A worker or customer could slip and be seriously hurt.

One of the most important features in any body shop is good lighting to reduce eye strain and help the employees perform a satisfactory repair job, whether it is bodywork or painting. The shop should also be heated and ventilated to remove as much dust as possible from the air, especially with the fiberglass and plastic fillers used today.

Electronic Control Modules and Air Conditioning

The technician must remove the electronic control modules which are installed at different locations in vehicles depending on the type of vehicle, if any MIG welding is to be done. Manufacturers' manuals should be checked to locate the modules and to remove them without damage. These modules must not get wet or dirty; place them in a plastic bag while the vehicle is being repaired. If wires are cut, check manufacturers' manuals to see if the wires may be spliced or not. If any parts are damaged, always replace them with the correct part (do not substitute).

Preliminary Steps. An accessory that often suffers damage in a front-end collision is the air-conditioning system. Moisture is the biggest enemy of the air-conditioning system as Freon gas and moisture will cause an acid to form. The air-conditioning system components will be damaged by corrosion because the acid is highly corrosive. The evaporator cores and condensers corrode from the inside

if acid is present and will fail shortly. Therefore, it is of the utmost importance that these components be protected while being serviced.

After the air-conditioning system has been discharged and dismantled, suitably sized plastic plugs are used to plug inlet and outlet fittings and hoses. If the system was damaged and discharged during a collision, the system should be protected by dismantling and plugging the appropriate hoses and fittings as soon as possible.

If the air-conditioning system has been opened for some time to the atmosphere, it must be recharged once it is operational using a special charging procedure to remove the moisture in the system. The receiver dehydrator moisture-absorbing material should always be replaced if the system has been opened for an extended period. In most cases the receiver dehydrator must be removed and replaced even if there is no visible outward damage. After the system has been properly installed and all hoses and connections are tight, the system can be recharged by a knowledgeable technician.

Safety Precautions

When a technician is dismantling an air-conditioning system, safety goggles should always be worn when opening refrigerant 12 lines. No welding or steam cleaning should be done near an air-conditioning system and no vapors should be discharged near open flames. The eyes must be protected from the liquid, and the breathing of fumes and smoke from the burning of the refrigerant 12 could be hazardous.

The temperature of liquid refrigerant 12 is approximately $-21°F$ or $-6°C$; if any of this liquid should touch the eyes, they could be damaged and a doctor should be called immediately. The eye or eyes should not be rubbed, but the affected areas should be splashed gently with quantities of cold water to gradually raise the temperature of the affected area to above freezing point. An antiseptic type of an oil may be used to provide a protective film over the eyeball and to prevent infection. If the skin should come in contact with refrigerant 12, it should be treated the same way as if it was frost bitten or frozen.

At any time when dismantling or disconnecting a fitting in the refrigeration unit, be sure the system has been discharged of all refrigerant. But even with the gauges reading zero, great care must be taken to avoid injury. The connections are opened very slowly, taking care to keep hands and face away from any possible leaks of the refrigerant should any still be present in the lines. At all times take great care and caution when working on an air-conditioning system.

Power Brakes

All hydraulic lines must be checked for any kinks, breaks, or leaks, and check the fasteners and holding clips. The power booster must be checked carefully, as well as all vacuum hoses, master cylinder, check valves, and fasteners. All damaged parts should be replaced; no repairs should be attempted to damaged hydraulic lines except by replacing with new parts. Remember that this is a high-pressure system for stopping the vehicle.

Power Steering

Power-steering components are often damaged in a collision, such as bent pulleys and brackets and damaged belts. The damaged parts, such as belts, pulleys, hoses, and brackets, should be replaced as required. Pulleys should never be straightened but replaced; brackets may be straightened if not too severely damaged. The drive belts and pulleys must be checked to see if they are in alignment.

The power-steering hoses should be routed as in the original assembly at the factory to prevent any contact with parts that could fray or cut them. All clips and fasteners in the original assembly should be used to hold the hoses in their proper location. Power-steering hoses must never be

spliced as the high-pressure hose will carry about 900 psi (6205 kPa).

Mechanical Systems

Mechanical components are usually serviced as a unit and are usually fairly simple to repair as long as the removal steps are reversed in the appropriate order. All mechanical systems mountings should be maintained and reinstalled properly. The drive line and mechanical structural components must be isolated and replaced as per manufacturers' specifications. These mechanical systems are usually removed and replaced as a unit. The wiring and some vacuum brake hose systems are usually held by quick-disconnect fittings.

It is of the utmost importance that all servicing of emission-control systems be done as per factory requirements. The proper adjustments and corrections must be made. The Clean Air Act must be followed, and any failure to repair and install all hoses and parts can be punishable by severe penalties for the technicians and shops that do not properly restore the emission control system.

7-1 REPAIRING FRONT-END COLLISION DAMAGE ON UNITIZED VEHICLES

In repairing any type of collision damage, the technician should first be familiar with the particular job before proceeding with repairs. The technician should study and diagnose the damage that has occurred from all angles and determine the direction of the damaging force or impact, as well as which parts were damaged by direct impact and which by indirect impact. The technician should consult with the shop supervisor or check the repair estimate to see how the repairs are to be made. He or she must know beforehand which parts are to be repaired and which replaced to be able to carry out the necessary repair operations efficiently in their proper sequence (Fig. 7-1).

FIGURE 7-1 Damage front end on an automobile.

In front-end collisions, where the frame or chassis has been damaged, this part must first be aligned before any sheet-metal parts can be reinstalled once they have been repaired. In cases of severe damage, where the damaged frame must either be replaced completely or repaired and aligned, it is often necessary to remove all the front-end sheet-metal parts. Before any of the front-end parts are removed, and this applies to standard as well as unitized high-strength steel (HSS) automobiles, they should be pulled out and roughly aligned using the damage dozer (Fig. 7-2) or other pulling equipment. This step not only corrects much of the direct damage, such as when the bumper and front section of the fender are pulled forward, but it also repositions and aligns much of the indirect damage that has occurred to the bumper brackets, inner construction of the front fender, grille panel, underpans, and supporting brackets, thus making their removal, repair, and replacement much easier.

When a front-wheel-drive vehicle is brought into the shop for collision repairs, the estimating manual must be checked carefully to find out which parts are HSS and HSLA types of steel (Fig. 7-3). If the estimating book does not show where these metals occur, the only safe way to repair the vehicle is to treat every part repaired or replaced as if it is HSS or HSLA type of steel.

When the hood was opened and removed, the repairs required as per the estimate were examined very carefully. Figure 7-4 shows that the left side of the vehicle was driven back, damaging beyond repair the radiator support fender, inner skirt, shield, and upper side rail side. Figure 7-5 shows the side rail, which was mashed as indicated by the chalk marks. This side rail was also damaged further back and sagged at the left front cowl area. Figure 7-6 shows the right rail, which was damaged mainly on the upper part as it was mashed together. There was also some damage on the shield, which must be repaired.

FIGURE 7-2A Pulling out a damaged bumper with a pulldozer. (B) Pulling out a damaged fender with a pulldozer and clamp anchoring rack. (Courtesy of E.S.D. Enterprises Ltd.)

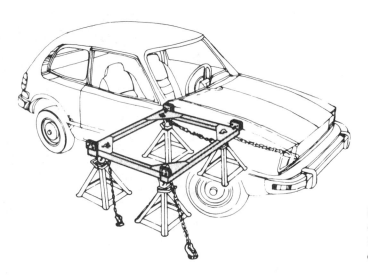

FIGURE 7-2C Quadriclamp anchoring rack. (Courtesy of Blackhawk, Division of Applied Power of Canada Ltd.)

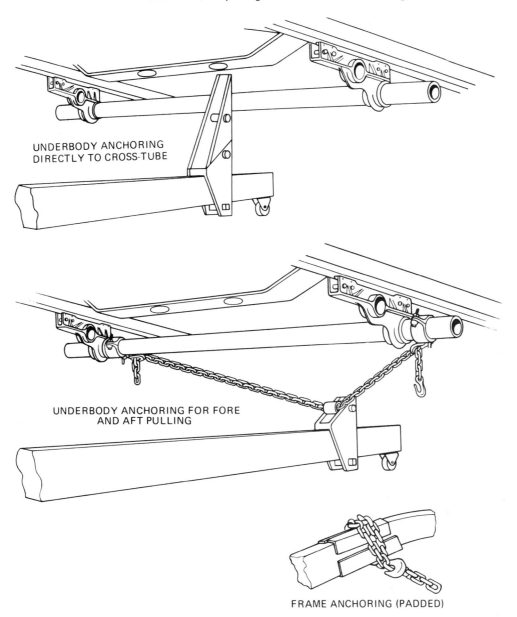

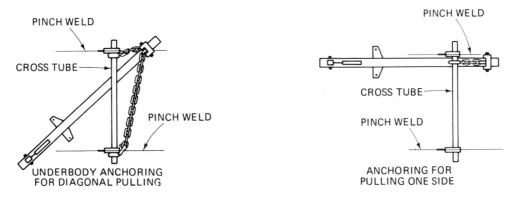

FIGURE 7-2D Methods of anchoring the damage dozer. (Courtesy of Blackhawk, Division of Applied Power of Canada Ltd.)

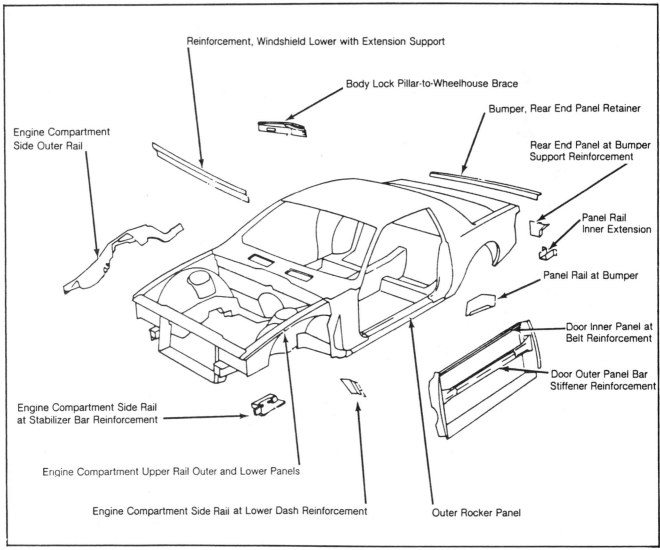

Reinforcement, Windshield Lower with Extension Support

Body Lock Pillar-to-Wheelhouse Brace

Bumper, Rear End Panel Retainer

Rear End Panel at Bumper Support Reinforcement

Engine Compartment Side Outer Rail

Panel Rail Inner Extension

Panel Rail at Bumper

Door Inner Panel at Belt Reinforcement

Door Outer Panel Bar Stiffener Reinforcement

Engine Compartment Side Rail at Stabilizer Bar Reinforcement

Engine Compartment Upper Rail Outer and Lower Panels

Engine Compartment Side Rail at Lower Dash Reinforcement

Outer Rocker Panel

The model shown is a General Motors Firebird body.

FIGURE 7-3   Estimating manual section showing where HSS or HSLA steel is typically used. (Courtesy of *Mitchell Estimating Guide*)

The left front door was opened and the rug on the floor pulled back so that the floor section could be checked for the amount of damage present (Fig. 7-7).

The vehicle was stripped of all front-end parts that were bolted to the inner top shield section and the radiator support. This includes the right and left fenders and skirts, the bumper assembly, and the grille assembly. The vehicle was rolled on the frame rack and raised by using hydraulic jacks to enable the positioning of the rocker panel to frame clamps; adjustable brackets allow correct positioning of the frame clamps. Four of these clamps were installed, one at each corner of the body section, from the rear of the cowl area and ahead of the back wheels at the rear door area. All flanges on rocker panels as well as clamp jaws are cleaned thoroughly before being placed and tightened at their proper location (Fig. 7-8).

The engine transmission, transaxle, and McPherson struts were not removed at this time due to the tension that was exerted on the lower cross-member assembly (Fig. 7-8), which was also bent slightly and needed to be straightened and aligned so that both the vehicle and engine cradle cross member would fit together.

When repairing vehicles involved in a front-end collision, it is often necessary that the whole power train be removed to facilitate the required repairs. (The power train is removed only if time may be gained by its removal or the vehicle cannot be repaired otherwise.) This involves disconnecting the exhaust system at the motor and the speedometer cable and shifting linkage at the transmission. The wiring harness must be removed from the engine accessories, lights, and horn. The bolts, clips, holding brake lines, McPherson struts, and steering linkage must be

FIGURE 7-4 Damaged radiator support and shield.

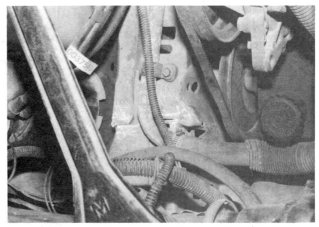

FIGURE 7-6 Damaged right rail, upper section.

FIGURE 7-7 Damaged floor area.

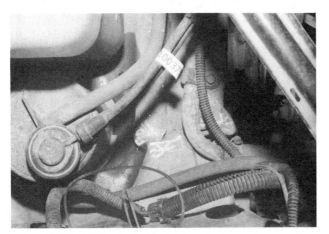

FIGURE 7-5 Damaged left rail, upper front.

FIGURE 7-8 Installing holding clamps from frame rack to vehicle.

removed and put away in a box for safe keeping until the vehicle is to be put together again. The radiator hoses clamps are loosened to remove them from the radiator. Always check the radiator for the manufacturing tag as this will be required if a new one has to be ordered.

Once everything is loosened, the body is lifted off the

power train and then can be moved onto the type of equipment the shop uses for lifting this type of vehicle. At this time the power train should be examined carefully for damage that could not be seen when it was part of the vehicle. If any is found that is not on the estimate, the estimator for the insurance company should be notified immediately so as to arrange for the repair or replacement of these parts, such as in Fig. 7-9.

Once the vehicle was tied down, the damage was checked so as to plan the hookups that would be necessary to return the different areas such as the cowl, which had moved back, damaged left shield (Fig. 7-10), and also the left rail (Fig. 7-11) to their proper locations. The cross-member assembly was also slightly distorted. The right side rail and inner shield were also damaged, as well as the right cross-member rail where the chalk marks are visible (Fig. 7-12).

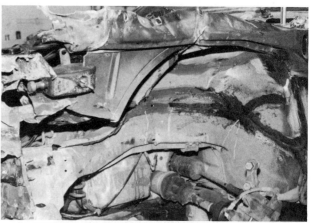

FIGURE 7-11   Damaged left rail and inner shield.

FIGURE 7-9   Damaged alternator.

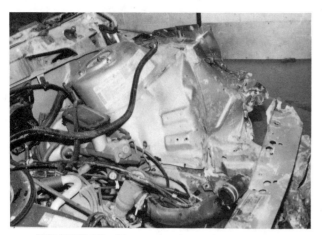

FIGURE 7-10   Shows the damaged left shield.

FIGURE 7-12   Damaged right inner skirt, rail and cross member.

When pulling must be done, it should be preplanned by determining the appropriate attaching points; the pulling directions should be evaluated so that the direction of the movement can be carefully monitored as it gets close to the reference points on the blueprints. Because of the high-strength and the heat-sensitive characteristics of the unibody type of structure, pulling should never be done with one pull for alignment and/or straightening in one step. A multiple-pull system is preferable, as it will pull out and unravel the damage in the reverse order that it occurred. These pulls should be done slowly and allow time to work and relax the metal and to check the progress toward proper alignment.

Unibody structures are extremely strong in the direction of their design loads, but a pulling clamp could possibly overstress and damage the area or panel it is attached to. It is desirable to spread and distribute the load over more of the structure with additional clamps.

In lighter collisions, the radiator support is often repaired; the radiator must first be removed from its support and repaired, recored, or replaced by a new or used radiator. It should not be installed, however, until all other repair operations to the front-end have been completed in order not to subject it to unnecessary vibration and abuse. Installing the radiator last often makes the assembling of parts much easier for the technician.

The radiator support can often be straightened, depending on the extent of the damage and its construction. It is straightened by first checking its center opening for squareness, by taking diagonal measurements from one top corner to the opposite lower corner of the radiator support, using jig holes, mounting nuts, mounting brackets, or accurately measured-off chalk marks as reference points. Hydraulic jacking equipment or a pull dozer is used in swaying and squaring the radiator support in the direction of the shorter diagonal measurement obtained. The support is normalized by hammering down any folds or wrinkles in the metal, either cold or in conjunction with heat (neutral to slightly carburizing flame), making sure that all breaks in the support have been welded beforehand. The radiator support is allowed to cool off completely before the hydraulic pressure is released. This step will eliminate all possibility of the support returning to its former bent or distorted, out-of-square position.

Great care must also be taken to reshape and straighten all outer portions of the radiator support correctly, especially the areas onto which the fenders, side panels, underpans, and headlights are fastened. Doing so will eliminate many of the alignment problems so often encountered and will ensure a better fit between the hood and fenders.

The radiator support on unitized (HSS) automobiles is solidly spot-welded into position on the front side rails at the factory; its lower section serves as a front cross-member. If only slightly damaged, it is aligned and straightened as on standard automobiles; but if badly damaged, it is removed completely by breaking all spot welds. It is replaced with a new panel that is accurately fitted into position using centering gauges and then spot welded in with a MIG welder.

Front-end-damaged unitized, high-strength-steel automobiles may require pulling out as much as possible before the front bumper, grille, radiator, battery, hood, and front fenders are individually removed. Often the motor, transmission, and front suspension must also be removed so that indirect damage extending to the rear seat area of the floor pan, cowl assembly, rack-and-pinion steering mounting panel, strut towers, and side rails can be repaired.

In correcting minor front-end damage, the side rails, front fender inner panels, strut towers, and radiator support are usually simultaneously pulled back to their original position and straightened, while under tension, using centering and strut tower gauges with a body and frame

FIGURE 7-13A Pulling of rail and inner skirt. (B) Squaring of engine cradle (typical).

straightening machine or a pull dozer anchored by means of a cross tube and underbody clamps or a quadriclamp rack (Fig. 7-2C and D).

The right side rail and inner shield were pulled ahead to enable the removal of the bolt holding the cross member to the rail (Fig. 7-13A and B). Once this was accomplished, the end of the engine cradle cross-member rail was repaired where it was slightly bent and then squared according to the specifications (Fig. 7-14).

In vehicles that use an engine cradle cross member, it is usually replaced if it is more than slightly damaged. This is because there are many attaching points on this particular part. These are the engine mounts, rack-and-pinion steering, lower control arms, and steering mechanisms. Therefore, due to the need for a high degree of accuracy, plus the cost of the labor to repair it, the cross member is usually changed. Figure 7-15 shows a typical engine cradle cross member.

Whenever this part is removed, the four large bolts at each corner should be marked so that they will be reinserted into the same hole when the parts are installed.

BOTTOM VIEW

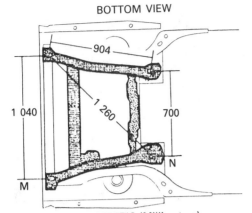

1. ALL DIMENSIONS ARE METRIC (Millimeters)
2. ALL CONTROL POINTS ARE SYMMETRICAL SIDE TO SIDE
3. ALL TOLERANCES ± 3mm

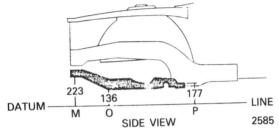

(B)

FIGURE 7-14 Schematic of engine cradle

FIGURE 7-15 Typical engine cradle cross member and bushings.

Each bolt cuts its own thread as it is inserted into the steel bracket in the rail.

In correcting major front-end damage, where the previously mentioned parts are badly damaged (crushed and torn), the parts are simultaneously pulled out to their approximate position, and all adjacent sheet-metal panels to which they are spot-welded are accurately aligned and straightened, while under tension, before they are removed

and replaced with new parts. All damage to the floor, cowl assembly, and strut towers is corrected first and in the order mentioned, so that all doors fit and open and close properly. This is accomplished by simultaneously applying multiple corrective pulls with a body and frame straightening machine to the top of the cowl assembly, strut tower, side rail, and fender inner panel, and aligning and straightening all folds, buckles, and creases, one by one, while panels are kept under tension, until all parts are brought back to their correct shape and position. Their correct position is determined by means of different types of gauges mounted on the automobile body according to the manufacturer's specification.

On this particular vehicle the left side upper rail, inner skirt, and lower inner and outer rails were extensively damaged. But to repair the vehicle properly, the main part of the body must be pulled back into the proper measurement and fit before these critical parts of the front section can be removed. Figure 7-16A shows the damage and Fig. 7-16B shows three separate hookups that were used to pull the lower rails, inner skirt, strut tower, and top rail all at the same time.

This will not only pull the rails and inner skirt ahead but also the cowl area and floor on the left side. The area is slightly overpulled and normalized. If heat is used on HSS or HSLA steel, a temperature stick should be used so as not to overheat a part that is being saved; remember, this type of metal must not be overheated and not heated for more than 3 minutes overall. In certain cases a come-along with a clamp bolted to a pinch-weld flange at the front of the top door opening and another clamp at the pinch-weld flange on top of the rocker panel is used to help pull the front roof panel and door opening area down (Fig. 7-17).

At other times, when the middle section of the door opening needs to be pushed as well as pulled ahead, a helper jack such as in Fig. 7-18 can be used with clamps that are

FIGURE 7-16A Damaged left rails and inner skirt.

FIGURE 7-16B Pulling the lower rails, inner skirt, strut tower, and upper rail.

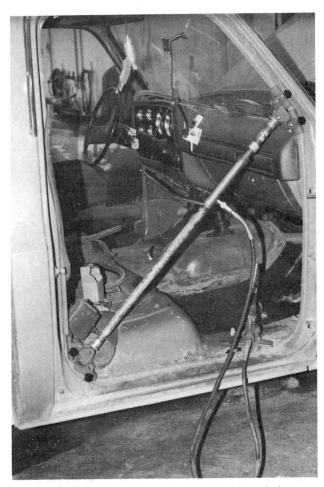

FIGURE 7-18   Jack used with clamps to help push the door post ahead.

FIGURE 7-17 Come-along pulling the roof panel and door opening down.

built with a groove in them so they can be slipped over the pinch-weld flanges and secured with bolts, which are threaded into that part of the clamp.

Many different types of gauging and pulling equipment are used in repair shops. On a severe collision, the gauges are used to analyze the amount of damage before the pulls are attached to the vehicle. A measuring tape and a tram rod may also be used very successfully to perform these analyses. The type of equipment available and the capabilities of the technicians will usually determine what equipment will be used. Figure 7-19A and B shows technicians hanging the gauges and aligning a laser-beam system to measure a vehicle.

Figure 7-20 shows a Nike Dataliner system with the different gauges and laser beam attached to make three vector pulls, which will be used to pull the lower rail and inner skirt back to their proper locations; this vehicle has been hit on the left front corner.

When the pulls in Fig. 7-16B were relaxed, the dimensions of the left strut tower were checked and found to be slightly inboard, and the door opening had to be moved ahead slightly so that the door would close properly; there was still slight tension present. A vector type of setup was used on the side of the tower and the top rail and inner skirt were also pulled at the same time (Fig. 7-21).

In some cases when a frame rail and inner shield are hit, the spot welds holding them together will break, causing the two panels to separate, as in Fig. 7-22. When the rail and inner shield are pulled back into their proper locations, they can be spot welded together again if they are not damaged beyond repair.

FIGURE 7-21 Side and front pull.

FIGURE 7-19A Installing measuring devices.
(B) Calibrating the laser beam attachments.

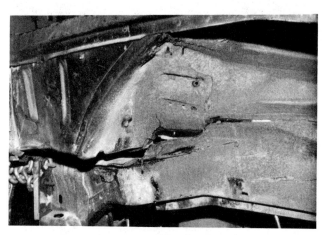

FIGURE 7-22 Rail separated from inner shield
due to spot welds breaking.

FIGURE 7-20 Dataliner set up for pulls.

Centering gauges were then installed on the vehicle at their proper location and adjusted for the datum line. There was one gauge at the rear cross member, one gauge at the rear door area, one gauge at the cowl area, one strut gauge on the strut towers, and one on the engine cradle cross member, according to the manufacturer's specifications (Fig. 7-23).

In some cases when the vehicle is hit hard enough and the upper rail, inner shield, and lower rails collapse as they are driven back, the force of some of the impact is transmitted to a certain degree to the cowl. This causes the cowl to move back, which makes the door bind on the locking mechanism, bends and lifts the windshield post, bends and raises the front of the rocker panel, and raises and moves the floor back. This condition will show as a partial twist on the side on which it was hit; it should be repaired first. To remove this condition, it is necessary to remove the lower part of the clamp assembly at the damaged

FIGURE 7-23 Centering gauges mounted on the vehicle.

FIGURE 7-25 Jack pulling upper rail, inner skirt, cowl, and door frame ahead.

location. A chain is wrapped around the beam of the frame rack and rocker panel clamp, and a jack is inserted between the chains as in Fig. 7-24.

As the jack tightens the chain, which in turn will put pressure on the clamp and pull the rocker panel down, a pull should also be made on the skirt area to pull the upper rail, inner skirt, cowl, and door frame ahead (Fig. 7-25). The use of this pressure will pull down the rocker panel and remove the false twist; the rocker panel should stay in place if the reinforcements have been properly normalized and the area overpulled slightly as required. This pull will also lower the windshield post and make it conform to the door frame and reposition the door in the door frame, making it fit the door frame properly with the appropriate gap all around. The strut tower gauge (Fig. 7-26A) is not only used to check the height of the section to see if it is on datum, but is also used to check if the towers are centered and within specifications from side to side (Fig. 7-26B).

When the right rail had been pulled to specifications

FIGURE 7-26A Strut tower gauge installed on vehicle.

FIGURE 7-24 Jack used to pull rocker panel down.

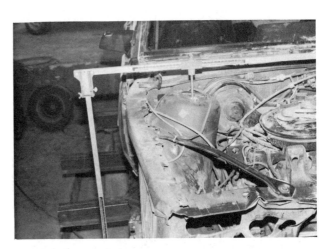

FIGURE 7-26B Strut gauge showing that the strut tower is not in alignment.

and alignment, the radiator support was removed using a carbide burr of the appropriate size for the spot welds in an air tool to cut through the spot welds (Fig. 7-27). A twist drill may also be used, but it is not as fast and accurate. The radiator support was removed and then the spot welds on the lower front inner shield were also broken to enable the lifting of the lower front section of the shield. This allowed the room required to cut and remove the inner front section of the inner rail, which had been badly damaged (Fig. 7-28). A section of the correct length was cut from a new rail, and this was inserted on the rail and held as in Fig. 7-29A. This was then butt welded and spot welded as required onto the outer rail. The inner lower shield was then spot welded as required. The welds were then cleaned

FIGURE 7-29A   New section held clamped on the outer rail.

FIGURE 7-27   Removing spot welds.

FIGURE 7-29B   Opened up side rail and reinforced area.

properly using a wire brush and then primed with a zinc-rich primer.

The left top rail, inner shield, and lower rails were properly aligned, normalized, and worked cold as much as possible using the appropriate tools. These parts were removed, except for the inner lower rail, which was kept in alignment, and the required repairs were done, especially on the front section. All the outer, overlapping, joining edges on the new replacement panels were then cleaned of all primer and paint using either a disk grinder or power-driven wire brush. Holes for plug welding were punched with a hole-punching tool, duplicating factory spot welds

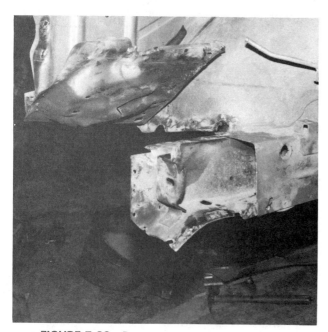

FIGURE 7-28   Removing a section of the rail.

as much as possible, before the new panels were fitted together and firmly clamped into position on the body of the automobile.

CAUTION: If a side rail or any structural member cannot be straightened cold, remember that it is made of high-strength steel (HSS) and must not be overheated. Use a temperature-indicating crayon and apply heat sparingly with an oxyacetylene torch using a neutral or slightly carburizing flame. Keep the heat concentrated on the repair area so as not to destroy the structural strength of the side rail.

Sometimes it is advantageous for the technician to open up the side rail to gain access to the damaged area, especially when the damage is located in a double-constructed or reinforced area of the side rail (Fig. 7-29B). Access is gained by breaking the spot welds along the top and bottom of the side rail, vertically cutting the side at one end of the portion to be removed, and pulling or bending it away from the rest of the side rail; or the side may be cut vertically at both ends and removed completely. The damaged section of the side rail is then repaired quite easily, and the side removed is straightened or replaced before it is MIG-welded back in place.

The outer rail was installed against the inner rail to check for fit. As the fit was good, a few screws and vise grips were used to hold them in place while the lower part of the radiator support was installed to check for fit (Fig. 7-30). Centering gauges were also used to assure proper centering and height. The upper rail and inner shield were then prepared and installed on the rail; all edges to be spot welded were cleaned of paint and then prepared for spot welding before being installed on the lower rails (Fig. 7-31). These parts were held together with metal screws and vise grips.

FIGURE 7-31 Top rail and inner skirt installed on lower rails.

NOTE: It is very important that all structural panels on automobiles of unitized HSS construction to which the front suspension components are directly mounted be accurately brought back or replaced with new parts positioned at the precise location required. This is to ensure that the front suspension has the required steering angles as per specifications. Also, the proper relationship to the rear suspension parts must be restored, such as tracking and the positional angles of the rear wheels.

The radiator support was also prepared for assembly and spot welding (Fig. 7-32). Once assembled according to guiding assembly holes, the parts were spot welded together using a MIG welder. Once the radiator support was assembled, it was then positioned onto the frame rails in the proper location using a centering gauge to center it properly (Fig. 7-33).

After the radiator support was installed, the front section was checked for fit by using length, height, and

FIGURE 7-30 Checking the fit of the new outer rail.

FIGURE 7-32 Radiator support ready for spot welding.

FIGURE 7-33 Radiator support installed using centering gauges.

FIGURE 7-35 Proper arrangement and quality of spot welds.

diagonal measurements. Once every part was lined up properly, the radiator support was spot welded with a MIG welder, as in Fig. 7-34, to reproduce factory-quality welds, as in Fig. 7-35, with proper penetration and enough surface metal to fill the hole punched into the metal surface.

All welds and panel joints are thoroughly cleaned with a hand or power-driven wire brush and treated with a metal conditioner before a brushable seam or medium-bodied sealer and petroleum base undercoating are applied (Fig. 7-36).

When the sealing operation has been completed and the sealing material has dried sufficiently, the panels must be prepared and painted to match the color used on the front section before the power train is reinstalled. Remember to always use zinc-rich primer as a first step on the bare metal. This is done so that the new panels will have the antirusting integrity restored to match the factory quality. All inner rails, box sections, and outer rails should be

FIGURE 7-34 MIG spot welding.

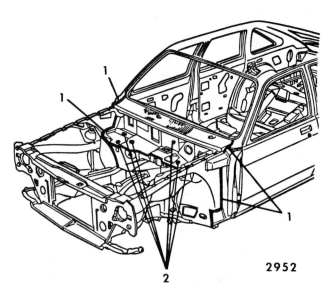

2952

1. **APPLY A BRUSHABLE SEAM SEALER OR MEDIUM–BODIED SEALER**

2. **STUDS AND BRACKETS MUST BE SEALED WITH CAULK**

FIGURE 7-36 Sealing the front end. (Courtesy of General Motors of Canada Ltd.)

undercoated to restore the original factory quality (see Chapter 8).

The fenders and hood should be installed on the front end to check if there is a proper gap and fit at the hood and cowl air intake panel, the hood side edge to fender edge, and the front door front edge and fender rear edge, as in Fig. 7-37.

Many technicians will try the panels on a vehicle to see how they fit in relation to the other parts that are being repaired. This method will assure that the panels fit the repaired area once the repairs are finished.

As the vehicle is being reassembled, the energy absorbers if damaged are replaced, and the chrome-plated or shiny aluminum bumpers are replaced with new or rebuilt units (see Appendix B). Damaged reinforcement bars are also changed with new parts or rebuilt exchange units (see Appendix B).

FIGURE 7-37 Typical front end assembled to check for fit.

If the damage to the bumper brackets is only minor, they are usually straightened. If extensively damaged, however, the brackets are replaced with new ones.

Many high-strength-steel (HSS) constructed automobiles have bumper fascia (face bars) made of thermosetting plastic and bumper reinforcements made of martensitic steel (Fig. 7-38). Fascia with minor damage such as small punctures, gouges, and tears can be repaired using the structural adhesive repair method (Chapter 5), but manufacturers recommend that bumper reinforcements be replaced rather than repaired.

Strongly reinforced hoods and adjoining cowl air-intake panels are generally not repaired when badly damaged. But if only minor damage has occurred, with very little if any damage to the large flat central section of the hood, it can be repaired by aligning and roughing-out both the inner construction and the outer panel simultaneously by using hydraulic jacking equipment (Fig. 7-39A) or the damage dozer (Fig. 7-39B). This operation can be performed either on or off the automobile, with or without a straightening fixture.

After the hood hookups have been made, the paint is removed from all sharp buckles, bends, and ridges in both the inner construction and the outer panel, using the torch and a steel wire brush. The torch, which is then adjusted to a carburizing flame, is used to heat up the buckles, bends, and ridges to a blue color. The buckles, in turn, are stretched out and hammered down as the hood is pushed back to its original shape and contour.

CAUTION: When working on HSS bodies, do not overheat or overpull hood inner construction.

NOTE: The crown of the outer panel on the hood must be accurately roughed out and aligned to as near its original

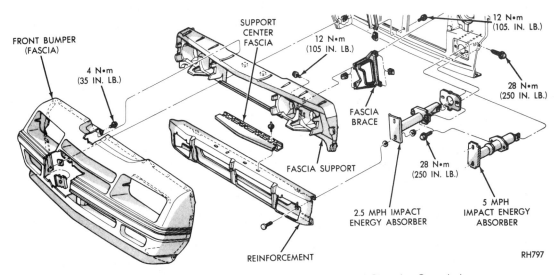

FIGURE 7-38 Front bumper fascia. (Courtesy of Chrysler Canada.)

(A)

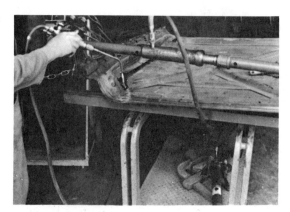

(B)

FIGURE 7-39A Using hydraulic jacking equipment. (B) Roughing out hood with the damage dozer.

height and shape as possible before any spring-hammering and straightening of the flat, more central portions of the outer panel are attempted.

All accessible dents, V channels, valleys, and ridges in the outer panel are eliminated and straightened by bumping, dinging, and spring-hammering, respectively, while those in enclosed and inaccessible areas are removed and straightened with spoons, pick bars, or picks, or they are pulled out and roughly straightened by using body solder, pull plates, or pull rods or by means of the nail welder and slide hammer method (Fig. 7-40).

Accessible areas are metal-finished in the usual way, while inaccessible, roughly straightened areas are plastic-filled.

Before the repaired front-end parts are assembled, any damage to the cowl, front doors, and windshield must be corrected. If the front doors are out of adjustment and do not close properly, either the front door opening will have to be aligned or the door hinges will have to be adjusted or straightened, depending largely on the make and model of the automobile and the type of hinges used. All damage to the cowl assembly must be repaired so that the front fenders, hood, and windshield will fit and function properly. If the windshield has been broken and there is no visible evidence or reason for its breaking, before it is replaced with a new windshield the pinch-weld flange around the window opening should be closely examined for sharp metal high spots that might have caused the windshield to break.

After all damaged front-end parts have been repaired, assembled, and adjusted properly, the radiator is installed and filled with a coolant before the automobile is moved into the paint shop for refinishing.

All front-end sheet-metal parts, such as front fenders, grille, headlights, battery, bumper isolators, front bumper, and radiator, are installed and adjusted before the automobile (Fig. 7-41) is moved into the paint shop.

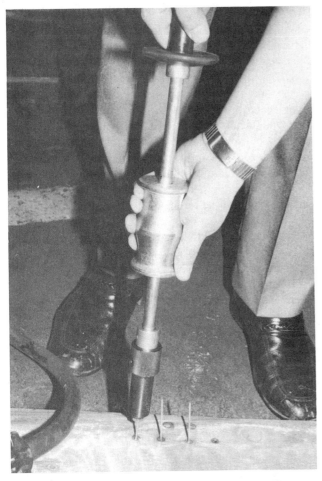

FIGURE 7-40 Spot welded nails and slide hammer being used to roughly align a panel.

FIGURE 7-41 Automobile ready for refinishing in the paint shop.

7-2 REPAIRING SIDE COLLISION DAMAGE

In repairing an automobile that has been severely damaged directly in the center of the side (Fig. 7-42), the first thing the repairperson must do—after carefully studying and

FIGURE 7-42 Automobile with center sidesway damage.

diagnosing the damage—is to remove the front and rear doors, seats, and trim from the center post; if the turret top is damaged, remove the headlining either partially (only on the damaged side) or completely, whichever is more practical. The floor mats, floor pan insulators or heat shields, must also be removed so that hydraulic jacking equipment and the damage dozer or frame-straightening machine can be used in correcting the damage that has occurred not only to the sill or rocker panel assembly and floor but also to the center body pillar, doors, turret top, and roof rail. Generally, the sill or rocker panel assembly and floor have been driven in to such an extent that the technician has no alternative but to replace the rocker panel completely (Fig. 7-43).

Heavy plates are spot-welded to the damaged rocker panel if it is repairable, or holes are cut into its side. By properly anchoring the end of the horizontal telescoping

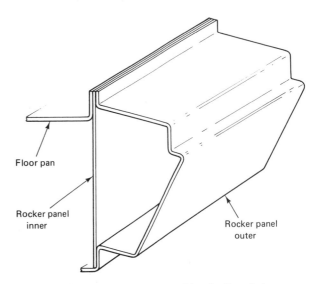

FIGURE 7-43 Rocker panel (typical) end view.

beam of the damage dozer either to the base of the center body pillar on the opposite side of the body or to the frame side rail, and then applying a steady and uniform pull at various points along the damaged rocker panel assembly or base of the center body pillar (Figs. 7-44 and 7-45), the damage to the floor and rocker panel is gradually pulled out. A variety of rams and spreaders are also simultaneously employed.

When a frame-straightening machine is employed, the damage is pulled out by applying a number of corrective outward pulls on the driven-in floor, rocker panel, and post, and simultaneously exerting another stretching pull (lengthwise) on the damaged side, using chains hooked to the top and bottom hinge areas of the cowl so as to bring the side back to its original length (Fig. 7-46).

The procedure outlined is generally followed in the correction of all major side collision damage, especially in the repairing of late-model, high-strength-steel automobiles.

Remember that, whenever possible, the stretching pull applied on the damaged floor and rocker panel should always be greater than the outward pull exerted. Any breaking of spot welds or tearing of metal encountered while pulling should immediately be MIG-welded, before corrective pulling is resumed.

All folds and creases in the floor panel and surrounding metal are gradually eliminated, one by one, by spring-hammering and straightening them while under constant pulling pressure, using body pull hooks, pull plates, and pull clamps together with chains, at the cowl, center pillar, and rear door areas.

The turret top and roof rail can also be aligned and roughed-out by applying an outward pull on the top section of the center pillar, just where it joins the roof rail, using body- and frame-straightening equipment (Fig. 7-47A). This can also be done without repositioning or changing the damage dozer hookup by merely using another hydraulic jack, positioned farther up on the damage dozer tower (Fig. 7-47B). As the turret top and roof rail are slowly pulled out, the crown of the roof panel and surrounding damaged areas are roughed-out and straightened by lifting the sheet metal (V channels and valleys) with the hydraulic jack and attachments (Fig. 7-48) and spring-hammering the ridges and metal dinging, as previously described.

After the floor has been straightened, the rocker panel assembly is removed completely with a pneumatic chisel, the cutting torch (wherever its services are required), or a spot-weld cutter, or by drilling out the spot welds (Fig. 7-49).

NOTE: Most manufacturers of 1980- or later-model automobiles with structural members made of high-strength steel recommend that, if a torch or cutoff grinder must be used in the removal of a damaged body section or on salvage

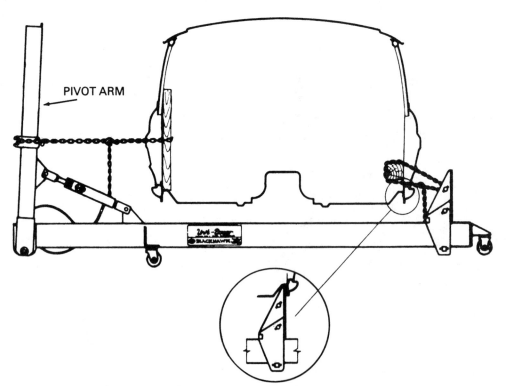

FIGURE 7-44 Anchoring the pulldozer. (Courtesy of Blackhawk, Division of Applied Power of Canada Ltd.)

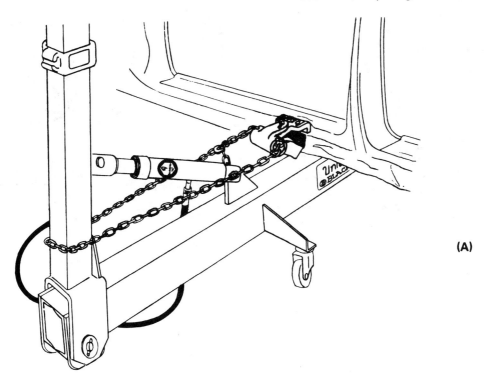

(A)

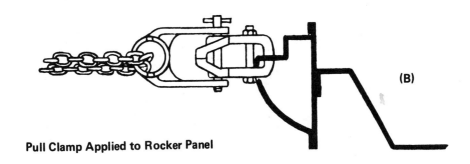

Pull Clamp Applied to Rocker Panel

(B)

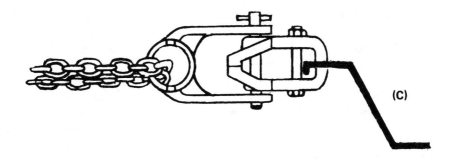

(C)

FIGURE 7-45 Using pull clamps properly to pull on sheet metal. (Courtesy of Blackhawk, Division of Applied Power of Canada Ltd.)

FIGURE 7-46 Side and front stretch and pull hookups.

FIGURE 7-47 Pulling out the turret top, roof rail, quarter-panel, and rocker panel at the same time using multiple hookups.

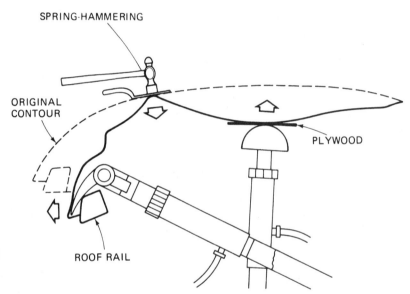

FIGURE 7-48 Using hydraulic jacks to push the roof rails and roof panel to original contour while spring-hammering the metal to relax sharp creases and buckles.

parts, at least 2 inches (50.8 mm) of additional metal be left on the part to be used. Once the part has been removed, the heat-affected area is cut off at the factory seams using a pneumatic chisel or hacksaw so as not to destroy the properties of the high-strength steel.

The replacement rocker panel assembly and bottom of center door pillar are tack-welded into position and their locations accurately rechecked by hanging the new replacement or repaired doors on the body before they are solidly spot welded into place with the MIG welder (Figs. 7-50, 7-51, 7-52).

When spot welding high-strength-steel replacement panels, always try to duplicate factory methods, as much as possible. Use the same number and size of spot welds and place them in precisely the same location as at the

factory. Following this procedure not only gives a factorylike appearance to the installation, but ensures the original structural strength of the repair.

Rocker panels, if not too badly rusted out or damaged, can often be repaired by merely replacing the outer section with a slip-over repair panel (Fig. 7-53). The old or covered-up portion need not necessarily be removed, just roughly aligned, enabling the new panel to fit properly. Its top edge is then spot welded into place, and its bottom edge is spot welded to the vertical portion of the old rocker panel assembly (Fig. 7-54). The overlapping panel joint at the rear quarter-panel is first spot welded, sunk down, solder filled, and metal finished in the usual way.

Another method of repairing localized damage in rocker panels is by cutting a door into the upper section of the rocker panel directly underneath the scuff plate. This

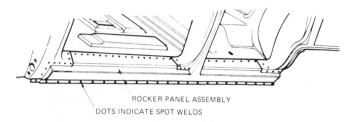

ROCKER PANEL ASSEMBLY
DOTS INDICATE SPOT WELDS

FIGURE 7-49   Removing rocker panel assembly.

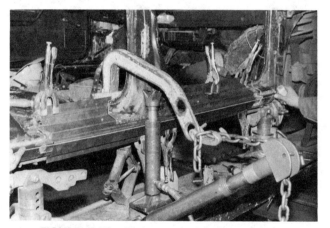

FIGURE 7-50   Fitting and clamping replacement rocker panel into position on body before tack welding.

FIGURE 7-51   Bottom of center pillar raised into position on rocker panel for spot welding.

step provides access to the damaged area and enables the repairperson to straighten and metal finish the panel quite easily (Fig. 7-55).

The body must now be checked for alignment. If the opposite side of the automobile has not been damaged and its doors, trunk lid, and hood fit and function properly, the diagonal measurement readings obtained from the door openings can be used in aligning the door openings on the damaged side (described and illustrated in Section 7-3).

The front and rear doors are frequently repaired by replacing their badly damaged outer panels with new repair panels. The outer panels are removed by using a disk sander, with a No. 24 or P24 grit closed-coat sanding disk to grind down the edges (hem) of the door panels and separate them from the door frame flange (Fig. 7-56). The door panels are cut at the top, either at the bead line (which often is covered with a chrome molding) or at the bottom portion of the window opening (Fig. 7-57). The door is then turned over in its straightening fixture, and the remaining portions of the spot-welded flange are removed from the door frame flange by back and forth bending, hammering on the vise grips, or a pneumatic chisel (Figs. 7-58 and 7-59). Any damage to the framework (inner construction) of the doors

FIGURE 7-52 Doors hung and fitted in door openings on body.

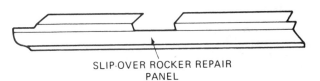

SLIP-OVER ROCKER REPAIR PANEL

FIGURE 7-53 Slip-over rocker repair panel.

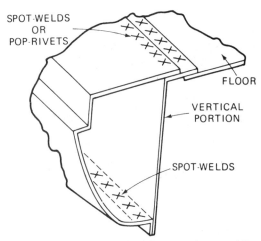

SPOT-WELDS OR POP-RIVETS

FLOOR

VERTICAL PORTION

SPOT-WELDS

FIGURE 7-54 Typical rocker panel assembly.

FIGURE 7-55 Opening cut into rocker panel.

FIGURE 7-56 Grinding through outer edges (hem) of door panels.

BELT LINE

FIGURE 7-57 Door replacement panel.

must now be corrected before the new repair panel, which has been accurately cut down to the required size (partial replacement) and has had anticorrosion material and seam sealer applied to its inner surface (Fig. 7-60), is positioned and tack-welded into place at points A and B, as shown in Fig. 7-57. The repair panel is fitted and clamped firmly to the door frame flange at points C, D, E, and F with vise-grip welding clamps. The toe dolly is held tightly against the outer edge of the repair panel, just next to each of the welding clamps, and the repair panel flange is turned over the door frame flange with the body hammer (Fig. 7-61) and tack welded before the vise-grip welding clamps are

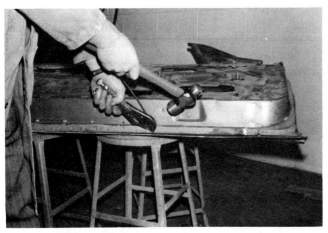

FIGURE 7-58 Removing spot-welded flange with a hammer and vise grips.

FIGURE 7-59 Spot-welded flange (hem) being removed from door frame with pneumatic chisel.

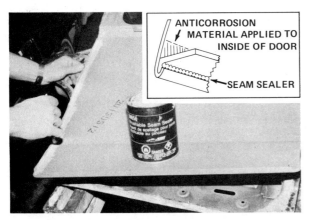

FIGURE 7-60 Applying seam sealer to outer edge of door panel.

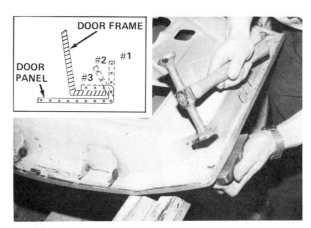

FIGURE 7-61 Turning over the door frame flange.

removed. The door is then hung on its hinges and its alignment and fit are checked on the automobile.

The door must fit perfectly into its opening, and any twist or bends in its framework or inner construction must be eliminated before the remaining portions of the repair panel flange are turned over and spot welded every $1\frac{1}{2}$ to 2 inches (38 to 51 mm). The tack-welded butt joints at points A and B are welded completely and the door is metal finished before it is installed on the automobile.

When the panel is replaced at the bead line, either a plain or a recessed lap joint may be used in joining the new panel to the upper section of the door panel. Pop rivets or metal screws spaced approximately 2 inches (51 mm) apart are used to keep the panel in alignment while it is being spot welded.

Frequently, in major side collisions, door hinges damaged beyond repair must be replaced. Some are fastened by means of bolts, making removal and installation of new hinges rather simple and easy. Others are solidly welded to both the door frame and the door pillar, making replacement more difficult.

Some manufacturers have started using adhesives to hold the door outer panel on the door frame at the factories. Suppliers have provided a two-component adhesive to use in the repair shop. The operations required to remove the outer panel and repair the inner panel are the same, but when the outer panel is to be installed some of the methods will vary. The door frame edge and outer panel are cleaned thoroughly and a special primer is applied (Fig. 7-62) using a special disposable brush; the primer is allowed to dry. Then a two-component cartridge of adhesive is inserted in a special tool that will push the adhesive into a tube that deposits a bead on the panel edge (Fig. 7-63).

Since this adhesive is a two-component material, it has a limited amount of working time. The outer repair panel edge is turned over using the same method previously used. Then the door should be installed on the vehicle as soon as possible. The outer panel can still be moved slightly;

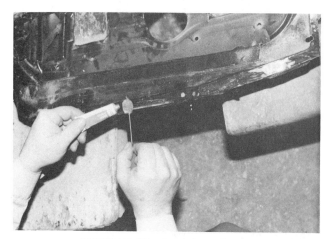

FIGURE 7-62 Applying primer.

FIGURE 7-63 Applying bead of adhesive.

it should be centered in the opening to fit properly and held in place with vise clamps if possible and spot welded using a MIG welder once on each side toward the top of the panel to hold it in place while the adhesive cures. Any adhesive sticking out between the two panels should be smoothed with a squeegee. The panel may then be undercoated properly on the inside of the door to prevent noise and rust.

Replacing doors on vehicles that have welded-on hinges, that is, one-half of the hinge is welded on the door frame and the other half on the door shell (Fig. 7-64), requires special care. The old half-hinge on the damaged door is removed from the panel and cleaned; then a $\frac{1}{4}$-inch (6 mm) hole is drilled through both top and lower hinges. Having carefully measured the exact location from the old panel, this measurement is transferred to the new door panel (Fig. 7-65). An oversized hole is drilled at both the top and lower hinge position; this will allow the hinges to be held on the door by using a $\frac{1}{4}$-inch (6 mm) bolt and oversized washer and regular nut, which is tightened to hold the door in place on the hinges when it is installed and fitted to the door opening. The hinges are then MIG welded as in the factory to retain the integrity that was built into the vehicle. The panel is then refinished as required with the proper paint materials.

Auto manufacturers of later-than-1980 models recommend that doors with no damage to the framework or guard rails or beams be repaired or repaneled, depending on the extent of damage, but that doors with damage to framework and guard rails made of high-strength and martensitic steel be replaced rather than repaired.

FIGURE 7-64 Position of welded-on hinges.

reducing the springback of the framework when the pressure is released.

Very often when a roof panel and rail are driven in, the metal in the roof panel will be stretched at the point of impact. After the damage has been pulled out, a high area

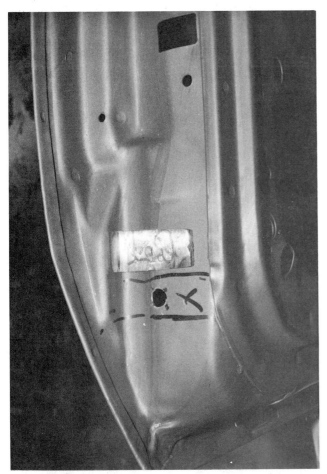

FIGURE 7-65 Holes drilled in door panel to allow for adjustment.

When the upper framework or window opening has become damaged and pushed out of shape, it can be corrected by positioning the hydraulic jack in the opening (Fig. 7-66). Pressure is then applied and the framework is pushed or forced back as well as up. The window frame is then spring-hammered, normalizing the metal and greatly

FIGURE 7-67 High area on roof panel at point of impact.

FIGURE 7-66 Straightening the window frame.

FIGURE 7-68 Used rocker panel and center post positioned for spot welding.

of metal will be present (Fig. 7-67). This area must not be more than roughed-out and aligned until the center door post and rocker panel have been checked for proper location and fit before being spot welded at the proper location on the vehicle (Fig. 7-68). When the rocker panel and center door post are positioned and fitted, they are spot welded to hold them in place. The quarter-panel and doors are mounted and fitted and aligned to the openings; a few more spot welds, metal screws, and clamps are used to hold these parts in place prior to the welding operations required (Fig. 7-69). Then all the welding operations are completed. To shrink this area properly, the first pin-shrink spots should be done past the area of the false stretched area that surrounds the high stretched spot (Fig. 7-67).

The shrinking is done in a sequence that surrounds the area and gradually moves toward the high area using pin shrinks. When the metal area is level, it is repaired using the regular methods.

All joints and panel seams in the floor panel, rocker panel, and door pillars are sealed with a brushable sealer

FIGURE 7-69 Used parts assembled to the vehicle.

FIGURE 7-70 Vehicle ready for delivery.

and undercoated or primed and painted, as at the factory, before the headlining, upholstery, floor pan insulators or heat shields, floor mats, seats, center pillar, and door trim are installed and the automobile refinished. Figure 7-70 shows the vehicle ready to be delivered to the customer.

7-3 REPAIRING TURRET-TOP DAMAGE

When the turret top on an automobile has not been damaged too badly and only minor repairs to its supporting inner construction or roof rails are necessary, the turret top is generally repaired. When the roof rails onto which the turret top (roof panel) is spot welded (Fig. 7-71) have been extensively damaged, it is advisable to replace rather than repair both the turret top and the roof rails.

Turret tops on many newer automobiles are of single-panel construction. When extensively damaged, replacement is necessary. Minor damage, such as that caused by hailstones (if not too extensive), is usually repaired by filling the pits with plastic filler or body solder.

The vehicle in Fig. 7-71 was examined carefully and it was found on the left-hand side, when the doors were partially opened, that the gap was much wider at the top of the door (Fig. 7-72) than at the bottom. This showed that the roof panel assembly had been forced back. This led to installing centering gauges on the bottom section of the vehicle. The gauges showed that the rear section of the vehicle at the rear cross member was lower than the specified datum line height. The impact of the roll-over had moved the roof assembly back, which then put pressure on the rear section of the vehicle, forcing it down.

Repairing of the damaged turret top is started by first preparing it for the straightening operation. This process involves removing the seats, headlining, trim panels, and wind cord from all body pillars and door openings. The floor mats, windshield, and rear window glasses are then removed, as well as any broken door glass. The dashboard,

FIGURE 7-71 Rolled-over vehicle.

FIGURE 7-72 Wider door-to-quarter opening gap.

instrument panel, and parcel rack behind the lazyback of the rear seat are covered with heavy wrapping paper, blankets, or canvas to protect them from being soiled and scratched while the necessary repairs are being made.

To repair the turret top, the insulation and sound-deadening material, which generally consists of sheets of spun fiberglass or asphalt-saturated felt paper, must be removed. Before this step can be taken, however, the turret top's reinforcing cross braces or bows must be removed after their exact locations on the inside of the roof rails have been clearly marked off. The insulation is removed by heating up the turret top from the outside with the welding torch, adjusted to a carburizing flame using a large tip. When sufficiently hot, the adhesive on the inside becomes soft, allowing the insulation to come off clean and easy without tearing, so that it can be put back after the turret top has been repaired.

Next, the turret top's inner construction is aligned and straightened. Roof rails that have not been badly bent or crushed, but merely pushed down, can quite easily be raised and restored to their original shape and position by using

the hydraulic jack and suitable attachments (Fig. 7-73). If the roof rails have not only been pushed down but also driven inward, decreasing the distance between the roof rails and damaging the curvature of the side and crown of the turret top at the drip molding, the damage is corrected by positioning the hydraulic jack between the roof rails and spreading them apart (Fig. 7-74) until the right curvature of the side rail is obtained.

When the windshield header-bar reinforcement has been driven down and back, causing the windshield opening to decrease in both length and width, it is corrected by means of hydraulic jacking equipment. A similar pushing setup is employed in aligning and straightening the rear window reinforcement.

Great care must be exercised when using hydraulic jacking equipment so as not to squash and buckle the inner construction when it is repositioned and aligned. This condition can be avoided by using sufficient padding material, generally pieces of hardwood, angle iron, or steel plates, to spread the force or pressure over a large area.

After the inner construction has been aligned and straightened, the damaged turret top (roof panel) is gradually raised with a hydraulic pushing setup and a small piece of plywood or Masonite, starting at its outer edges and gradually working round and round toward its center. In pushing up damaged metals, especially on turret tops, heavy-duty extension tubes are used, together with a slip-lock extension, to obtain the desired length. The floor panel is well padded with suitable pieces of wood, and the flex head at the top end of the pushing setup allows the angle of the plywood or Masonite to change as the roof panel is pushed up.

The turret-top metal is aligned, shaped, and straightened as it is pushed up by spring-hammering all high ridges, metal dinging and shrinking wherever necessary. Before the turret top can be metal finished, however, the whole body of the automobile must be aligned.

FIGURE 7-73 Pushing inner construction back to original position.

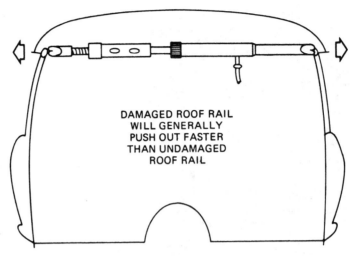

FIGURE 7-74A Pushing damaged roof rails as required.

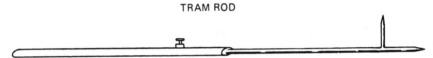

TRAM ROD

FIGURE 7-74B Typical tram rod.

Body Alignment

Before checking the alignment of a badly damaged automobile body, the technician must be sure that all frame misalignments have been corrected. Upholstery and glass must be removed and all badly damaged areas roughed out. All sills, door pillars, roof rails, header bars, and other reinforcing brackets must be straightened. If it is necessary to remove any of the damaged parts to straighten them, they must be reinstalled and welded solidly back into place before any attempt is made at aligning the body.

NOTE: All welding of structural members on newer automobiles of high-strength-steel construction should be done *only* by the MIG welding process.

Parts that have been severely damaged (with sharp bends and folds) may have to be heated to keep them from cracking or breaking as they are straightened. The damaged areas should not, however, be heated to more than a dull or cherry red under any circumstances.

There are two ways of aligning or squaring up an automobile body—by using a tram rod (Fig. 7-74) or with a steel measuring tape. The alignment is determined by taking two opposite diagonal measurements, using either body bolts or accurately measured-off chalk marks as reference points. It is very important that all measurements be taken from bare metal areas. If the two opposite diagonal measurements are the same, that particular section or area of the body is in alignment (Fig. 7-75). When an automobile has been damaged on both sides, it is rather difficult

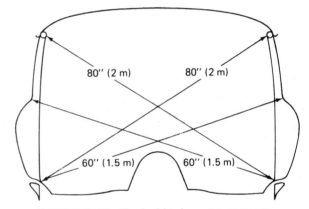

FIGURE 7-75 Typical body measurements.

to align the body because both sides are out of alignment. In such a case, the correct diagonal measurements are obtained from an undamaged automobile of similar make, year, model, and body style, and the damaged body is aligned accordingly.

If the two opposite diagonal measurements are not the same, it not only indicates that the body is out of alignment in that particular section or area but also shows that the body must be forced over (using hydraulic jacking equipment) in the direction of the shorter diagonal reading. The distance that the body will have to be forced over will, in most cases, be a little more than half the difference between the two diagonal measurement readings. This will compensate for a certain amount of springback that generally occurs when the corrective pressure of the hydraulic jack is released. Figures 7-76 and 7-77 clearly illustrate

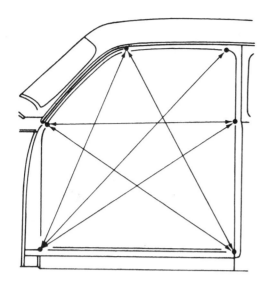

FRONT DOOR OPENING MEASURING POINTS

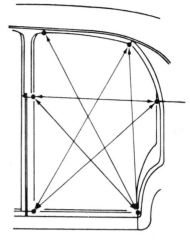

REAR DOOR OPENING MEASURING POINTS

FIGURE 7-76 Typical side body measuring points.

some of the reference points from which diagonal measurement readings of various sections of an automobile body are taken.

The turret top is metal finished by removing the paint and outlining the low spots with the disk sander, using either a No. 16 or PI6 or No. 24 or P24 grit open-coat sanding disk. The low spots are raised with a suitable pick hammer and dolly, starting with the outer crown area and gradually working round and round toward the center of the roof panel (Fig. 7-78). When most of the low spots outlined by the disk sander have been raised, the turret top is filed, picked, and filed again (Fig. 7-79) until all damaged metal has been filed completely smooth and finished perfectly. The turret top is then given a final disk sanding, using a No. 24 or P24 grit closed-coat disk first, followed by a sanding with a No. 36 or P36 grit disk, and finished with a No. 50 or P50 grit closed-coat disk. The roof rails above the doors and the windshield and rear window openings, after they have been carefully checked to ensure proper fit of their glasses, are also metal finished whenever necessary.

All bare metal areas that are covered up or concealed by the turret top's insulation upholstery, moldings, and glass, and particularly all welded and shrunk areas, must be thoroughly cleaned and primed before the parts and materials are again installed. If, however, the damage to a turret top is so extensive that it cannot be repaired and must be replaced with either a similar used turret top from another automobile or with a new roof panel, the damaged roof panel must not be removed before all damage to the turret top, its inner construction (roof rails, windshield, and rear window upper reinforcements), and body pillars have been roughed-out and aligned as previously described.

Due to the impact that moved the roof panel assembly back and lowered the rear section, the vehicle was put on the frame rack and tied down with the four sill pinch-weld flange clamps. Then two pull plates were installed on the front section of the roof. These were connected with chains to two pull rams on the towers. The roof panel was pulled ahead (Fig. 7-78) to bring it back to its proper location. Using the doors, windshield, back window, and the appropriate measurements, the roof panel was positioned at its correct location. The pull on the roof panel helped to pull the rear section back in place, assisted also by two push rams at the rear cross member. The reinforcements were normalized as required and the rear section and roof assembly remained at their proper location. When the vehicle rolled over, the right front fender, inner shield, upper rail, and radiator support were driven down. So while the vehicle was on the frame rack, the gauges were installed on the front section (Fig. 7-79); these, plus a visual check, revealed that the front section was pushed down and had been twisted slightly. The front of the vehicle at the lower engine cradle cross member was chained down to the rack side lower beams; then a hydraulic jack (Fig. 7-80) was used to raise the radiator support edge back to the proper height and remove the slight twist condition. After these alignment procedures were completed, the vehicle was removed from the frame rack and rolled to its stall in the shop. The turret top was then removed from the rest of the body by locating and breaking the spot welds and beads along the eave troughs, panel joints, and top edge in the door openings.

The paint was removed by heating it with the welding torch, using a carburizing flame in the areas of the spot welds and, while still hot, brushing the paint away with a

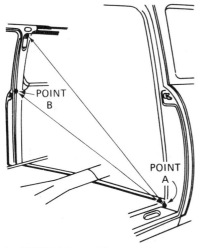

LOCK PILLAR DIAGONAL MEASURING
POINTS (TUDOR AND COUPES)

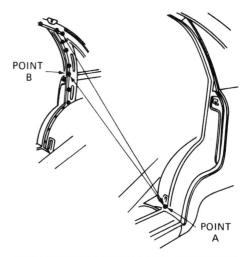

REAR LOCK PILLAR DIAGONAL MEASURING
POINTS (FORDOR)

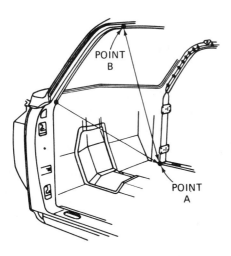

FRONT PILLAR DIAGONAL MEASURING
POINTS (FORDOR, TUDOR AND COUPES)

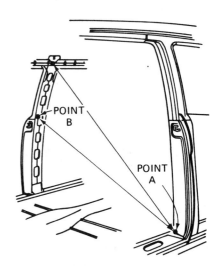

CENTER PILLAR DIAGONAL MEASURING
POINTS (FORDOR)

FIGURE 7-77 Typical body measuring points.

FIGURE 7-78 Pulling roof panel ahead.

FIGURE 7-79 Gauges showing twisted section.

FIGURE 7-80 Hydraulic jack raising the upper section of the radiator support.

steel wire brush. This process will bring many of the hidden, hard-to-locate spot welds into full view.

Solder-filled panel joints are generally quite easily located by either looking at or feeling the inner surface of the roof panel. The spot welds are weakened by partially drilling through them with a $\frac{1}{4}$ inch (6 mm) drill or a high-speed air tool with a carbide burr with the pneumatic chisel. Besides the paint, solder fills used in metal finishing the panel joints must also be removed by melting the solder and either brushing or wiping the joints until all traces of body solder have been removed. The spot welds, which can now be clearly seen, are broken in the same way. After all turret-top spot welds have been broken, the roof panel is removed from the automobile and all necessary repairs to the roughed-out roof rails, windshield, and rear window reinforcements are carried out (Fig. 7-81).

Since the right center door pillar or B pillar had been damaged extensively, it was removed and replaced with a new pillar, which was positioned and held with vise grips

while it was checked for proper fit before it was spot welded to the rocker panel (Fig. 7-82) and the roof side rail. The installation of the B pillar provided an accurate distance between the undamaged rocker panel and the roof rail and permitted the preliminary installation of the roof panel to check for proper fit (Fig. 7-83), which was held with a few vise grips.

The windshield and back window, with the edge protected by using one or two layers of masking tape on its inside edge, were then positioned carefully and installed in their openings. This is done to check to see if the openings and the glass fit together properly and have the proper gap all around their edges (Fig. 7-84).

The replacements panel was fitted and held down tightly in its proper position by means of self-locking welding clamps or C clamps, while it was first tack welded and then checked once more for fit before it was solidly spot welded into place. The roof panel was then spot welded using a MIG welder as recommended for high-strength steel.

FIGURE 7-82 Lower B pillar spot welded to the rocker panel.

FIGURE 7-81 Roof rails with roof panel removed.

FIGURE 7-83 Roof panel installed to check for fit.

FIGURE 7-84 Checking gap in the windshield opening.

FIGURE 7-86 Braze welding of A pillar.

FIGURE 7-87 Repaired and refinished vehicle.

The flange was then simply spot welded to the adjoining inner construction and the holes neatly filled as the turret top was welded into place, giving it a factorylike appearance (Fig. 7-85).

The joint on the A or windshield pillar, which was a lap joint, was braze welded as done at the factory (Fig. 7-86), taking great care to just heat the metal to its proper cherry red color before braze welding together (Fig. 7-86).

All panel joints were solder filled and all minor irregularities in the turret top, eave trough or drip molding, windshield, and rear window openings were metal finished. The spot-welded turret-top flange was properly sealed all around in the area of the eave trough or drip molding.

All welds and covered-up bare metal areas were primed before the insulation, headlining, windshield, rear window, upholstery, floor mats, and seats were installed, and the automobile was moved to the paint shop to be refinished. Figure 7-87 shows the vehicle once it was completely refinished.

Another method, probably one of the fastest and most economical methods, of repairing turret top or roll-over damage (Fig. 7-88) is to replace the turret top completely as one whole unit or assembly with a used salvaged assembly, rather than repair and replace individual parts.

After the body has been prepared for the straightening operation by removing all glass, seats, headlining, trim panels, and floor mats, the body is brought into alignment by correcting the windshield, door, deck-lid, and rear window openings, making certain that all doors open and close properly (Fig. 7-89).

The damaged roof panel is roughed out first (after the body has been brought into alignment) (Fig. 7-90), and then the windshield pillars, center door pillars, and rear-quarter window (sailing) panels on both sides of the automobile and the salvaged roof replacement assembly are very accurately marked off (Fig. 7-91) with a measuring tape, scratch awl or marking pencil, a right-angled flexible piece of heavy paper or cardboard used as a square, and masking tape.

The roughed-out roof panel is then removed by running the panel cutter around its outer edges (Fig. 7-92A

FIGURE 7-85 Spot welding roof panel and top of B pillar using a MIG welder.

FIGURE 7-88 Rolled-over vehicle.

FIGURE 7-91 Marking where panels are to be cut.

FIGURE 7-89 Aligning roof rails.

FIGURE 7-92A Cutting roof with panel cutter.

FIGURE 7-90 Aligning roof panel.

and B), exposing the turret top's inner construction and body pillars, making the portions of the turret top remaining on the car much lighter in weight and cutting at the marked-off lines much easier. Cutting is done with either a hacksaw or panel cutter, whichever is more practical (Fig. 7-93). The salvaged turret-top assembly is also prepared for installation in the same manner, taking care to prepare the roof

FIGURE 7-92B Vehicle with cut panel removed.

FIGURE 7-93 Cutting sail panel with hacksaw.

FIGURE 7-95 MIG welding sail panel.

panel assembly and vehicle body with offset butt joints at the A, B, and C pillar and sail panel.

After the remaining portions of the turret top have been removed from the automobile, the salvaged replacement assembly is lifted onto the car, positioned, and firmly clamped down by using vise grips, welding clamps, or C clamps, and then MIG tack welded firmly in place (Fig. 7-94).

After the overall size and shape of all body openings have been rechecked, including the opening and closing of all doors, the turret top is solidly welded in position (Fig. 7-95) with a continuous-wire-feed MIG welder using offset butt joints at pillars A, B, and C and the sail panel.

All welded pillar and panel joints are metal finished by either countersinking or forging of the weld beads wherever possible and practical and by leveling or cleaning the weld beads with the disk grinder and filling them and all surrounding surface irregularities with body solder or plastic filler (Fig. 7-96).

The top of the doors' "glass-opening" framework,

FIGURE 7-96 Trimming plastic filler on sail panel.

which was roughed out and straightened earlier to make possible accurate alignment and fitting of doors in their respective openings, is metal finished at this time.

The undersides of all weld joints, body-opening flanges, and other bare metal-finished areas that will be covered up by chrome trim, glass, or upholstery are well primed before the glass, headlining, trim panels, upholstery, seats, and floor mats are reinstalled and the automobile is moved into the paint shop.

7-4 REPAIRING REAR-END COLLISION DAMAGE

An automobile that has been badly damaged in the rear so that its bumper, quarter-panels, deck lid, floor, and wheel housings have been driven in and forward, bending its frame and causing an overlapping of the rear doors and the quarter-panels (Fig. 7-97A, B, and C), can generally be restored to its original condition if the repair operations are carried out in their proper order or sequence and with the right equipment.

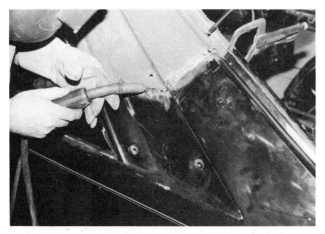

FIGURE 7-94 Panel held in place with vise grips and spot welded.

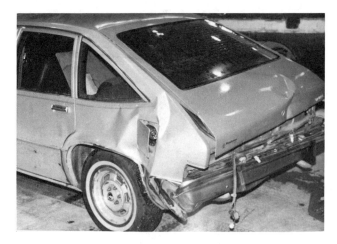

FIGURE 7-97 Typical rear-end collision damage.

The first step in repairing this type of damage is to prepare the automobile for the roughing-out and straightening operations by placing it on supporting safety stands, high enough so that the damage can be accurately diagnosed with measuring equipment and centering and tracking gauges, and then repaired using alignment equipment, such as the damage dozer or the body and frame straightener (Fig. 7-98). The damaged frame or side rails in unitized construction, being the strongest members in the rear section of an automobile, are first pulled out. Pulling can be done by using a damage dozer hooked to the bumper, bumper bracket (after the bumper face bar and guards have been removed), or a pull plate bolted to the side rail, with the other end of the horizontal beam anchored to the center section of the body or frame. One of the latest and strongest methods of anchoring portable body and frame straighteners, especially when repairing automobiles of unitized, high-strength-steel construction, is the quadri-clamp anchoring rack. The rack enables the repairer to apply single and also multiple corrective pulls and prevents additional unwanted damage to the underbody (rocker panels) of the

automobile while pulling. Damage can also be pulled out using frame- and body-straightening equipment and similar hookups. The damage to the frame and quarter-panels in a rear-end collision can also be corrected by firmly fastening the automobile in a stationary frame-straightening machine and then attaching hydraulic pulling rams to the vertical towers and the frame and quarter-panels (Fig. 7-98A and B). All pulling must be done slowly and very carefully (at the proper angle), stopping frequently not only to inspect the damaged frame (or side rails) and adjoining sheet-metal sections but also to align and roughly straighten them (spring-hammering and metal dinging) as each panel is pulled back to its original position and shape. This operation tends to normalize the sheet metal into its drawn-back position and greatly minimizes the elastic or springback property that sheet metal possesses.

It must be mentioned, however, that in most instances a number of changes in positioning of the damage dozer and several different hookups (Fig. 7-99) will be required before all the damage is roughed out, aligned, and corrected.

The frame alignment or centering gauges, which were

FIGURE 7-98 Pulling quarter-panel, rear cross member, floor, and frame rail simultaneously.

previously installed and used in determining the extent and type of damage that has occurred, should be visually checked regularly as the damage is being pulled out and alignment progresses (Fig. 7-100).

NOTE: It is very important that all structural panels, especially on automobiles of unitized (HSS) construction, to which the rear suspension components are directly mounted, be accurately brought back to their original position and shape so that the proper relationship of the rear suspension parts, not only to each other but also to the front suspension parts, is restored (Fig. 7-101).

In rear-end collisions, with no frame, side rail, or floor damage, but where the quarter-panel has been badly damaged, the damage is repaired by applying corrective stretching pulls directly on the quarter-panel. It is roughed out, aligned, and straightened, while under tension, or replaced if necessary.

FIGURE 7-100 Centering gauges mounted and ready for checking.

FIGURE 7-99 View of several different corrective hookups.

FIGURE 7-101 View of trunk floor and rear suspension mounting structural panels.

Sometimes, as is also done on front frame rails that were damaged in a front-end collision, it is necessary also to gain access to the rear frame rails. Due to the damage and to help relieve the buckles as it is pulled, it is necessary to cut doors or openings in the trunk floor panel and sometimes the quarter-panel (Fig. 7-102A, B, and C). Figure 7-103A shows where the rail was damaged from a top view. With these openings it is possible to reshape the frame section as it is pulled. The floor section that was removed is straightened and welded back in place (Fig. 7-103B). Cutting a hole in the quarter-panel which was to be changed as per the estimate facilitated the repairs on the frame rail and shows the floor section when it was reinstalled (Fig. 7-103C).

There are occasions when a vehicle is hit in the rear section hard enough that the frame rail will even sag at the rear door area. When using centering gauges as the different operations of pulling are carried out, it is of the utmost importance that the gauge showing sag should be installed as in Fig. 7-103D. The gauge must always be installed in front of the mash in the frame rail above the rear axle. This is the only way to be able to use the gauge to show a true sag condition.

After the side rails, center floor pan, and deck lower panel have been pulled out and roughly aligned and straightened as much as possible, the damaged quarter-panels are pulled out, using the frame-straightening machine (Fig. 7-104). By stretching out or pulling back the quarter-panels, the vertical floor pan extensions, the lower turret-top panel, the rear door locking pillars, and to some extent the wheel housings are repositioned.

The wheel housings generally require additional assistance and are pushed back into their proper positions and shape by placing the hydraulic jack with suitable attachments in the wheel housings and stretching them or restricting them from becoming elongated by means of a clamp and rachet hoist puller ("come-along"), or a pulling ram setup (Fig. 7-104B). After the wheel housings have been pushed back into their proper positions, and while the tension of the hydraulic jack is still on the quarter-panel,

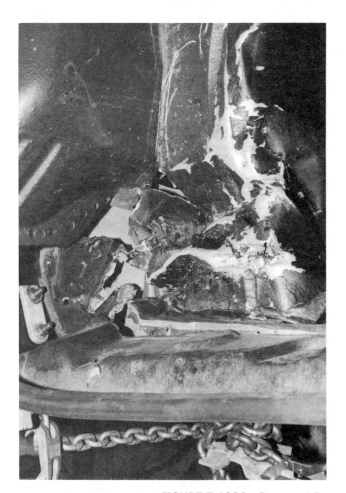

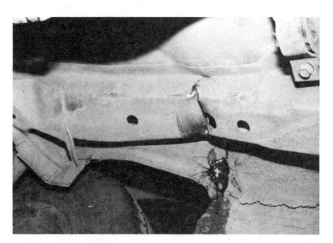

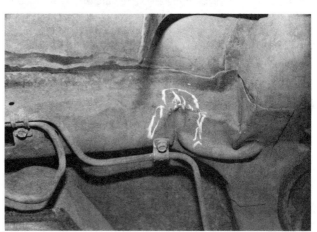

FIGURE 7-102A Damaged floor area, left corner. (B) Damaged rear frame rail. (C) Damaged cross member between suspension points (right and left).

FIGURE 7-103A   Trunk floor cut away.

FIGURE 7-103B   Floor section reinstalled.

all high ridges caused by the bulging out of the quarter-panels at their sides are spring-hammered and both wheel housings and quarter-panels are simultaneously aligned and roughly straightened. This step eliminates the overlap of the rear door and the quarter-panel, making the door opening large enough for the door to open and close properly.

After all the damaged sheet metal has been roughly aligned, the number of body panels that can be repaired or that will have to be replaced will depend greatly on the extent and severity of the rear-end collision (Fig. 7-105A and B). If the damage is so great that all sheet metal except the side rails and wheel housings have to be replaced, the damaged panels are then removed as required. The side rails, rear cross member, wheel housings, and floor pan (over the differential housing) are straightened perfectly or replaced (Fig. 7-106A) now that all areas are accessible and aligned according to factory specifications. Replacement quarter-panels can be installed as received from the manufacturer, which may make it necessary to remove a portion of the vinyl top covering, eave-trough chrome molding, and the rear window glass; or the quarter-panels

can be cut down in size and installed without removing any parts. The new quarter-panels are then placed into position on the body and aligned so that the new deck lid fits properly before they are tack welded into place (Fig. 7-106B).

In some cases of extensive repair, a complete rear section from a wrecked vehicle that is undamaged and in good condition is used to repair the vehicle. The rear damaged section is cut off across the rocker panel, C pillar, and sail panel (Fig. 7-107). The used part or rear clip is cut at the same location, except slightly longer; this permits the removal of any metal that was damaged due to heat when it was cut off. This will also allow enough material for offset butt weld, lap welds, and the trimming of the parts to get an accurate fit.

Sometimes the roof panel and rear section are damaged in the same accident. If the vehicle is to be repaired and still remain within the cost allocated for the particular job, a rear section and roof clip may be used.

When using welding equipment, always employ preventive methods to avoid damage to the vehicle from welding operations. Since MIG welding was to be used in

FIGURE 7-103C   Hole cut in quarter-panel.

FIGURE 7-104A Stretching out quarter-panel, wheel housing, and adjacent panels to correct rear door opening.

FIGURE 7-104B Restricting wheel housing from tearing or elongating.

FIGURE 7-103D Gauge held in position by magnets.

our example, cardboard cut to fit and a tarpaulin were used to prevent the hot metal sparks from damaging glass and upholstery (Fig. 7-108).

Due to having cut the quarter-panel higher up than the joint on the dog leg, an insert of the same metal was shaped and placed where the weld was going to be done (Fig. 7-109). While being held with a vise grip, it was spot welded to the section of the dog leg remaining on the vehicle.

The replacement quarter-panel was then prepared for the necessary welding operations, such as punching $\frac{5}{16}$-inch (8 mm) holes for plug welds. The areas where it was to be butt welded and lap welded were also prepared. The quarter-panel was then fitted and aligned in place to fit the deck lid, right rear door, wheel house outer edge, and lower floor extensions. When the gaps between the required panels were of the appropriate width, the quarter-panel was held in place with vise grips and tack spot welds were placed at the

FIGURE 7-106B   Preliminary fit of a quarter panel.

FIGURE 7-105A   Roughed out and aligned left quarter-panel ready for final repairs. (B) Roughed out and aligned right quarter-panel ready for removal.

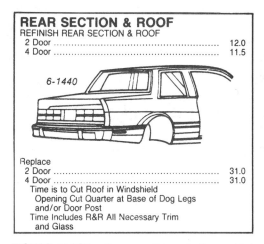

REAR SECTION & ROOF
REFINISH REAR SECTION & ROOF
  2 Door 12.0
  4 Door 11.5

6-1440

Replace
  2 Door 31.0
  4 Door 31.0
  Time is to Cut Roof in Windshield
    Opening Cut Quarter at Base of Dog Legs
    and/or Door Post
  Time Includes R&R All Necessary Trim
    and Glass

FIGURE 7-107   Rear section of the vehicle from auto salvage. (Courtesy of Mitchell Manuals, Inc.)

FIGURE 7-106A   Vehicle ready for the replacement of the quarter-panel.

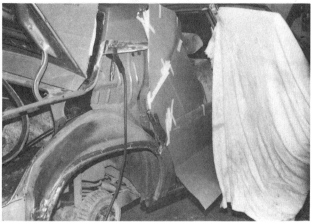

FIGURE 7-108   Vehicle prepared for MIG welding.

FIGURE 7-109 Metal insert in dog leg.

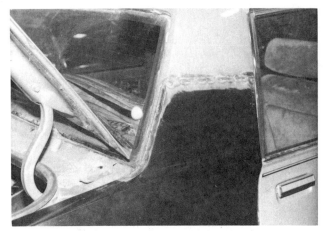

FIGURE 7-111 Welded quarter-panel.

proper areas (Fig. 7-110). The quarter-panel was then spot welded as required; the sail panel lap joint was welded solid, but it was done by welding about 1.5 inches (38 mm) at a time and alternating from one area to the other. This was done to let the heat dissipate and prevent warping of the panel. The butt weld on the dog leg was welded using the same method (Fig. 7-111). When the joints were all welded, they were cleaned and the weld ground down with a grinder (Fig. 7-112).

The new, used, or repaired deck lid can be installed for fitting on the automobile; however, the deck lid hinges, which may also be badly bent, are straightened quite easily. In most cases, the hinges will bend as shown at points A and B in Fig. 7-113. The bend at point A controls the upward and downward position of the deck lid.

If the sharpness of the bend at A is increased by bending the hinge in the C direction, the deck lid is raised up higher in its opening when in its closed position. If the bend in the hinge at point A is decreased by bending it in the D direction, the deck lid is lowered in its opening.

FIGURE 7-112 Welded areas ground down to prepare for plastic filler as required.

On the other hand, if the hinge at point B is bent in the E direction, the deck lid moves forward in its opening; but when bent in the F direction, the deck lid mover farther back in its opening.

Generally, the hinges, if repairable, can be straightened without removing them from the car (Fig. 7-114). The hinges are merely stabilized and kept from moving at either points A or B and bent by lifting up or pulling down on the deck lid.

If the quarter-panel is rusted out or badly damaged in only one particular area, it is often repaired by installing a partial replacement instead of replacing the whole quarter panel, as illustrated in Fig. 7-115. The size of the replacement section is clearly marked off on the quarter-panel, allowing enough metal to flange the edges of the opening after the damaged section has been cut out with the pneumatic chisel.

After the opening edges have been flanged, the

FIGURE 7-110 Quarter-panel held in place by vise grips and spot welds.

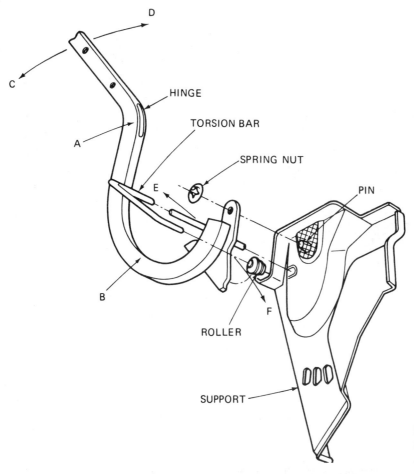

FIGURE 7-113 Typical deck lid hinge. (Courtesy of Chrysler Canada.)

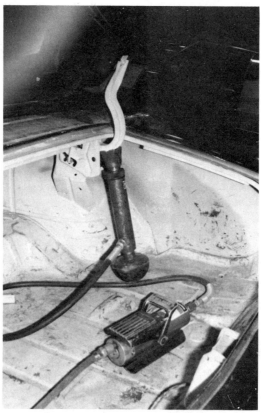

FIGURE 7-114 Straightening the deck lid hinge.

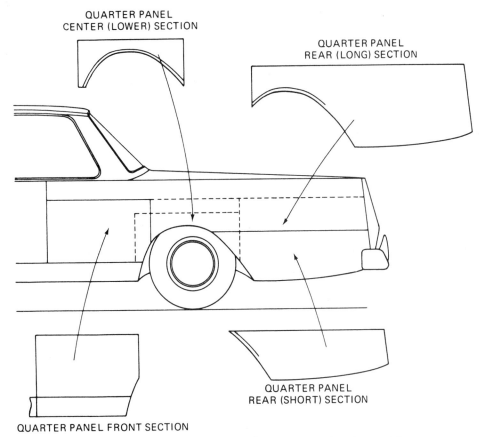

QUARTER PANEL
CENTER (LOWER) SECTION

QUARTER PANEL
REAR (LONG) SECTION

QUARTER PANEL
REAR (SHORT) SECTION

QUARTER PANEL FRONT SECTION

FIGURE 7-115 Different parts of quarter-panel replacement sections.

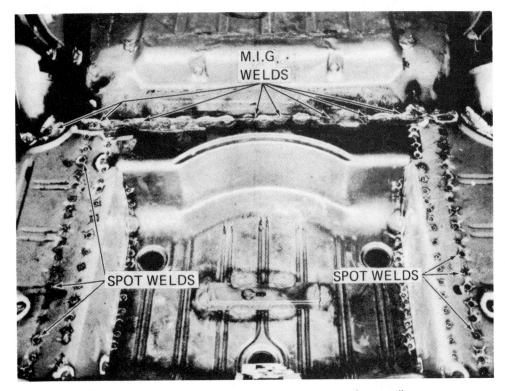

FIGURE 7-116 Spot welding new floor section to frame rails.

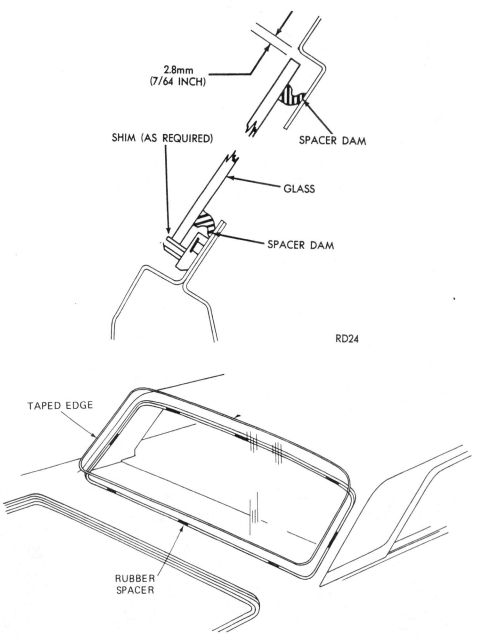

FIGURE 7-117 Installation of back window. (Courtesy of Chrysler Canada.)

replacement section is fitted into position and kept in alignment by means of metal screws or pop-rivets while the new section is spot welded into place.

The quarter-panel is then metal finished by solder-filling the recessed lap joints or by using plastic filler and finished in the usual manner. The deck lower panel is similarly positioned and tack welded in place on the car. Body straps are frequently used with either a hydraulic pulling ram, rachet hoist puller ("come-along"), or friction jack to pull the quarter-panels or front fenders together.

The damaged floor pan, which sometimes has to be removed in order to complete the straightening of the side rails, is also MIG spot welded (Fig. 7-116). The body is given another final check for alignment before all replacement panels are solidly welded in place. The deck lid opening, which may sometimes undergo slight changes due to expansion and contraction of metal when the new replacement panels are solidly welded into place, often has to be corrected by spreading the quarter-panels apart with the hydraulic jack.

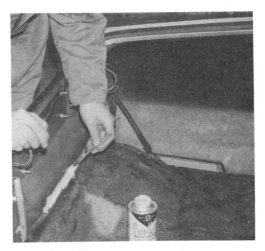

FIGURE 7-119 Sealing body joints, seams, and openings.

FIGURE 7-118 Finishing repairs on (A) quarter-panel and (B) deck lid.

FIGURE 7-120 Repaired automobile ready for delivery.

The rear window opening also has to be checked for alignment, first by taking diagonal measurements from a point in the lower corner of one side to a point in the upper corner of the opposite side, using inner-construction holes or joints as reference points. The outer edge of the rear window glass is then covered with several layers of masking tape to prevent chipping the glass as it is placed into the opening; its curvature is checked with that of the window frame.

A twist in the framework of the rear window opening, which may cause the installed glass to crack, can be located by either gluing or taping a number of small rubber spacers, all of equal thickness, into position at various points on the pinch-weld flange. The rubber dam, used on later-model automobiles (Fig. 7-117), can also be used instead of the rubber spacers. The glass, when placed into the opening and properly centered, should lie flat and square, making solid contact with all the rubber spacers or the dam if the window opening is properly aligned.

All straightened sheet-metal and replacement panels are then metal finished by first grinding down all spot welds to a smooth finish, hammering out all small dents, and solder filling or plastic filling the panel joints (Fig. 7-118). The rear window glass is now installed, and all body joints, seams, and openings are carefully sealed with a high-grade sealer to prevent moisture, water, and dust from entering the interior of the automobile (Fig. 7-119). If the sealing operation is performed before the automobile is refinished, the body sealer is also covered with a coat of paint, which gives a factory-finished appearance to the repaired automobile (Fig. 7-120) after all the remaining parts have been installed.

QUESTIONS

7-1. What are the important facts a repairperson must have before starting to repair a damaged automobile?

7-2. Out of what material are many of the underpans and wheel housing panels on the newer, unitized, high-strength-steel automobiles made, and how are they repaired?

7-3. What methods are used in straightening damaged radiator supports?

7-4. If the radiator support is not repaired properly, what problems will the repairperson encounter?

7-5. How is a badly damaged radiator support on unitized (HSS) automobiles replaced?

7-6. How are fascia bumpers on late-model automobiles repaired?

7-7. How are the sharp buckles, bends, and ridges eliminated from the inner construction and outer panel of a hood?

7-8. What methods are used in roughing-out inaccessible outer panels on hoods?

7-9. Describe and illustrate with a sketch how a front door opening is aligned.

7-10. What precautionary measure should be taken when the windshield has been broken in a front-end collision and there is no visible evidence or reason for its breaking?

7-11. In minor front-end damage on unitized (HSS) automobiles, how are the front fender inner panels, strut towers, side rails, and radiator support pulled out and straightened?

7-12. In repairing major front-end damage, what damage is repaired first, and how is this accomplished?

7-13. Why is repairing of front-end damage with a pulldozer more cumbersome and slower than with a body and frame straightener or frame machine?

7-14. What equipment is used to determine the correct position of the strut towers, front fender inner panels, side rails, and radiator support as they are pulled out and straightened or replaced?

7-15. How are the outer, overlapping, joining edges of replacement panels cleaned in preparation for welding?

7-16. How is a side rail or any structural member repaired if it cannot be straightened cold?

7-15. How can the overheating of high-strength steel be avoided?

7-16. Describe how an inaccessible, reinforced area on a badly damaged side rail is straightened.

7-17. Is the sectioning of load-bearing structural members and panels recommended, and how should they be installed?

7-18. What protective treatment is given all welds and panel joints before the motor, transmission, steering, and suspension parts are installed?

7-19. In repairing side collision damage, how are the floor and rocker panels repaired?

7-20. In what way are the roof rail and turret top aligned?

7-21. If a cutting torch is used in the removal of a body section or salvage parts, how should the cutting be done?

7-22. How are the top and bottom edges of the new rocker panel fastened to the old rocker panel assembly?

7-23. Can localized damage to rocker panels be repaired? If so, how?

7-24. Describe how a replacement panel is installed on a door.

7-25. Is the repairing of doors with badly damaged framework and guard rails on automobiles later than 1980 models recommended, and why?

7-26. Describe and illustrate with a sketch how the window opening on a door is corrected.

7-27. What preparations must be made before a damaged turret top can be repaired?

7-28. How are badly bent roof rails repaired?

7-29. What hydraulic setup and attachments are used in pushing up a turret top, and how is this operation carried out?

7-30. Describe how a badly damaged body is aligned.

7-31. What type and grit of sanding disks are used in metal finishing a turret top?

7-32. Why must the roof rails, windshield, and rear window openings be metal finished?

7-33. In what way are covered-up or concealed bare metal areas protected before parts are installed?

7-34. What method is employed in breaking the spot welds when a turret top has to be replaced?

7-35. Describe how a replacement roof panel is prepared for spot welding and how it is positioned and held in place.

7-36. How are the newly installed roof panel and adjoining parts metal finished?

7-37. What is one of the fastest and most economical methods of repairing turret-top damage?

7-38. Describe how the damage to the rear end is roughed out and aligned.

7-39. What equipment provides the strongest method of anchoring portable body and frame straighteners?

7-40. When repairing rear-end collision damage, especially on automobiles of unitized (HSS) construction, why is it so important that all structural panels be accurately straightened?

7-41. How are damaged panels removed that have to be replaced?

7-42. What kind of equipment is used in repairing side rails and the rear cross member?

7-43. Describe and illustrate with a sketch how a deck lid hinge is straightened.

7-44. How are partial and whole quarter-panel replacements made?

7-45. Explain how a rear window glass is used in checking the alignment of its opening.

7-46. Why should all the body panel seams be sealed, and why must this be done before the automobile is refinished?

## CHAPTER EIGHT

Restoration of Rust Protection

SAFETY TIP

It is common knowledge that accidents are usually caused by negligence. Only by paying careful attention to accident causes can they be reduced. Many of the products used in a body shop are highly combustible—lacquers, reducers, thinners, and other dangerous chemicals. Moreover, because the vehicles are sometimes dismantled in assemblies, they clutter up the floor or the alleys between the cars.

Combustibles are always a fire hazard and the containers holding such products as thinners, reducers, and paints should be kept closed and stored in fireproof cupboards. There should also be no welding or smoking close to the paint area, and proper signs signifying such restrictions should be prominently displayed. All painting should be done in a spray booth with exhaust fans that meet the requirements of local laws.

The painter should always wear a suitable respirator and have the exhaust fan on when painting or working with thinners and reducers. The inhalation of thinner, reducer, or paint fumes could possibly result in physical ailments.

8-1 DESCRIPTION OF RUST PROTECTION

The automobile industry has gone through tremendous changes, which were brought about in part by the shortage of oil. The public and governments desired vehicles that would be fuel efficient. This in turn made the manufacturers design new, lighter automobiles.

The new designs and methods of manufacturing have had the result that every panel in the vehicle is used to support and add strength to the vehicle. All these panels are part of the unibody structural integrity of the automobile. With all these panels being used as parts of the structure, it has become very important that they be very resistant to corrosion. These panels are made of a lighter-gauge metal, and rust is not only a detriment to appearance but also weakens the metal.

Manufacturers have introduced different types of materials to help combat the corrosion problem; these metals include one- and two-sided galvanized steel, zincrometal, aluminum H.S.S., HSLA steel, and plastics.

Manufacturers also have to contend with the increasing use of salt on highways to help control snow and ice conditions. The chimneys of the nation, whether home or industry, are pouring chemicals in the atmosphere, which in turn pollute the air and cause more corrosion on automobiles.

With the high cost of automobiles, the motoring public is keeping its vehicles much longer than before. The new customer wants his or her vehicle to last longer and be much more resistant against corrosion and its effects. Manufacturers are using new undercoating materials and methods to prevent the vehicles from rusting from the inside out. They are also using different primers, sealers and color coats to help prevent the rusting of panels, both inside and out.

Rustproofing

The completely welded autobody is submerged in a tank that contains a cleaning chemical, which is then followed by a neutralizing water rinse. The vehicle body is then immersed into a conversion coating bath, which will give a surface that will be very receptive to the primer; this is also neutralized with a water wash.

The vehicle moves to the next stage, where it is submerged in a tank of a tough primer that is electrodeposited on the vehicle; this procedure coats the vehicle inside and out uniformly and seals all joints and seams. This process deposits the epoxy primer to a film thickness of approximately 1.6 mils or 4 micrometers. The primer is baked to cure the material and to evaporate the solvents. This is followed with a coat of primer-surfacer, which is sprayed on exterior exposed surfaces by robot equipment.

This is followed by the color coats, which are sprayed on the body. Most manufacturers apply on the inside, enclosed, corrosion-prone areas a coating of either petroleum-based or wax undercoating for additional protection.

Thus manufacturers are producing vehicles that are much more corrosion proof than before. This places the onus on the repair industry, when a vehicle is repaired, to maintain corrosion protection integrity; corrosion protection must be restored to the original equipment manufacturer's specifications to ensure that the warranty remains valid.

The repair shop that prides itself on its quality of work will obtain not only the knowledge, but also the equipment and material to do the work properly. Corrosion-resistant materials should not only be applied to the newer vehicles, but also to the older units owned by their customers. This prevents the job from coming back to be redone due to corrosion and a peeling film on repaired areas. Remember that the materials used should be materials from the original manufacturer (Fig. 8-1). Materials should not be intermixed, which could cause a failure in the system; materials from the same company are designed to work together and are compatible.

There are no mysteries in restoring the corrosion protection of a vehicle, just basic steps. The first operation is the phosphate treatment of the metal and then the application of the conversion coating; always follow label directions for the material used. The treated metal must be prepared to give good adherence for the material that will be applied, which has basically the same characteristics as the material applied at the factory. These corrosion-resistant pigment primers are composed of chromates and epoxy resins, which give long-term adherence and dry usually in 1 hour. These primers may be used on fiberglass, steel, or aluminum, and almost all types of primer-surfacers or top coats will adhere to them. A primer-surfacer is used if filling

FIGURE 8-1 Materials used to refinish repaired area. (Courtesy of Inter-Industry Conference on Auto Collision Repair)

of sand scratches is needed; otherwise, a good-quality primer-sealer may be used instead.

The typical autobody technician may not be too interested in how corrosion starts, but he or she should know the basics so as to understand why corrosion should be prevented when a repair is done. Corrosion or, as it is commonly known, rust occurs on steel and has costly consequences; it is the product of the complex chemical reaction of metal in an oxygen-rich environment. A chemical flow of electrons causes the breakdown of the metal and forms various oxygen compounds, such as iron oxides, zinc oxides, and aluminum oxides.

This corrosion or rusting of the body of the vehicle can be delayed by two main methods; these are (1) zinc coating or galvanizing of steel or (2) covering the steel with paint. Any steel left without a protective coating will rust due to the effects of moisture, salt, and impurities in the atmosphere. The higher the concentrations of impurities and moisture are, the faster the metal will produce iron oxides or rust, which does not adhere to the surface of the steel, but just falls off. This will continue until the steel part is completely rusted away.

A properly applied paint system will protect the metal from the effects of the moisture and impurities in the air. If the surface paint film is broken or scratched to the metal surface, the metal surface is no longer protected from the effects of corrosion. This corrosion will spread between the paint film and the steel; and if the adherence of the paint film to the metal is poor, it will raise the affected areas, causing the paint to fall off. Severe rusting will quickly follow on areas that are not protected properly. The areas that are not cleaned properly and have impurities between the paint film and the metal may react and cause rust if the oxygen in the air passes through the paint film; this gradually destroys the protection of the paint film.

Previous methods to prevent rust were to have a chemically clean metal surface that was protected by a paint film and undercoatings to seal the surface from the effects of air and moisture. These techniques were found to be insufficient to protect the metal; therefore, manufacturers are using zinc to give additional protection to the steel. Through experiments it has been found that, when two different types of metal are in contact, a chemical reaction occurs in the more chemically active of these two different metals, which will corrode. This reaction can be used to an advantage by placing a more chemically active material with steel; this reaction will protect the steel and prevent it from rusting. The chemical reaction causes one metal or material to sacrifice itself while giving protection to the less active metal. Zinc is a very active metal and, being fairly inexpensive, it can be chemically applied to sheet metal to galvanize it, or it may be mixed in a powdered form to the resins used to make primers and paint. These two are the most used methods to protect metal from corrosion.

The zinc on galvanized steel forms a barrier between the atmosphere and the steel, and as the zinc corrodes it will form a layer of zinc oxide on the surface of the steel exposed to the air. But unlike iron oxide, which falls, zinc oxide remains on the zinc coating. This action forms a barrier between the zinc on the metal and the surrounding air.

When the vehicle's painted surface is scratched, the zinc coating on the affected area will form a zinc oxide film to protect the steel under the coating. Therefore, it can be seen that the zinc provides a chemical galvanic protection, and it also forms a zinc oxide as a repair to protect the exposed steel. Thus it is of the utmost importance that the zinc protection applied to vehicles never be removed when repairing vehicles, replacing parts, or sectioning and welding, because this will take away the protection from corrosion at the affected areas.

Air pollutants, such as the ashes from combustion, dust, chemical solvents, and sulphur dioxide, cause the breakdown of the paint film and rusting. The areas that are particularly prone to rusting are joints, seams, and pockets in the sheet-metal stamping used to build vehicles. Since these pollutants are usually carried by rain or air, they penetrate the smallest crevices or seams. This action damages the coatings in time, causing rust to form; corrosion may progress rapidly and penetrate under the protective coatings that were applied previously.

8-2 CORROSION PROTECTION RESTORATION

When a vehicle is involved in a collision, some of the protective materials will be damaged, not only in the areas of direct impact but also in the areas of indirect damage. Also, the force of the impact will cause paint to chip, caulking to become loose or break, and some seals to pull apart. When repairs are done, it is important that all affected areas be repaired by the autobody technician so as to preserve the rust protection built into the vehicle.

Repair methods require the cutting of metal body panels, usually by using a plasma torch, hacksaw, or a zip gun, which may damage protective coatings. They can be further damaged by repair pulling operations, as well as by the temperatures used in MIG welding, which may cause the zinc to vaporize from the weld zone. The use of grinders and abrasives will also cause the loss of zinc protection. All these areas require proper repair methods to reestablish corrosion protection. After all repair operations have been done, all damaged and repaired areas must be refinished using the proper materials and methods.

Careful methods must be used to prevent corrosion and jobs that have to be redone. If the proper steps are not used, it may cause premature component failure due to corrosion affecting an area in a major structural component.

This may only show up after another accident, but many times a component breaking prematurely could impair the integrity of the vehicle for road use or in the event of a collision. Therefore, it must be remembered that it is of the utmost importance that all repairs be carried out as required.

It is of the utmost importance that the proper materials be used when restoring the corrosion protection after the repairs have been done. These operations must be done as recommended by the manufacturer, using materials that are compatible with one another. Remember that all surfaces must be cleaned thoroughly and be free of oil, grease, dirt, wax, grinding residues, and oxidation.

The paint surface must be wiped properly with a wax, grease, oil, and road tar removing solvent; reducer or other motor-designed solvents should not be used for this operation. The solvent is applied liberally to the surface so as to float the contaminants; this is then removed by wiping with clean rags or paper towels while the surface is wet to remove and pick up the contaminants. The rag is turned over often, or if paper towels are used, they are changed often to assure a satisfactory clean-up. Never use rags that have been treated with silicones or any material that helps to pick up dust.

A phosphoric acid-based cleaner is used to chemically clean and remove rust from the surface. This metal conditioner will clean and etch the metal; after a couple of minutes, it is washed off with water, if so recommended by the material manufacturer.

Conversion coating is used to leave a uniform zinc phosphate coating on the sheet metal, which is chemically bonded to it. This forms a good base for adherence of the primers and will stop rust from creeping under the primer coat. The conversion coating should be used on the steel even if it is coated galvanized metal to give good adhesion for the paint. The conversion coating is then applied as per label directions and allowed to work for 3 to 5 minutes. Only an area as big as can be worked comfortably should be coated and rinsed with water before the solution dries. If it should dry before rinsing, it must be done over. Then the surface is washed off with cold water and a sponge rinsed in clean water; this should then be wiped with a dry cloth and allowed to air dry.

Once the surface has air dried, the next steps for refinishing the surface may be done, but never touch the clean metal with your hands once the surface has been cleaned.

With the different methods of construction used in the building of the body of a vehicle, the corrosion-protection methods will vary somewhat. These different types of construction are the closed body sections, such as rocker panel assemblies and body frame rails, exposed interior surfaces such as hood sections, aprons or skirts and floor pans, exposed joints such as quarter-panel to trunk floor, quarter to wheel-house joints, and any other exposed surfaces such as door skins, quarter-panels, and fenders.

An exposed panel is a panel that is readily accessible without removing welded components.

Closed Body Sections

The most important areas to be protected during a repair job are the interior surfaces of closed body sections. These enclosed sections include the underbody structures, such as the frame rails front and rear and the rocker panels. The reason that these panels must be protected are that they are the principal load-bearing structural members of the unitized body. Adverse effects may be caused by any corrosion to these sections, such as to the durability and crash worthiness of the unitized vehicle.

It is not recommended that metal conditioner and conversion coating be used inside closed sections; this is due to being unable to remove the chemicals and moisture from the seams on the inside. The primers used should be able to adhere adequately in these enclosed areas without using conversion coatings. This does not mean that the sections must not be cleaned; they must be thoroughly degreased and cleaned, and, due to their closed construction, this must be done before the part is welded into the required position.

After the parts have been cleaned, a zinc-rich weld-through primer is applied to the joint areas (Figs. 8-2 through 8-6). The weld zones will be protected by the zinc in the primer, which will deter the starting of any corrosion by galvanic action in the weld zones. This zinc-rich primer should not be applied in too thick a coating because it may have a bad effect on the weld. Remember that weld-through primers should only be applied over bare steel, not over any primer or paint film or on any surface of galvanized sheet metal. This primer should only be applied to the welding area, because this primer has poor adhesion characteristics. All welding residue and excess primer should be removed from the area of the joint after the welding operation.

A wire brush is not the best tool to be used when

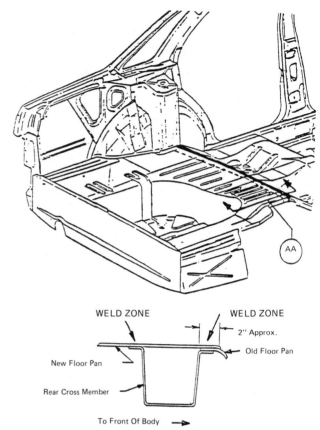

FIGURE 8-2 Areas where weld-through primer should be used. (Courtesy of Inter-Industry Conference on Auto Collision Repair)

cleaning the weld area, as it may leave scratches in the existing primer that might not be filled by the coat of new primer being applied. The new primer may not follow and penetrate into all the scratches, leaving small voids where corrosion may start. A better system to use is a plastic abrasive or a sandblaster to thoroughly clean the weld area.

Metal conditioners and conversion coatings should not be used on areas that have been sandblasted. Due to

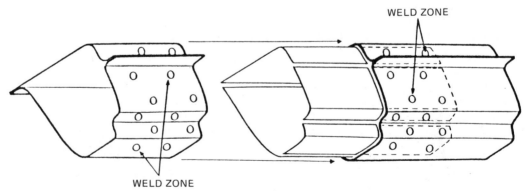

FIGURE 8-3 Area where weld-through primer should be used. (Courtesy of Inter-Industry Conference on Auto Collision Repair)

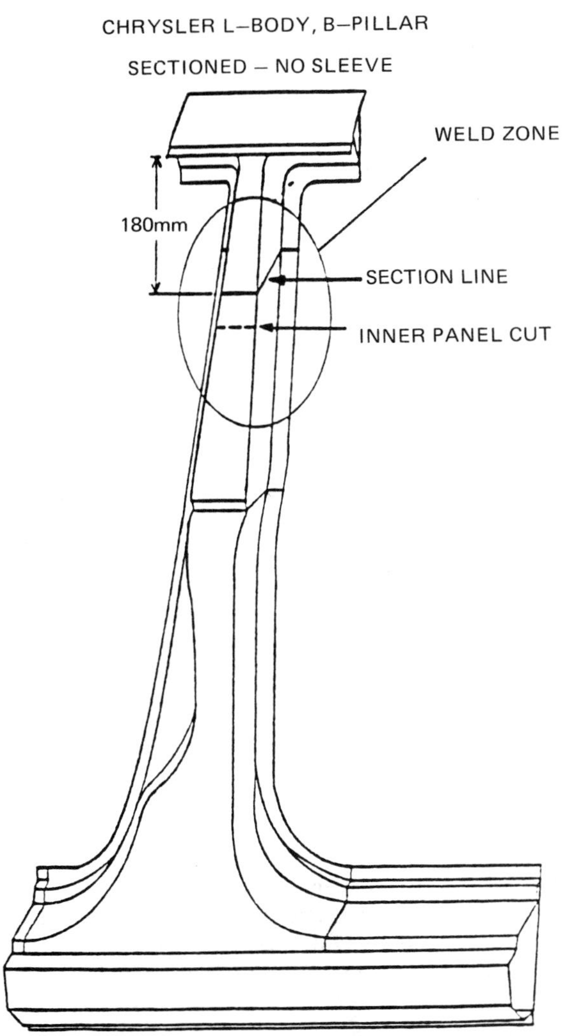

CHRYSLER L–BODY, B–PILLAR

SECTIONED – NO SLEEVE

WELD ZONE

180mm

SECTION LINE

INNER PANEL CUT

FIGURE 8-4 Area where weld-through primer should be used. (Courtesy of Inter-Industry Conference on Auto Collision Repair)

joints because they are not exposed to damage like exterior surfaces. These interior joints usually have seams that must not be treated with metal conditioner and conversion coating due to their being difficult to rinse clean. The area is allowed to air dry, after which the proper primer is applied. Due to the importance of the adhesion and corrosion resistance required by the bare sheet metal, only an approved primer should be used.

The primer that most resembles the factory E-coat system is the two-part epoxy primer or, if recommended, a self-etching primer may be used. This coat of epoxy primer is followed by any approved material used in the refinishing process. Ordinary lacquer-based primer should not be used on bare metal, even after the metal treatment, due to its inability to provide proper adhesion. Lacquer-based primers should not be used on bare metal of unibody vehicles built in the 1980s.

Replacement parts as bought from the manufacturer have a coating applied to them at the factory that is not designed to serve as a primer. The replacement parts should be primed to give good adherence of the color coat. The part should be cleaned with a wax and grease remover, and the surface is then examined for scratches or runs. If any imperfections are present, the area should be sanded smooth, but not necessarily to remove the coating applied at the factory. The panel should be scuff sanded and then the part is primed before applying the color coat. If in doubt about the coating of the part, check with the manufacturer of the part.

8-3 SEALING OF JOINTS

The joints and seams of a vehicle body must be sealed to prevent the trapping of corrosive materials, and sometimes it is required to fill sizable gaps between panels. The sealing is done after the weld area has been cleaned properly and primed as required. The next operation is the sealing of the panel joints with seam sealer, which is used to keep out exhaust fumes, dust, and water that may penetrate through gaps in the body joints. The four different types of sealers used can be separated into four slightly different types: brushable seam sealer, thin-bodied sealer, heavy-bodied sealer, and solid sealers.

Brushable seam sealers (Fig. 8-7) resist automotive fluids like brake fluid, transmission fluid, and gasoline and salt. This type of sealer is designed to hold the brushmarks and is used on interior seams where the overall appearance is not of great importance.

Thin-bodied sealers (Fig. 8-8) are used to fill seams that are less than $\frac{1}{8}$ inch (3 mm) wide. This type of sealer will remain flexible to resist vibration, but will shrink slightly to show the shape of the joint; it may be used with success in filling the gap between the roof and rear body

the sandblasting, the metal is quite rough and not as smooth as it appears; therefore, due to the roughness of the metal, it would not be possible to remove all the chemicals from the joints. Therefore, an application of two-component epoxy primer should be applied directly to the bare steel that was sandblasted.

The required vinyl wash epoxy primer is applied to the inside of the enclosed area after it has been cleaned properly. A pressure-pot spray with a wand must be used to apply the epoxy primer once the section has been welded in place. This is done through existing factory jig holes or holes drilled for that purpose, which will be closed with a plug once the job is finished. This primer should be allowed to dry per manufacturer's recommendations.

Interior exposed surfaces are cleaned thoroughly with a wax and grease removing solvent. The usual metal conditioner and conversion coating should not be used on these

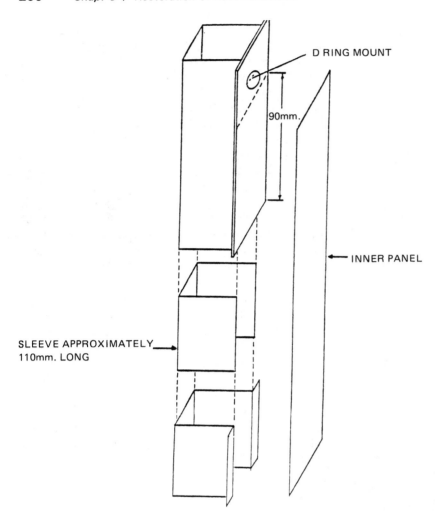

D RING MOUNT

90mm.

INNER PANEL

SLEEVE APPROXIMATELY
110mm. LONG

FIGURE 8-5 Area where weld-through primer should be used. (Courtesy of Inter-Industry Conference on Auto Collision Repair)

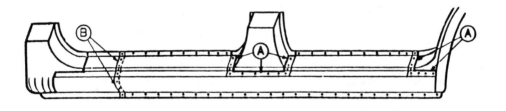

USE WELD—THROUGH PRIMER
IN ALL JOINT AREAS IF BARE STEEL

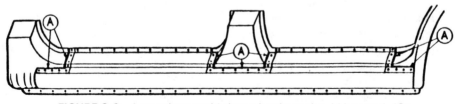

FIGURE 8-6 Area where weld-through primer should be used. (Courtesy of Inter-Industry Conference on Auto Collision Repair)

FIGURE 8-7 Use of brushable seam sealer. (Courtesy of Inter-Industry Conference on Auto Body Repair)

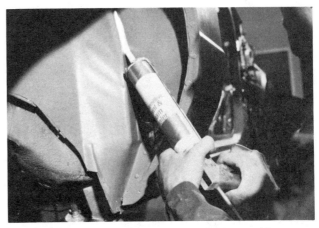

FIGURE 8-9 Heavy-bodied sealers, cartridge type. (Courtesy of Inter-Industry Conference on Auto Collision Repair)

panel on pickup trucks and must adhere to primed or bare metal. This type of sealer is usually referred to as a flow-grade or drip-check sealer.

Heavy-bodied sealers can be worked to hide an overlap seam or coach joint if required, or may be left in a bead form. This type of sealer shrinks very little, has good flexibility to withstand cracking, and does not sag easily (Fig. 8-9). It is used to fill gaps and seams that are $\frac{1}{8}$ to $\frac{1}{4}$ inch or (3 to 6 mm.) in width. It can be purchased in a solid or a squeeze tube from the suppliers of this type of material.

The last remaining sealer is the solid type. It is sold in a strip caulking shape and is designed to be pressed and worked in, usually by fingers and thumb, where it is required (Fig. 8-10). This type of sealer is used to eliminate wind, wind noises, and water leaks, usually where two panels are joined; it is flexible, resists moisture, and is paintable.

A good-quality seam sealer should be paintable and

adhere solidly to primed or bare metal. The sealer must be dry before it is painted; the required dry time will vary depending on the type of sealer, the temperature and humidity, and the thickness of application. The lower the temperature and the higher the humidity, the longer is the dry time. The sealer must also be very flexible to enable it to flex as required with the unibody components without cracking.

At times the heavier-bodied sealer must be worked to make it conform to the joint. A finger wet in water or solvent can be used to shape the material without having the sealer stick to it. A smaller type of paint brush with fairly stiff bristles should be used on brushable sealer, and it should be brushed only in one direction to make it look like a factory application. Silicone sealer should never be used to seal seams on a vehicle body. It has lower adherence than other sealers, it is not paintable, and it will attract dirt and dust gradually.

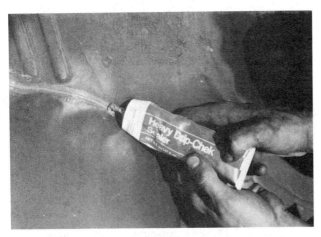

FIGURE 8-8 Thin-bodied sealers. (Courtesy of Inter-Industry Conference on Auto Collision Repair)

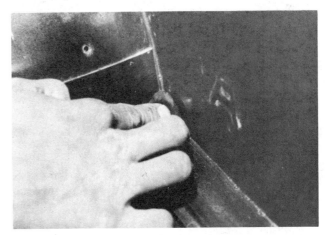

FIGURE 8-10 Use of heavy-bodied sealer. (Courtesy of Inter-Industry Conference on Auto Collision Repair)

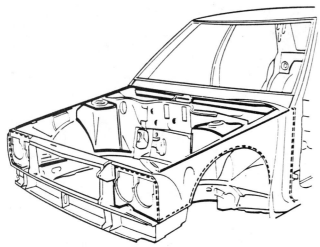

FIGURE 8-11 Sealing location for front section of the vehicle exposed joints. (Courtesy of Inter-Industry Conference on Auto Collision Repair)

Figures 8-11 through 8-14 show typical areas where the types of sealers discussed are used on unibody vehicles.

As discussed earlier, outside exposed surfaces must have greater resistance to nicks and chips than interior surfaces. Therefore, preparation for refinishing must be done properly to assure adhesion of the primer and color coat. In summary, exterior surfaces must be degreased and dried; then the metal conditioner is applied and rinsed with water. Next the conversion coating is applied, rinsed off with clean water, and then dried. Once dried, the two-part epoxy

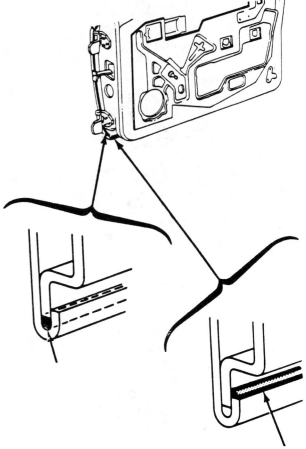

FIGURE 8-13 Sealing door seams. (Courtesy of Inter-Industry Conference on Auto Collision Repair)

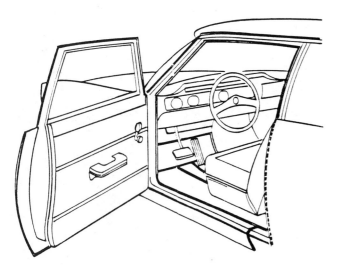

FIGURE 8-12 Sealing of seams, door opening. (Courtesy of Inter-Industry Conference on Auto Collision Repair)

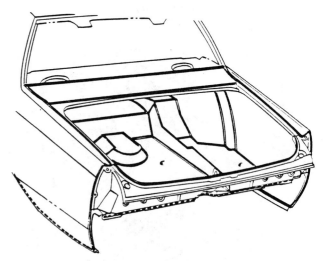

FIGURE 8-14 Sealing seams in rear section. (Courtesy of Inter-Industry Conference on Auto Collision Repair)

primer is applied, followed by primer-surfacer and the color coat to match the existing factory finish.

CAUTION: Oxides may form when dissimilar metal parts are placed together. Corrosion can occur when aluminum and stainless steel parts are installed together, and must be prevented. Manufacturers usually install barriers made of plastic pads to separate different types of metal. When holes have to be drilled in a repaired or new panel, it should be primed properly to coat the inside edge of the holes before mounting trim parts that are made of stainless steel or aluminum. There is a great variety of trim parts on the market, and if unsure of installation methods, manufacturers' manuals should be checked for proper installation.

8-4 ANTICORROSION MATERIALS AND APPLICATION

Vehicle manufacturers have been using more and better anticorrosion materials to protect their vehicles from the effects of corrosion. It is of the utmost importance that the autobody technician be able to restore them after a repair operation. The basic anticorrosion compounds are either petroleum or wax based and are applied after the color coat has dried. Manufacturer-recommended equipment should be used to apply the anticorrosion material to the inside of closed sections and underbody surfaces. The equipment used is usually an airless or pressure-feed type, but for some surfaces syphon feed is also recommended.

When anticorrosion materials are to be applied to inner closed sections, conventional syphon spray gun equipment or aerosols cannot do the type of work required, because they cannot reach the surfaces as required. This type of work requires special wands and pressure equipment so as to reach the inside cavities and joints (Figs. 8-15 and 16).

The pressure type of equipment uses compressed air to push the fluid through the wand or nozzle, which breaks it up into a fine, atomized spray pattern. This material is introduced into the inside of closed sections and, when sprayed, it is spread evenly and rapidly into the areas that require protection.

When doing a closed section, the wand is inserted into the cavity through a hole to the farthest area requiring the coating. When spraying areas such as inner fender panels, quarter-panels, or closed sections, a flexible nylon tube with nozzle should be used so as to get to all hard-to-reach areas. As soon as the spraying operation is begun, the wand is pulled out at an even rate sufficient to coat the enclosed section evenly.

Some anticorrosion materials are also effective when coating over previously rusted sections and will retard any corrosion in these areas. This is very important when repairs

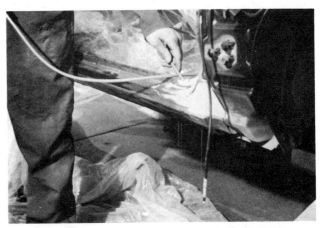

FIGURE 8-15 Applying anticorrosion material through holes to a closed section. (Courtesy of Inter-Industry Conference on Auto Collision Repair)

are done with recycled parts or an older vehicle. The size of the shop and the amount of work done will govern the type of equipment and the size of the material containers in which the material is bought.

Remember that all the recommended procedures in preparing a repaired area must be followed before the application of the anticorrosion materials. The spray equipment should be cleaned as needed, but at least once a week with a cleaning solvent or mineral spirit. The mineral spirit should be sprayed through all the wands and then hung to dry. If proper cleaning maintenance is not done, the gun and wand will become plugged and prevent any application until the equipment is cleaned properly.

When undercoating or rust proofing an area or even a whole vehicle, a checklist (Fig. 8-17A, B, C, and D) should be used so as to assure that no areas are missed. If

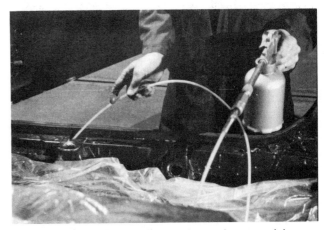

FIGURE 8-16 Applying anticorrosion material through holes into the rear lower trunk panel. (Courtesy of Inter-Industry Conference on Auto Collision Repair)

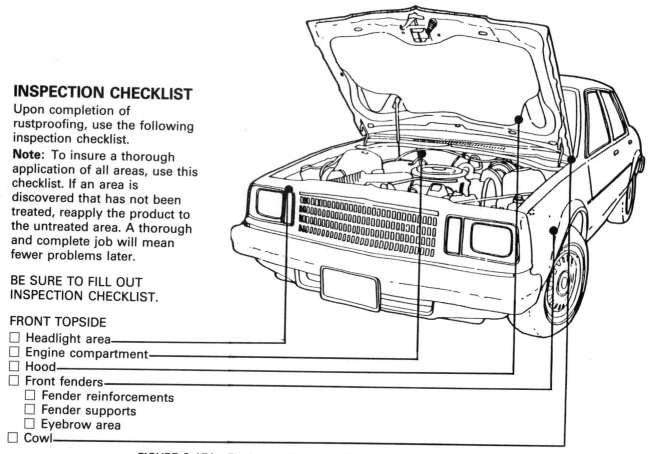

INSPECTION CHECKLIST

Upon completion of rustproofing, use the following inspection checklist.

Note: To insure a thorough application of all areas, use this checklist. If an area is discovered that has not been treated, reapply the product to the untreated area. A thorough and complete job will mean fewer problems later.

BE SURE TO FILL OUT INSPECTION CHECKLIST.

FRONT TOPSIDE
- ☐ Headlight area
- ☐ Engine compartment
- ☐ Hood
- ☐ Front fenders
  - ☐ Fender reinforcements
  - ☐ Fender supports
  - ☐ Eyebrow area
- ☐ Cowl

FIGURE 8-17A   Final inspection checklist, front top side. (Courtesy of Inter-Industry Conference on Auto Collision Repair)

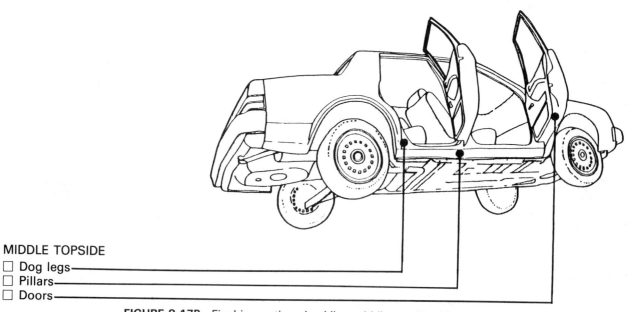

MIDDLE TOPSIDE
- ☐ Dog legs
- ☐ Pillars
- ☐ Doors

FIGURE 8-17B   Final inspection checklist, middle topside. (Courtesy of Inter-Industry Conference on Auto Collision Repair)

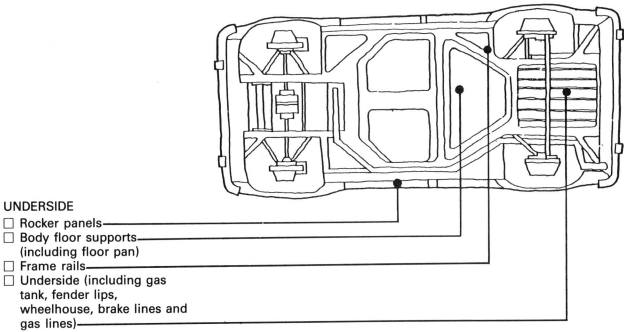

UNDERSIDE

☐ Rocker panels
☐ Body floor supports
  (including floor pan)
☐ Frame rails
☐ Underside (including gas
  tank, fender lips,
  wheelhouse, brake lines and
  gas lines)

FIGURE 8-17C Final inspection checklist, underside. (Courtesy of Inter-Industry Conference on Auto Collision Repair)

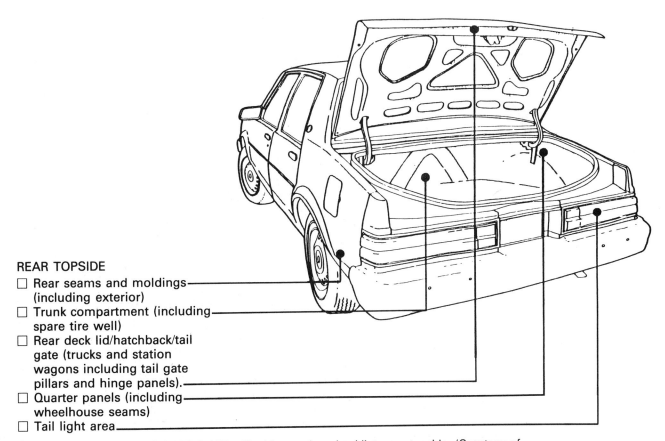

REAR TOPSIDE

☐ Rear seams and moldings
  (including exterior)
☐ Trunk compartment (including
  spare tire well)
☐ Rear deck lid/hatchback/tail
  gate (trucks and station
  wagons including tail gate
  pillars and hinge panels).
☐ Quarter panels (including
  wheelhouse seams)
☐ Tail light area

FIGURE 8-17D Final inspection checklist, rear topside. (Courtesy of Inter-Industry Conference on Auto Collision Repair)

an area is discovered that has not been treated, the material should be applied to the untreated section. Doing a good job will mean less problems later.

Spraying the underside of the vehicle, as in Fig. 8-18, should be done at a maximum pressure of 30 psi (207 kPa). However, caution must be taken not to spray the material on brake linings, brakes, and the catalytic converter. The entire underside is coated using the small wand, and the frame as well as cross members are done by inserting the long flexible wand with its 360° tip. The spraying is begun when the wand is in place and should be pulled out slowly from closed sections. The spraying is stopped when the colored end of the wand becomes visible. The exterior of the gas tank is coated, as well as the inside of the gas door and the gas filler tube area.

For the bottom panels (Fig. 8-19), a pressure of 80 psi (550 kPa) should be used. The long flexible wand with a 360° spraying tip is inserted into the rocker panel's drain holes; it may be necessary to remove the plugs if any are used. The wand is inserted and gently and smoothly pulled out as spraying begins. The spraying is stopped when the colored end of the wand becomes visible. If access is limited to the drain holes, a small wand is inserted into the drain hole and spraying is done by directing the spray in all possible directions.

When the trunk area is to be sprayed, it is usually done using an air pressure of 60 psi (415 kPa). All areas that are not to be sprayed should be covered to prevent application in the wrong area. The small wand is usually used to spray into all the existing holes; the spray gun is moved so that the material is sprayed in all directions of the trunk lid. For the bottom section of the trunk compart-

UNDERCARRIAGE OF VEHICLE

USE 30 PSI
CAUTION: DO NOT SPRAY
BRAKES, BRAKE LINING OR
CATALYTIC CONVERTER.

Coat entire underside using small wand.

Coat entire frame and cross members by inserting long flexible wand with 360° tip. When wand is in place, begin to spray while slowly pulling wand out. Stop spraying when red end of wand becomes visible.

Coat exterior of gas tank, inside gas door, and gas filler area.

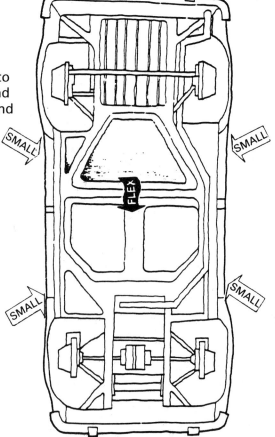

FIGURE 8-18 Spraying the underside of the vehicle. (Courtesy of Inter-Industry Conference on Auto Collision Repair)

BOTTOM PANELS

USE 80 PSI

Insert long flex wand with 360°
tip into rocker panel drain holes.
(Remove plugs, if any.) When
wand is in place, begin to spray
while slowly pulling wand out.
Stop spraying when red end of
wand becomes visible.

Note: If access is limited to
drain holes, use small wand in
drain holes, spraying in all
directions.

Coat all bottom inside panels of
vehicle including:
   Front fenders
   Rocker Panels
   Bottom area of door panels
   Bottom areas of rear quarter
     panels

FIGURE 8-19 Spraying the bottom of the vehicle using the correct wand. (Courtesy of Inter-Industry Conference on Auto Collision Repair)

ment, the inside of the quarter-panels, inside walls, and tail lights are sprayed (Fig. 8-20).

Basic Rules When Spraying Anticorrosion Material

When spraying anticorrosion material, certain methods must be used. Seat-belt retractors must be removed before spraying the coating in this particular area. Only the lower parts of the doors 2 to 4 inches (5 to 10 cm) high should be sprayed. This is done to keep the moving parts free of the rust proofer, and all windows should be closed. The corrosion material should be applied at a temperature of at least 65°F (18°C) for an ideal treatment with anticorrosion material.

Before any spraying is done, the spray pattern should be checked and if needed corrected by adjusting the air pressure. The container should always be checked before starting to see if enough material is available to complete the job. If the spraying to be done could get into the passenger area, these areas should be masked and the pressure of the spray gun reduced. To ensure that a quality job is done and to provide long-term protection, all interior cavity surfaces must be coated in the shop by a protective film. This is accomplished by using slow and even spraying

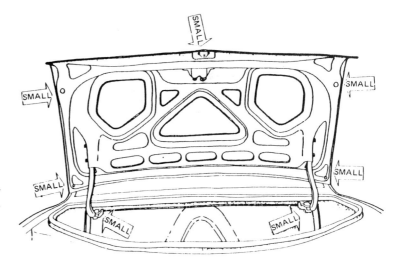

FIGURE 8-20 Spraying the inner side of the trunk lid and compartment. (Courtesy of Inter-Industry Conference on Auto Collision Repair)

of the film in the interior of these closed sections; it can be improved if required by moving the hose back and forth. The spray gun, hose, and nozzle should be cleaned with a solvent such as kerosene.

IMPORTANT: Once the anticorrosion material has dried, usually about 1 hour, all water drain holes must be cleared if required.

CAUTION NOTES: The following items should not be coated due to the reasons given.

Bumper energy-absorbing units. Foreign material on the sliding member may alter the performance of the energy-absorbing unit.

Cruise-control transducer. Foreign material could plug the filter and result in either an inoperative unit or erratic speed control.

Exhaust system. If the components of the exhaust system are coated, it may result in a fire or objectional odors.

Antenna motor drain holes or mast. If these holes are plugged, water will collect inside the motor or the mount. This trapped water will cause damage by corroding the parts or by freezing.

Propeller shaft. The propeller shaft or driveshaft should never be sprayed with undercoating as it could cause an imbalance. This could result in a vibration while the vehicle is in motion.

Vents. Coated vents, such as used on differentials or transmissions, will result in a pressure rise caused by the blockage. This rise in pressure will force fluids or lubricants past the seals of the component.

Brake drums, rotors, and backing plates. Any material sprayed on any brake friction surfaces could cause erratic braking action.

Transmission oil pan, engine oil pan, radiator, power steering cooler tube, air-conditioning condenser, and rear axle. These parts should never be sprayed. The coating will result in higher operating temperatures and shorten the service of the component.

Air filters. Coating will shorten the life of the filter.

Door latch mechanism. Coating sprayed on this component will cause it to be hard-operating or binding.

Seat-belt retractors. Many vehicles have seat-belt retractors located in the quarter-panel behind the body lock pillar. Coating in this area could stop the retractors from working and cause appearance problems. If they are in the way of the spray operation, the retractors should be removed.

QUESTIONS

8-1. What type of primer is used at the factory to protect the body of vehicles?

8-2. To what thickness is the E-coat primer applied at the factory?

8-3. What is used to treat metal before priming it?

8-4. What causes the corrosion of the steel used in the vehicle body?

8-5. How is the repaired area cleaned to assure adherence from the start of the repair to the application of the color coat?

8-6. Explain how zinc is used to protect steel.

8-7. What should be used to clean the weld zone?

8-8. What is a conversion coating and how is it applied?

8-9. How are closed sections prepared for the repair operation?

8-10. What type of primer should be used to give protection to the steel before welding is done?

8-11. Describe how an enclosed area is protected to prevent corrosion after repairs have been done.

8-12. What type of primer must be used on base steel to get maximum adherence?

8-13. What type of sealer may be used to fill the gaps when a quarter-panel is installed?

8-14. What is used to prevent corrosion from occurring between aluminum and steel?

8-15. Describe how an enclosed area is sprayed with anticorrosion material using a pressure-feed gun.

Labor Conversion Chart and Metric Tables

*Pages 276–279 are reproduced courtesy of Mitchell Information Services, Inc.

CONVERSION TABLE

C1

Operation Allowances to Dollars

FOR DOLLAR RATES ENDING WITH 50 CENTS, ADD THIS COLUMN TO YOUR RATE COLUMN.

Time	$10	$11	$12	$13	$14	$15	$16	$17	$18	$19	$20	.50	$21	$22	$23	$24	$25	$26	$27	$28	$29	$30
0.1	1.00	1.10	1.20	1.30	1.40	1.50	1.60	1.70	1.80	1.90	2.00	.05	2.10	2.20	2.30	2.40	2.50	2.60	2.70	2.80	2.90	3.00
0.2	2.00	2.20	2.40	2.60	2.80	3.00	3.20	3.40	3.60	3.80	4.00	.10	4.20	4.40	4.60	4.80	5.00	5.20	5.40	5.60	5.80	6.00
0.3	3.00	3.30	3.60	3.90	4.20	4.50	4.80	5.10	5.40	5.70	6.00	.15	6.30	6.60	6.90	7.20	7.50	7.80	8.10	8.40	8.70	9.00
0.4	4.00	4.40	4.80	5.20	5.60	6.00	6.40	6.80	7.20	7.60	8.00	.20	8.40	8.80	9.20	9.60	10.00	10.40	10.80	11.20	11.60	12.00
0.5	5.00	5.50	6.00	6.50	7.00	7.50	8.00	8.50	9.00	9.50	10.00	.25	10.50	11.00	11.50	12.00	12.50	13.00	13.50	14.00	14.50	15.00
0.6	6.00	6.60	7.20	7.80	8.40	9.00	9.60	10.20	10.80	11.40	12.00	.30	12.60	13.20	13.80	14.40	15.00	15.60	16.20	16.80	17.40	18.00
0.7	7.00	7.70	8.40	9.10	9.80	10.50	11.20	11.90	12.60	13.30	14.00	.35	14.70	15.40	16.10	16.80	17.50	18.20	18.90	19.60	20.30	21.00
0.8	8.00	8.80	9.60	10.40	11.20	12.00	12.80	13.60	14.40	15.20	16.00	.40	16.80	17.60	18.40	19.20	20.00	20.80	21.60	22.40	23.20	24.00
0.9	9.00	9.90	10.80	11.70	12.60	13.50	14.40	15.30	16.20	17.10	18.00	.45	18.90	19.80	20.70	21.60	22.50	23.40	24.30	25.20	26.10	27.00
1.0	10.00	11.00	12.00	13.00	14.00	15.00	16.00	17.00	18.00	19.00	20.00	.50	21.00	22.00	23.00	24.00	25.00	26.00	27.00	28.00	29.00	30.00
1.1	11.00	12.10	13.20	14.30	15.40	16.50	17.60	18.70	19.80	20.90	22.00	.55	23.10	24.20	25.30	26.40	27.50	28.60	29.70	30.80	31.90	33.00
1.2	12.00	13.20	14.40	15.60	16.80	18.00	19.20	20.40	21.60	22.80	24.00	.60	25.20	26.40	27.60	28.80	30.00	31.20	32.40	33.60	34.80	36.00
1.3	13.00	14.30	15.60	16.90	18.20	19.50	20.80	22.10	23.40	24.70	26.00	.65	27.30	28.60	29.90	31.20	32.50	33.80	35.10	36.40	37.70	39.00
1.4	14.00	15.40	16.80	18.20	19.60	21.00	22.40	23.80	25.20	26.60	28.00	.70	29.40	30.80	32.20	33.60	35.00	36.40	37.80	39.20	40.60	42.00
1.5	15.00	16.50	18.00	19.50	21.00	22.50	24.00	25.50	27.00	28.50	30.00	.75	31.50	33.00	34.50	36.00	37.50	39.00	40.50	42.00	43.50	45.00
1.6	16.00	17.60	19.20	20.80	22.40	24.00	25.60	27.20	28.80	30.40	32.00	.80	33.60	35.20	36.80	38.40	40.00	41.60	43.20	44.80	46.40	48.00
1.7	17.00	18.70	20.40	22.10	23.80	25.50	27.20	28.90	30.60	32.30	34.00	.85	35.70	37.40	39.10	40.80	42.50	44.20	45.90	47.60	49.30	51.00
1.8	18.00	19.80	21.60	23.40	25.20	27.00	28.80	30.60	32.40	34.20	36.00	.90	37.80	39.60	41.40	43.20	45.00	46.80	48.60	50.40	52.20	54.00
1.9	19.00	20.90	22.80	24.70	26.60	28.50	30.40	32.30	34.20	36.10	38.00	.95	39.90	41.80	43.70	45.60	47.50	49.40	51.30	53.20	55.10	57.00
2.0	20.00	22.00	24.00	26.00	28.00	30.00	32.00	34.00	36.00	38.00	40.00	1.00	42.00	44.00	46.00	48.00	50.00	52.00	54.00	56.00	58.00	60.00
2.1	21.00	23.10	25.20	27:30	29.40	31.50	33.60	35.70	37.80	39.90	42.00	1.05	44.10	46.20	48.30	50.40	52.50	54.60	56.70	58.80	60.90	63.00
2.2	22.00	24.20	26.40	28.60	30.80	33.00	35.20	37.40	39.60	41.80	44.00	1.10	46.20	48.40	50.60	52.80	55.00	57.20	59.40	61.60	63.80	66.00
2.3	23.00	25.30	27.60	29.90	32.20	34.50	36.80	39.10	41.40	43.70	46.00	1.15	48.30	50.60	52.90	55.20	57.50	59.80	62.10	64.40	66.70	69.00
2.4	24.00	26.40	28.80	31.20	33.60	36.00	38.40	40.80	43.20	45.60	48.00	1.20	50.40	52.80	55.20	57.60	60.00	62.40	64.80	67.20	69.60	72.00
2.5	25.00	27.50	30.00	32.50	35.00	37.50	40.00	42.50	45.00	47.50	50.00	1.25	52.50	55.00	57.50	60.00	62.50	65.00	67.50	70.00	72.50	75.00
2.6	26.00	28.60	31.20	33.80	36.40	39.00	41.60	44.20	46.80	49.40	52.00	1.30	54.60	57.20	59.80	62.40	65.00	67.60	70.20	72.80	75.40	78.00
2.7	27.00	29.70	32.40	35.10	37.80	40.50	43.20	45.90	48.60	51.30	54.00	1.35	56.70	59.40	62.10	64.80	67.50	70.20	72.90	75.60	78.30	81.00
2.8	28.00	30.80	33.60	36.40	39.20	42.00	44.80	47.60	50.40	53.20	56.00	1.40	58.80	61.60	64.40	67.20	70.00	72.80	75.60	78.40	81.20	84.00
2.9	29.00	31.90	34.80	37.70	40.60	43.50	46.40	49.30	52.20	55.10	58.00	1.45	60.90	63.80	66.70	69.60	72.50	75.40	78.30	81.20	84.10	87.00
3.0	30.00	33.00	36.00	39.00	42.00	45.00	48.00	51.00	54.00	57.00	60.00	1.50	63.00	66.00	69.00	72.00	75.00	78.00	81.00	84.00	87.00	90.00
3.1	31.00	34.10	37.20	40.30	43.40	46.50	49.60	52.70	55.80	58.90	62.00	1.55	65.10	68.20	71.30	74.40	77.50	80.60	83.70	86.80	89.90	93.00
3.2	32.00	35.20	38.40	41.60	44.80	48.00	51.20	54.40	57.60	60.80	64.00	1.60	67.20	70.40	73.60	76.80	80.00	83.20	86.40	89.60	92.80	96.00
3.3	33.00	36.30	39.60	42.90	46.20	49.50	52.80	56.10	59.40	62.70	66.00	1.65	69.30	72.60	75.90	79.20	82.50	85.80	89.10	92.40	95.70	99.00
3.4	34.00	37.40	40.80	44.20	47.60	51.00	54.40	57.80	61.20	64.60	68.00	1.70	71.40	74.80	78.20	81.60	85.00	88.40	91.80	95.20	98.60	102.00
3.5	35.00	38.50	42.00	45.50	49.00	52.50	56.00	59.50	63.00	66.50	70.00	1.75	73.50	77.00	80.50	84.00	87.50	91.00	94.50	98.00	101.50	105.00
3.6	36.00	39.60	43.20	46.80	50.40	54.00	57.60	61.20	64.80	68.40	72.00	1.80	75.60	79.20	82.80	86.40	90.00	93.60	97.20	100.80	104.40	108.00
3.7	37.00	40.70	44.40	48.10	51.80	55.50	59.20	62.90	66.60	70.30	74.00	1.85	77.70	81.40	85.10	88.80	92.50	96.20	99.90	103.60	107.30	111.00
3.8	38.00	41.80	45.60	49.40	53.20	57.00	60.80	64.60	68.40	72.20	76.00	1.90	79.80	83.60	87.40	91.20	95.00	98.80	102.60	106.40	110.20	114.00
3.9	39.00	42.90	46.80	50.70	54.60	58.50	62.40	66.30	70.20	74.10	78.00	1.95	81.90	85.80	89.70	93.60	97.50	101.40	105.30	109.20	113.10	117.00
4.0	40.00	44.00	48.00	52.00	56.00	60.00	64.00	68.00	72.00	76.00	80.00	2.00	84.00	88.00	92.00	96.00	100.00	104.00	108.00	112.00	116.00	120.00
4.1	41.00	45.10	49.20	53.30	57.40	61.50	65.60	69.70	73.80	77.90	82.00	2.05	86.10	90.20	94.30	98.40	102.50	106.60	110.70	114.80	118.90	123.00
4.2	42.00	46.20	50.40	54.60	58.80	63.00	67.20	71.40	75.60	79.80	84.00	2.10	88.20	92.40	96.60	100.80	105.00	109.20	113.40	117.60	121.80	126.00
4.3	43.00	47.30	51.60	55.90	60.20	64.50	68.80	73.10	77.40	81.70	86.00	2.15	90.30	94.60	98.90	103.20	107.50	111.80	116.10	120.40	124.70	129.00
4.4	44.00	48.40	52.80	57.20	61.60	66.00	70.40	74.80	79.20	83.60	88.00	2.20	92.40	96.80	101.20	105.60	110.00	114.40	118.80	123.20	127.60	132.00
4.5	45.00	49.50	54.00	58.50	63.00	67.50	72.00	76.50	81.00	85.50	90.00	2.25	94.50	99.00	103.50	108.00	112.50	117.00	121.50	126.00	130.50	135.00
4.6	46.00	50.60	55.20	59.80	64.40	69.00	73.60	78.20	82.80	87.40	92.00	2.30	96.60	101.20	105.80	110.40	115.00	119.60	124.20	128.80	133.40	138.00
4.7	47.00	51.70	56.40	61.10	65.80	70.50	75.20	79.90	84.60	89.30	94.00	2.35	98.70	103.40	108.10	112.80	117.50	122.20	126.90	131.60	136.30	141.00
4.8	48.00	52.80	57.60	62.40	67.20	72.00	76.80	81.60	86.40	91.20	96.00	2.40	100.80	105.60	110.40	115.20	120.00	124.80	129.60	134.40	139.20	144.00
4.9	49.00	53.90	58.80	63.70	68.60	73.50	78.40	83.30	88.20	93.10	98.00	2.45	102.90	107.80	112.70	117.60	122.50	127.40	132.30	137.20	142.10	147.00
5.0	50.00	55.00	60.00	65.00	70.00	75.60	80.00	85.00	90.00	95.00	100.00	2.50	105.00	110.00	115.00	120.00	125.00	130.00	135.00	140.00	145.00	150.00
5.1	51.00	56.10	61.20	66.30	71.40	76.50	81.60	86.70	91.80	96.90	102.00	2.55	107.10	112.20	117.30	122.40	127.50	132.60	137.70	142.80	147.90	153.00
5.2	52.00	57.20	62.40	67.60	72.80	78.00	83.20	88.40	93.60	98.80	104.00	2.60	109.20	114.40	119.60	124.80	130.00	135.20	140.40	145.60	150.80	156.00
5.3	53.00	58.30	63.60	68.90	74.20	79.50	84.80	90.10	95.40	100.70	106.00	2.65	111.30	116.60	121.90	127.20	132.50	137.80	143.10	148.40	153.70	159.00
5.4	54.00	59.40	64.80	70.20	75.60	81.00	86.40	91.80	97.20	102.60	108.00	2.70	113.40	118.80	124.20	129.60	135.00	140.40	145.80	151.20	156.60	162.00
5.5	55.00	60.50	66.00	71.50	77.00	82.50	88.00	93.50	99.00	104.50	110.00	2.75	115.50	121.00	126.50	132.00	137.50	143.00	148.50	154.00	159.50	165.00
5.6	56.00	61.60	67.20	72.80	78.40	84.00	89.60	95.20	100.80	106.40	112.00	2.80	117.60	123.20	128.80	134.40	140.00	145.60	151.20	156.80	162.40	168.00
5.7	57.00	62.70	68.40	74.10	79.80	85.50	91.20	96.90	102.60	108.30	114.00	2.85	119.70	125.40	131.10	136.80	142.50	148.20	153.90	159.60	165.30	171.00
5.8	58.00	63.80	69.60	75.40	81.20	87.00	92.80	98.60	104.40	110.20	116.00	2.90	121.80	127.60	133.40	139.20	145.00	150.80	156.60	162.40	168.20	174.00
5.9	59.00	64.90	70.80	76.70	82.60	88.50	94.40	100.30	106.20	112.10	118.00	2.95	123.90	129.80	135.70	141.60	147.50	153.40	159.30	165.20	171.10	177.00
6.0	60.00	66.00	72.00	78.00	84.00	90.00	96.00	102.00	108.00	114.00	120.00	3.00	126.00	132.00	138.00	144.00	150.00	156.00	162.00	168.00	174.00	180.00
6.1	61.00	67.10	73.20	79.30	85.40	91.50	97.60	103.70	109.80	115.90	122.00	3.05	128.10	134.20	140.30	146.40	152.50	158.60	164.70	170.80	176.90	183.00
6.2	62.00	68.20	74.40	80.60	86.80	93.00	99.20	105.40	111.60	117.80	124.00	3.10	130.20	136.40	142.60	148.80	155.00	161.20	167.40	173.60	179.80	186.00
6.3	63.00	69.30	75.60	81.90	88.20	94.50	100.80	107.10	113.40	119.70	126.00	3.15	132.30	138.60	144.90	151.20	157.50	163.80	170.10	176.40	182.70	189.00
6.4	64.00	70.40	76.80	83.20	89.60	96.00	102.40	108.80	115.20	121.60	128.00	3.20	134.40	140.80	147.20	153.60	160.00	166.40	172.80	179.20	185.60	192.00

C-2

CONVERSION TABLE

Operation Allowances to Dollars

FOR DOLLAR RATES ENDING WITH 50 CENTS, ADD THIS COLUMN TO YOUR RATE COLUMN.

Time	$10	$11	$12	$13	$14	$15	$16	$17	$18	$19	$20	.50	$21	$22	$23	$24	$25	$26	$27	$28	$29	$30
6.5	65.00	71.50	78.00	84.50	91.00	97.50	104.00	110.50	117.00	123.50	130.00	3.25	136.50	143.00	149.50	156.00	162.50	169.00	175.50	182.00	188.50	195.00
6.6	66.00	72.60	79.20	85.80	92.40	99.00	105.60	112.20	118.80	125.40	132.00	3.30	138.60	145.20	151.80	158.40	165.00	171.60	178.20	184.80	191.40	198.00
6.7	67.00	73.70	80.40	87.10	93.80	100.50	107.20	113.90	120.60	127.30	134.00	3.35	140.70	147.40	154.10	160.80	167.50	174.20	180.90	187.60	194.30	201.00
6.8	68.00	74.80	81.60	88.40	95.20	102.00	108.80	115.60	122.40	129.20	136.00	3.40	142.80	149.60	156.40	163.20	170.00	176.80	183.60	190.40	197.20	204.00
6.9	69.00	75.90	82.80	89.70	96.60	103.50	110.40	117.30	124.20	131.10	138.00	3.45	144.90	151.80	158.70	165.60	172.50	179.40	186.30	193.20	200.10	207.00
7.0	70.00	77.00	84.00	91.00	98.00	105.00	112.00	119.00	126.00	133.00	140.00	3.50	147.00	154.00	161.00	168.00	175.00	182.00	189.00	196.00	203.00	210.00
7.1	71.00	78.10	85.20	92.30	99.40	106.50	113.60	120.70	127.80	134.90	142.00	3.55	149.10	156.20	163.30	170.40	177.50	184.60	191.70	198.80	205.90	213.00
7.2	72.00	79.20	86.40	93.60	100.80	108.00	115.20	122.40	129.60	136.80	144.00	3.60	151.20	158.40	165.60	172.80	180.00	187.20	194.40	201.60	208.80	216.00
7.3	73.00	80.30	87.60	94.90	102.20	109.50	116.80	124.10	131.40	138.70	146.00	3.65	153.30	160.60	167.90	175.20	182.50	189.80	197.10	204.40	211.70	219.00
7.4	74.00	81.40	88.80	96.20	103.60	111.00	118.40	125.80	133.20	140.60	148.00	3.70	155.40	162.80	170.20	177.60	185.00	192.40	199.80	207.20	214.60	222.00
7.5	75.00	82.50	90.00	97.50	105.00	112.50	120.00	127.50	135.00	142.50	150.00	3.75	157.50	165.00	172.50	180.00	187.50	195.00	202.50	210.00	217.50	225.00
7.6	76.00	83.60	91.20	98.80	106.40	114.00	121.60	129.20	136.80	144.40	152.00	3.80	159.60	167.20	174.80	182.40	190.00	197.60	205.20	212.80	220.40	228.00
7.7	77.00	84.70	92.40	100.10	107.80	115.50	123.20	130.90	138.60	146.30	154.00	3.85	161.70	169.40	177.10	184.80	192.50	200.20	207.90	215.60	223.30	231.00
7.8	78.00	85.80	93.60	101.40	109.20	117.00	124.80	132.60	140.40	148.20	156.00	3.90	163.80	171.60	179.40	187.20	195.00	202.80	210.60	218.40	226.20	234.00
7.9	79.00	86.90	94.80	102.70	110.60	118.50	126.40	134.30	142.20	150.10	158.00	3.95	165.90	173.80	181.70	189.60	197.50	205.40	213.30	221.20	229.10	237.00
8.0	80.00	88.00	96.00	104.00	112.00	120.00	128.00	136.00	144.00	152.00	160.00	4.00	168.00	176.00	184.00	192.00	200.00	208.00	216.00	224.00	232.00	240.00
8.1	81.00	89.10	97.20	105.30	113.40	121.50	129.60	137.70	145.80	153.90	162.00	4.05	170.10	178.20	186.30	194.40	202.50	210.60	218.70	226.80	234.90	243.00
8.2	82.00	90.20	98.40	106.60	114.80	123.00	131.20	139.40	147.60	155.80	164.00	4.10	172.20	180.40	188.60	196.80	205.00	213.20	221.40	229.60	237.80	246.00
8.3	83.00	91.30	99.60	107.90	116.20	124.50	132.80	141.10	149.40	157.70	166.00	4.15	174.30	182.60	190.90	199.20	207.50	215.80	224.10	232.40	240.70	249.00
8.4	84.00	92.40	100.80	109.20	117.60	126.00	134.40	142.80	151.20	159.60	168.00	4.20	176.40	184.80	193.20	201.60	210.00	218.40	226.80	235.20	243.60	252.00
8.5	85.00	93.50	102.00	110.50	119.00	127.50	136.00	144.50	153.00	161.50	170.00	4.25	178.50	187.00	195.50	204.00	212.50	221.00	229.50	238.00	246.50	255.00
8.6	86.00	94.60	103.20	111.80	120.40	129.00	137.60	146.20	154.80	163.40	172.00	4.30	180.60	189.20	197.80	206.40	215.00	223.60	232.20	240.80	249.40	258.00
8.7	87.00	95.70	104.40	113.10	121.80	130.50	139.20	147.90	156.60	165.30	174.00	4.35	182.70	191.40	200.10	208.80	217.50	226.20	234.90	243.60	252.30	261.00
8.8	88.00	96.80	105.60	114.40	123.20	132.00	140.80	149.60	158.40	167.20	176.00	4.40	184.80	193.60	202.40	211.20	220.00	228.80	237.60	246.40	255.20	264.00
8.9	89.00	97.90	106.80	115.70	124.60	133.50	142.40	151.30	160.20	169.10	178.00	4.45	186.90	195.80	204.70	213.60	222.50	231.40	240.30	249.20	258.10	267.00
9.0	90.00	99.00	108.00	117.00	126.00	135.00	144.00	153.00	162.00	171.00	180.00	4.50	189.00	198.00	207.00	216.00	225.00	234.00	243.00	252.00	261.00	270.00
9.1	91.00	100.10	109.20	118.30	127.40	136.50	145.60	154.70	163.80	172.90	182.00	4.55	191.10	200.20	209.30	218.40	227.50	236.60	245.70	254.80	263.90	273.00
9.2	92.00	101.20	110.40	119.60	128.80	138.00	147.20	156.40	165.60	174.80	184.00	4.60	193.20	202.40	211.60	220.80	230.00	239.20	248.40	257.60	266.80	276.00
9.3	93.00	102.30	111.60	120.90	130.20	139.50	148.80	158.10	167.40	176.70	186.00	4.65	195.30	204.60	213.90	223.20	232.50	241.80	251.10	260.40	269.70	279.00
9.4	94.00	103.40	112.80	122.20	131.60	141.00	150.40	159.80	169.20	178.60	188.00	4.70	197.40	206.80	216.20	225.60	235.00	244.40	253.80	263.20	272.60	282.00
9.5	95.00	104.50	114.00	123.50	133.00	142.50	152.00	161.50	171.00	180.50	190.00	4.75	199.50	209.00	218.50	228.00	237.50	247.00	256.50	266.00	275.50	285.00
9.6	96.00	105.60	115.20	124.80	134.40	144.00	153.60	163.20	172.80	182.40	192.00	4.80	201.60	211.20	220.80	230.40	240.00	249.60	259.20	268.80	278.40	288.00
9.7	97.00	106.70	116.40	126.10	135.80	145.50	155.20	164.90	174.60	184.30	194.00	4.85	203.70	213.40	223.10	232.80	242.50	252.20	261.90	271.60	281.30	291.00
9.8	98.00	107.80	117.60	127.40	137.20	147.00	156.80	166.60	176.40	186.20	196.00	4.90	205.80	215.60	225.40	235.20	245.00	254.80	264.60	274.40	284.20	294.00
9.9	99.00	108.90	118.80	128.70	138.60	148.50	158.40	168.30	178.20	188.10	198.00	4.95	207.90	217.80	227.70	237.60	247.50	257.40	267.30	277.20	287.10	297.00
10.0	100.00	110.00	120.00	130.00	140.00	150.00	160.00	170.00	180.00	190.00	200.00	5.00	210.00	220.00	230.00	240.00	250.00	260.00	270.00	280.00	290.00	300.00
10.5	105.00	115.50	126.00	136.50	147.00	157.50	168.00	178.50	189.00	199.50	210.00	5.25	220.50	231.00	241.50	252.00	262.50	273.00	283.50	294.00	304.50	315.00
11.0	110.00	121.00	132.00	143.00	154.00	165.00	176.00	187.00	198.00	209.00	220.00	5.50	231.00	242.00	253.00	264.00	275.00	286.00	297.00	308.00	319.00	330.00
11.5	115.00	126.50	138.00	149.50	161.00	172.50	184.00	195.50	207.00	218.50	230.00	5.75	241.50	253.00	264.50	276.00	287.50	299.00	310.50	322.00	333.50	345.00
12.0	120.00	132.00	144.00	156.00	168.00	180.00	192.00	204.00	216.00	228.00	240.00	6.00	252.00	264.00	276.00	288.00	300.00	312.00	324.00	336.00	348.00	360.00
12.5	125.00	137.50	150.00	162.50	175.00	187.50	200.00	212.50	225.00	237.50	250.00	6.25	262.50	275.00	287.50	300.00	312.50	325.00	337.50	350.00	362.50	375.00
13.0	130.00	143.00	156.00	169.00	182.00	195.00	208.00	221.00	234.00	247.00	260.00	6.50	273.00	286.00	299.00	312.00	325.00	338.00	351.00	364.00	377.00	390.00
13.5	135.00	148.50	162.00	175.50	189.00	202.50	216.00	229.50	243.00	256.50	270.00	6.75	283.50	297.00	310.50	324.00	337.50	351.00	364.50	378.00	391.50	405.00
14.0	140.00	154.00	168.00	182.00	196.00	210.00	224.00	238.00	252.00	266.00	280.00	7.00	294.00	308.00	322.00	336.00	350.00	364.00	378.00	392.00	406.00	420.00
14.5	145.00	159.50	174.00	188.50	203.00	217.50	232.00	246.50	261.00	275.50	290.00	7.25	304.50	319.00	333.50	348.00	362.50	377.00	391.50	406.00	420.50	435.00
15.0	150.00	165.00	180.00	195.00	210.00	225.00	240.00	255.00	270.00	285.00	300.00	7.50	315.00	330.00	345.00	360.00	375.00	390.00	405.00	420.00	435.00	450.00
15.5	155.00	170.50	186.00	201.50	217.00	232.50	248.00	263.50	279.00	294.50	310.00	7.75	325.50	341.00	356.50	372.00	387.50	403.00	418.50	434.00	449.50	465.00
16.0	160.00	176.00	192.00	208.00	224.00	240.00	256.00	272.00	288.00	304.00	320.00	8.00	336.00	352.00	368.00	384.00	400.00	416.00	432.00	448.00	464.00	480.00
16.5	165.00	181.50	198.00	214.50	231.00	247.50	264.00	280.50	297.00	313.50	330.00	8.25	346.50	363.00	379.50	396.00	412.50	429.00	445.50	462.00	478.50	495.00
17.0	170.00	187.00	204.00	221.00	238.00	255.00	272.00	289.00	306.00	323.00	340.00	8.50	357.00	374.00	391.00	408.00	425.00	442.00	459.00	476.00	493.00	510.00
17.5	175.00	192.50	210.00	227.50	245.00	262.50	280.00	297.50	315.00	332.50	350.00	8.75	367.50	385.00	402.50	420.00	437.50	455.00	472.50	490.00	507.50	525.00
18.0	180.00	198.00	216.00	234.00	252.00	270.00	288.00	306.00	324.00	342.00	360.00	9.00	378.00	396.00	414.00	432.00	450.00	468.00	486.00	504.00	522.00	540.00
18.5	185.00	203.50	222.00	240.50	259.00	277.50	296.00	314.50	333.00	351.50	370.00	9.25	388.50	407.00	425.50	444.00	462.50	481.00	499.50	518.00	536.50	555.00
19.0	190.00	209.00	228.00	247.00	266.00	285.00	304.00	323.00	342.00	361.00	380.00	9.50	399.00	418.00	437.00	456.00	475.00	494.00	513.00	532.00	551.00	570.00
19.5	195.00	214.50	234.00	253.50	273.00	292.50	312.00	331.50	351.00	370.50	390.00	9.75	409.50	429.00	448.50	468.00	487.50	507.00	526.50	546.00	565.50	585.00
20.0	200.00	220.00	240.00	260.00	280.00	300.00	320.00	340.00	360.00	380.00	400.00	10.00	420.00	440.00	460.00	480.00	500.00	520.00	540.00	560.00	580.00	600.00
30.0	300.00	330.00	360.00	390.00	420.00	450.00	480.00	510.00	540.00	570.00	600.00	15.00	630.00	660.00	690.00	720.00	750.00	780.00	810.00	840.00	870.00	900.00
40.0	400.00	440.00	480.00	520.00	560.00	600.00	640.00	680.00	720.00	760.00	800.00	20.00	840.00	880.00	920.00	960.00	1000.00	1040.00	1080.00	1120.00	1160.00	1200.00

CONVERSION TABLE

C-3

Operation Allowances to Dollars

FOR DOLLAR RATES ENDING WITH 50 CENTS, ADD THIS COLUMN TO YOUR RATE COLUMN.

Time	$31	$32	$33	$34	$35	$36	$37	$38	$39	$40	.50	$41	$42	$43	$44	$45	$46	$47	$48	$49	$50
0.1	3.10	3.20	3.30	3.40	3.50	3.60	3.70	3.80	3.90	4.00	.05	4.10	4.20	4.30	4.40	4.50	4.60	4.70	4.80	4.90	5.00
0.2	6.20	6.40	6.60	6.80	7.00	7.20	7.40	7.60	7.80	8.00	.10	8.20	8.40	8.60	8.80	9.00	9.20	9.40	9.60	9.80	10.00
0.3	9.30	9.60	9.90	10.20	10.50	10.80	11.10	11.40	11.70	12.00	.15	12.30	12.60	12.90	13.20	13.50	13.80	14.10	14.40	14.70	15.00
0.4	12.40	12.80	13.20	13.60	14.00	14.40	14.80	15.20	15.60	16.00	.20	16.40	16.80	17.20	17.60	18.00	18.40	18.80	19.20	19.60	20.00
0.5	15.50	16.00	16.50	17.00	17.50	18.00	18.50	19.00	19.50	20.00	.25	20.50	21.00	21.50	22.00	22.50	23.00	23.50	24.00	24.50	25.00
0.6	18.60	19.20	19.80	20.40	21.00	21.60	22.20	22.80	23.40	24.00	.30	24.60	25.20	25.80	26.40	27.00	27.60	28.20	28.80	29.40	30.00
0.7	21.70	22.40	23.10	23.80	24.50	25.20	25.90	26.60	27.30	28.00	.35	28.70	29.40	30.10	30.80	31.50	32.20	32.90	33.60	34.30	35.00
0.8	24.80	25.60	26.40	27.20	28.00	28.80	29.60	30.40	31.20	32.00	.40	32.80	33.60	34.40	35.20	36.00	36.80	37.60	38.40	39.20	40.00
0.9	27.90	28.80	29.70	30.60	31.50	32.40	33.30	34.20	35.10	36.00	.45	36.90	37.80	38.70	39.60	40.50	41.40	42.30	43.20	44.10	45.00
1.0	31.00	32.00	33.00	34.00	35.00	36.00	37.00	38.00	39.00	40.00	.50	41.00	42.00	43.00	44.00	45.00	46.00	47.00	48.00	49.00	50.00
1.1	34.10	35.20	36.30	37.40	38.50	39.60	40.70	41.80	42.90	44.00	.55	45.10	46.20	47.30	48.40	49.50	50.60	51.70	52.80	53.90	55.00
1.2	37.20	38.40	39.60	40.80	42.00	43.20	44.40	45.60	46.80	48.00	.60	49.20	50.40	51.60	52.80	54.00	55.20	56.40	57.60	58.80	60.00
1.3	40.30	41.60	42.90	44.20	45.50	46.80	48.10	49.40	50.70	52.00	.65	53.30	54.60	55.90	57.20	58.50	59.80	61.10	62.40	63.70	65.00
1.4	43.40	44.80	46.20	47.60	49.00	50.40	51.80	53.20	54.60	56.00	.70	57.40	58.80	60.20	61.60	63.00	64.40	65.80	67.20	68.60	70.00
1.5	46.50	48.00	49.50	51.00	52.50	54.00	55.50	57.00	58.50	60.00	.75	61.50	63.00	64.50	66.00	67.50	69.00	70.50	72.00	73.50	75.00
1.6	49.60	51.20	52.80	54.40	56.00	57.60	59.20	60.80	62.40	64.00	.80	65.60	67.20	68.80	70.40	72.00	73.60	75.20	76.80	78.40	80.00
1.7	52.70	54.40	56.10	57.80	59.50	61.20	62.90	64.60	66.30	68.00	.85	69.70	71.40	73.10	74.80	76.50	78.20	79.90	81.60	83.30	85.00
1.8	55.80	57.60	59.40	61.20	63.00	64.80	66.60	68.40	70.20	72.00	.90	73.80	75.60	77.40	79.20	81.00	82.80	84.60	86.40	88.20	90.00
1.9	58.90	60.80	62.70	64.60	66.50	68.40	70.30	72.20	74.10	76.00	.95	77.90	79.80	81.70	83.60	85.50	87.40	89.30	91.20	93.10	95.00
2.0	62.00	64.00	66.00	68.00	70.00	72.00	74.00	76.00	78.00	80.00	1.00	82.00	84.00	86.00	88.00	90.00	92.00	94.00	96.00	98.00	100.00
2.1	65.10	67.20	69.30	71.40	73.50	75.60	77.70	79.80	81.90	84.00	1.05	86.10	88.20	90.30	92.40	94.50	96.60	98.70	100.80	102.90	105.00
2.2	68.20	70.40	72.60	74.80	77.00	79.20	81.40	83.60	85.80	88.00	1.10	90.20	92.40	94.60	96.80	99.00	101.20	103.40	105.60	107.80	110.00
2.3	71.30	73.60	75.90	78.20	80.50	82.80	85.10	87.40	89.70	92.00	1.15	94.30	96.60	98.90	101.20	103.50	105.80	108.10	110.40	112.70	115.00
2.4	74.40	76.80	79.20	81.60	84.00	86.40	88.80	91.20	93.60	96.00	1.20	98.40	100.80	103.20	105.60	108.00	110.40	112.80	115.20	117.60	120.00
2.5	77.50	80.00	82.50	85.00	87.50	90.00	92.50	95.00	97.50	100.00	1.25	102.50	105.00	107.50	110.00	112.50	115.00	117.50	120.00	122.50	125.00
2.6	80.60	83.20	85.80	88.40	91.00	93.60	96.20	98.80	101.40	104.00	1.30	106.60	109.20	111.80	114.40	117.00	119.60	122.20	124.80	127.40	130.00
2.7	83.70	86.40	89.10	91.80	94.50	97.20	99.90	102.60	105.30	108.00	1.35	110.70	113.40	116.10	118.80	121.50	124.20	126.90	129.60	132.30	135.00
2.8	86.80	89.60	92.40	95.20	98.00	100.80	103.60	106.40	109.20	112.00	1.40	114.80	117.60	120.40	123.20	126.00	128.80	131.60	134.40	137.20	140.00
2.9	89.90	92.80	95.70	98.60	101.50	104.40	107.30	110.20	113.10	116.00	1.45	118.90	121.80	124.70	127.60	130.50	133.40	136.30	139.20	142.10	145.00
3.0	93.00	96.00	99.00	102.00	105.00	108.00	111.00	114.00	117.00	120.00	1.50	123.00	126.00	129.00	132.00	135.00	138.00	141.00	144.00	147.00	150.00
3.1	96.10	99.20	102.30	105.40	108.50	111.60	114.70	117.80	120.90	124.00	1.55	127.10	130.20	133.30	136.40	139.50	142.60	145.70	148.80	151.90	155.00
3.2	99.20	102.40	105.60	108.80	112.00	115.20	118.40	121.60	124.80	128.00	1.60	131.20	134.40	137.60	140.80	144.00	147.20	150.40	153.60	156.80	160.00
3.3	102.30	105.60	108.90	112.20	115.50	118.80	122.10	125.40	128.70	132.00	1.65	135.30	138.60	141.90	145.20	148.50	151.80	155.10	158.40	161.70	165.00
3.4	105.40	108.80	112.20	115.60	119.00	122.40	125.80	129.20	132.60	136.00	1.70	139.40	142.80	146.20	149.60	153.00	156.40	159.80	163.20	166.60	170.00
3.5	108.50	112.00	115.50	119.00	122.50	126.00	129.50	133.00	136.50	140.00	1.75	143.50	147.00	150.50	154.00	157.50	161.00	164.50	168.00	171.50	175.00
3.6	111.60	115.20	118.80	122.40	126.00	129.60	133.20	136.80	140.40	144.00	1.80	147.60	151.20	154.80	158.40	162.00	165.60	169.20	172.80	176.40	180.00
3.7	114.70	118.40	122.10	125.80	129.50	133.20	136.90	140.60	144.30	148.00	1.85	151.70	155.40	159.10	162.80	166.50	170.20	173.90	177.60	181.30	185.00
3.8	117.80	121.60	125.40	129.20	133.00	136.80	140.60	144.40	148.20	152.00	1.90	155.80	159.60	163.40	167.20	171.00	174.80	178.60	182.40	186.20	190.00
3.9	120.90	124.80	128.70	132.60	136.50	140.40	144.30	148.20	152.10	156.00	1.95	159.90	163.80	167.70	171.60	175.50	179.40	183.30	187.20	191.10	195.00
4.0	124.00	128.00	132.00	136.00	140.00	144.00	148.00	152.00	156.00	160.90	2.00	164.00	168.00	172.00	176.00	180.00	184.00	188.00	192.00	196.00	200.00
4.1	127.10	131.20	135.30	139.40	143.50	147.60	151.70	155.80	159.90	164.00	2.05	168.10	172.20	176.30	180.40	184.50	188.60	192.70	196.80	200.90	205.00
4.2	130.20	134.40	138.60	142.80	147.00	151.20	155.40	159.60	163.80	168.00	2.10	172.20	176.40	180.60	184.80	189.00	193.20	197.40	201.60	205.80	210.00
4.3	133.30	137.60	141.90	146.20	150.50	154.80	159.10	163.40	167.70	172.00	2.15	176.30	180.60	184.90	189.20	193.50	197.80	202.10	206.40	210.70	215.00
4.4	136.40	140.80	145.20	149.60	154.00	158.40	162.80	167.20	171.60	176.00	2.20	180.40	184.80	189.20	193.60	198.00	202.40	206.80	211.20	215.60	220.00
4.5	139.50	144.00	148.50	153.00	157.50	162.00	166.50	171.00	175.50	180.00	2.25	184.50	189.00	193.50	198.00	202.50	207.00	211.50	216.00	220.50	225.00
4.6	142.60	147.20	151.80	156.40	161.00	165.60	170.20	174.80	179.40	184.00	2.30	188.60	193.20	197.80	202.40	207.00	211.60	216.20	220.80	225.40	230.00
4.7	145.70	150.40	155.10	159.80	164.50	169.20	173.90	178.60	183.30	188.00	2.35	192.70	197.40	202.10	206.80	211.50	216.20	220.90	225.60	230.30	235.00
4.8	148.80	153.60	158.40	163.20	168.00	172.80	177.60	182.40	187.20	192.00	2.40	196.80	201.60	206.40	211.20	216.00	220.80	225.60	230.40	235.20	240.00
4.9	151.90	156.80	161.70	166.60	171.50	176.40	181.30	186.20	191.10	196.00	2.45	200.90	205.80	210.70	215.60	220.50	225.40	230.30	235.20	240.10	245.00
5.0	155.00	160.00	165.00	170.00	175.00	180.00	185.00	190.00	195.00	200.00	2.50	205.00	210.00	215.00	220.00	225.00	230.00	235.00	240.00	245.00	250.00
5.1	158.10	163.20	168.30	173.40	178.50	183.60	188.70	193.80	198.90	204.00	2.55	209.10	214.20	219.30	224.40	229.50	234.60	239.70	244.80	249.90	255.00
5.2	161.20	166.40	171.60	176.80	182.00	187.20	192.40	197.60	202.80	208.00	2.60	213.20	218.40	223.60	228.80	234.00	239.20	244.40	249.60	254.80	260.00
5.3	164.30	169.60	174.90	180.20	185.50	190.80	196.10	201.40	206.70	212.00	2.65	217.30	222.60	227.90	233.20	238.50	243.80	249.10	254.40	259.70	265.00
5.4	167.40	172.80	178.20	183.60	189.00	194.40	199.80	205.20	210.60	216.00	2.70	221.40	226.80	232.20	237.60	243.00	248.40	253.80	259.20	264.60	270.00
5.5	170.50	176.00	181.50	187.00	192.50	198.00	203.50	209.00	214.50	220.00	2.75	225.50	231.00	236.50	242.00	247.50	253.00	258.50	264.00	269.50	275.00
5.6	173.60	179.20	184.80	190.40	196.00	201.60	207.20	212.80	218.40	224.00	2.80	229.60	235.20	240.80	246.40	252.00	257.60	263.20	268.80	274.40	280.00
5.7	176.70	182.40	188.10	193.80	199.50	205.20	210.90	216.60	222.30	228.00	2.85	233.70	239.40	245.10	250.80	256.50	262.20	267.90	273.60	279.30	285.00
5.8	179.80	185.60	191.40	197.20	203.00	208.80	214.60	220.40	226.20	232.00	2.90	237.80	243.60	249.40	255.20	261.00	266.80	272.60	278.40	284.20	290.00
5.9	182.90	188.80	194.70	200.60	206.50	212.40	218.30	224.20	230.10	236.00	2.95	241.90	247.80	253.70	259.60	265.50	271.40	277.30	283.20	289.10	295.00

C-4

CONVERSION TABLE

Operation Allowances to Dollars

FOR DOLLAR RATES ENDING WITH 50 CENTS, ADD THIS COLUMN TO YOUR RATE COLUMN.

Time	$31	$32	$33	$34	$35	$36	$37	$38	$39	$40	.50	$41	$42	$43	$44	$45	$46	$47	$48	$49	$50
6.0	186.00	192.00	198.00	204.00	210.00	216.00	222.00	228.00	234.00	240.00	3.00	246.00	252.00	258.00	264.00	270.00	276.00	282.00	288.00	294.00	300.00
6.1	189.10	195.20	201.30	207.40	213.50	219.60	225.70	231.80	237.90	244.00	3.05	250.10	256.20	262.30	268.40	274.50	280.60	286.70	292.80	298.90	305.00
6.2	192.20	198.40	204.60	210.80	217.00	223.20	229.40	235.60	241.80	248.00	3.10	254.20	260.40	266.60	272.80	279.00	285.20	291.40	297.60	303.80	310.00
6.3	195.30	201.60	207.90	214.20	220.50	226.80	233.10	239.40	245.70	252.00	3.15	258.30	264.60	270.90	277.20	283.50	289.80	296.10	302.40	308.70	315.00
6.4	198.40	204.80	211.20	217.60	224.00	230.40	236.80	243.20	249.60	256.00	3.20	262.40	268.80	275.20	281.60	288.00	294.40	300.80	307.20	313.60	320.00
6.5	201.50	208.00	214.50	221.00	227.50	234.00	240.50	247.00	253.50	260.00	3.25	266.50	273.00	279.50	286.00	292.50	299.00	305.50	312.00	318.50	325.00
6.6	204.60	211.20	217.80	224.40	231.00	237.60	244.20	250.80	257.40	264.00	3.30	270.60	277.20	283.80	290.40	297.00	303.60	310.20	316.80	323.40	330.00
6.7	207.70	214.40	221.10	227.80	234.50	241.20	247.90	254.60	261.30	268.00	3.35	274.70	281.40	288.10	294.80	301.50	308.20	314.90	321.60	328.30	335.00
6.8	210.80	217.60	224.40	231.20	238.00	244.80	251.60	258.40	265.20	272.00	3.40	278.80	285.60	292.40	299.20	306.00	312.80	319.60	326.40	333.20	340.00
6.9	213.90	220.80	227.70	234.60	241.50	248.40	255.30	262.20	269.10	276.00	3.45	282.90	289.80	296.70	303.60	310.50	317.40	324.30	331.20	338.10	345.00
7.0	217.00	224.00	231.00	238.00	245.00	252.00	259.00	266.00	273.00	280.00	3.50	287.00	294.00	301.00	308.00	315.00	322.00	329.00	336.00	343.00	350.00
7.1	220.10	227.20	234.30	241.40	248.50	255.60	262.70	269.80	276.90	284.00	3.55	291.10	298.20	305.30	312.40	319.50	326.60	333.70	340.80	347.90	355.00
7.2	223.20	230.40	237.60	244.80	252.00	259.20	266.40	273.60	280.80	288.00	3.60	295.20	302.40	309.60	316.80	324.00	331.20	338.40	345.60	352.80	360.00
7.3	226.30	233.60	240.90	248.20	255.50	262.80	270.10	277.40	284.70	292.00	3.65	299.30	306.60	313.90	321.20	328.50	335.80	343.10	350.40	357.70	365.00
7.4	229.40	236.80	244.20	251.60	259.00	266.40	273.80	281.20	288.60	296.00	3.70	303.40	310.80	318.20	325.60	333.00	340.40	347.80	355.20	362.60	370.00
7.5	232.50	240.00	247.50	255.00	262.50	270.00	277.50	285.00	292.50	300.00	3.75	307.50	315.00	322.50	330.00	337.50	345.00	352.50	360.00	367.50	375.00
7.6	235.60	243.20	250.80	258.40	266.00	273.60	281.20	288.80	296.40	304.00	3.80	311.60	319.20	326.80	334.40	342.00	349.60	357.20	364.80	372.40	380.00
7.7	238.70	246.40	254.10	261.80	269.50	277.20	284.90	292.60	300.30	308.00	3.85	315.70	323.40	331.10	338.80	346.50	354.20	361.90	369.60	377.30	385.00
7.8	241.80	249.60	257.40	265.20	273.00	280.80	288.60	296.40	304.20	312.00	3.90	319.80	327.60	335.40	343.20	351.00	358.80	366.60	374.40	382.20	390.00
7.9	244.90	252.80	260.70	268.60	276.50	284.40	292.30	300.20	308.10	316.00	3.95	323.90	331.80	339.70	347.60	355.50	363.40	371.30	379.20	387.10	395.00
8.0	248.00	256.00	264.00	272.00	280.00	288.00	296.00	304.00	312.00	320.00	4.00	328.00	336.00	344.00	352.00	360.00	368.00	376.00	384.00	392.00	400.00
8.1	251.10	259.20	267.30	275.40	283.50	291.60	299.70	307.80	315.90	324.00	4.05	332.10	340.20	348.30	356.40	364.50	372.60	380.70	388.80	396.90	405.00
8.2	254.20	262.40	270.60	278.80	287.00	295.20	303.40	311.60	319.80	328.00	4.10	336.20	344.40	352.60	360.80	369.00	377.20	385.40	393.60	401.80	410.00
8.3	257.30	265.60	273.90	282.20	290.50	298.80	307.10	315.40	323.70	332.00	4.15	340.30	348.60	356.90	365.20	373.50	381.80	390.10	398.40	406.70	415.00
8.4	260.40	268.80	277.20	285.60	294.00	302.40	310.80	319.20	327.60	336.00	4.20	344.40	352.80	361.20	369.60	378.00	386.40	394.80	403.20	411.60	420.00
8.5	263.50	272.00	280.50	289.00	297.50	306.00	314.50	323.00	331.50	340.00	4.25	348.50	357.00	365.50	374.00	382.50	391.00	399.50	408.00	416.50	425.00
8.6	266.60	275.20	283.80	292.40	301.00	309.60	318.20	326.80	335.40	344.00	4.30	352.60	361.20	369.80	378.40	387.00	395.60	404.20	412.80	421.40	430.00
8.7	269.70	278.40	287.10	295.80	304.50	313.20	321.90	330.60	339.30	348.00	4.35	356.70	365.40	374.10	382.80	391.50	400.20	408.90	417.60	426.30	435.00
8.8	272.80	281.60	290.40	299.20	308.00	316.80	325.60	334.40	343.20	352.00	4.40	360.80	369.60	378.40	387.20	396.00	404.80	413.60	422.40	431.20	440.00
8.9	275.90	284.80	293.70	302.60	311.50	320.40	329.30	338.20	347.10	356.00	4.45	364.90	373.80	382.70	391.60	400.50	409.40	418.30	427.20	436.10	445.00
9.0	279.00	288.00	297.00	306.00	315.00	324.00	333.00	342.00	351.00	360.00	4.50	369.00	378.00	387.00	396.00	405.00	414.00	423.00	432.00	441.00	450.00
9.1	282.10	291.20	300.30	309.40	318.50	327.60	336.70	345.80	354.90	364.00	4.55	373.10	382.20	391.30	400.40	409.50	418.60	427.70	436.80	445.90	455.00
9.2	285.20	294.40	303.60	312.80	322.00	331.20	340.40	349.60	358.80	368.00	4.60	377.20	386.40	395.60	404.80	414.00	423.20	432.40	441.60	450.80	460.00
9.3	288.30	297.60	306.90	316.20	325.50	334.80	344.10	353.40	362.70	372.00	4.65	381.30	390.60	399.90	409.20	418.50	427.80	437.10	446.40	455.70	465.00
9.4	291.40	300.80	310.20	319.60	329.00	338.40	347.80	357.20	366.60	376.00	4.70	385.40	394.80	404.20	413.60	423.00	432.40	441.80	451.20	460.60	470.00
9.5	294.50	304.00	313.50	323.00	332.50	342.00	351.50	361.00	370.50	380.00	4.75	389.50	399.00	408.50	418.00	427.50	437.00	446.50	456.00	465.50	475.00
9.6	297.60	307.20	316.80	326.40	336.00	345.60	355.20	364.80	374.40	384.00	4.80	393.60	403.20	412.80	422.40	432.00	441.60	451.20	460.80	470.40	480.00
9.7	300.70	310.40	320.10	329.80	339.50	349.20	358.90	368.60	378.30	388.00	4.85	397.70	407.40	417.10	426.80	436.50	446.20	455.90	465.60	475.30	485.00
9.8	303.80	313.60	323.40	333.20	343.00	352.80	362.60	372.40	382.20	392.00	4.90	401.80	411.60	421.40	431.20	441.00	450.80	460.60	470.40	480.20	490.00
9.9	306.90	316.80	326.70	336.60	346.50	356.40	366.30	376.20	386.10	396.00	4.95	405.90	415.80	425.70	435.60	445.50	455.40	465.30	475.20	485.10	495.00
10.0	310.00	320.00	330.00	340.00	350.00	360.00	370.00	380.00	390.00	400.00	5.00	410.00	420.00	430.00	440.00	450.00	460.00	470.00	480.00	490.00	500.00
10.5	325.50	336.00	346.50	357.00	367.50	378.00	388.50	399.00	409.50	420.00	5.25	430.50	441.00	451.50	462.00	472.50	483.00	493.50	504.00	514.50	525.00
11.0	341.00	352.00	363.00	374.00	385.00	396.00	407.00	418.00	429.00	440.00	5.50	451.00	462.00	473.00	484.00	495.00	506.00	517.00	528.00	539.00	550.00
11.5	356.50	368.00	379.50	391.00	402.50	414.00	425.50	437.00	448.50	460.00	5.75	471.50	483.00	494.50	506.00	517.50	529.00	540.50	552.00	563.50	575.00
12.0	372.00	384.00	396.00	408.00	420.00	432.00	444.00	456.00	468.00	480.00	6.00	492.00	504.00	516.00	528.00	540.00	552.00	564.00	576.00	588.00	600.00
12.5	387.50	400.00	412.50	425.00	437.50	450.00	462.50	475.00	487.50	500.00	6.25	512.50	525.00	537.50	550.00	562.50	575.00	587.50	600.00	612.50	625.00
13.0	403.00	416.00	429.00	442.00	455.00	468.00	481.00	494.00	507.00	520.00	6.50	533.00	546.00	559.00	572.00	585.00	598.00	611.00	624.00	637.00	650.00
13.5	418.50	432.00	445.50	459.00	472.50	486.00	499.50	513.00	526.50	540.00	6.75	553.50	567.00	580.50	594.00	607.50	621.00	634.50	648.00	661.50	675.00
14.0	434.00	448.00	462.00	476.00	490.00	504.00	518.00	532.00	546.00	560.00	7.00	574.00	588.00	602.00	616.00	630.00	644.00	658.00	672.00	686.00	700.00
14.5	449.50	464.00	478.50	493.00	507.50	522.00	536.50	551.00	565.50	580.00	7.25	594.50	609.00	623.50	638.00	652.50	667.00	681.50	696.00	710.50	725.00
15.0	465.00	480.00	495.00	510.00	525.00	540.00	555.00	570.00	585.00	600.00	7.50	615.00	630.00	645.00	660.00	675.00	690.00	705.00	720.00	735.00	750.00
15.5	480.50	496.00	511.50	527.00	542.50	558.00	573.50	589.00	604.50	620.00	7.75	635.50	651.00	666.50	682.00	697.50	713.00	728.50	744.00	759.50	775.00
16.0	496.00	512.00	528.00	544.00	560.00	576.00	592.00	608.00	624.00	640.00	8.00	656.00	672.00	688.00	704.00	720.00	736.00	752.00	768.00	784.00	800.00
16.5	511.50	528.00	544.50	561.00	577.50	594.00	610.50	627.00	643.50	660.00	8.25	676.50	693.00	709.50	726.00	742.50	759.00	775.50	792.00	808.50	825.00
17.0	527.00	544.00	561.00	578.00	595.00	612.00	629.00	646.00	663.00	680.00	8.50	697.00	714.00	731.00	748.00	765.00	782.00	799.00	816.00	833.00	850.00
17.5	542.50	560.00	577.50	595.00	612.50	630.00	647.50	665.00	682.50	700.00	8.75	717.50	735.00	752.50	770.00	787.50	805.00	822.50	840.00	857.50	875.00
18.0	558.00	576.00	594.00	612.00	630.00	648.00	666.00	684.00	702.00	720.00	9.00	738.00	756.00	774.00	792.00	810.00	828.00	846.00	864.00	882.00	900.00
18.5	573.50	592.00	610.50	629.00	647.50	666.00	684.50	703.00	721.50	740.00	9.25	758.50	777.00	795.50	814.00	832.50	851.00	869.50	888.00	906.50	925.00
19.0	589.00	608.00	627.00	646.00	665.00	684.00	703.00	722.00	741.00	760.00	9.50	779.00	798.00	817.00	836.00	855.00	874.00	893.00	912.00	931.00	950.00
19.5	604.50	624.00	643.50	663.00	682.50	702.00	721.50	741.00	760.50	780.00	9.75	799.50	819.00	838.50	858.00	877.50	897.00	916.50	936.00	955.50	975.00
20.0	620.00	640.00	660.00	680.00	700.00	720.00	740.00	760.00	780.00	800.00	10.00	820.00	840.00	860.00	880.00	900.00	920.00	940.00	960.00	980.00	1000.00
30.0	930.00	960.00	990.00	1020.00	1050.00	1080.00	1110.00	1140.00	1170.00	1200.00	10.00	1230.00	1260.00	1290.00	1320.00	1350.00	1380.00	1410.00	1440.00	1470.00	1500.00
40.0	1240.00	1280.00	1320.00	1360.00	1400.00	1440.00	1480.00	1520.00	1560.00	1600.00	20.00	1640.00	1680.00	1720.00	1760.00	1800.00	1840.00	1880.00	1920.00	1960.00	2000.00

METRIC TABLES

Linear	One METER (m) : 10 decimeter (dm) : 100 centimeter (cm) : 1000 millimeters (mm) 1000 meters : One kilometer (km)
Square	One SQUARE METER (m^2) : 100 square decimeters (dm^2) : 10,000 square centimeters (cm^2) : 1,000,000 square millimeters (mm^2)
Cubic	One CUBIC METER (m^3) : 1000 cubic decimeters (dm^3) : 1,000,000 cubic centimeters (cm^3)
Capacity	One LITER (l) : 10 deciliters (dl) : 1000 centiliters (cl) 100 Liters: One hectoliter (hl)
Weight	One KILOGRAM (kg) : 100 decagrams (dkg) : 1000 grams (g) 100 Kilograms : One metric cent (q) 1000 kilograms : One ton (t)
Pressure	KILOGRAM PER SQUARE CENTIMETER (kg/cm^2) One kilogram per square centimeter : One ATMOSPHERE (atm)
Temperature	CENTIGRADE degree (°C) : CELSIUS degree (°C)

CONVERSION TABLE
INCH FRACTIONS AND DECIMALS TO METRIC EQUIVALENTS

INCHES Fractions	Decimals	m m	INCHES Fractions	Decimals	m m	INCHES Fractions	Decimals	m m
-	.0004	.01	-	.4331	11	31/32	.96875	24.606
-	.004	.10	7/16	.4375	11.113	-	.9843	25
-	.01	.25	29/64	.4531	11.509	1	1.000	25.4
1/64	.0156	.397	15/32	.46875	11.906	-	1.0236	26
-	.0197	.50	-	.4724	12	1 1/32	1.0312	26.194
-	.0295	.75	31/64	.48437	12.303	1 1/16	1.062	26.988
1/32	.03125	.794	-	.492	12.5	-	1.063	27
-	.0394	1	1/2	.500	12.700	1 3/32	1.094	27.781
3/64	.0469	1.191	-	.5118	13	-	1.1024	28
-	.059	1.5	33/64	.5156	13.097	1 1/8	1.125	28.575
1/16	.0625	1.588	17/32	.53125	13.494	-	1.1417	29
5/64	.0781	1.984	35/64	.54687	13.891	1 5/32	1.156	29.369
-	.0787	2	-	.5512	14	-	1.1811	30
3/32	.094	2.381	9/16	.5625	14.288	1 3/16	1.1875	30.163
-	.0984	2.5	-	.571	14.5	1 7/32	1.219	30.956
7/64	.1093	2.776	37/64	.57812	14.684	-	1.2205	31
-	.1181	3	-	.5906	15	1 1/4	1.250	31.750
1/8	.1250	3.175	19/32	.59375	15.081	-	1.2598	32
-	.1378	3.5	39/64	.60937	15.478	1 9/32	1.281	32.544
9/64	.1406	3.572	5/8	.6250	15.875	-	1.2992	33
5/32	.15625	3.969	-	.6299	16	1 5/16	1.312	33.338
-	.1575	4	41/64	.6406	16.272	-	1.3386	34
11/64	.17187	4.366	-	.6496	16.5	1 11/32	1.344	34.131
-	.177	4.5	21/32	.65625	16.669	1 3/8	1.375	34.925
3/16	.1875	4.763	-	.6693	17	-	1.3779	35
-	.1969	5	43/64	.67187	17.066	1 13/32	1.406	35.719
13/64	.2031	5.159	11/16	.6875	17.463	-	1.4173	36
-	.2165	5.5	45/64	.7031	17.859	1 7/16	1.438	36.513
7/32	.21875	5.556	-	.7087	18	-	1.4567	37
15/64	.23437	5.953	23/32	.71875	18.256	1 15/32	1.469	37.306
-	.2362	6	-	.7283	18.5	-	1.4961	38
1/4	.2500	6.350	47/64	.73437	18.653	1 1/2	1.500	38.100
-	.2559	6.5	-	.7480	19	1 17/32	1.531	38.894
17/64	.2656	6.747	3/4	.7500	19.050	-	1.5354	39
-	.2756	7	49/64	.7656	19.447	1 9/16	1.562	39.688
9/32	.28125	7.144	25/32	.78125	19.844	-	1.5748	40
-	.2953	7.5	-	.7874	20	1 19/32	1.594	40.481
19/64	.29687	7.541	51/64	.79687	20.241	-	1.6142	41
5/16	.3125	7.938	13/16	.8125	20.638	1 5/8	1.625	41.275
-	.3150	8	-	.8268	21	-	1.6535	42
21/64	.3281	8.334	53/64	.8281	21.034	1 21/32	1.6562	42.069
-	.335	8.5	27/32	.84375	21.431	1 11/16	1.6875	42.863
11/32	.34375	8.731	55/64	.85937	21.828	-	1.6929	43
-	.3543	9	-	.8662	22	1 23/32	1.719	43.656
23/64	.35937	9.128	7/8	.8750	22.225	-	1.7323	44
-	.374	9.5	57/64	.8906	22.622	1 3/4	1.750	44.450
3/8	.3750	9.525	-	.9055	23	-	1.7717	45
25/64	.3906	9.922	29/32	.90625	23.019	1 25/32	1.781	45.244
-	.3937	10	59/64	.92187	23.416	-	1.8110	46
13/32	.4062	10.319	15/16	.9375	23.813	1 13/16	1.8125	46.038
-	.413	10.5	-	.9449	24	1 27/32	1.844	46.831
27/64	.42187	10.716	61/64	.9531	24.209	-	1.8504	47

Millimeters

|||||||||||||||||||||||||||||||||||||||||||||||||||||||||||||||||||||||||||||||||||||||||||||||||||||||||||||||||||||||||||||||||||||||||||||||||||||||||||||||||

10   20   30   40   50   60   70   80   90   100   110   120   130   140 150

CONVERSION TABLE
INCH FRACTIONS AND DECIMALS TO METRIC EQUIVALENTS

INCHES Fractions	Decimals	m m	INCHES Fractions	Decimals	m m	INCHES Fractions	Decimals	m m
1 7/8	1.875	47.625	-	3.0709	78	-	4.7244	120
-	1.8898	48	-	3.1102	79	4 3/4	4.750	120.650
1 29/32	1.9062	48.419	3 1/8	3.125	79375	4 7/8	4.875	123.825
-	1.9291	49	-	3.1496	80	-	4.9212	125
1 15/16	1.9375	49.213	3 3/16	3.1875	80.963	5	5.000	127
-	1.9685	50	-	3.1890	81	-	5.1181	130
1 31/32	1.969	50.006	-	3.2283	82	5 1/4	5.250	133.350
2	2.000	50.800	3 1/4	3.250	82.550	5 1/2	5.500	139.700
-	2.0079	51	-	3.2677	83	-	5.5118	140
-	2.0472	52	-	3.3071	84	5 3/4	5.750	146.050
2 1/16	2.062	52.388	3 5/16	3.312	84.1377	-	5.9055	150
-	2.0866	53	-	3.3464	85	6	6.000	152.400
2 1/8	2.125	53.975	3 3/8	3.375	85.725	6 1/4	6.250	158.750
-	2.126	54	-	3.3858	86	-	6.2992	160
-	2.165	55	-	3.4252	87	6 1/2	6.500	165.100
2 3/16	2.1875	55.563	3 7/16	3.438	87.313	-	6.6929	170
-	2.2047	56	-	3.4646	88	6 3/4	6.750	171.450
-	2.244	57	3 1/2	3.500	88.900	7	7.000	177.800
2 1/4	2.250	57.150	-	3.5039	89	-	7.0866	180
-	2.2835	58	-	3.5433	90	-	7.4803	190
2 5/16	2.312	58.738	3 9/16	3.562	90.4877	7 1/2	7.500	190.500
-	2.3228	59	-	3.5827	91	-	7.8740	200
-	2.3622	60	-	3.622	92	8	8.000	203.200
2 3/8	2.375	60.325	3 5/8	3.625	92.075	-	8.2677	210
-	2.4016	61	-	3.6614	93	8 1/2	8.500	215.900
2 7/16	2.438	61.913	3 11/16	3.6875	93.663	-	8.6614	220
-	2.4409	62	-	3.7008	94	9	9.000	228.600
-	2.4803	63	-	3.7401	95	-	9.0551	230
2 1/2	2.500	63.500	3 3/4	3.750	95.250	-	9.4488	240
-	2.5197	64	-	3.7795	96	9 1/2	9.500	241.300
-	2.559	65	3 13/16	3.8125	96.838	-	9.8425	250
2 9/16	2.562	65.088	-	3.8189	97	10	10.000	254.000
-	2.5984	66	-	3.8583	98	-	10.2362	260
2 5/8	2.625	66.675	3 7/8	3.875	98.425	-	10.6299	270
-	2.638	67	-	3.8976	99	11	11.000	279.400
-	2.6772	68	-	3.9370	100	-	11.0236	280
2 11/16	2.6875	68.263	3 15/16	3.9375	100.013	-	11.4173	290
-	2.7165	69	-	3.9764	101	-	11.8110	300
2 3/4	2.750	69.850	4	4.000	101.600	12	12.000	304.800
-	2.7559	70	4 1/16	4.062	103.188	13	13.000	330.200
-	2.7953	71	4 1/8	4.125	104.775	-	13.7795	350
2 13/16	2.8125	71.438	-	4.1338	105	14	14.000	355.600
-	2.8346	72	4 3/16	4.1875	106.363	15	15.000	381
-	2.8740	73	4 1/4	4.250	107.950	-	15.7480	400
2 7/8	2.875	73.025	4 5/16	4.312	109.538	16	16.000	406.400
-	2.9134	74	-	4.3307	110	17	17.000	431.800
2 15/16	2.9375	74.613	4 3/8	4.375	111.125	-	17.7165	450
-	2.9527	75	4 7/16	4.438	112.713	18	18.000	457.200
-	2.9921	76	4 1/2	4.500	114.300	19	19.000	482.600
3	3.000	76.200	-	4.5275	115	-	19.6850	500
-	3.0315	77	4 9/16	4.562	115.888	20	20.000	508
3 1/16	3.062	77.788	4 5/8	4.625	117.475	21	21.000	533.400

Millimeters

10   20   30   40   50   60   70   80   90   100   110   120   130   140   150

METRIC CONVERSION EQUIVALENTS

Linear Measure

Inch to metric			Metric to Inch		
1 inch	25.400	millimeters	1 millimeter	0.0393700	inch
1 inch	2.540	centimeters	1 centimeter	0.393700	inch
1 foot	304.800	millimeters	1 meter	39.3700	inches
1 foot	30.480	centimeters	1 meter	3.2808	feet
1 foot	0.3048	meter	1 meter	1.0936	yards
1 yard	91.4400	centimeters	1 kilometer	0.62137	mile
1 yard	0.9144	meter			
1 mile	1,609.35	meters			
1 mile	1.609	kilometers			

Area

Square Inch to Metric			Metric to Square Inch		
1 square inch	645.16	square millimeters	1 square millimeter	0.00155	square inch
1 square inch	6.4516	square centimeters	1 square centimeter	0.1550	square inch
1 square foot	929.00	square centimeters	1 square meter	10.7640	square feet
1 square foot	0.0929	square meter	1 square meter	1.196	square yards
1 square yard	0.836	square meter	1 square kilometer	0.38614	square mile
1 square mile	2.5889	square kilometers			

Cubic Measure

Cubic Inch to Metric			Metric to Cubic Inch		
1 cubic inch	16.387	cubic centimeters	1 cubic centimeter	0.0610	cubic inch
1 cubic foot	0.02832	cubic meter	1 cubic meter	85.314	cubic feet
1 cubic yard	0.765	cubic meter	1 cubic meter	1.308	cubic yards

Capacity

Imperial to Metric			Metric to Imperial		
1 fluid ounce	28.413	milliliters	1 milliliter	0.035195	fluid ounce
1 fluid ounce	0.2841	liter	1 centiliter	0.35195	fluid ounce
1 pint	0.56826	liter	1 deciliter	3.5195	fluid ounces
1 quart	1.13652	liters	1 liter	0.88	quart
1 gallon	4.546	liters	1 hectoliter	21.9969	gallons

Weight

Avoirdupois to Metric			Metric to Avoirdupois		
1 grain	64.7989	milligrams	1 gram	15.432	grains
1 ounce	28.35	grams	1 dekagram	0.353	ounce
1 pound	0.4536	kilogram	1 kilogram	2.2046	pounds
1 short ton (2000 lbs.)	907.200	kilograms	1 metric cent	220.46	pounds
1 short ton (2000 lbs.)	9.072	metric cents	1 ton	2204.6	pounds
1 short ton (2000 lbs.)	0.9072	ton	1 ton	1.102	short tons

METRIC CONVERSION EQUIVALENTS

Pressure

Pounds/Inches to Metric		Metric to Pounds/Inches	
1 pound per square inch	0.0703 kilogram per square centimeter	1 kilogram/square centimeter	14.223 pounds/square inch
1 pound per square inch	0.0703 atmosphere (metric)	1 kilogram/square centimeter	1 atmosphere

Temperature

Canadian to Metric		Metric to Canadian	
1 Fahrenheit degree (°F)	1.8 × (°C) plus 32	1 centigrade (Celsius) degree (°C)	0.556 × (°F minus 32)

METRIC BOLT AND NUT IDENTIFICATION

Common metric fastener strength property classes are 9.8 and 10.9 with the class identification embossed on the head of each bolt. Customary (inch) strength classes range from grade 2 to 8 with line identification embossed on each bolt head. Markings correspond to two lines less than the actual grade (i.e. grade 7 bolt will exhibit 5 embossed lines on the bolt head). Some metric nuts will be marked with single digit strength identification numbers on the nut face. The following figure illustrates the different strength markings.

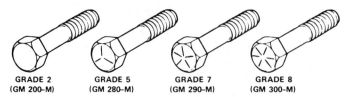

| GRADE 2 | GRADE 5 | GRADE 7 | GRADE 8 |
| (GM 200-M) | (GM 280-M) | (GM 290-M) | (GM 300-M) |

Customary (inch) bolts – Identification marks correspond to bolt strength – Increasing numbers represent increasing strength.

Metric Bolts – Identification class numbers correspond to bolt strength – Increasing numbers represent increasing strength.

MANUFACTURERS IDENTIFICATION

NUT STRENGTH IDENTIFICATION

CROSS RECESS SCREW HEAD

IDENTIFICATION MARKS (4)

1943

Exchange Bumpers, Reinforcements, and Urethane Fascia

*Courtesy of the Auto Body Connection, Erie, Pa., Marketing Division
of Lake Erie Bumper Plating Corp.

AMERICAN MOTORS

Alliance, Encore
83-85 Front Cover..................	154.00	
83-85 Rear Covers.................	146.00	

Concord, Spirit, Eagle, AMX
78-80 Fronts - alum...............	157.00	95.00
78-83 CONCORD Fronts - alum........	157.00	
81-86 Fronts - alum...............	106.00	
78-80 Rears - alum................	152.00	95.00
78-83 CONCORD Rears - alum........	152.00	
81-86 Rears - alum................	106.00	

Gremlin, Hornet
73-78 Fronts.....................	164.00	95.00
73-78 Rears......................	169.00	95.00

LeCar
76-79 Front Cover.................	225.00
80-83 Front Cover.................	191.00
76-79 Rear Cover..................	238.00
80-83 Rear Cover..................	202.00

Matador
74-78 Fronts.....................	178.00	127.00
74-78 Rears......................	182.00	127.00

Pacer
75-80 Fronts-Rears................	150.00	95.00

Jeep J Series, Wagoneer, Cherokee
74-78 F - R Ends chrome...........	106.00
74-78 F - R Ends primed...........	69.00
74-78 F - R Centers chrome........	90.00
74-78 F - R Centers primed........	55.00
79-86 Fronts-Rears alum...........	165.00

Jeep CJ5, CJ6, CJ7
76-85 Fronts-Rears chrome.........	96.00
76-85 Fronts-Rears primed.........	66.00

BUICK

Full Size Buick
73-85 Fronts (RWD)................	214.00	CALL
86 Front Cover (FWD)...........	158.00	
86 Front Face Bar (FWD)........	118.00	
85-86 ELECTRA Front Cover (FWD)....	142.00	
85-86 Front Face Bar (FWD)........	126.00	
73-85 Rears (RWD).................	180.00	CALL
74-79 ELECTRA Rears...............	210.00	146.00
77-85 Station Wagon Rears.........	149.00	120.00
80-85 ELECTRA Rears (RWD).........	180.00	120.00

Full Size Buick
86 Rear Upper Cover (FWD)......	199.00
86 Rear Lower Face Bar (FWD)...	126.00
85-86 ELECTRA Rear Cover (FWD)....	196.00
85-86 ELECTRA Rear Face Bar (FWD).	126.00

Regal, Century, Special
73-81 Fronts.....................	153.00	120.00
81-85 REGAL Fronts...............	145.00	120.00
82-85 CENTURY Front Cover.........	170.00	104.00
85-86 SOMERSET Front Cover........	119.00	
85-86 SOMERSET Front Face Bar.....	75.00	
73-77 Rears......................	147.00	108.00
78-86 Rears......................	161.00	116.00
78-85 Station Wagon Rears.........	147.00	114.00
82-85 CENTURY Rear Covers.........	170.00	79.00
85-86 SOMERSET Rear Cover.........	101.00	
85-86 SOMERSET Rear Face Bar......	82.00	

Riviera
79-85 Fronts.....................	171.00	102.00
86 Front Cover.................	166.00	86.00
79-85 Rears......................	248.00	112.00
86 Rear Upper Cover...........	115.00	
86 Rear Lower Cover...........	109.00	107.00

Skyhawk
82-86 Front Cover.................	154.00	112.00
82-86 Rear Cover..................	136.00	119.00

Skylark, Apollo
75-79 Fronts.....................	120.00	102.00
80-85 Fronts - alum...............	126.00	
86 Front Cover.................	119.00	
86 Front Face Bar.............	75.00	
75-79 Rears......................	128.00	92.00
80-85 Rears - alum...............	140.00	
86 Rear Cover.................	101.00	
86 Rear Face Bar.............	82.00	

CADILLAC

Cimarron
82-84 Fronts.....................	130.00
85-86 Front Uppers...............	130.00
85-86 Front Lower................	100.00
82-86 Rears......................	121.00

Some items on this page may not be in stock at all times - CALL FOR AVAILABILITY

SEE REAR SECTION FOR ITEMS GUARANTEED TO BE IN STOCK AT ALL TIMES

CADILLAC

	Bumper	Rein

Deville, Fleetwood

	Bumper	Rein
77-79 Front Upper	225.00	
77-79 Front Lower	275.00	143.00
77-86 Front Ends ea. (RWD)	112.00	
80-86 Front Center (RWD)	310.00	143.00
85-86 F - R Lower (FWD)	255.00	
85-86 F - R Cover (FWD)	190.00	34.00
73-86 Rear Centers (RWD)	310.00	132.00
73-86 Rear Ends ea. (RWD)	115.00	

Eldorado

	Bumper	Rein
74-78 Front Uppers	260.00	
74-78 Front Lowers	59.00	
74-78 Front Inner Ends ea	73.00	
74-78 F - R Ends ea	121.00	
79-85 Fronts	365.00	163.00
86 Front Upper Cover	138.00	126.00
74-78 Rear Center	330.00	146.00
79-85 Rears	360.00	85.00
86 Rear Upper Cover	104.00	98.00

Seville

	Bumper	Rein
75-79 Front Upper	342.00	
75-79 Front Lower	252.00	147.00
80-85 Fronts	337.00	163.00
75-79 Rears	319.00	74.00
80-85 Rears	332.00	79.00

CHEVROLET

Camaro, Z-28

	Bumper	Rein
78-81 Front Cover	175.00	65.00
82-84 Front Cover	175.00	81.00
85-86 Front Cover	175.00	50.00
82-84 Z-28 Front Cover	246.00	81.00
85-86 Z-28 Front Cover	246.00	50.00
78-81 Rear Cover	140.00	135.00
82-86 Rear Cover	140.00	41.00
78-81 Z-28 Rear Cover	160.00	135.00
82-86 Z-28 Rear Cover	160.00	41.00

Cavalier

	Bumper	Rein
82-83 F - R Chrome	121.00	
82-83 F - R Primed	90.00	
82-83 Front Cover	166.00	78.00
84-86 Front Cover	51.00	110.00
82-83 Rear Cover	105.00	119.00
84-86 Rear Cover	62.00	110.00

Celebrity

	Bumper	Rein
82-86 Fronts - Rears	122.00	

Chevelle, Malibu

	Bumper	Rein
73-83 Fronts	127.00	100.00
73-83 Rears	123.00	100.00
73-83 Station Wagon Rears	139.00	114.00

Chevette

	Bumper	Rein
76-82 F - R Chrome	82.00	
76-82 F - R Primed	76.00	
83-86 F - R Chrome	123.00	
83-86 F - R Primed	82.00	

Citation

	Bumper	Rein
80-85 Fronts	108.00	
80-85 Rears	125.00	

Corvette

	Bumper	Rein
73-86 Fronts Covers	146.00	77.00
74-86 Rear Covers	300.00	CALL

Full Size Chevrolet

	Bumper	Rein
74-86 Fronts	138.00	133.00
74-86 Rears	149.00	120.00

Monte Carlo

	Bumper	Rein
76-77 Fronts	117.00	113.00
78-80 Front Cover	200.00	167.00
81-86 Front Cover	169.00	119.00
70-77 Rears	123.00	105.00
78-80 Rear Cover	180.00	150.00
81-86 Rear Cover	152.00	121.00

Monza

	Bumper	Rein
75-81 Fronts	130.00	58.00
75-81 Rears	130.00	

Nova

	Bumper	Rein
75-79 Fronts	128.00	98.00
85 Front Cover	94.00	98.00
75-79 Rears	128.00	92.00
85 Rear Cover	94.00	98.00

Chevrolet Luv

	Bumper	Rein
73-80 Fronts	90.00	
81-84 Front Center	90.00	
81-84 Front Ends ea	45.00	
76-80 Rears	90.00	
81-84 Rears	133.00	

Chevrolet S-10, S-15

	Bumper	Rein
82-86 Fronts Chrome	106.00	
82-86 Fronts Primed	74.00	
82-86 Rears Chrome	110.00	
82-86 Rears Primed	74.00	

Full Size Chevrolet - GMC Trucks

	Bumper	Rein
73-80 Fronts Chrome	85.00	
73-80 Fronts Primed	73.00	
81-82 Fronts Chrome	99.00	
81-86 Fronts Primed	86.00	
83-86 Fronts Chrome	116.00	
67-86 Rears Chrome	129.00	
67-86 Rears Primed	81.00	

Some items on this page may not be in stock at all times - CALL FOR AVAILABILTY

SEE REAR SECTION FOR ITEMS GUARANTEED TO BE IN STOCK AT ALL TIMES

CHEVROLET

Full Size Chevrolet - GMC Vans

71-86 Fronts Chrome	119.00	
71-86 Fronts Primed	65.00	
71-86 Rears Chrome	119.00	
71-86 Rears Primed	55.00	

GMC Mini Van

85-86 Front Chrome	122.00	
85-86 Front Primed	67.00	
85-86 Rear Chrome	125.00	
85-86 Rear Primed	88.00	

CHRYSLER - DODGE - PLYMOUTH

Aries - Reliant

81-84 Front Covers	98.00	59.00
85-86 Front Covers	130.00	49.00
81-84 Rear Covers	80.00	49.00
85-86 Rear Covers	130.00	50.00

Aspen - Volare

76-80 Fronts	156.00	65.00
76-80 Rears	140.00	84.00

Challenger

78-80 Fronts	147.00	63.00
81-83 Front Covers	187.00	100.00
78-80 Rears	140.00	63.00
81-83 Rears Covers	187.00	107.00

Champ, Colt, Arrow

77-82 Fronts Chrome	100.00	56.00
77-82 Fronts Primed	86.00	56.00
77-82 Rears Chrome	100.00	56.00
77-82 Rears Primed	86.00	56.00

Cordoba, Charger, Magnum

75-79 Fronts	145.00	118.00
80-83 Fronts	178.00	
80-83 LS Front Cover	275.00	
75-79 Rears	136.00	108.00
80-83 Rears Chrome	147.00	
80-83 Rears - alum	205.00	

Dart, Swinger, Sport

73-76 Fronts	118.00	60.00
73-76 Rears	125.00	60.00

Dodge 400, 600

82-85 Front Covers	118.00	44.00
86 Front Covers	85.00	56.00
82-85 Rear Covers	80.00	49.00
86 Rear Covers	130.00	64.00

Gran Fury

74-77 Fronts	162.00	95.00
80-81 Fronts - alum	254.00	
82-86 Fronts	156.00	
74-77 Rears	135.00	90.00
80-81 Rears Chrome	141.00	
80-81 Rears - alum	220.00	
82-86 Rears	147.00	

LeBaron, Diplomat, E Class

77-86 Fronts Chrome	156.00	65.00
82-85 Front Covers	102.00	42.00
86 Front Covers	85.00	56.00
77-86 Rears Chrome	147.00	84.00
77-86 Wagon Rears Chrome	140.00	
82-84 Rear Covers	80.00	49.00
85-86 Rear Covers	130.00	50.00
86 E Class Rear Cover	85.00	56.00
82-86 Wagon Rear Covers	130.00	49.00

Laser, Daytona

84-86 Front Covers exc turbo	137.00	95.00
84-86 Rear Covers	101.00	40.00

Monaco, Coronet, Fury

75-78 Fronts	160.00	110.00
75-78 Rears	150.00	90.00

Newport, New Yorker

79-81 Fronts - alum	254.00	
82-86 Fronts	156.00	
79-81 Rears - alum	220.00	
79-86 Rears Chrome	147.00	

Omni, Horizon

78-86 Fronts - alum	120.00	
78-84 Omni Front Cover	135.00	103.00
78-84 Horizon Front Covers	154.00	103.00
78-86 Rears - alum	120.00	
78-84 Rear Covers	84.00	91.00

Dodge D-50, Arrow

79-85 Fronts Chrome	96.00	
79-85 Fronts Primed	80.00	

Dodge, Plymouth Trucks

72-86 Fronts Chrome	153.00	
72-86 Fronts Primed	87.00	
72-86 Rears Chrome	150.00	
72-86 Rears Primed	90.00	

Dodge, Plymouth Vans

71-85 Fronts Chrome	142.00	
86 Front Chrome	160.00	
71-85 Rears Primed	86.00	
86 Rears Primed	97.00	

Some items on this page may not be in stock at all times - CALL FOR AVILABILITY
SEE REAR SECTION FOR ITEMS GUARANTEED TO BE IN STOCK AT ALL TIMES

CHRYSLER-DODGE-PLYMOUTH
Dodge, Plymouth, Mini Vans

84–86 Fronts–Rears – Alum.......... 140.00

DATSUN

200SX

	BUMPER	REIN
76–79 Fronts..................... 100.00		
80–81 Front Covers.............. 100.00		92.00
82–83 Front Covers.............. 220.00		106.00
84–86 Front Covers.............. 290.00		167.00
76–79 Rears..................... 109.00		
80–81 Rear Covers.............. 107.00		95.00
82–83 Rear Covers.............. 160.00		106.00
84–86 Rear Covers.............. 208.00		172.00

210, B210

75–82 Fronts..................... 70.00
75–82 Rears..................... 70.00

240Z, 260Z, 280Z

75–76 Fronts..................... 227.00		
77–78 Fronts..................... 274.00		
79–81 Front Covers.............. 169.00		95.00
82–83 Front Covers.............. 135.00		89.00
75–78 Rears..................... 232.00		
79–81 Rear Covers.............. 150.00		85.00
82–83 Rear Covers.............. 126.00		103.00

310

79–82 Fronts..................... 125.00
79–82 Rears..................... 95.00

510

77–81 Fronts..................... 96.00
77–81 Rears..................... 90.00

620

73–79 Fronts..................... 55.00

720

80–82 Front Center Chrome.......... 58.00
80–82 Front Center Primed.......... 52.00
83–85 Front Chrome................. 80.00
83–85 Front Primed................. 66.00

810

76–80 Fronts..................... 109.00		58.00
81–84 Front Cover.............. 101.00		101.00
85–86 Front Cover.............. 141.00		133.00
76–80 Rears..................... 109.00		38.00
81–84 Rear Cover.............. 92.00		100.00
85–86 Rear Cover.............. 122.00		146.00

F10

77–79 Fronts..................... 100.00
77–79 Rears..................... 87.00

Pulsar

83–86 Coupe Front Cover.......... 197.00		76.00
83–85 H-Back Front Cover.......... 77.00		81.00
83–86 Coupe Rear Cover.......... 161.00		76.00
83–85 H-Back Rear Cover.......... 81.00		76.00

Sentra

82–86 Front Covers................ 93.00		60.00
82–83 Rear Covers................ 81.00		38.00
84–86 Rear Covers................ 92.00		67.00

Stanza

82–86 Front Cover................. 253.00   79.00
82–86 Rear Cover................. 239.00   79.00

FORD-LINCOLN-MERCURY
Continental, Lincoln, Towncar

74–79 Fronts..................... 277.00		174.00
80–86 Fronts Chrome................ 242.00		116.00
80–83 Fronts – alum................ 384.00		141.00
70–83 Rears Chrome................ 236.00		117.00
80–83 Rears – alum................ 384.00		202.00
84–86 Rears Chrome................ 185.00		58.00

Escort, Lynx

81–85 (March) Fronts Chrome....... 110.00
85–86 (April) Front Chrome....... 116.00
81–85 (March) Fronts – alum....... 170.00
85–86 (April) Front – alum........ 196.00
81–85 (March) Rears Chrome....... 110.00
85–86 (April) Rear Chrome........ 116.00
81–85 (March) Rears – alum....... 170.00
85–86 (April) Rear – alum........ 196.00

EXP, LN-7

82–85 Front Covers................ 249.00   190.00
82–85 Rear Covers................ 136.00   117.00

Fairmont, Zephyr

78–83 Fronts – alum................ 170.00
78–83 Rears – alum................ 170.00

Fiesta

78–82 Fronts – alum................ 140.00
78–82 Rears – alum................ 140.00

Full Size Ford, LTD, Galaxie

73–78 Fronts..................... 114.00		114.00
79–86 Fronts Chrome................ 150.00		120.00
82–86 Fronts – alum................ 262.00		120.00
73–78 Rears..................... 121.00		120.00
79–86 Rears Chrome................ 139.00		113.00
79–86 Rears – alum................ 259.00		

Some items on this page may not be in stock at all times – CALL FOR AVAILABILITY
SEE REAR SECTION FOR ITEMS GUARANTEED TO BE IN STOCK AT ALL TIMES

FORD-LINCOLN-MERCURY

Granada, Monarch, Versailles

	BUMPER	REIN
75-80 Fronts	120.00	116.00
81-82 Fronts	153.00	
75-80 Rears	106.00	113.00
81-82 Rears	136.00	75.00

Grand Marquis, Monterey

	BUMPER	REIN
73-78 Fronts	188.00	126.00
79-86 Fronts Chrome	150.00	120.00
80-81 Fronts - alum	280.00	120.00
82-86 Fronts - alum	296.00	120.00
73-78 Rears	177.00	126.00
73-78 Station Wagon Rears	121.00	120.00
79-86 Rears Chrome	139.00	113.00
79-86 Rears - alum	259.00	

Mark IV, V, VI, VII

	BUMPER	REIN
75-76 Fronts	280.00	174.00
77-79 Fronts	241.00	137.00
80-83 Fronts Chrome	220.00	120.00
80-83 Fronts - alum	340.00	141.00
84-86 Fronts	200.00	52.00
72-76 Rears	341.00	93.00
77-79 Rears	287.00	137.00
80-83 Rears Chrome	236.00	117.00
80-83 Rears - alum	384.00	202.00
84-86 Rears	170.00	22.00

Maverick, Comet

	BUMPER	REIN
74-77 Fronts	135.00	107.00
74-77 Rears	115.00	111.00

Midsize LTD II, Marquis

	BUMPER	REIN
77-79 Fronts	141.00	119.00
83-86 Fronts	143.00	
77-79 Rears	112.00	128.00
83-86 Rears	153.00	113.00

Mustang, Capri

	BUMPER	REIN
74-78 Front Covers	250.00	54.00
79-86 Front Covers	250.00	100.00
74-78 Rear Covers	250.00	64.00
79-86 Rear Covers	110.00	77.00

Pinto, Bobcat

	BUMPER	REIN
74-76 Fronts	145.00	119.00
77-78 Front - alum	180.00	
79-80 Front - alum	245.00	
74-76 Rears	147.00	130.00
77-80 Rears - alum	199.00	

Tempo, Topaz

	BUMPER	REIN
84-85 Fronts Chrome	121.00	
84-85 Fronts - alum	140.00	
86 Front Chrome	137.00	

Tempo, Topaz

	BUMPER	REIN
84-85 Rears Chrome	121.00	
84-85 Rears - alum	140.00	
86 Rear Chrome	137.00	

Thunderbird, Cougar

	BUMPER	REIN
77-79 Fronts	141.00	119.00
80-86 Front Covers	120.00	131.00
81-82 Front Chrome	153.00	
77-79 Rears	112.00	128.00
80-86 Rear Covers	129.00	130.00
81-82 Rear Chrome	136.00	75.00

Ford Courier

	BUMPER	REIN
77-82 Fronts	72.00	

Ford Vans

	BUMPER	REIN
68-86 Fronts Chrome	105.00	
68-86 Fronts Primed	75.00	
68-86 Rears Chrome	105.00	
68-86 Rears Primed	75.00	

Full Size Ford Trucks

	BUMPER	REIN
64-86 Fronts Chrome	110.00	
64-86 Fronts Primed	86.00	
73-86 Rears Chrome	113.00	
73-86 Rears Primed	70.00	

Ranger, Bronco II

	BUMPER	REIN
82-86 Fronts Chrome	110.00	
82-86 Fronts Primed	89.00	

HONDA

Accord

	BUMPER	REIN
76-81 Fronts	60.00	43.00
82 Front Covers	148.00	
83 Front Covers	134.00	
84-85 Front Cover	113.00	
76-81 Rears	60.00	39.00
82 Rear Covers	102.00	
83 Rear Covers	130.00	
84-85 Rear Cover	113.00	105.00

Civic

	BUMPER	REIN
74-79 Fronts	72.00	41.00
80-81 Fronts	101.00	
82-85 Front Covers	106.00	
84-85 Fronts Chrome	106.00	
74-77 Rears	99.00	
78-79 Rears	68.00	41.00
80-81 Rears	82.00	
82-85 Rear Covers	86.00	
84-85 Rears Chrome	86.00	

Some items on this page may not be in stock at all times - CALL FOR AVAILABILITY
SEE REAR SECTION FOR ITEMS GUARANTEED TO BE IN STOCK AT ALL TIMES

HONDA

Prelude

79-82 Fronts Primed	148.00	
83-86 Front Cover	124.00	
79-82 Rears Primed	146.00	
83-86 Rear Cover	113.00	

GLC

76-84 Fronts Chrome	66.00	
76-84 Fronts Primed	43.00	
76-84 Rears Chrome	63.00	
76-84 Rears Primed	43.00	
82-83 Station Wagon Rears	75.00	

RX7

81-83 Front Cover	189.00	

626

79-80 Front Centers	89.00	
81-85 Front Covers	154.00	80.00
79-80 Rear Centers	89.00	
81-85 Rear Covers	154.00	56.00

B1800, B2000, B2200

77-81 Fronts	64.00	
82-84 Fronts Chrome	84.00	
82-84 Fronts Primed	65.00	

OLDSMOBILE

Cutlass Ciera

82-86 Front Covers	200.00	180.00
82-84 Rear Covers	195.00	157.00
85-86 Rear Covers	195.00	76.00

Cutlass Supreme

75-77 Fronts	186.00	110.00
78-79 Front Uppers	134.00	
78-79 Front Lowers	186.00	120.00
79-86 Front one piece	186.00	120.00
81-86 Front Upper Cover	196.00	
81-86 Front Lowers Chrome	186.00	120.00
74-77 Rears one piece	165.00	
74-77 Station Wagon Rears	147.00	108.00
76-77 Rear Lowers	165.00	120.00
76-77 Rear Upper Ends ea	88.00	
78-86 Rears one piece	161.00	116.00
78-86 Station Wagon Rears	139.00	114.00
81-86 Rear Upper Covers	137.00	
81-86 Rear Lowers Chrome	165.00	116.00

Firenza

82-86 Front Covers	120.00	113.00
82-86 Rear Covers	106.00	119.00

Oldsmobile 88, 98

76-86 Fronts (RWD)	227.00	133.00
85-86 Front Upper Cover (FWD)	183.00	
85-86 Front Lower (FWD)	125.00	
74-76 Rears	212.00	127.00
77-79 Rear Lowers	154.00	142.00
77-79 Rear Ends ea	74.00	
77-86 Station Wagon Rear	149.00	120.00
80-86 Rears (RWD)	154.00	127.00
85-86 Rear Upper Cover (FWD)	183.00	
85-86 Rear Lower (FWD)	164.00	

Omega

75-79 Fronts	120.00	102.00
80-84 Fronts - alum	170.00	
75-79 Rears	128.00	92.00
80-84 Rears - alum	150.00	

Starfire

79-80 Fronts	130.00	58.00
79-80 Rears	130.00	

Toronado

77-78 Fronts	234.00	147.00
79-85 Fronts	170.00	120.00
86 Front Cover	108.00	63.00
75-78 Rear Centers	297.00	128.00
75-78 Rear Ends ea	80.00	
79-85 Rears	248.00	112.00
86 Rear Cover	105.00	79.00

PONTIAC

Bonneville, Catalina

73-81 Fronts	185.00	147.00
82-86 Front Cover	88.00	116.00
74-81 Rears	200.00	142.00
77-81 Station Wagon Rears	149.00	120.00
82-86 Rear Covers	116.00	118.00
82-86 Station Wagon Rears	139.00	114.00

Firebird

74-78 Front Covers	202.00	102.00
79-84 Front Covers	202.00	81.00
85-86 Front Covers	180.00	112.00
74-75 Rear Covers	280.00	88.00
76-78 Rear Covers	159.00	88.00
79-81 Rear Covers	159.00	112.00
82-86 Rear Covers	159.00	41.00

Some items on this page may not be in stock at all times CALL FOR AVAILABILITY
SEE REAR SECTION FOR ITEMS GUARANTEED TO BE IN STOCK AT ALL TIMES

PONTIAC

Gran Prix

	BUMPER	REIN
73–80 Fronts	237.00	154.00
81–86 Fronts	169.00	118.00
81–86 Front Cover Ends ea	70.00	
73–77 Rears	261.00	
78–80 Rears	248.00	118.00
81–86 Rear Lowers	205.00	118.00
81–86 Rear Upper Covers	116.00	

LeMans, Tempest, Grand Am

	BUMPER	REIN
71–77 Fronts	144.00	110.00
78–81 Front Covers	156.00	
inner		116.00
outer		57.00
73–77 Rears	132.00	118.00
74–77 Station Wagon Rears	147.00	118.00
78–81 Rear Covers	116.00	
inner		118.00
outer		57.00
78–81 Station Wagon Rears	139.00	114.00

Parisienne

	BUMPER	REIN
83–86 Fronts	138.00	133.00
83–86 Rears	149.00	120.00

Pontiac T 1000

	BUMPER	REIN
81–82 Fronts	82.00	
83–86 Fronts	123.00	
81–82 Rears	82.00	
83–86 Rears	123.00	

Pontiac J 2000, Sunbird

	BUMPER	REIN
76–80 Fronts	130.00	58.00
82–86 Front Covers	171.00	112.00
76–80 Rears	130.00	
82–86 Rear Covers	111.00	119.00
82–86 Station Wagon Rears	121.00	

Pontiac 6000

	BUMPER	REIN
82–86 Front Cover	147.00	133.00
82–84 Rear Covers	111.00	127.00
85–86 Rear Covers	111.00	76.00

Ventura, Phoenix

	BUMPER	REIN
71–79 Fronts	120.00	102.00
80–84 Front Covers	136.00	100.00
73–79 Rears	128.00	92.00
80–84 Rear Covers	127.00	93.00

SUBARU

Brat

	BUMPER	REIN
77–84 Fronts	70.00	48.00
77–84 Rears	74.00	

Stage 2, 1600, 1800

	BUMPER	REIN
74–79 Fronts	70.00	
80–84 Fronts	74.00	
74–79 Rears	74.00	
80–84 Rears	79.00	

TOYOTA

Camry

	BUMPER	REIN
83–86 Front Covers	99.00	101.00
83–86 Rear Covers	99.00	92.00

Celica

	BUMPER	REIN
75–77 Fronts	93.00	63.00
78–79 Front Covers	70.00	94.00
80–81 Front Covers	104.00	94.00
82–85 Front Covers	103.00	94.00
75–77 Rears	108.00	71.00
78–85 Rear Covers	91.00	94.00

Corolla

	BUMPER	REIN
75–79 Fronts	84.00	53.00
80–86 Front Covers	84.00	86.00
75–79 Rears	91.00	53.00
80–86 Rear Covers	84.00	86.00

Corona

	BUMPER	REIN
74–78 Fronts	99.00	71.00
79–82 Front Covers	99.00	101.00
74–78 Rears	104.00	71.00
79–80 Rear Covers	99.00	116.00
81–82 Rear Covers	179.00	116.00

Cressida

	BUMPER	REIN
76–80 Fronts	94.00	80.00
81–85 Fronts Covers	106.00	124.00
76–79 Rears	112.00	80.00
80 Rears	87.00	90.00
81–85 Rear Covers	106.00	124.00

Starlet

	BUMPER	REIN
81–84 Front Covers	94.00	98.00
81–84 Rear Covers	94.00	98.00

Supra

	BUMPER	REIN
79–85 Front Covers	99.00	116.00
79–81 Rear Covers	99.00	107.00
82–83 Rear Covers	220.00	107.00
84–85 Rear Covers	99.00	107.00

Some items on this page may not be in stock at all times – CALL FOR AVAILABILITY

SEE REAR SECTION FOR ITEMS GUARANTEED TO BE IN STOCK AT ALL TIMES

TOYOTA

Tercel

```
80-86 Front Covers................. 94.00    98.00
80-86 Rear Covers.................. 94.00    98.00
```

Toyota Pick up

```
72-85 Front Chrome................. 58.00
72-85 Front Primed................. 46.00
```

VOLKSWAGON

Beetle, Superbeetle

```
74-78 Fronts - Rears.............. 152.00
```

Dasher

```
74-77 Fronts...................... 151.00
78-81 Front Covers................ 250.00    92.00
74-77 Rears....................... 151.00
78-81 Rear Covers................. 250.00    99.00
```

Jetta

```
80-84 Front Covers................. 94.00   134.00
80-84 Rear Covers.................. 85.00   134.00
```

Rabbit, VW Pick-up

```
75-80 Fronts...................... 168.00
81-84 Fronts - alum............... 95.00
75-80 Rears....................... 162.00
81-84 Rears - alum................ 95.00
```

Scirocco

```
74-77 Fronts...................... 236.00
78-81 Front Covers................ 135.00   200.00
82-84 Front Covers................ 114.00   134.00
74-77 Rears....................... 207.00
78-81 Rear Covers................. 135.00   200.00
82-84 Rear Covers................. 135.00   101.00
```

Some items on this page may not be in stock at all times - CALL FOR AVAILABILITY

SEE REAR SECTION FOR ITEMS GUARANTEED TO BE IN STOCK AT ALL TIMES

AMERICAN MOTORS/RENAULT

Alliance, Encore
83-85 Front Covers   RENALLI-F83P-U 154.00

Concord, Eagle
79-83 Fronts   Plain   AMCCONC-F79P-A 157.00

           W/Guards   AMCCONC-F79G-A 157.00

81-86 Eagle Fronts Plain   AMCEAGL-F81P-A 106.00

            W/Guards   AMCEAGL-F81G-A 106.00

BUICK

Full Size Buick
80-85 Fronts (RWD)   GMCBUIC-F80S 214.00

80-85 Electra Front (RWD)   GMCELEC-F80S 214.00

80-85 Front Reinforcement (RWD)   REGBUIC-F80-ST 120.00

80-85 Rears (RWD) Exc. Station Wagon   GMCBUIC-R80S 180.00

80-85 Electra Rear   GMCELEC-R80S 180.00

79-85 Station Wagon Rear Reinforcement   REGCHEV-R77SW-ST 120.00

Century
78-81 Front Reinforcement   REGREGA-F80-S........ 120.00

82-85 Front Cover   GMCCENT-F82P-U....... 170.00

82-85 Front Reinforcement   REGCENT-F812. .... 104.00

78-81 Rear Reinforcement Exc. Sta. Wgn.   REGREGA-R78-S........ 116.00

84-85 Rear Cover Exc. Station Wagon   GMCCENT-R84P-U....... 170.00

Regal
78-80 Front Reinforcement   REGREGA-F80-S 120.00

81-86 2 Door Front Face Bar   GMCREGA-F81S2 .... 145.00

81-86 2 Door Front Reinforcement   REGREGA-F812-S 120.00

81-86 4 Door Front Reinforcement   REGREGA-F80-S 120.00

78-80 Rear Reinforcement Exc. Sta. Wgn.   REGREGA-R78-S 116.00

81-86 2 Door Rear Face Bar   GMCREGA-R81S2 .... 161.00

82-86 4 Door Rear Reinforcement Exc. S/W REGREGA-R78-S 116.00

ALL ITEMS ON THIS PAGE ARE GUARANTEED TO BE AVAILABLE

FOR SHIPMENT WITHIN 48 HOURS

BUICK

Skyhawk

Description	Reference Number	List
82-86 Front Cover	GMCSKYH-F82P-U	154.00
82-86 Rear Cover	GMCSKYH-R82P-U	136.00

CADILLAC

Deville, Fleetwood

Description	Reference Number	List
77-79 Front Upper Center	GMCCADI-F77SCU	225.00
77-79 Front Lower Center	GMCCADI-F77SCLO	275.00
77-79 Front Ends Right	GMCCADI-F77SR	112.00
Left	GMCCADI-F77SL	112.00
80-86 Front Center (RWD)	GMCCADI-F80SC	310.00
80-86 Front Ends (RWD) Right	GMCCADI-F80SR	112.00
Left	GMCCADI-F80SL	112.00
80-86 Front Reinforcement (RWD)	REGCADI-F80-A	143.00
80-86 Rear Ends (RWD) Right	GMCCADI-R80SR	115.00
Left	GMCCADI-R80SL	115.00

CHEVROLET

Camaro, Z-28

Description	Reference Number	List
78-81 Front Cover	GMCCAMA-F78P-U	175.00
82-84 Front Cover	GMCCAMA-F82P-U	175.00
82-84 Z-28 Front Cover	GMCZ28--F82P-U	246.00
85-86 Front Cover	GMCCAMA-F85P-U	175.00
85-86 Z-28 Front Cover	GMCZ28--F85P-U	246.00
78-81 Rear Cover	GMCCAMA-R78P-U	140.00
82-86 Rear Cover	GMCCAMA-R82P-U	140.00
82-86 Z-28 Rear Cover	GMCZ28--R82P-U	160.00

Cavalier

Description	Reference Number	List
82-83 Front Chrome	GMCCAVA-F82S	121.00
82-83 Front Primed	GMCCAVA-F82SPA	90.00
82-83 Front Cover	GMCCAVA-F82P-U	166.00
82-83 Front Reinforcement	REGCAVA-F82HB	78.00
84-86 Front Cover	GMCCAVA-F84P-U	51.00
84-86 Front Reinforcement	REGCAVA-F84.	110.00
84-86 Rear Cover Exc. Sta. Wgn.	GMCCAVA-R84P-U	62.00

ALL ITEMS ON THIS PAGE ARE GUARANTEED TO BE AVAILABLE

FOR SHIPMENT WITHIN 48 HOURS

CHEVROLET

Celebrity
82-83 Front	GMCCELE-F82S	.... 122.00
84-85 Front	GMCCELE-F84S	.... 122.00

Chevelle, Malibu
78-83 Front Plain	GMCMALI-F78P	.... 127.00
W/Cushions	GMCMALI-F78S	.... 127.00

Chevette
76-82 Front Chrome Plain	GMCCVET-F76P	.... 82.00
W/Cushions	GMCCVET-F76S	.... 82.00
76-82 Fronts Primed Plain	GMCCVET-F76PPA	...... 76.00
W/Cushions	GMCCVET-F76SPA	...... 76.00
76-82 Rears Chrome Plain	GMCCVET-R76P	.... 82.00
W/Cushions	GMCCVET-R76S	.... 82.00
76-82 Rears Primed Plain	GMCCVET-R76PPA	...... 76.00
W/Cushions	GMCCVET-R76SPA	...... 76.00

Citation
80-85 Fronts Plain	GMCCITI-F80P	.... 108.00
W/Cushions	GMCCITI-F80S	.... 108.00

Full Size Chevrolet
80-86 Front Plain	GMCCHEV-F80P	.... 138.00
W/Cushions	GMCCHEV-F80S	.... 138.00
80-86 Front Reinforcement	REGCHEV-F80-ST	...... 133.00
77-86 Station Wagon Rear Reinforcement	REGCHEV-R77SW-ST	.... 120.00

Monte Carlo
78-80 Front Cover	GMCMOCA-F78P-U	...... 200.00
78-80 Front Reinforcement Steel	REGMOCA-F78-ST	...... 167.00
81-86 Front Cover Exc. SS	GMCMOCA-F81P-U	...... 169.00
81-86 Front Reinforcement	REGMOCA-F81-ST	...... 119.00
78-80 Rear Cover	GMCMOCA-R78P-U	...... 180.00
81-86 Rear Cover	GMCMOCA-R81P-U	...... 152.00

ALL ITEMS ON THIS PAGE ARE GUARANTEED TO BE AVAILABLE
FOR SHIPMENT WITHIN 48 HOURS

CHEVROLET

Monza
75-80 Front Chrome W/Cushions   GMCMONZ-F75S 130.00

Chevrolet Luv
76-80 Front   GMCCHLU-F76P 90.00

81-84 Front Center Chrome   GMCCHLU-F81PC 90.00

Chevrolet S-10, S-15
82-86 Front Chrome Plain   GMCS-10-F82P 106.00

              W/Cushions   GMCS-10-F82S 106.00

82-86 Front Primed Plain   GMCS-10-F82PPA 74.00

              W/Cushions   GMCS-10-F82SPA 74.00

Full Size Chevrolet Trucks
73-80 Front Chrome Plain   GMCCHTK-F73P 85.00

              W/Cushions   GMCCHTK-F73S 85.00

73-80 Front Primed Plain   GMCCHTK-F73PPA 73.00

              W/Cushions   GMCCHTK-F73SPA 73.00

81-82 Front Chrome Plain   GMCCHTK-F81P 99.00

              W/Cushions   GMCCHTK-F81S 99.00

81-82 Front Primed Plain   GMCCHTK-F81PPA 86.00

              W/Cushions   GMCCHTK-F81SPA 86.00

83-86 Front Chrome Plain   GMCCHTK-F83P 116.00

              W/Cushions   GMCCHTK-F83S 116.00

83-86 Front Primed Plain   GMCCHTK-F83PPA 86.00

              W/Cushions   GMCCHTK-F83SPA 86.00

73-80 Rears Chrome Plain   GMCCHTK-R73P 129.00

              W/Cushions   GMCCHTK-R73S 129.00

73-80 Rears Primed Plain   GMCCHTK-R73PPA 81.00

              W/Cushions   GMCCHTK-R73SPA 81.00

81-86 Rears Chrome Plain   GMCCHTK-R81P 129.00

81-86 Rears Primed Plain   GMCCHTK-R81PPA 81.00

ALL ITEMS ON THIS PAGE ARE GUARANTEED TO BE AVAILABLE

FOR SHIPMENT WITHIN 48 HOURS

AUTO BODY CONNECTION

Marketing Division of

NEW AFTER MARKET REINFORCEMENT BARS

DESCRIPTION	REFERENCE PART #	AFTER MARKET LIST PRICE	BODY SHOP PRICE
CHRYSLER			
81-84 Reliant/Aries Front	4103346	46.00	34.50
78-83 Omni/Horizon 2 Door Front	5216104	103.00	77.25
FORD			
80-85 Full Size Ford/Mercury Front	E2AZ17A792A	120.00	90.00
80-83 Lincoln Mark VI Front	E2VY17A792C	120.00	90.00
77-80 Granada/Monarch/Versailles Front	E00217A792B	116.00	87.00
79-85 Mustang/Capri Front	E02217757B	100.00	75.00
GENERAL MOTORS			
80-85 Buick Full Size Front (EXC Fwd)	25500772	120.00	90.00
80-86 Caprice/Impala/Parisienne Front	14005687	133.00	99.75
80-85 Olds Full Size (EXC Fwd) Front	22509628	133.00	99.75
77-79 Olds Full Size Rear	554331	142.00	106.50
80-85 Olds Full Size (EYC Fwd) Rear	22509629	127.00	96.00
77-85 Full Size GM Station Wagon Rear	10018059	120.00	80.00
80-86 Deville/Fleetwood (RWD) Front	1616415	143.00	107.25
79-85 Toronado Front	561403	120.00	90.00
84 Cavalier Front	14069235	110.00	82.50
85-86 Cavalier Front	14086672	110.00	82.50
82-85 Century Front	25509363	104.00	78.00
82-84 Cutlass Ciera Front	22511216	180.00	135.00
78-80 Cutlass/Century/Regal Front	22502372	120.00	90.00
81-85 Cutlass/Regal 4 Door Front	22502372	120.00	90.00
81-85 Cutlass 2 Door Front	22506302	120.00	90.00
81-85 Regal 2 Door Front	25505367	120.00	90.00
76-77 Cutlass Rear	551047	120.00	90.00
78-80 Cutlass/Regal Rear	22502043	116.00	87.00
81-85 Cutlass/Regal (4 Dr.) Rear	22502043	116.00	87.00
78-80 Monte Carlo Front	14006589	167.00	125.25
81-85 Monte Carlo Front	16502839	119.00	89.25

BUFFALO
800-848-1200
716-873-9700

CLEVELAND
800-531-3770
216-531-4455

ERIE
800-458-0518 (NY,OH)
800-352-0056 (PA)
814-452-6728

NEW AFTER MARKET URETHANE BUMPERS (FASCIA)

DESCRIPTION	REFERENCE PART #	AFTER MARKET LIST PRICE	BODY SHOP PRICE
AMERICAN MOTORS			
83-85 Renault/Alliance	8983501175	154.00	115.50
CHRYSLER			
80-83 Cordoba LS Front	X546TX9	275.00	206.25
82-84 New Yorker Front	4103379	102.00	76.50
84-85 Laser-Daytona Front	4270904	137.00	102.75
78-83 Omni 024 Front	4194865	135.00	101.25
81-84 K-Car Front	4103698	98.00	73.50
85 K-Car Front	4334003	130.00	97.50
81-84 K-Car Rear	X586AW3	80.00	60.00
81-84 K-Car Rear SW	X569VX2	80.00	60.00
85 K-Car Rear	4334052	130.00	97.50
85 K-Car Rear SW	4334062	130.00	97.50
FORD			
79-84 Capri Front	E4CY8190B	250.00	187.50
81-82 Cougar XR7 Front	E1WY170957A	120.00	277.50
74-78 Mustang Front	D6ZZ17757A	250.00	187.50
79-82 Mustang Front	E0ZZ8200A	250.00	187.50
83-84 Mustang Front	E3ZZ8200A	250.00	187.50
85-86 Mustang Front	E5ZZ8190A	250.00	187.50
81-82 Thunderbird Front	E1SZ17D957A	120.00	277.50
83-85 Thunderbird/Cougar Front	E4SZ17D957A	120.00	277.50
74-78 Mustang Rear	D6ZZ17906A	250.00	187.50
79-84 Mustang Rear	E1ZZ17K835A	110.00	82.50
BUICK			
82-85 Century Front	25509104	170.00	127.50
82-85 Skyhawk Front	25509911	154.00	115.50
84-85 Century Rear	25509260	170.00	127.50
82-85 Skyhawk Rear	25509974	136.00	102.00
CHEVROLET			
78-81 Camaro Front	14016390	175.00	131.25
82-84 Camaro Front	5972942	175.00	131.25
85-86 Camaro Front	16503478	175.00	131.25
82-84 Z-28 Front	16500112	246.00	184.50
85-86 Z-28 Front	16503496	246.00	184.50
82-83 Cavalier Front	14020778	166.00	124.50
84-86 Cavalier Front	14080869	51.00	38.25
78-80 Monte Carlo Front	14009708	200.00	150.00
81-86 Monte Carlo Front	5972840	169.00	126.75
78-81 Camaro Rear	14013415	140.00	105.00
82-85 Camaro Rear	5972941	140.00	105.00
82-84 Z-28 Air Dam	5973208	91.00	68.25
82-84 Z-28 Rear	5973208	160.00	120.00
84-86 Cavalier Rear	14080870	62.00	46.50
78-80 Monte Carlo Rear	14009711	180.00	135.00
81-86 Monte Carlo Rear	5972949	152.00	114.00
OLDSMOBILE			
82-84 Ciera Front	22511159	200.00	150.00
85-86 Ciera Front	22522863	200.00	150.00
81-86 Supreme Front Upper	5972521	196.00	147.00
82-84 Ciera Rear	22511536	195.00	146.25
81-85 Supreme Rear Upper	5972519	137.00	102.75

NEW AFTER MARKET URETHANE BUMPERS (FASCIA)

DESCRIPTION	REFERENCE PART #	AFTER MARKET LIST PRICE	BODY SHOP PRICE
PONTIAC			
82-83 J 2000 Front	10019625	171.00	128.25
82-85 J 6000 Front	10018219	147.00	110.25
77-78 Firebird Front	547092	202.00	151.50
79-81 Firebird Front	10004629	202.00	151.50
82-84 Firebird Front	10020286	202.00	151.50
78-80 LeMans Front	10009018	156.00	117.00
80-82 Phoenix Front	10012952	136.00	102.00
84-85 Sunbird Front	10026827	171.00	128.25
82-85 Bonneville Front	10027167	88.00	66.00
79-81 Firebird Rear	10004176	159.00	119.25
82-84 Firebird Rear	10021598	159.00	119.25
76-78 Firebird Rear	526899	159.00	119.25
78-85 Bonneville - LeMans Rear	10027207	116.00	87.00
81-85 Gran Prix End Cap (Right)	10017375	70.00	52.50
81-85 Gran Prix End Cap (Left)	10017376	70.00	52.50
CADILLAC			
84½ - 86 DeVille	1632851	190.00	142.50
IMPORTS			
DATSUN			
79-81 280ZX Front	62050P7100	169.00	126.75
80-81 200SX Front	62050N8500	100.00	75.00
82-83 200SX Front	62050N8561	220.00	165.00
82-83 280ZX Front	62050P9120	135.00	101.25
82-83 Sentra Front	6205004A00	93.00	69.75
84-85 Sentra Front	6202036A00	93.00	69.75
79-81 280ZX Rear	85858P7100	150.00	112.50
82-83 Sentra Rear	8505004A00	81.00	60.75
84-85 Sentra Rear	8502036A00	92.00	69.00
MAZDA			
81-85 RX 7 Front	FA0150030A	189.00	141.75
83-85 626 Front	G032500310	154.00	115.50
TOYOTA			
78-79 Celica Front	52119-14020	70.00	52.50
78-79 Celica Front (Cushion)	5261114010		
82-83 Celica Front	52119-14902	91.00	68.25
80-83 Corolla Front	52119-12041	84.00	63.00
80-83 Corolla Front (Cushion)	5261112040		
81-82 Tercel Front	52119-16021	94.00	70.50
HONDA			
84-85 Civic Front	62511SB4000	106.00	79.50
84-85 Civic Rear	84111SB4660	86.00	64.50
TOTAL			
TOTAL FROM PAGE 1			
GRAND TOTAL			

PRICE & ORDER FORM IMPACT STRIPS

ALL SETS OR PARTS INDIVIDUALLY BOXED

OEM LIST	AUTO & YEAR MODEL	REFERENCE PART #	AFTER MARKET LIST PRICE	BODY SHOP PRICE
87.00	Monte Carlo 81-86 F	5934283	65.00	48.75
43.25	Monte Carlo 81-86 R	5934240	31.00	23.25
138.75	Monte Carlo 78-80 F (Set of 3)		104.00	78.00
98.85	Monte Carlo 78-80 F Upper	5932320	74.00	55.50
19.95	Monte Carlo 78-80 F Lower (2 Req.)	5932321	15.00	11.25
122.75	Monte Carlo 78-80 R (Set of 3)		87.00	65.25
77.75	Monte Carlo 78-80 R Upper	5932325	57.00	42.75
22.50	Monte Carlo 78-80 R Lower (2 Req.)	5932334	15.00	11.25
55.50	Cutlass Supreme 81-86 F (Set of 2)	None	39.00	29.25
68.90	Cutlass Supreme 81-86 R (Set of 4)	None	48.00	36.00
55.58	Phoenix 80-82 F Chrome	10007827	40.00	30.00
55.58	Phoenix 80-82 R Chrome	10007460	40.00	30.00
53.68	LeMans - Grand Am 78-80 F	10006386	39.00	29.25
61.00	LeMans - Grand Am 78-80 R	10006388	40.00	30.00
37.42	Thunderbird - Cougar 83-86 F	E3SZ17C829A	28.00	21.00
37.42	Thunderbird - Cougar 83-86 R	E3SZ17C830A	28.00	21.00
37.42	Thunderbird 80-82 F Chrome	E0SZ17C829A	32.00	24.00
37.42	Thunderbird 80-82 F Black Center	E0SZ17C829B	32.00	24.00
37.42	Thunderbird - Cougar 80-82 R Chrome	E0SZ17C830B	32.00	24.00
37.42	Thunderbird 80-82 R Black Center	E0SZ17C830B	32.00	24.00
34.14	Cougar 80-82 F (Set of 3)	None	28.00	21.00
36.74	Mustang 74-78 F or R Chrome	D4ZZ17B970B	19.00	14.25
27.60	Mustang 74-78 F or R Black & White	D7ZZ17C829B	19.00	14.25
54.65	K-Car 81-83 F Tan & Chrome	X288AT3	44.50	33.37
54.65	K-Car 81-83 F Black & Chrome	X288AX9	44.50	33.37
54.65	K-Car 81-83 R Tan & Chrome	X287AT3	44.50	33.37
54.65	K-Car 81-83 R Black & Chrome	X287AX9	44.50	33.37
54.65	LeBaron-New Yorker 82-84 Black & Chrome	X284AX9	44.50	33.37
	TOTAL			
	GRAND TOTAL BUMPERS & STRIPS			

DESCRIPTION	REFERENCE NUMBER	LIST

CHEVROLET

Full Size Chev. Vans

78-86 Front Chrome	GMCCHVN-F78P	119.00
78-86 Front Primed	GMCCHVN-F78PPA	65.00
78-86 Rear Chrome	GMCCHVN-R78P	119.00
78-86 Rear Primed	GMCCHVN-R78PPA	55.00

CHRYSLER

Aries, Reliant

81-84 Front Cover	CHRKCAR-F81P-U	98.00
81-84 Front Reinforcement	RECKCAR-F81.	59.00
85-86 Front Cover	CHRKCAR-F85P-U	130.00
81-84 Rear Cover	CHRKCAR-R81P-U	80.00
84-85 Rear Cover Station Wagon	CHRKCAR-R84PSW-U	80.00
85-86 Rear Cover Exc. Station Wagon	CHRKCAR-R85P-U	130.00

Champ, Colt H.B.

79-84 Front Chrome	CHRCOLT-F79PHB	100.00
79-84 Front Primed	CHRCOLT-F79PHBPA	86.00
79-84 Rear Chrome	CHRCOLT-R79PHB	100.00
79-84 Rear Primed	CHRCOLT-R79PHBPA	86.00

LeBaron, E Class

82-86 Front Cover Exc. G.T.S.	CHRLBAR-F82P-U	102.00
82-86 Rear Cover Exc. G.T.S.	CHRKCAR-R81P-U	80.00
84-85 Rear Cover Station Wagon	CHRKCAR-R84PSW-U	130.00

Omni, Horizon

78-86 4 Door Front Plain	CHROMNI-F78P-A	120.00
W/Cushions	CHROMNI-F78S-A	120.00
79-83 2 Door OMNI Front Cover	CHROMNI-F79P2-U	135.00
79-85 Front Reinforcement	RECOMNI-F79-S	103.00
78-86 4 Door Rear Plain	CHROMNI-F78P-A	120.00
W/Cushions	CHROMNI-F78S-A	120.00

ALL ITEMS ON THIS PAGE ARE GUARANTEED TO BE AVAILABLE

FOR SHIPMENT WITHIN 48 HOURS

DESCRIPTION	REFERENCE NUMBER	LIST

CHRYSLER

Dodge D-50, Arrow

79-82 Front Chrome	CHRD-50-F79P	96.00
78-82 Front Primed	CHRD-50-F79PPA	80.00
83-85 Front Chrome	CHRD-50-F83P	96.00
83-85 Front Primed	CHRD-50-F83PPA	80.00

Dodge, Plymouth Trucks

72-82 Front Chrome Plain	CHRDOTK-F72P	153.00
72-82 Front Primed Plain	CHRDOTK-F72PPA	87.00
83-85 Front Chrome Plain	CHRDOTK-F83P	153.00
83-85 Front Primed Plain	CHRDOTK-F83PPA	87.00
72-85 Rear Chrome Plain	CHRDOTK-R72P	150.00
72-85 Rear Primed Plain	CHRDOTK-R72PPA	90.00

Dodge, Plymouth Vans

79-85 Front Chrome Plain	CHRDOVN-F79P	142.00
79-85 Front Primed Plain	CHRDOVN-F79PPA	86.00
78-85 Rear Chrome Plain	CHRDOVN-R78P	104.00
78-85 Rear Primed Plain	CHRDOVN-R78PPA	86.00

Dodge, Plymouth Mini Vans

84-86 Front Plain	CHRCAVN-F84P-A	140.00
W/Cushions	CHRCAVN-F84S-A	140.00
84-86 Rear Plain	CHRCAVN-R84P-A	140.00
W/Cushions	CHRCAVN-R84S-A	140.00

DATSUN

200SX

80-81 Front Cover	DAT200S-F80P-U	100.00
82-83 Front Cover	DAT200S-F82P-U	220.00

210, B210

76 Front	DAT210--F75PLA	70.00
77-78 Front	DAT210--F77P	70.00
79-82 Front Plain	DAT210--F79P	70.00
W/Cushions	DAT210--F80S	70.00

ALL ITEMS ON THIS PAGE ARE GUARANTEED TO BE AVAILABLE
FOR SHIPMENT WITHIN 48 HOURS

DESCRIPTION	REFERENCE NUMBER	LIST

DATSUN NISSAN

210, B210

75-76 Rear	DAT210--R75P	70.00
77-78 Rear	DAT210--R77P	70.00
79 Rear Exc. Station Wagon	DAT210--R79P	70.00
80-82 Rear Exc. Station Wagon	DAT210--R80P	70.00

260Z, 280Z

77-78 Front Center	DAT280Z-F77P	274.00
79-81 Front Cover	DAT280Z-F79P-U	169.00
82-83 Front Cover	DAT280Z-F82P-U	135.00

310

79 Front Center	DAT310--F79P	125.00
80 Front Center	DAT310--F80P	125.00
81-82 Front Center	DAT310--F81P	125.00

510

78-79 Front Center	DAT510--F78P	96.00
80-81 Front Center	DAT510--F80S	96.00

620

73-79 Front	DAT620--F73P	55.00

720

80-82 2WD Front Center Chrome	DAT720--F80P2WD	58.00
80-82 2WD Front Center Primed	DAT720--F80P2WP	52.00
80-82 4WD Front Center Chrome	DAT720--F80P4WD.....	58.00
80-82 4WD Front Center Primed	DAT720--F80P4WP	52.00
83-85 2WD Front Chrome	DAT720--F83P2WD	80.00
83-85 2WD Front Primed	DAT720--F83P2WP	66.00
83-85 4WD Front Chrome	DAT720--F83P4WD	80.00
83-85 4WD Front Primed	DAT720--F83P4WP	66.00

ALL ITEMS ON THIS PAGE ARE GUARANTEED TO BE AVAILABLE

FOR SHIPMENT WITHIN 48 HOURS

DESCRIPTION	REFERENCE NUMBER	LIST

DATSUN NISSAN

810, Maxima

81-85 Front Cover	DAT810--F81P-U	101.00

Sentra

82-85 Front Cover	DATSENT-F82P-U	93.00
82-85 Front Reinforcement	REDSENT-F82.	60.00

FORD-MERCURY

Escort, Lynx

81-85 (March) Front Alum. Plain	FMCESCO-F81P-A	170.00
W/Cushions	FMCESCO-F81S-A	170.00
81-85 (March) Rear Alum. Plain	FMCESCO-R81P-A	170.00
W/Cushions	FMCESCO-R81S-A	170.00

Fairmont, Zephyr

78-83 Front Alum. Plain or w/guards	FMCFMON-F78P-A	170.00
80-83 Front Alum. W/Cushions	FMCFMON-F80S-A	170.00
78-83 Rear Alum. Plain or w/guards	FMCFMON-R78P-A	170.00

Fiesta

78-80 Front Alum. Plain	FMCFIES-F78P-A	140.00
W/Cushions	FMCFIES-F78S-A	140.00
78-80 Rear Alum. Plain	FMCFIES-F78P-A	140.00
W/Cushions	FMCFIES-F78S-A	140.00

Full Size

80-86 Front Reinforcement Steel	REFFORD-F80-ST	120.00

Granada, Monarch

77-80 Front Reinforcement Steel	REFGRAN-F77LA	116.00

Mustang, Capri

65-66 Mustang Front	FMCMUST-F65P	110.00
67-68 Mustang Front	FMCMUST-F67P	110.00
74-78 Mustang Front Cover	FMCMUST-F74P-U	250.00
79-82 Mustang Front Cover	FMCMUST-F79P-U	250.00
83-84 Mustang Front Cover	FMCMUST-F83P-U	250.00

ALL ITEMS ON THIS PAGE ARE GUARANTEED TO BE AVAILABLE
FOR SHIPMENT WITHIN 48 HOURS

Mustang, Capri

Description	Reference Number	List
79-84 Capri Front Cover	FMCCAPI-F79P-U	250.00
85-86 Mustang Front Cover	FMCMUST-F85P-U	250.00
79-86 Front Reinforcement	REFMUST-F79-ST	100.00
74-78 Rear Cover	FMCMUST-R74P-U	250.00
79-84 Rear Cover	FMCMUST-R79P-U	110.00

Tempo, Topaz

Description	Reference Number	List
84-85 Front Alum. Plain	FMCTEPO-F84P-A	140.00
W/Cushions	FMCTEPO-F84S-A	140.00
84-85 Rear Alum. Plain	FMCTEPO-R84P-A	140.00
W/Cushions	FMCTEPO-R84S-A	140.00

Thunderbird, Cougar

Description	Reference Number	List
81-82 T-Bird Front Cover	FMCTHUN-F81P-U	120.00
81-82 Cougar XR7 Front Cover	FMCCOUG-F81P-U	120.00
83-86 Front Cover	FMCTHUN-F83P-U	120.00

Ford Courier

Description	Reference Number	List
78-82 Front Chrome	FMCCOUR-F78P	72.00

Ford Van

Description	Reference Number	List
75-86 Front Chrome	FMCFOVN-F75P	105.00
75-86 Front Primed	FMCFOVN-F75PPA	75.00
75-86 Rear Chrome	FMCFOVN-R75P	105.00
75-86 Rear Primed	FMCFOVN-R75PPA	75.00

Full Size Ford Trucks

Description	Reference Number	List
64-77 Front Chrome Plain	FMCFOTK-F64P	110.00
W/Cushions	FMCFOTK-F64S	110.00
64-77 Front Primed Plain	FMCFOTK-F64PPA	86.00
W/Cushions	FMCFOTK-F64SPA	86.00
78-79 Front Chrome Plain	FMCFOTK-F78P	110.00
W/Cushions	FMCFOTK-F78S	110.00

ALL ITEMS ON THIS PAGE ARE GUARANTEED TO BE AVAILABLE
FOR SHIPMENT WITHIN 48 HOURS

FORD

Full Size Ford Trucks

78-79 Front Primed Plain	FMCFOTK-F78PPA	86.00
W/Cushions	FMCFOTK-F78SPA	86.00
80-86 Front Chrome Plain	FMCFOTK-F80P	110.00
W/Cushions	FMCFOTK-F80S	110.00
80-86 Front Primed Plain	FMCFOTK-F80PPA	86.00
W/Cushions	FMCFOTK-F80SPA	86.00

Ranger, Bronco II

82-85 Front Chrome Plain	FMCRANG-F82P	110.00
W/Cushions	FMCRANG-F82S	110.00
82-85 Front Primed Plain	FMCRANG-F82PPA	89.00
W/Cushions	FMCRANG-F82SPA	89.00

HONDA

Accord

76-79 Front	HONACCO-F76S	60.00
80-81 Front	HONACCO-F80S	60.00
76-79 Rear	HONACCO-R76S	60.00
80-81 Rear	HONACCO-R80S	60.00

Civic

74-77 Front	HONCIVI-F74P	72.00
78-79 Front	HONCIVI-F78P	72.00
80-81 Front Chrome	HONCIVI-F80S	101.00
80-81 Front Primed	HONCIVI-F80SPA	80.00
74-77 Rear	HONCIVI-F74P	72.00
78-79 Rear	HONCIVI-R78P	68.00
80-81 Rear Chrome	HONCIVI-R80S	82.00
80-81 Rear Primed	HONCIVI-R80SPA	58.00

MAZDA

RX7

81-83 Front Cover	MAZRX7--F81P-U	189.00

ALL ITEMS ON THIS PAGE ARE GUARANTEED TO BE AVAILABLE
FOR SHIPMENT WINTHIN 48 HOURS

MAZDA

626

83-85 Front Cover	MAZ626--F83P-U	154.00

OLDSMOBILE

Cutlass Ciera

82-84 Front Cover	GMCCIER-F82P-U	200.00
82-84 Front Reinforcement Alum	REGCIER-F82-A	180.00
85-86 Front Cover	GMCCIER-F85P-U	200.00
82-84 Rear Cover Exc. S/W	GMCCIER-R82P-U	195.00

Cutlass, Supreme

78 Supreme Front Upper	GMCCUTL-F78SUSUP ...	134.00
80 Supreme Front	GMCCUTL-F80SSUP	186.00
78-80 ALL Front Reinforcement	REGREGA-F80-S	120.00
81-86 4 Door Front	GMCCUTL-F80SSUP	186.00
81-86 4 Door Front Reinforcement	REGREGA-F80-S	120.00
81-86 2 Door Front Upper Cover	GMCCUTL-F81PU-U	196.00
81-86 2 Door Front Lower Chrome	GMCCUTL-F81PLOST ...	186.00
81-86 2 Door Front Reinforcement	REGCUTL-F81.	120.00
76-77 2 Door Rear Upper Right	GMCCUTL-R76SRU2	88.00
Left	GMCCUTL-R76SLU2	88.00
76-77 Rear Reinforcement Exc. S/W	REGCUTL-R76.	120.00
78-80 Rear Reinforcement Exc. S/W	REGREGA-R78-S	116.00
81-86 4 Door Rear Reinforcement Exc. S/W	REGREGA-R78-S	116.00
81-86 2 Door Rear Cover	GMCCUTL-R81PU-U	137.00

Oldsmobile 88, 98

80-86 Front (RWD)	GMCOLDS-F80S	227.00
80-86 Front Reinforcement (RWD)	REGOLDS-F80-ST	133.00
77-79 Rear Reinforcement	REGOLDS-R77.	142.00
77-86 S/W Rear Reinforcement	REGCHEV-R77SW-ST ...	120.00
80-86 Rear Reinforcement (RWD)	REGOLDS-R80-ST	127.00

ALL ITEMS ON THIS PAGE ARE GUARANTEED TO BE AVAILABLE
FOR SHIPMENT WITHIN 48 HOURS

OLDSMOBILE

Omega
80-83 Front Alum. Plain	GMCOMEG-F80P-A	..... 170.00
W/Cushions	GMCOMEG-F80S-A	..... 170.00
84-85 Front Alum. Plain	GMCOMEG-F84P-A	..... 170.00
W/Cushions	GMCOMEG-F84S-A	..... 170.00

Starfire
79-80 Front W/Cushions	GMCMONZ-F75S	.... 130.00

Toronado
79-85 Front Reinforcement	REGTORO-F79-S	...... 120.00

PONTIAC

Bonneville, Catalina
82-86 Front Cover	GMCPONT-F82P-U	..... 88.00
82-86 Rear Cover Exc. S/W	GMCTEMP-R78P-U	..... 116.00
77-81 Sta. Wgn. Rear Reinforcement	REGCHEV-R77SW-ST	... 120.00

Firebird
77-78 Front Cover	GMCFIRE-F77P-U	..... 202.00
79-81 Front Cover	GMCFIRE-F79P-U	..... 202.00
82-84 Front Cover	GMCFIRE-F82P-U	..... 202.00
76-78 Rear Cover	GMCFIRE-R76P-U	..... 159.00
79-81 Rear Cover	GMCFIRE-R79P-U	..... 159.00

Gran Prix
81-86 Front Cover Right	GMCGRPX-F81PR-U	.... 70.00
Left	GMCGRPX-F81PL-U	.... 70.00
81-86 Rear Upper Cover	GMCGRPX-R81PU-U	.... 116.00

LeMans
78-80 Front Cover	GMCTEMP-F78P-U	..... 156.00
81 Front Cover	GMCTEMP-F81P-U	..... 156.00
78-81 Rear Cover Exc. S/W	GMCTEMP-R78P-U	..... 116.00

ALL ITEMS ON THIS PAGE ARE GUARANTEED TO BE AVAILABLE
FOR SHIPMENT WITHIN 48 HOURS

PONTIAC

Parisienne

83-86 Front Plain	GMCCHEV-F80P	138.00
W/Cushions	GMCCHEV-F80S	138.00
83-86 Front Reinforcement	REGCHEV-F80-ST	133.00
83-86 S/W Rear Reinforcement	REGCHEV-R77SW-ST	120.00

Pontiac T-1000

81-82 Front Plain	GMCCVET-F76P	82.00
W/Cushions	GMCCVET-F76S	82.00
81-82 Rear Plain	GMCCVET-R76P	82.00
W/Cushions	GMCCVET-R76S	82.00

Pontiac J 2000, Sunbird

76-80 Front W/Cushion	GMCMONZ-F75S	130.00
82-83 Front Cover	GMC2000-F82P-U	171.00
84-85 Front Cover	GMC2000-F84P-U	171.00

Pontiac 6000

82-84 Front Cover Exc. STE	GMC6000-F82P-U	147.00

Phoenix

80-82 Front Cover	GMCPHOE-F80P-U	136.00

TOYOTA

Celica

75-77 Front	TOYCELI-F74PLA	93.00
78-79 Front Cover	TOYCELI-F78P-U	70.00
80-81 Front Cover	TOYCELI-F80P-U	104.00
82-85 Front Cover	TOYCELI-F82P-U	103.00

Corolla

75-79 Front	TOYCORL-F75P	84.00
80-81 Coupe Front Cover	TOYCORL-F80PCP-U	84.00
75-79 Rear	TOYCORL-R75P	91.00

ALL ITEMS ON THIS PAGE ARE GUARANTEED TO BE AVAILABLE
FOR SHIPMENT WITHIN 48 HOURS

TOYOTA

Tercel

81-82 Front Cover	TOYTERC-F81P-U	94.00

Toyota Pick-up

79-81 2WD Front Chrome	TOYHILU-F79P2W	58.00
Primed	TOYHILU-F79P2WP	46.00
79-81 4WD Front Chrome	TOYHILU-F79P4W	58.00
Primed	TOYHILU-F79P4WP	46.00
82-83 2WD Front Chrome	TOYHILU-F82P2W	58.00
Primed	TOYHILU-F82P2WP	46.00
82-83 4WD Front Chrome	TOYHILU-F82P4W	58.00
Primed	TOYHILU-F82P4WP	46.00
84-85 4WD Front Chrome	TOYHILU-F84P4W	58.00
Primed	TOYHILU-F84P4WP	46.00

VOLKSWAGON

Beetle, Superbeetle

68-73 Front	VW-BEET-F68P	60.00
74-79 Front	VW-BEET-F74P	152.00
68-73 Rear	VW-BEET-R68P	60.00
74-79 Rear	VW-BEET-R74P	152.00

Rabbit, VW Pick-up

75-80 Front Chrome	VW-RABB-F75S	168.00
81-83 Front Alum Plain	VW-RABB-F81P-A	95.00
W/Cushions	VW-RABB-F81S-A	95.00
75-79 Rear Chrome	VW-RABB-R75S	162.00
81-84 Rear Alum Plain	VW-RABB-R81P-A	95.00
W/Cushions	VW-RABB-R81S-A	95.00

**ALL ITEMS ON THIS PAGE ARE GUARANTEED TO BE AVAILABLE
FOR SHIPMENT WITHIN 48 HOURS**

Jobber Steel Body Parts

*Courtesy of Pro Auto Ltd., Winnipeg, Manitoba

STEEL: FENDERS, HOODS, DOORS & TAILGATES

MAKE	MODEL	YEARS	PARTS STOCKED
AUDI	FOX	73-76	L FENDER 59.22 R FENDER 59.22
		77-79	L FENDER 66.62 R FENDER 66.62
	5000	78-79	L FENDER 88.85 R FENDER 88.85
		80-83	L FENDER 88.85 R FENDER 88.85
	4000	80-83	L FENDER 81.45 R FENDER 81.45
AMC	CONCORDE	79-83	L FENDER 133.29 R FENDER 133.29
BMW	1600-2002	67-76	L FENDER 88.85 R FENDER 88.85
	320i	77-83	L FENDER 88.85 R FENDER 88.85
	528-530i	75-81	L FENDER 96.25 R FENDER 96.25
	318i	84	L FENDER 96.25 R FENDER 96.25
	528e	82-85	L FENDER 96.25 R FENDER 96.25
CHRYSLER	ARIES/RELIANT	81-84	L FENDER 78.50 R FENDER 78.50 HOOD 140.70 GRILL 44.40

STEEL: FENDERS, HOODS, DOORS & TAILGATES

MAKE	MODEL	YEARS	PARTS STOCKED
CHRYSLER	ASPEN/VOLARE	76-79	L FENDER *103.60* R FENDER *103.60*
	ASPEN	80	L FENDER *103.60* R FENDER *103.60*
	CARAVELLE R.W.D.	80-82	L FENDER *103.60* R FENDER *103.60*
	DIPLOMAT	80-82	L FENDER *103.60* R FENDER *103.60*
	LE BARON R.W.D.	80-82	L FENDER *103.60* R FENDER *103.60*
	NEW YORKER R.W.D.	80-85	L FENDER *103.60* R FENDER *103.60*
	VOLARE	80	L FENDER *103.60* R FENDER *103.60*
	LE BARON F.W.D. (W OR W/O CORNER LAMPS)	82-83	L FENDER *81.50* R FENDER *81.50*
	NEW YORKER	82-83	L FENDER *81.50* R FENDER *81.50*
	COLT F.W.D.	79-82	L FENDER *59.25* R FENDER *59.25* HOOD *96.25* GRILL *37.00*
	DODGE 400 (W OR W/O CORNER LAMPS)	82-83	L FENDER *81.45* R FENDER *81.45*
	DODGE 600 F.W.D.	82-83	L FENDER *81.45* R FENDER *81.45*

STEEL: FENDERS, HOODS, DOORS & TAILGATES

MAKE	MODEL	YEARS	PARTS STOCKED	
CHRYSLER	DODGE PICKUP	72-80	L FENDER	*81.45*
			R FENDER	*81.45*
			HOOD	*133.30*
			DOOR	*n/a*
			TAILGATE	*81.45*
		81-85	L FENDER	*103.60*
			R FENDER	*103.60*
	RAMCHARGER	72-80	L FENDER	*81.45*
			R FENDER	*81.45*
			HOOD	*133.30*
			DOOR	*n/a*
			TAILGATE	*81.45*
		81-85	L FENDER	*103.60*
			R FENDER	*103.60*
	TRAIL DUSTER	72-80	L FENDER	*81.45*
			R FENDER	*81.45*
			HOOD	*133.30*
			DOOR	*n/a*
			TAILGATE	*81.45*
		81-85	L FENDER	*103.60*
			R FENDER	*103.60*
	D50 PICKUP IMPORT	79-83	GRILL	*44.40*
		79-85	HOOD	*103.60*
		79-86	L FENDER	*81.45*
			R FENDER	*81.45*
	HORIZON/OMNI 4DR	78-82	L FENDER	*59.25*
			R FENDER	*59.25*

STEEL: FENDERS, HOODS, DOORS & TAILGATES

MAKE	MODEL	YEARS	PARTS STOCKED
CHRYSLER	HORIZON/OMNI 2DR	79-83	L FENDER 66.65 R FENDER 66.65 HOOD 118.50
	MAGIC WAGON	83-85	L FENDER 96.25 R FENDER 96.25 HOOD · 125.90
	CARAVAN	83-85	L FENDER 96.25 R FENDER 96.25 HOOD 125.90
DATSUN	B210	74-78	L FENDER 59.25 R FENDER 59.25 HOOD 74.00 GRILL 41.45
	210	79	L FENDER 66.65 R FENDER 66.65 HOOD 74.05
		80-81	L FENDER 66.65 R FENDER 66.65 HOOD 78.50 GRILL 37.00
	310	79-82	L FENDER 66.65 R FENDER 66.65 GRILL 48.85 HOOD 103.65
	510	78-81	L FENDER 66.65 R FENDER 66.65 HOOD 74.05 GRILL 59.25
	620 PICKUP	72-79	L FENDER 59.25 R FENDER 59.25 HOOD 74.05 GRILL 37.00 BUMPER 37.00

STEEL: FENDERS, HOODS, DOORS & TAILGATES

MAKE	MODEL	YEARS	PARTS STOCKED	
DATSUN	720 PICKUP	80-85	L FENDER	66.65
			R FENDER	66.65
			HOOD	103.65
			GRILL	45.50
			L DOOR	125.90
			R DOOR	125.90
			TAILGATE	103.65
	SENTRA	82-85	L FENDER	51.80
			R FENDER	51.80
			HOOD	74.05
			GRILL	59.25
	240/60/80Z	70-78	L FENDER	103.60
			R FENDER	103.60
			HOOD	140.70
			H/L EXT. PANEL	44.40
	280ZX	79-82	L FENDER	118.50
			R FENDER	118.50
		79-83	HOOD (TURBO)	214.77
	200SX	80-81	L FENDER	78.50
			R FENDER	78.50
	MAXIMA	81-84	L FENDER	78.50
			R FENDER	78.50
	STANZA	82-83	L FENDER	74.00
			R FENDER	74.00
	300ZX	84-86	L FENDER	148.10
			R FENDER	148.10
			HOOD (TURBO)	259.25
FORD	COURIER	77-83	L FENDER	37.00
			R FENDER	37.00
			HOOD	96.25
			TAILGATE	74.00
			GRILL	66.65

STEEL: FENDERS, HOODS, DOORS & TAILGATES

MAKE	MODEL	YEARS	PARTS STOCKED
FORD	ECONOLINE VAN	75-84	L FENDER 37.00 R FENDER 37.00 HOOD 96.25 DOORS 176.40
	ESCORT/LYNX	81-85	L FENDER 37.00 R FENDER 37.00 HOOD 103.60 GRILL 22.20
	FAIRMONT/FUTURA	78-83	L FENDER 81.50 R FENDER 81.50 HOOD 103.60
	ZEPHYR	78-83	L FENDER 81.50 R FENDER 81.50 HOOD 103.60
	FIESTA	78-80	L FENDER 37.00 R FENDER 37.00 HOOD 74.00
	FORD PICKUP	73-79	L FENDER 37.00 R FENDER 37.00 HOOD 140.70 DOORS 11.10 TAILGATE 74.05
		80-86	L FENDER 74.00 R FENDER 74.00 HOOD 148.15 DOORS 125.90 TAILGATE 81.50
	GRANADA	75-80	L FENDER 78.50 R FENDER 78.50
	MONARCH	75-80	L FENDER 78.50 R FENDER 78.50
	VERSAILLES	75-80	L FENDER 78.50 R FENDER 78.50

STEEL: FENDERS, HOODS, DOORS & TAILGATES

MAKE	MODEL	YEARS	PARTS STOCKED
FORD	MUSTANG	79-86	L FENDER *51.80* R FENDER *51.80* HOOD *155.50*
	RANGER PICKUP	83-86	L FENDER *66.65* R FENDER *66.65* HOOD *125.90*
GM	SKYLARK	80-86	L FENDER *81.50* R FENDER *81.50*
	BUICK CENTURY	78-79	L FENDER *74.00* R FENDER *74.00*
	CAMARO (SPECIFY Z28)	74-77	L FENDER *118.50* R FENDER *118.50* HOOD *155.50*
		78-81	L FENDER *118.50* R FENDER *118.50* HOOD *155.50*
		82-85	L FENDER *96.25* R FENDER *96.25* HOOD *185.15*
	FIREBIRD (SPECIFY TRANS AM)	82-85	L FENDER *118.50* R FENDER *118.50*
	CAVALIER	82-84	L FENDER *59.25* R FENDER *59.25* HOOD *119.00*
	CITATION	80-85	L FENDER *59.25* R FENDER *59.25* HOOD *118.50*
		82-85	GRILL *37.00*

STEEL: FENDERS, HOODS, DOORS & TAILGATES

MAKE	MODEL	YEARS	PARTS STOCKED
GM	CHEVETTE/ACADIAN	76-82	L FENDER 41.45 R FENDER 41.45
		79-86	L FENDER 81.50 R FENDER 81.50 HOOD 103.60 GRILL 29.60
	MALIBU (W OR W/O MARKER LITE)	78/81	L FENDER 88.85 R FENDER 88.85
	MONZA	76-80	L FENDER 74.00 R FENDER 74.00
	SKYHAWK	76-80	L FENDER 74.00 R FENDER 74.00
	NOVA	75-79	L FENDER 78.50 R FENDER 78.50
	CUTLASS SALON	78-79	L FENDER 125.90 R FENDER 125.90
	CUTLASS SUPREME	78-80	L FENDER 125.90 R FENDER 125.90
	CUTLASS SUPREME 2DR	80-84	L FENDER 59.25 R FENDER 59.25
	CUTLASS CIERA	82-84	L FENDER 103.60 R FENDER 103.60
	OLDS 88/98	80-85	L FENDER 74.00 R FENDER 74.00

STEEL: FENDERS, HOODS, DOORS & TAILGATES

MAKE	MODEL	YEARS	PARTS STOCKED	
GM	GM S10/S15	82-85	L FENDER	74.00
			R FENDER	74.00
			HOOD	118.50
			DOORS	170.35
			TAILGATE	125.90
			GRILL	51.80
	CHEVY VAN	71-82	L FENDER	37.00
			R FENDER	37.00
		78-83	L DOOR	192.55
			R DOOR	192.55
			HOOD	96.25
	CHEVY/GMC PICKUP	73-80	L FENDER	59.25
			R FENDER	59.25
			HOOD	133.30
			DOORS	81.50
			TAILGATE	74.00
			L ROCKER	18.50
			R ROCKER	18.50
			L PARTIAL QUARTER	29.95
			R PARTIAL QUARTER	29.95
		81-84	L FENDER	74.00
			R FENDER	74.00
			HOOD	133.50
			DOORS	81.50
			TAILGATE	74.00
HONDA	ACCORD	76-81	L FENDER	51.85
			R FENDER	51.85
			HOOD	81.50
			GRILL	51.80
			BUMPER	37.00
		82-83	L FENDER	96.25
			R FENDER	96.25
			GRILL	59.25
		84-85	L FENDER	96.25
			R FENDER	96.25
			HOOD	148.15

STEEL: FENDERS, HOODS, DOORS & TAILGATES

MAKE	MODEL	YEARS	PARTS STOCKED
HONDA	CIVIC	73-79	L FENDER 51.85 R FENDER 51.85
		80-81	L FENDER 59.25 R FENDER 59.25 HOOD 96.25 GRILL 51.85
		82-83	L FENDER 74.00 R FENDER 74.00 HOOD 125.90 GRILL 51.80
		84-85	L FENDER 103.65 R FENDER 103.65
	CIVIC CVCC WAGON	75-79	L FENDER 66.65 R FENDER 66.65
	PRELUDE	79-85	L FENDER 74.00 R FENDER 74.00
MAZDA	GLC	77-80	L FENDER 59.25 R FENDER 59.25
		81-85	L FENDER 66.65 R FENDER 66.65 HOOD 81.50 GRILL 29.60
	626	79-86	L FENDER 74.00 R FENDER 74.00 GRILL 44.40
	RX7	79-84	L FENDER 103.65 R FENDER 103.65 HOOD
	MAZDA PICKUP B2000	77-84	L FENDER 66.65 R FENDER 66.65 HOOD 103.65 GRILL 66.65 TAILGATE 88.85

STEEL: FENDERS, HOODS, DOORS & TAILGATES

MAKE	MODEL	YEARS	PARTS STOCKED
MERCEDES BENZ	220/230/250/280C	68-76	L FENDER *118.50* R FENDER *118.50*
	230/240/280/300	73-76	L FENDER *118.50* R FENDER *118.50*
	280/300/300D	77-83	L FENDER *118.50* R FENDER *118.50*
RENAULT	RS LE CAR	76-84	L FENDER *44.40* R FENDER *44.40* HOOD *74.40*
	ALLIANCE	83-84	L FENDER *74.00* R FENDER *74.00*
SUBARU	BRAT	77-78	L FENDER *74.00* R FENDER *74.00* HOOD *125.90*
	1600/1800	80-82	L FENDER *74.00* R FENDER *74.00* HOOD *125.90* GRILL *44.40*
TOYOTA	CELICA (SPECIFY SUPRA)	78-85	L FENDER *96.25* R FENDER *96.25*
	COROLLA KE 30	75-79	L FENDER *59.25* R FENDER *59.25* HOOD *74.00*
	SEDAN WAGON	80-81	L FENDER *66.65* R FENDER *66.65* HOOD *74.00*
	COUPE	80-81	L FENDER *66.65* R FENDER *66.65*
	COUPE SEDAN	82-83	L FENDER *74.00* R FENDER *74.00*

STEEL: FENDERS, HOODS, DOORS & TAILGATES

MAKE	MODEL	YEARS	PARTS STOCKED
TOYOTA	SEDAN LIFTBACK	84-85	L FENDER 74.40 R FENDER 74.40
	CRESSIDA	78-82	L FENDER 81.50 R FENDER 81.50
	TERCEL	81-86	L FENDER 66.65 R FENDER 66.65 GRILL 81.45
	PICKUP HILUX	72-78	L FENDER 66.65 R FENDER 66.65 HOOD 66.65 DOORS 125.90
	PICKUP HILUX 2WD/4WD	79-82	L FENDER 66.65 R FENDER 66.65 HOOD 74.00 DOORS 125.90 TAILGATE n/a GRILL n/a
		83-85	L FENDER 125.90 R FENDER 125.90 HOOD 125.90 GRILL 44.40
VOLKSWAGEN	DASHER	74-77	L FENDER 66.65 R FENDER 66.65
	JETTA	80-84	L FENDER 66.65 R FENDER 66.65 HOOD 106.65
	RABBIT	75-79	L FENDER 51.85 R FENDER 51.85 HOOD 103.65 GRILL n/a
		80-84	L FENDER 74.40 R FENDER 74.40 HOOD 106.65

STEEL: FENDERS, HOODS, DOORS & TAILGATES

MAKE	MODEL	YEARS	PARTS STOCKED
VOLKSWAGEN	SCIROCCO	75-81	L FENDER *118.50* R FENDER *118.50* HOOD *177.75*
VOLVO	140	69-74	L FENDER *81.50* R FENDER *81.50*
	240	75-82	L FENDER *88.85* R FENDER *88.85*

Write-in Estimate Worksheets

ESTIMATOR'S REPORT

	CLAIM NUMBER
Insurance Company _____	
Estimate, Inspection and Location Date _____	

ADJUSTER'S NAME	ESTIMATOR'S NAME	DATE OF COMPLETION	DATE OF LOSS

INSURED

NAME AND ADDRESS

VEHICLE

LICENSE (POLICY) NUMBER	GVW	MILEAGE	AMOUNT OF DEDUCTIBLE
YEAR, MAKE & MODEL		SERIAL NUMBER	

DESCRIPTION OF WORK TO BE DONE	RE-PAIR	REPLACE NEW	L.K.Q.	QTY.	PART NUMBER	PARTS COST	HRS.	LABOR COST

This is purely an estimate and not a definite contract price. Owing to the impossibility of determining damage of concealed parts, we reserve the right to submit a further estimate for approval or otherwise. Prices subject to change without notice.
Authorization to Repair

_____

I _____ the registered owner of the above described
vehicle authorize the repairs to proceed.

TOTAL PARTS COST ▶	
TOTAL LABOR COST ▶	
SHOP MATERIAL	
PAINT LABOR	
PAINT MATERIAL	
SUB TOTAL	
TAX	
TOTAL COST ▶	

ONLY APPROVED ADDITIONS PAID

ESTIMATOR'S REPORT

Insurance Company _____ | CLAIM NUMBER

Estimate, Inspection and Location Date _____

| ADJUSTER'S NAME | ESTIMATOR'S NAME | DATE OF COMPLETION | DATE OF LOSS |

INSURED   VEHICLE

NAME AND ADDRESS	LICENSE (POLICY) NUMBER	GVW	MILEAGE	AMOUNT OF DEDUCTIBLE
	YEAR, MAKE & MODEL		SERIAL NUMBER	

DESCRIPTION OF WORK TO BE DONE	RE-PAIR	REPLACE NEW	L.K.Q.	QTY.	PART NUMBER	PARTS COST	HRS.	LABOR COST

This is purely an estimate and not a definite contract price. Owing to the impossibility of determining damage of concealed parts, we reserve the right to submit a further estimate for approval or otherwise. Prices subject to change without notice.
Authorization to Repair
_____

I_____ the registered owner of the above described
vehicle authorize the repairs to proceed.

TOTAL PARTS COST ▶	
TOTAL LABOR COST ▶	
SHOP MATERIAL	
PAINT LABOR	
PAINT MATERIAL	
SUB TOTAL	
TAX	
TOTAL COST ▶	

ONLY APPROVED ADDITIONS PAID

ESTIMATOR'S REPORT

Insurance Company _____

| CLAIM NUMBER |

Estimate, Inspection and Location Date _____

ADJUSTER'S NAME	ESTIMATOR'S NAME	DATE OF COMPLETION	DATE OF LOSS

INSURED

VEHICLE

NAME AND ADDRESS	LICENSE (POLICY) NUMBER	GVW	MILEAGE	AMOUNT OF DEDUCTIBLE
	YEAR, MAKE & MODEL		SERIAL NUMBER	

DESCRIPTION OF WORK TO BE DONE	RE-PAIR	REPLACE NEW	REPLACE L.K.Q.	QTY.	PART NUMBER	PARTS COST	HRS.	LABOR COST

This is purely an estimate and not a definite contract price. Owing to the impossibility of determining damage of concealed parts, we reserve the right to submit a further estimate for approval or otherwise. Prices subject to change without notice.
Authorization to Repair
_____

I_____ the registered owner of the above described
vehicle authorize the repairs to proceed.

TOTAL PARTS COST ▶	
TOTAL LABOR COST ▶	
SHOP MATERIAL	
PAINT LABOR	
PAINT MATERIAL	
SUB TOTAL	
TAX	
TOTAL COST ▶	

ONLY APPROVED ADDITIONS PAID

ESTIMATOR'S REPORT

Insurance Company _____

	CLAIM NUMBER

Estimate, Inspection and Location Date _____

ADJUSTER'S NAME	ESTIMATOR'S NAME	DATE OF COMPLETION	DATE OF LOSS

INSURED   VEHICLE

NAME AND ADDRESS	LICENSE (POLICY) NUMBER	GVW	MILEAGE	AMOUNT OF DEDUCTIBLE
	YEAR, MAKE & MODEL		SERIAL NUMBER	

DESCRIPTION OF WORK TO BE DONE	RE-PAIR	REPLACE NEW	L.K.Q.	QTY.	PART NUMBER	PARTS COST	HRS.	LABOR COST

This is purely an estimate and not a definite contract price. Owing to the impossibility of determining damage of concealed parts, we reserve the right to submit a further estimate for approval or otherwise. Prices subject to change without notice.

Authorization to Repair
_____

I_____ the registered owner of the above described vehicle authorize the repairs to proceed.

TOTAL PARTS COST ▶	
TOTAL LABOR COST ▶	
SHOP MATERIAL	
PAINT LABOR	
PAINT MATERIAL	
SUB TOTAL	
TAX	
TOTAL COST ▶	

ONLY APPROVED ADDITIONS PAID

ESTIMATOR'S REPORT

Insurance Company _____

CLAIM NUMBER

Estimate, Inspection and Location Date _____

ADJUSTER'S NAME	ESTIMATOR'S NAME	DATE OF COMPLETION	DATE OF LOSS

INSURED

VEHICLE

NAME AND ADDRESS			

LICENSE (POLICY) NUMBER	GVW	MILEAGE	AMOUNT OF DEDUCTIBLE
YEAR, MAKE & MODEL		SERIAL NUMBER	

DESCRIPTION OF WORK TO BE DONE	RE-PAIR	REPLACE NEW	REPLACE L.K.Q.	QTY.	PART NUMBER	PARTS COST	HRS.	LABOR COST

This is purely an estimate and not a definite contract price. Owing to the impossibility of determining damage of concealed parts, we reserve the right to submit a further estimate for approval or otherwise. Prices subject to change without notice.
Authorization to Repair _____

I _____ the registered owner of the above described
vehicle authorize the repairs to proceed.

TOTAL PARTS COST ▶	
TOTAL LABOR COST ▶	
SHOP MATERIAL	
PAINT LABOR	
PAINT MATERIAL	
SUB TOTAL	
TAX	
TOTAL COST ▶	

ONLY APPROVED ADDITIONS PAID

ESTIMATOR'S REPORT

Insurance Company _____

	CLAIM NUMBER

Estimate, Inspection and Location Date _____

ADJUSTER'S NAME	ESTIMATOR'S NAME	DATE OF COMPLETION	DATE OF LOSS

INSURED   VEHICLE

NAME AND ADDRESS	LICENSE (POLICY) NUMBER	GVW	MILEAGE	AMOUNT OF DEDUCTIBLE
	YEAR, MAKE & MODEL		SERIAL NUMBER	

DESCRIPTION OF WORK TO BE DONE	RE-PAIR	REPLACE NEW	REPLACE L.K.Q.	QTY.	PART NUMBER	PARTS COST	HRS.	LABOR COST

This is purely an estimate and not a definite contract price. Owing to the impossibility of determining damage of concealed parts, we reserve the right to submit a further estimate for approval or otherwise. Prices subject to change without notice.
Authorization to Repair
_____

I_____ the registered owner of the above described vehicle authorize the repairs to proceed.

TOTAL PARTS COST ▶	
TOTAL LABOR COST ▶	
SHOP MATERIAL	
PAINT LABOR	
PAINT MATERIAL	
SUB TOTAL	
TAX	
TOTAL COST ▶	

ONLY APPROVED ADDITIONS PAID

ESTIMATOR'S REPORT

Insurance Company _____

CLAIM NUMBER

Estimate, Inspection and Location Date _____

ADJUSTER'S NAME	ESTIMATOR'S NAME	DATE OF COMPLETION	DATE OF LOSS

INSURED

VEHICLE

NAME AND ADDRESS	LICENSE (POLICY) NUMBER	GVW	MILEAGE	AMOUNT OF DEDUCTIBLE
	YEAR, MAKE & MODEL		SERIAL NUMBER	

DESCRIPTION OF WORK TO BE DONE	RE-PAIR	REPLACE NEW	L.K.Q.	QTY.	PART NUMBER	PARTS COST	HRS.	LABOR COST

This is purely an estimate and not a definite contract price. Owing to the impossibility of determining damage of concealed parts, we reserve the right to submit a further estimate for approval or otherwise. Prices subject to change without notice.

Authorization to Repair _____

I_____ the registered owner of the above described vehicle authorize the repairs to proceed.

TOTAL PARTS COST ▶	
TOTAL LABOR COST ▶	
SHOP MATERIAL	
PAINT LABOR	
PAINT MATERIAL	
SUB TOTAL	
TAX	
TOTAL COST ▶	

ONLY APPROVED ADDITIONS PAID

ESTIMATOR'S REPORT

Insurance Company _____

	CLAIM NUMBER

Estimate, Inspection and Location Date _____

ADJUSTER'S NAME	ESTIMATOR'S NAME	DATE OF COMPLETION	DATE OF LOSS

INSURED   VEHICLE

NAME AND ADDRESS	LICENSE (POLICY) NUMBER	GVW	MILEAGE	AMOUNT OF DEDUCTIBLE
	YEAR, MAKE & MODEL		SERIAL NUMBER	

DESCRIPTION OF WORK TO BE DONE	RE-PAIR	REPLACE NEW	L.K.Q.	QTY.	PART NUMBER	PARTS COST	HRS.	LABOR COST

This is purely an estimate and not a definite contract price. Owing to the impossibility of determining damage of concealed parts, we reserve the right to submit a further estimate for approval or otherwise. Prices subject to change without notice.
Authorization to Repair

_____

I_____ the registered owner of the above described
vehicle authorize the repairs to proceed.

TOTAL PARTS COST ▶	
TOTAL LABOR COST ▶	
SHOP MATERIAL	
PAINT LABOR	
PAINT MATERIAL	
SUB TOTAL	
TAX	
TOTAL COST ▶	

ONLY APPROVED ADDITIONS PAID

ESTIMATOR'S REPORT

Insurance Company _____ | CLAIM NUMBER

Estimate, Inspection and Location Date _____

ADJUSTER'S NAME	ESTIMATOR'S NAME	DATE OF COMPLETION	DATE OF LOSS

INSURED VEHICLE

NAME AND ADDRESS	LICENSE (POLICY) NUMBER	GVW	MILEAGE	AMOUNT OF DEDUCTIBLE
	YEAR, MAKE & MODEL		SERIAL NUMBER	

DESCRIPTION OF WORK TO BE DONE	RE-PAIR	REPLACE NEW	L.K.Q.	QTY.	PART NUMBER	PARTS COST	HRS.	LABOR COST

This is purely an estimate and not a definite contract price. Owing to the impossibility of determining damage of concealed parts, we reserve the right to submit a further estimate for approval or otherwise. Prices subject to change without notice.
Authorization to Repair
_____

I _____ the registered owner of the above described vehicle authorize the repairs to proceed.

TOTAL PARTS COST ▶	
TOTAL LABOR COST ▶	
SHOP MATERIAL	
PAINT LABOR	
PAINT MATERIAL	
SUB TOTAL	
TAX	
TOTAL COST ▶	

ONLY APPROVED ADDITIONS PAID

ESTIMATOR'S REPORT

Insurance Company _____ | CLAIM NUMBER

Estimate, Inspection and Location Date _____

| ADJUSTER'S NAME | ESTIMATOR'S NAME | DATE OF COMPLETION | DATE OF LOSS |

INSURED   VEHICLE

| NAME AND ADDRESS | LICENSE (POLICY) NUMBER | GVW | MILEAGE | AMOUNT OF DEDUCTIBLE |
| | YEAR, MAKE & MODEL | | SERIAL NUMBER | |

DESCRIPTION OF WORK TO BE DONE	RE-PAIR	REPLACE NEW	L.K.Q.	QTY.	PART NUMBER	PARTS COST	HRS.	LABOR COST

This is purely an estimate and not a definite contract price. Owing to the impossibility of determining damage of concealed parts, we reserve the right to submit a further estimate for approval or otherwise. Prices subject to change without notice.
Authorization to Repair

I _____ the registered owner of the above described vehicle authorize the repairs to proceed.

TOTAL PARTS COST ▶	
TOTAL LABOR COST ▶	
SHOP MATERIAL	
PAINT LABOR	
PAINT MATERIAL	
SUB TOTAL	
TAX	
TOTAL COST ▶	

ONLY APPROVED ADDITIONS PAID

Index

Unitized Body-Frame Construction

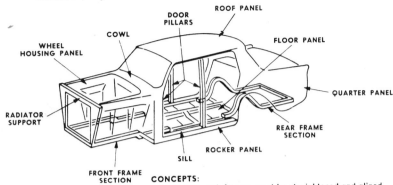

CONCEPTS:
1. Bodies and frames must be straightened and alined together.
2. Body panels must not be removed or replaced until after the body and frame have been alined.
3. Multiple hook-ups are the secret to Body-Frame correction work.
4. More power is needed to straighten unitized vehicles than for conventional frames.

FIGURE 6-45B Unitized body-frame construction. (Courtesy of Bear Manufacturing Co.)

be straightened on the vehicle as much as possible. This is to increase or gain as much support as possible when pressure is applied when straightening the body and reinforcing structures.

2. The power train and suspension assemblies on older unitized and newer unitized HSS-constructed vehicles are removed as required.

3. A wire brush is used to clean the buckled or cracked areas.

4. All breaks in the frame and body panels are welded to avoid further tearing of the metal while the frame and body are being straightened.

5. After all welding is completed, HSS welded areas are primed with a zinc primer.

Body-frame damage is always removed in the opposite direction from that of the impact. In most cases, the damage is removed by pulling instead of pushing. The use of heat is minimized; as much of the work as possible is done by cold-working. The work can be done on either a frame rack or a movable straightening system (Fig. 6-46).

With the unlimited power available, the operator must be careful not to tear body panels and frame members as they are being pulled out. Thus a hammer is used to relax the buckles until a silver streak appears in the center of the buckle; then and only then is heat applied. Using a large tip and a neutral or slightly carburizing flame, the body technician heats the area to the required temperature as more pressure is applied to the frame member.

When a frame is being straightened, it is always necessary to overcorrect to allow for springback. Unitized construction does not require as much overcorrection as the conventional type of frame. As the frame is being straightened, the body panels should also be pulled, for this saves time and helps to relieve strains on both the body and frame.

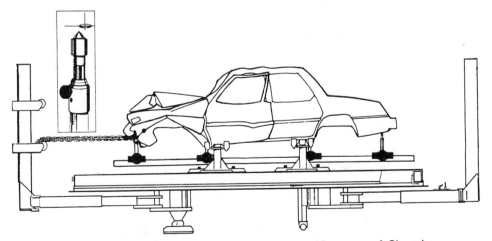

FIGURE 6-46 Accu-rack and Exacto gauge. (Courtesy of Chart Industries Ltd.)

The stretch and pull hookup is first attached on the side of the vehicle having the most damage. This hookup serves as the basic hookup that is used to remove all other types of frame misalignment except twist.

When a collision of any consequence occurs, damage to the structure will seldom be in a single direction (Fig. 6-47). The damage from the collision will usually affect the vehicle in several directions simultaneously and will occur in an orderly fashion. When a vehicle is hit in the front (Fig. 6-48), it will cause a shortness of length first, then height, width, side movement, and so on. Visualize the damage as it occurs because the repair will logically have to reverse the sequence. Therefore, the hookups will have to pull out the damage in the proper sequence, either alone or with the other damage, in the reverse order in which it happened. To avoid problems with overpulling some areas and underpulling others, this method should be followed strictly while still trying to achieve overall dimensions.

The type of equipment available in the shop will vary some of the hookups, but the new unitized vehicles must be anchored with four pinch-weld clamp systems on the rocker panels. It may be necessary to have additional tie-downs to control height and side movement.

Proper alignment of the sheet metal will not occur until the internal stresses from the impact are relieved. This will allow the dimensions to remain when the corrective hookups are released. The stress relief may be done cold in some cases, and in other cases heat must be applied.

As the corrective forces are applied, movement will occur in the areas where secondary damage has occurred. As these secondary damaged areas move, work the ridges and buckles slowly while raising low metal (Fig. 6-49).

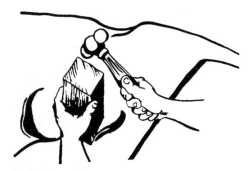

FIGURE 6-49 Relieving stresses using a block of wood and hammer. (Courtesy of Chart Industries Ltd.)

If the metal should tear, it should be rewelded as realignment occurs. This type of construction and metal must be worked slowly to allow time for the metal to reposition itself in its proper shape or space.

Since HSS is used in most structural members, care must be used when applying heat. Heat-stress relief will work best at the critical temperature of approximately 900°F (371°C). The structured member being heated turns blue in color. Some manufacturers may recommend slightly higher heat, but never more than 1400°F (760°C). These ranges are acceptable for most HSS specifications depending on the domestic manufacturer, as long as the area is not heated for more than a total of 3 minutes. A heat crayon (Fig. 6-50) should be used to guide the repairer for higher-temperature exposure of panel.

Heat should be applied along the edges of the damaged members, around spot welds, because this is where

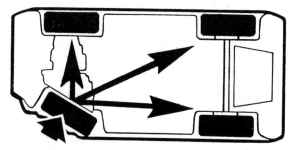

FIGURE 6-47 Direction that damage travels. (Courtesy of Chart Industries Ltd.)

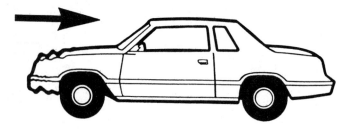

FIGURE 6-48 Crushing due to front-end collision. (Courtesy of Chart Industries Ltd.)